Great Celebrations Start With The Yearbook!

Dear Friend,

New ideas make decorating fun. And there is no better place than the 2005 Wilton Yearbook to find that next great decorating idea. In this new edition, decorators will gain inspiration, learn new techniques, and discover great products to create their best cakes.

One look at the cover and you'll know it's going to be an exciting year for decorators. It features an unforgettable heart cake made in our fun new SweetHeart Pan and introduces a great new way to decorate with fondant. The textures of stacked flowers and twisted fondant strips, dramatic neon and pastel colors and painted leaves make this a cake to remember.

It's just the start of the amazing fondant cakes featured in the 2005 Yearbook. You'll love our special section, "Fondant Fun!", featuring incredible designs like a baby shower quilt, a birthday scrapbook and individual fondant face cakes. Our new collection of fondant products makes it all happen. You'll find pre-tinted fondant and easy-to-use tools for cutting and stamping, along with great ways to paint and draw colorful accents on your cakes. These terrific new products make it easy for anyone to enjoy fondant decorating.

As always, the 2005 Yearbook is filled with many unique theme ideas to surprise you. Guests will love our island designs, including colorful tropical fish and a wonderful beach scene. You can also delight kids with their favorite animal face made in the new Animal Crackers pan.

Along with great cake ideas, the Yearbook will help you make simple treats something special. Even cupcakes can make a party sparkle with our new Cupcakes 'N More™ Dessert Stand. You'll also find easy ways for kids to get in on the fun. Our Gummy and Kandy Clay™ products let kids create fun candy shapes in their favorite flavors.

It's all waiting for you. Get ready to enjoy some great decorating moments with help from your 2005 Yearbook.

Vince Naccarato

Vince Naccarato
Chairman and CEO
Wilton Industries, Inc.

Cake Decorating!

THE 2005 WILTON YEARBOOK

The Ideas p. 4

ON OUR COVER
The New SweetHeart Pan ....p. 4

The contemporary shape of our new pan gives the traditional heart cake a fun twist! Check out the colorful fondant cake on our cover, create elegant designs decorated with a lavish fondant bow or icing roses and indulge in a rich truffle-topped ganache.

BIRTHDAY BLISS ....p. 6

The thrill of blowing out the candles never gets old—especially when the cake is custom-decorated for you! Find a design for every age—rocking horses, smiley faces, ice cream carousels, a '50s malt shop in fondant and more.

STAR POWER ....p. 30

You know how to make a birthday kid feel important—have a celebrity appear at the party! Decorate their favorite characters on fun cakes, cupcakes and candies.

HOLIDAYS YOUR WAY ....p. 44

Season after season, you'll be ready with desserts that perfectly capture the holiday flavor! Unleash the fun with some batty Halloween cakes, cookies and fudge. Bring Christmas joy with an inspiring manger scene or our gift-wrapping elves. Hunt down the perfect egg house cake for Easter, complete with textured fondant shutters and rooftop.

PROUDEST MOMENTS ......p. 72

The events you remember forever require a cake that's equally memorable. Our cathedral communion cake, a smiley face gelatin grad and a baby airport with storks ready for takeoff are just some of the designs that will be a major part of those special days.

VISIONS OF LOVE ....p. 82

Explore exciting new possibilities for your wedding day...design elements such as sugared pastel flowers, sunny yellow diamonds, dramatic candy plaque cake tops, and white dotted fantasy flowers with black dot accents. Create a similar sensation for showers and anniversaries with cakes and cupcakes that echo the look of our wedding cakes.

FONDANT FUN! ....p. 92

We've rolled, cut, shaped, stamped, painted and embossed fondant to give you cakes with amazing textural and color effects. Wait till you see our 3-D train, a layered floral bouquet for Mother's Day and the festive birthday scrapbook, all made with our new pre-tinted fondant, tools and accent icings.

Decorating Guide p. 104

It's easy to find the help you need! Includes step-by-step techniques, luscious recipes, construction guides and cutting charts, cookie and candy tips. Explore decorating further by attending classes at The Wilton School.

Product Shops p. 121

Everything you need to create the exciting ideas in this Yearbook! From decorating tips to famous Wilton bakeware, from character candles to elegant wedding ornaments, find it all here.

Index p. 224

CREATIVE DIRECTOR
Daniel Masini

ART DIRECTOR/CAKE DESIGNER
Steve Rocco

SENIOR CAKE DECORATOR
Mary Gavenda

CAKE DECORATORS
Susan Matusiak
Debbie Friedman
Diane Knowlton
Judy Wysocki
Anne Christopher
Mark Malak
Nancy Suffolk-Guerine
Lori Parrett

EDITOR/WRITER
Jeff Shankman

WRITERS
Mary Enochs
Marita Seiler
Tricia Despres
Jessica Radzak

PRODUCTION MANAGER
Challis Yeager

ASSISTANT PRODUCTION MANAGER
Mary Stahulak

GRAPHIC DESIGN/PRODUCTION
Alena Sokoloski
PreMediaONE
RNB Graphics
TBD Studios

PHOTOGRAPHY
Peter Rossi - PDR Productions
PreMediaONE
Alter Image

PHOTO STYLIST
Carey Thornton

ADMINISTRATIVE ASSISTANT
Sharon Gaeta

For photography purposes, many cakes in this book were decorated (by right- and left-handed decorators) with royal icing.

Printed in U.S.A.

IN U.S.A.
Wilton Industries, Inc.
2240 West 75th Street
Woodridge, IL 60517
www.wilton.com
Retail Customer Orders:
Phone: 800-794-5866
Fax: 888-824-9520
Website: www.wilton.com
Class Locations:
Phone: 800-942-8881
Website: www.wilton.com

IN CANADA
Wilton Industries, Canada, Ltd.
98 Carrier Drive
Etobicoke, Ontario M9W 5R1 Canada
Retail Customer Orders:
Phone: 416-679-0790
Fax: 416-679-0798
Class locations:
Phone: 416-679-0790, x200
E-mail: classprograms@wilton.ca

¡SE HABLA ESPAÑOL!
para mas informacion,
marque 800-436-5778

The new SweetHeart Pan is Here!

Create heart cakes with a fresh, fun attitude! The SweetHeart pan has graceful curves that bring an exciting new look to Valentine desserts, birthday cakes, Mother's Day gelatin molds and more. Here's just a taste of the great things you can do!

▲ Vibrant Vines

Opposites attract as pastel and neon fondant come together on this energetic heart design. Great texture accents the shape, from the embossed strips on the sides to the layered flowers on top.

Pan: SweetHeart, p. 159

Fondant: Ready-To-Use Rolled Fondant in White, Pastel Yellow, Pastel Pink (24 oz. each), Pastel and Neon Multi Packs, p. 122; Funny Flower Cut-Outs™, p. 123; Green Brush-On Color™, p. 124; Easy-Glide Fondant Smoother, Roll & Cut Mat, Rolling Pin, Brush Set, Color Tray, Cutter/Embosser, p. 125

Recipe: Buttercream Icing, p. 111

Also: 2005 Pattern Book (Small and Large Heart), p. 222; Cake Board, Fanci-Foil Wrap, p. 217; small plastic ruler, small paring knife

Prepare 2-layer 3 in. cake for rolled fondant (p. 105); cover with yellow fondant and smooth. Combine Pastel Pink with Neon Pink fondant from Multi Pack to achieve pink color used. Roll out fondant ⅛ in. thick and, using patterns, cut one large pink and one small white heart. Attach pink heart to cake and white heart to pink heart with damp brush. Mix orange fondant from Neon Multi Pack with 6 oz. white fondant. Cut out orange flowers using medium Cut-Out and pink flowers using small Cut-Out. Using damp brush, attach small to medium flowers, then attach flowers to cake. Roll ⅛ in. diameter white balls for flower centers, attach. Paint stems and leaves using Brush-On Color and bevel-tipped brush. Roll out large pieces of orange and pink fondant ⅛ in. thick and imprint lattice lines, ¼ in. apart, with wavy-edge wheel of Cutter/Embosser. Cut strips ¾ x 4½ in. Attach to cake, ¾ in. apart at top, with damp brush. Roll out green fondant ⅛ in. thick and cut ¼ in.x 4½ in. strips. Twist strips and attach between lattice strips, brushing areas where ends will rest with water. Press ends lightly and trim off excess. Roll ¼ in. diameter white balls and attach around center heart. Roll out white fondant ⅛ in. thick and cut four ½ x 12 in. strips. Brush back with water and loosely position around bottom border. Serves 12.

◀ Rose Garland

Less formal, more fun! A dynamic swirling background wraps around the vivid rose center heart for a boldly romantic approach.

Pan: SweetHeart, p. 159
Tips: 4, 5, 6, 102, 352, p. 136-137
Colors: Rose, Red-Red, Kelly Green, p. 127
Recipes: Buttercream, Royal Icings, p. 111
Also: Flower Nail, p. 134; Cake Board, Fanci-Foil Wrap, p. 217, Meringue Powder, p. 126; waxed paper, toothpick

In advance: In royal icing, make 16 tip 102 roses with tip 6 bases; make extras to allow for breakage and let dry. Ice smooth 2-layer 3 in. high cake and mark center heart area with toothpick, 1½ in. from edge. Pipe tip 4 swirls on cake sides and top around marked area. Position roses on marked heart. Add tip 352 leaves. Pipe tip 5 ball bottom border. Serves 12.

▶ Bold and Blue

The classic fondant bow has more presence (and texture) than ever when coated with white nonpareils. The cool blue fondant cake sets it off perfectly.

Pan: SweetHeart, p. 159
Colors: Royal Blue, Violet, Rose, p. 127
Fondant: White Ready-To-Use Rolled Fondant (72 oz. needed), p. 122; Easy-Glide Fondant Smoother, Rolling Pin, Roll & Cut Mat, p. 125
Recipe: Buttercream Icing, p. 111
Also: Gum-Tex™ Karaya, p. 125; Piping Gel, p. 126; White Nonpareils Sprinkle Decorations, p. 128; Cake Board, Fanci-Foil Wrap, p. 217; paring knife, cornstarch, cotton balls

In advance: Make fondant bow (p. 117) using approximately 20 oz. of white fondant kneaded with 2 teaspoons of Gum-Tex for added strength. Reserve remaining fondant mixture to make streamers and flat ribbon. To make streamers, cut 1½ in. wide strips, 5 and 6 in. long; cut V-shapes at one end and pinch together other end to fit under loops. Place pan flat, back side up, and position streamers, placing cotton balls beneath to shape; let dry, then remove.

Prepare 2-layer 4 in. high cake for rolled fondant (p. 105). Tint 36 oz. fondant light blue; cover cake and smooth with Easy-Glide Smoother. To make flat ribbon, using reserved fondant mixture, cut a 1½ x 18 in. strip; position on cake, trim off excess, then remove. Brush tops of all bow pieces with piping gel and immediately sprinkle with white nonpareils; let set. Position bow pieces on cake. Tint half of remaining fondant violet/rose combination, half blue. Roll ⅛ to ¼ in. diameter fondant balls and attach to cake with damp brush. Serves 12.

◀ Truffling with Your Affections

This pretty candy dish is actually a ganache-coated cake, topped with rich truffles. Nothing says love like chocolate!

Pans: SweetHeart, p. 159; Cooling Grid, p. 160
Recipes: Buttercream Icing, p. 111; Ganache Glaze, p. 112; Truffles (2 recipes needed), p. 112
Also: Candy Melts®† in White (1 pk. needed), Light Cocoa (4 pks. needed), p. 146; Cake Board, Fanci-Foil Wrap, p. 217; Parchment Triangles, p. 134; chopped walnuts, waxed paper

In advance: Make approximately 32 chocolate dipped truffles—some plain, some rolled in chopped walnuts and some topped with a swirl using melted white candy in cut parchment bag. Set aside.

Ice 1-layer cake smooth in buttercream. Position cake on cooling grid over drip pan and cover with ganache; let set. Position cake on foil-wrapped board. Position truffles on cake top. Cake serves 12.

†Brand confectionery coating.

Birthday Bliss!

It's the one day each year everyone gets to blow their own horn. A birthday cake should make some noise too! Think about what makes your birthday boy or girl great, then look here for the cake that says it best. You'll find shapes from rocking horses to race cars, merry-go-rounds to malt shops—ideas to make kids of any age smile!

Instructions for projects shown on these two pages are on page 8.

1
JONATHAN
HAPPY
BIRTHDAY

One-derful Time

This cute-as-a-button bear cake makes the perfect topper for our bright and bubbly pastel cake. He's holding a great big cookie just for a special toddler.

Pans: 10, 16 x 2 in. Round, p. 158; Stand-Up Cuddly Bear Set, p. 163
Tips: 1A, 4, 5, 8, 12, 16, 125, 233, p. 136-137
Colors: Rose, Royal Blue, Lemon Yellow, Kelly Green, Violet, Black, p. 127
Recipes: Buttercream Icing, p. 111; Roll-Out Cookie, p. 112
Also: 2005 Pattern Book (#1 Cookie), p. 222; Chocolate Ready-To-Use Decorator Icing, p. 126; White Ready-To-Use Rolled Fondant, p. 122; Cake Board, Fanci-Foil Wrap, p. 217; 18 in. Round Silver Cake Base, p. 217; Dowel Rods, p. 214; Cooling Grid, p. 160; 11¾ in. Lollipop Sticks, p. 149; Decorator Brush Set, p. 147; ice cream sugar cone, toothpick, craft knife, cornstarch

Roll out cookie dough and trace #1 pattern using toothpick. Cut cookie with knife, bake and cool. Ice cookie smooth. Outline cookie and print name with tip 5. Ice smooth 2-layer round cakes and prepare for stacked construction (p. 110). Trim right arm off bear cake and position bear on stacked cakes. Lighten a portion of chocolate icing with a little white and ice smooth footpads and inside ears. Pipe in tip 4 nose and eyes (pat smooth with finger dipped in cornstarch). Pipe in mouth and add outline smile with tip 4. Cover bear with tip 233 pull-out fur.

For hat, trim ice cream cone to 3½ in. high; ice smooth. Print tip 8 message on cakes. Tint 6 oz. portions of fondant green, violet, rose and blue. Roll out colors ⅛ in. thick and cut various size circles using both ends of tip 1A and large ends of tips 12 and 125. Attach circles to cakes and cone with damp brush. Pipe tip 8 ball top borders on 10 and 16 in. cakes and bottom border on 10 in. cake. Pipe tip 12 ball bottom border on 16 in. cake. Insert lollipop stick in bear's head, leaving 3 in. exposed. Position cone hat; pipe tip 16 pull-out star fringe. Attach lollipop sticks to back of cookie with icing and insert in cake . Shape a fondant arm, 1 in. diameter x 3 in. long. Attach to bear with a damp brush and shape paw around cookie. Cover arm with tip 233 pull-out fur. Serves 117.

Cutest Little Baby Face

Easy favors that hold guests' places, along with the memory of a special day.

Favor Accent: Bear Placecard Holders, p. 219
Also: Construction paper, baby photos, glue, scissors

Cut 3 in. construction paper circle; cut another 2½ in. circle out of center to create frame. Cut photo to fit and glue to back of frame. Position on placecard holders.

Candy Cake Centerpiece

Candy: Party Cakes Candy Making Kit (includes molds, Candy Melts®† in white, red, yellow and green, melting bags and decorating brush), p. 146; Blue Candy Melts, p. 146, plastic ruler

Follow kit instructions to mold three cake tiers with white candy. Also mold 18 swirl candies and two candle halves using painting method (p. 119). Refrigerate all until firm; unmold. Attach candle halves together with melted candy. Divide top tier into 4ths, each 1½ in. wide; divide middle tier into 6ths, each 1¾ in. wide; divide bottom tier into 8ths, each 2 in. wide. Using melted blue candy in cut bag, pipe zigzag garlands at division points, ¾ in. deep; refrigerate until firm. Attach tiers with melted candy. Add bead bottom borders using melted red candy in cut bag. Attach candle and swirls with melted candy.

The Crowd's Roaring!

Cookie: 101 Cookie Cutters Set, p. 142; Medium Non-Stick Cookie Pan, p. 157
Candy: Party Time Mold, p. 148; Candy Melts®† in Light Cocoa, White, p. 146; Primary and Garden Candy Color Sets, p. 147; Decorator Brush Set, p. 147
Also: Parchment Triangles, p. 134

Tint portions of melted white candy blue, pink and yellow using candy colors; reserve some white. Position small bear and number 1 cutter from set on cookie sheet and fill ¼ in. deep with melted candy. Refrigerate until firm; unmold. Mold hat and gift using painting method (p. 119); refrigerate until firm; unmold. Pipe facial features, bow and inside ears using melted candy in parchment bag cut with a small opening. Attach hat, number and gift to bear with melted candy. Pipe hands; let set. Each serves 1.

†Brand confectionery coating.

▶ First Birthday Fling

Pans: 6, 10, 14 x 2 in. Rounds, p. 158
Tips: 2, 3, 10, p. 136
Colors: Rose, Lemon Yellow, Kelly Green, Creamy Peach, Royal Blue, p. 127
Recipes: Buttercream, Color Flow Icings, p. 111
Also: 2005 Pattern Book (Top, Middle and Bottom Tier Rainbows), p. 222; Cake Circles, Fanci-Foil Wrap, p. 217; Dowel Rods, p. 214; Pastel Blue Rolled Fondant (72 oz. needed), p. 122; Color Flow Mix, p. 126; 4 in. Lollipop Sticks, p. 149; Pink #1 Numeral Candle, p. 151; Tumbling Bears Cake Toppers Set (2 sets needed), p. 155; waxed paper

Several days in advance: Make rainbow plaques using patterns and color flow icing. Using tip 2, outline each section with stiff consistency color flow, then fill in with thinned color flow. Let dry 48 hours. When dry, turn plaques over and reinforce by outlining and filling in entire plaque in one color. Make extras to allow for breakage and let dry overnight.

Prepare 1-layer 6, 10 and 14 in. rounds for stacked construction (p. 110). Prepare and cover cakes with rolled fondant (p. 105). Cakes will not be centered when stacked, so dowel rods will need to be positioned so that the 6 in. cake side aligns with the left edge of the 10 in. round and the 10 cake side aligns at the right edge of the 14 in. round. Assemble tiers.

Pipe tip 3 message in buttercream icing. Insert lollipop sticks into cake sides in a descending pattern to support rainbow plaques. Use 4 sticks in the 6 in. tier, 6 each in the 10 in. and 14 in. tiers. Position rainbow plaques, and pipe a section of tip 10 ball clouds at bottom border of each tier, to secure edge of plaque. Pipe a mound of tip 10 ball clouds on top tier, position candle. Position bears. Serves 103.

▼ Rock On

Pans: 3-D Rubber Ducky, p. 163; Oval Set (16½ x 12⅜ x 2 in. used), p. 159

Tips: 3, 4, 16, 18, 21, p. 136-137

Colors: Violet, Lemon Yellow, Royal Blue, Rose, Leaf Green, Black, p. 127

Recipes: Buttercream, Royal Icings, p. 111

Also: 2005 Pattern Book (Rockers, Saddle), p. 222; White Ready-To-Use Rolled Fondant (24 oz. needed), p. 122; Gum-Tex™ Karaya, p. 125; Meringue Powder, p. 126; Cake Boards, Fanci-Foil Wrap, p. 217; Hidden Pillars, p. 215; cornstarch, hot glue gun

In advance: Make rockers. Tint fondant as follows: 1 in. ball green, 3 in. ball rose, reserve 8 oz. white and tint remaining fondant violet with a little rose (add 1 teaspoon Gum-Tex to violet). Roll out violet fondant and cut 2 rockers using pattern; let dry on cornstarch-dusted surface. When dry, use tip 4 and royal icing to outline rockers and print name; set aside.

For legs, cover 4 in. of hidden pillars with white fondant (remaining 2 in. will be inserted into cake); smooth seams. Cover fondant area on legs with tip 16 stars in buttercream. Trace bottom of Rubber Ducky pan on cake board and cut board to fit. Wrap board with foil. Attach legs to bottom of board with hot glue gun.

Bake and cool 1-layer oval cake and duck "horse" cake using firm-textured batter such as pound cake. Ice oval cake smooth in buttercream; pipe tip 18 rosette top and bottom borders. Cut 2 cake boards to fit under horse cake, cover with foil and position cake. Fill in space between cake bottom and board with icing. Mound icing with spatula to create rounded muzzle. For ears, build up icing with tip 3 (smooth with finger dipped in cornstarch).

Using pink fondant and pattern, cut saddle; attach to cake with buttercream. Cut pink fondant triangles and attach inside ears. Cut ½ in. wide strips of pink and green fondant for bridle, harness and saddle trim; attach. Roll ¼ in. balls of white for eyes, pink for nostrils and green for saddle bolts, attach. Pipe tip 3 dot pupils and string mouth. Cover horse with tip 16 stars. Add tip 21 pull-out star mane and tail. Insert hidden pillar legs into cake; position horse cake on leg base, securing with icing. Attach rockers to legs with icing. Serves 56.

ANTHONY

Great New Pan!

Animal Crackers is the perfect shape for decorating kids' favorite animal faces! See details on p. 162.

▶ Go Bananas!

Pan: Animal Crackers, p. 162
Tips: 4, 6, 16, p. 136
Colors: Rose, Black, p. 127
Recipes:* Buttercream, Chocolate Buttercream Icings, p. 111
Also: Cake Circle, Fanci-Foil Wrap, p. 127, cornstarch

Trim ears off cake and position lower on head. Trace shape on cake circle, cut to fit and wrap with foil. Outline facial features with tip 4. Pipe in tip 6 eyes, pupils, inside ears, nostrils, mouth and tongue (pat smooth with finger dipped in cornstarch). Cover head with tip 16 stars. Serves 12.

***Note:** Add white to chocolate buttercream for shade used in inner face area.

◀ Deeply Mooooving

Our happy Holstein serves guests with their choice of chocolate or vanilla icing (if only cows gave milk the same way).

Pans: Animal Crackers, p. 162; Mini Loaf, p. 160; 12 x 2 in. Round, p. 158
Tips: 3, 18, p. 136
Colors: Black, Pink, p. 127
Recipes: Buttercream, Chocolate Buttercream Icings, p. 111
Also: Bubble Gum Light Pink Kandy Clay™**, p. 145; Cake Circles, Fanci-Foil Wrap, p. 217; 4 in. Lollipop Sticks, p. 149; cornstarch

Bake and cool 1-layer round cake, Animal Crackers cake and 4 mini loaves.

Cut ends of two loaf cakes in a curve and position against round cake for feet. Position Animal Crackers "head" cake on cake circle, then place on top portion of round cake "body." Cut one of the remaining loaf cakes horizontally in half; stack one half on top of a whole loaf cake and position under overhanging top portion of head cake to support. Pipe in eyes, mouth, nostrils and inside ears with tip 3 (smooth with finger dipped in cornstarch). Cover cow with tip 18 stars (nose and spots first). Knead 2 pieces of Kandy Clay to soften. Shape into horns, insert on lollipop sticks and insert in head. Serves 56.

**Brand edible modeling clay.

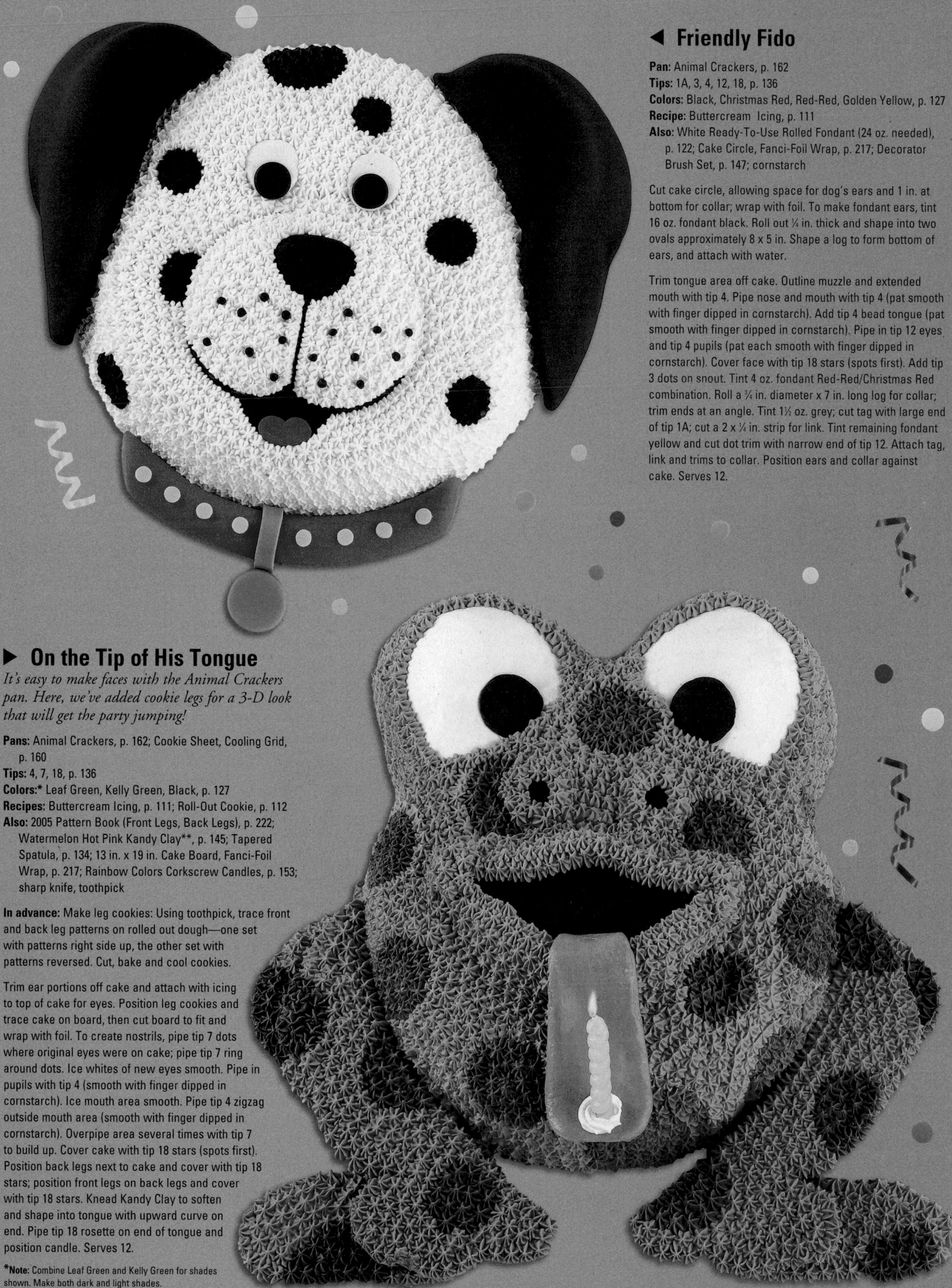

◀ Friendly Fido

Pan: Animal Crackers, p. 162
Tips: 1A, 3, 4, 12, 18, p. 136
Colors: Black, Christmas Red, Red-Red, Golden Yellow, p. 127
Recipe: Buttercream Icing, p. 111
Also: White Ready-To-Use Rolled Fondant (24 oz. needed), p. 122; Cake Circle, Fanci-Foil Wrap, p. 217; Decorator Brush Set, p. 147; cornstarch

Cut cake circle, allowing space for dog's ears and 1 in. at bottom for collar; wrap with foil. To make fondant ears, tint 16 oz. fondant black. Roll out ¼ in. thick and shape into two ovals approximately 8 x 5 in. Shape a log to form bottom of ears, and attach with water.

Trim tongue area off cake. Outline muzzle and extended mouth with tip 4. Pipe nose and mouth with tip 4 (pat smooth with finger dipped in cornstarch). Add tip 4 bead tongue (pat smooth with finger dipped in cornstarch). Pipe in tip 12 eyes and tip 4 pupils (pat each smooth with finger dipped in cornstarch). Cover face with tip 18 stars (spots first). Add tip 3 dots on snout. Tint 4 oz. fondant Red-Red/Christmas Red combination. Roll a ¾ in. diameter x 7 in. long log for collar; trim ends at an angle. Tint 1½ oz. grey; cut tag with large end of tip 1A; cut a 2 x ¼ in. strip for link. Tint remaining fondant yellow and cut dot trim with narrow end of tip 12. Attach tag, link and trims to collar. Position ears and collar against cake. Serves 12.

▶ On the Tip of His Tongue

It's easy to make faces with the Animal Crackers pan. Here, we've added cookie legs for a 3-D look that will get the party jumping!

Pans: Animal Crackers, p. 162; Cookie Sheet, Cooling Grid, p. 160
Tips: 4, 7, 18, p. 136
Colors:* Leaf Green, Kelly Green, Black, p. 127
Recipes: Buttercream Icing, p. 111; Roll-Out Cookie, p. 112
Also: 2005 Pattern Book (Front Legs, Back Legs), p. 222; Watermelon Hot Pink Kandy Clay**, p. 145; Tapered Spatula, p. 134; 13 in. x 19 in. Cake Board, Fanci-Foil Wrap, p. 217; Rainbow Colors Corkscrew Candles, p. 153; sharp knife, toothpick

In advance: Make leg cookies: Using toothpick, trace front and back leg patterns on rolled out dough—one set with patterns right side up, the other set with patterns reversed. Cut, bake and cool cookies.

Trim ear portions off cake and attach with icing to top of cake for eyes. Position leg cookies and trace cake on board, then cut board to fit and wrap with foil. To create nostrils, pipe tip 7 dots where original eyes were on cake; pipe tip 7 ring around dots. Ice whites of new eyes smooth. Pipe in pupils with tip 4 (smooth with finger dipped in cornstarch). Ice mouth area smooth. Pipe tip 4 zigzag outside mouth area (smooth with finger dipped in cornstarch). Overpipe area several times with tip 7 to build up. Cover cake with tip 18 stars (spots first). Position back legs next to cake and cover with tip 18 stars; position front legs on back legs and cover with tip 18 stars. Knead Kandy Clay to soften and shape into tongue with upward curve on end. Pipe tip 18 rosette on end of tongue and position candle. Serves 12.

***Note:** Combine Leaf Green and Kelly Green for shades shown. Make both dark and light shades.

◀ Cheers for the Birthday Girl!

Pan: 14 x 2 in. Square, p. 159
Tips: 2, 2A, 12, p. 136
Colors: Rose, Red-Red, Christmas Red, Brown, Lemon Yellow, Orange, Black, p. 127
Fondant: White Ready-To-Use Rolled Fondant (96 oz. needed), Natural Colors Multi Pack, Bold Tip Primary Colors FoodWriter™, p. 124; Cut-Outs™ in Alphabet/Numeral, and People, p. 123; Easy-Glide Fondant Smoother, Cutter/Embosser, Brush Set, Roll & Cut Mat, Rolling Pin, p. 125
Recipe: Buttercream Icing, p. 111
Also: Cake Boards, Fanci-Foil Wrap, p. 217

Tint 72 oz. white fondant light rose. Prepare 1-layer cake and cover with fondant (p. 105); smooth with Easy-Glide Smoother. Tint 6 oz. fondant red (combine Red-Red and Christmas Red). Roll fondant thin and cut letters and numbers with Cut-Outs. (Apostrophes are made from top curve of number 1, trimmed and shaped. Dashes are made by cutting letter "I" in half.) Also cut out skirts using skirt Cut-Out, imprint pleats using smooth wheel of Cutter/Embosser. Cut heads using head Cut-Out and Natural fondant colors. Cut shirts using white fondant and shirt Cut-Out. To keep neckline rounded for placement of heads, place head Cut-Out at top of shirt, then shape sleeves up as necessary. Push sleeves down on other shirts as necessary. Let all dry. Cut out knees for the kneeling girls using the small end of tip 2A, cut in half. Cut arms and legs for all girls and shoes for the bottom row girls using the shoe Cut-Out, trim off the toe end for legs; the arms are the curved portion of the shoe. Shoes for the middle and top row girls are made using small end of tip 12, cut in half. Use red FoodWriter to mark pleats on skirts and to draw letters, necklines, waistbands and cuffs on shirts.

Assemble fondant decorations beginning at bottom row of girls and working up. Attach all fondant pieces using brushstrokes of water. First, position skirts, shirts and heads, then add legs, shoes and arms. Position message. Mark eyes and mouths using black FoodWriter. Using tip 2 and buttercream icing, add string and dot hair and barrettes. Add tip 2 pull-out dot pompoms.

Roll 8 fondant ropes approximately ¼ in. thick and 14 in. long. Twist 2 ropes together for each side and attach to bottom border with brushstrokes of water. Serves 63.

▶ The Princess's Party

Even if they're not aspiring ballerinas, little girls will be swept off their feet by our baby bear. It's the full ruffled skirt that makes this a cake to remember.

Pan: Huggable Teddy Bear, p. 163
Tips: 3, 4, 16, 104, 127D, p. 136-137
Colors: Rose, Brown, Black, p. 127
Recipe: Buttercream Icing, p. 111
Also: 2005 Pattern Book (Crown), p. 222; Cake Boards, Fanci-Foil Wrap, p. 217; 4 in. Lollipop Sticks, p. 149

Ice cake sides smooth. Outline face, mouth, paws, pads and neckline with tip 4. Pipe in mouth, nose and eyes with tip 4. Cover cake top with tip 16 stars. Add tip 3 pull-out eyelashes. For skirt, pipe three rows of tip 127D ruffles. Pipe tip 104 waistband and bow. Add tip 16 star bottom border and random stars on cake sides. Trace crown pattern on cake board, cut out and wrap with foil. Cover crown except for top star with tip 16 stars; add tip 16 rosettes at points. Insert lollipop sticks in head and position crown. Cover top star with tip 16 stars. Serves 12.

▶ Birthday Whirligig

A merry-go-round is sure to turn kids' heads—especially with crazy cupcakes, baked in ice cream cones, on top.

Pans: 8, 12 x 2 in. Round, p. 158; Jumbo Muffin, p. 160
Tips: 1M, 21, p. 136
Recipe: Cone Cupcakes, p. 112
Also: Vanilla Ice Cream Mix (3 pks. needed), p. 126; Colored Sugars in Yellow, Lavender, Pink, p. 128; 14 in. Round Silver Cake Base, p. 217; Carousel Separator Set, p. 155; Cake Dividing Set, p. 131; Dowel Rods, p. 214; ice cream cup cones (24 needed), spice drops, candy-coated mint chocolate dots

Bake and cool 2-layer round cakes (for 8 in. cake, bake two 1½ in. high layers to make 3 in. high cake), 24 cone cupcakes (6 needed for cake, serve extras at party), and 1 plain jumbo cupcake. Prepare 2 packs of ice cream mix; fill cakes. Ice smooth cakes and plain cupcake with ice cream. Freeze to set.

Divide 8 in. cake into 8ths, 12 in. cake into 10ths. Prepare cakes for 2-plate and pillar construction. On both cakes, pipe tip 21 star garland 1½ in. deep. Cut spice drops in half and position on stars. Pipe tip 21 rosette top borders; position whole spice drops on rosettes. Position iced cupcake in center of 8 in. cake; attach candy-coated chocolates for top and bottom borders. On 8 in. cake, pipe tip 21 rosette bottom border, on 12 in. cake pipe tip 1M rosette bottom border; position candy-coated chocolates on rosettes, place in freezer. Prepare remaining ice cream mix. Pipe tip 1M swirl on cone cupcake tops, sprinkle with colored sugars, position spice drops and freeze to set. Position cones, pushing slightly into cake top. About 10 minutes before serving, assemble cakes. Cake serves 61; each cone serves 1.

▼ Frosty Flowers

Pan: 11 x 15 x 2 in. Sheet, p. 158
Tip: 4, p. 136
Color: Golden Yellow, p. 127
Cookie: Flower Stencil-A-Cookie™ Cutter & Stencil Set, p. 141; Cookie Sheet, Cooling Grid, p. 160
Recipe: Roll-Out Cookie, p. 112
Also: Vanilla Ice Cream Mix, p. 126; Pink Color Mist™, p. 127

Cut 2 cookies for each sandwich using flower cutter from set. Position stencil and spray cookies with Color Mist; remove stencil. Tint remaining dough yellow and thin with water to piping consistency. On top cookies only, pipe tip 4 center swirl in yellow dough. Bake and cool cookies.

Prepare ice cream mix following package directions. Pour into sheet pan, ½ in. thick, and freeze. Cut flower shapes and position between top and bottom cookies. Each serves 1.

▼ Park Paradise

Fun nature details really make this cake work for kids. Easy add-ons like pretzel rod trees, a mini pretzel campfire and piping gel lake add a touch of the great outdoors.

Pan: Guitar, p. 164
Tips: 1, 2, 2A, 3, 5, 8, 12, 16, 45, 233, 349, p. 136-137
Colors:* Sky Blue, Royal Blue, Kelly Green, Black, Copper, Red-Red, Christmas Red, Brown, Lemon Yellow, Golden Yellow, p. 127
Recipes: Buttercream, Royal Icings, p. 111
Also: Cake Board, Fanci-Foil Wrap, p. 217; Meringue Powder, p. 126; Piping Gel, p. 126; sugar ice cream cones, pretzel rods, mini pretzel rods, sugar wafer cookies (size for making ice cream sandwiches), black shoestring licorice, craft block, waxed paper, paring knife

In advance: Using royal icing, figure pipe kids (p. 118) with tips 2A, 3, 5, 8, 12, 16 and 349. Make trees using royal icing: Place cones on waxed paper. Cover cones with tip 16 pull-out star branches, piping from bottom up. Using royal icing, make campfire: Position mini pretzels in a circular stack on waxed paper. Pipe tip 349 pull-out flames. Let all dry.

Trim off keys on neck area of guitar cake. Place cake on foil-wrapped board extended 4 in. past neck area for piping "water." Ice cake smooth in buttercream. Pipe boards and corner poles on dock with tip 45 bands. Pipe tip 8 ball rocks and tip 233 pull-out grass. For tents, use knife to split wafer cookie into 3 flat sections. Remove icing and cut sections into 2½ x 2 in. pieces. Attach at an angle with royal icing; let dry. Tint piping gel blue and spread on board for water. For tallest tree, insert pretzel rod into cake. Pipe tip 16 rosette on top and position tree. Position kids, tents, trees and campfire. Serves 12.

***Note:** Combine Red-Red and Christmas Red for shade shown.

▶ Rocket Racer

Pans: First and Ten Football, p. 164; 6 x 2 in. Round, p. 158
Colors: Copper (skin tone), Brown, Leaf Green, Lemon Yellow, Violet, Rose, Royal Blue, Sky Blue, Black, p. 127
Fondant: White Ready-To-Use Rolled Fondant (72 oz. needed), p. 122; Round and Leaf Cut-Outs™, p. 123; FoodWriter™ in Fine Tip Primary Colors, p. 124; Halloween FoodWriters, p. 166; Easy-Glide Fondant Smoother, Rolling Pin, Brush Set, p. 125
Recipe: Buttercream Icing, p. 111
Also: 2005 Pattern Book (Helmet, Wing, Exhaust Pipes), p. 222; 6 in. Lollipop Sticks, p. 149; Cake Board, Fanci-Foil Wrap, p. 217; paring knife, scissors, cornstarch

Tint fondant as follows: 20 oz. violet with a little rose, 9 oz. green, 4 oz. royal blue/sky blue combination, 3 oz. brown, 2 oz. copper, 1 oz. black; reserve remainder white. Prepare cakes and cover with white and violet fondant (p. 105). Using patterns, cut wing and exhaust pipes from green fondant. Cut a 4½ in. circle for face from copper fondant. Cut flames from white fondant using large leaf Cut-Out. Let pieces dry on cornstarch-dusted surface. Position cakes. Roll ⅜ in. diameter blue fondant rope and position where cakes meet. Attach the following fondant decorations immediately after making by brushing back with water: Cut black portholes using medium round Cut-Out. For porthole frames, roll 3 green ropes, ⅜ in. diameter. Cover nose of spaceship with green fondant, roll 3 ropes of green fondant, ⅜ in. diameter and attach to nose. Roll violet rope ¾ in. diameter and attach as top opening of spaceship. Position face on top of round cake; draw facial features with FoodWriters. For nose, roll small ball of copper fondant and attach. For hair, cut 1½ in. wide strips of brown fondant and trim edges with scissors to make fringe; attach in bunches to top of head. Using blue fondant, make a ¾ in. diameter x 3½ in long log for arm; attach. Using black fondant, make a 3 in. long x ¼ diameter rope for steering wheel, attach. Using patterns, shape fondant helmet and hand; attach. Color flames with FoodWriters; attach to back of exhaust pipes using buttercream. Insert lollipop sticks in cake to support wing and exhaust pipes, leaving 3½ in. exposed. Attach wing and exhaust pipes with buttercream. Serves 24.

◀ Captain Kid

Serve up some swashbuckling sweets with our Little Pirate cake! Shiver their timbers with our easy-to-mold treasure chest, filled with a bounty of candy loot.

Pan: Little Pirate, p. 165
Tips: 3, 16, p. 136
Colors:* Royal Blue, Golden Yellow, Red-Red, Christmas Red, Violet, Kelly Green, Brown, Copper, Black, p. 127
Recipe: Buttercream Icing, p. 111
Also: 2005 Pattern Book (Sword, Sword Handle), p. 222; Cake Boards, Fanci-Foil Wrap, p. 217; Treasure Chest Candy Kit (includes molds, Candy Melts®† in light cocoa, yellow, green and red, melting bags and decorator brush), p. 146; granulated brown sugar, cornstarch, toothpick, cellophane tape

In advance: Make Candy Treasure Chest following kit directions. Set aside.

Trim treasure chest area off cake. Ice cake sides and background areas smooth. Using tip 3, outline and pipe in skull and crossbones (smooth with finger dipped in cornstarch), eye patch, eye and mouth. Outline face, body and clothes with tip 3; cover pirate and hat with tip 16 stars. Add tip 16 pull-out star hair, moustache, goatee and eyebrow. Pipe tip 3 ball nose (smooth with finger dipped in cornstarch). Trace sword pattern on board; cut out and wrap with foil. Trace sword handle pattern on cake with toothpick; outline and pipe in with tip 3. Insert sword into handle. Sprinkle granulated brown sugar around base of cake and position treasure chest. Serves 12.

***Note:** Combine Red-Red and Christmas Red for red shade shown. Combine Brown and Red-Red for brown shade shown.

†Brand confectionery coating.

◀ Well Wishes

Pans: Jumbo Muffin, p. 160; Petite Loaf, p. 160
Tips: 2, 107 (left-handed decorators use new Left-Handed Drop Flower Tips Set, p. 137), 349, p. 136-137
Colors: Leaf Green, Lemon Yellow, Violet, p. 127
Recipe: Royal Icing, p. 111
Also: Pink and White Candy Melts®†, p. 146; White Jumbo Baking Cups, p. 150; Meringue Powder, p. 126; 6 in. Lollipop Sticks, p. 149; Pillow Mints, p. 219; Parchment Triangles, p. 134

In advance: Using royal icing, make 5 each violet and yellow tip 107 drop flowers with tip 2 white dot centers. Make extras to allow for breakage; let dry.

Make candy shells in baking cups (p. 119) using melted candy, repeating process to make a thicker shell. Make candy plaques (p. 119) for roof in Petite Loaf Pan. Cut lollipop sticks to 4½ in. long. Attach to candy shell with melted candy. To assemble roof, pipe a line of melted candy in cut parchment bag on long edge of one plaque; attach second plaque at a 45° angle and refrigerate until firm. Attach roof to sticks with melted candy. Attach flowers with tip 2 and royal icing. Pipe tip 349 leaves. Fill shell with mints. Each serves 1.

◀ Getting His Sea Legs!

Candy: Kandy Clay™* Color Packs in Grape Purple, Marshmallow White and Chocolate Brown, Scissors/Sculpting Tool Set, Play Mat/Rolling Pin Set, p. 145

Using purple Kandy Clay, roll a ball for head. Using Sculpting Tool, carve a smile line. To make facial features, roll flat balls of purple for cheeks, flat balls of white for eyes and nose and small balls of brown for pupils. To make hat, roll a white ball with flat bottom. Make a flat log of white for brim; attach with drops of water. To make legs, roll small logs of purple. Attach all pieces with drops of water. Each serves 1.

*Brand edible modeling clay.

▼ Petal Perk-Ups

Pan: 10½ x 15½ x 1 in. Jelly Roll, p. 160
Color: Lemon Yellow, p. 127
Fondant: White Ready-To-Use Rolled Fondant (24 oz. needed), p. 122; Pink IcingWriter™, p. 124; FoodWriter™ in Bold Tip/Primary Colors, p. 124; Round Cut-Outs™, p. 123; Brush Set, p. 125
Recipe: Buttercream Icing, p. 111
Also: Flower Stencil-A-Cookie™ Cutter and Stencil Set, p. 141; Cake Board, Fanci-Foil Wrap, p. 217

From 1 in. high cake, cut cakes using flower cutter. For each cake, tint a 4 in. ball of fondant lemon yellow and a 1 in. ball dark lemon yellow. Prepare cakes and cover with lemon yellow fondant. Draw petals and dots with pink Icing Writer. Roll out dark yellow fondant and cut flower center using medium round Cut-Out; attach to flower with damp brush. Roll tiny balls of white fondant for eyes; flatten and attach with damp brush. Draw pupils and mouth with black FoodWriter. Each serves 1.

▶ Dino Bites

Pan: Mini Dinosaur, p. 161; Cookie Sheet, Cooling Grid, p. 160
Tips: 2, 2A, 3, 6, 8, 10, 352, p. 136-137
Colors: Violet, Leaf Green, Lemon Yellow, Black, p. 127
Recipes: Buttercream Icing, p. 111
Also: White Candy Melts®†, p. 146, toothpick

Cover cakes with melted candy (p. 118); let set. Using buttercream, pipe tip 10 right leg (below head). Pipe tip 2A body with tail. Add tip 10 leg near tail. Overpipe stomach with tip 3 lines. Pipe tip 6 outline lower jaw. Pipe tip 8 face and eyebrows. Add tip 6 ball eyes and tip 2 dot pupils and nostrils. Pipe tip 2 pull-out arms with dot fingers. Pipe tip 352 spikes. Each serves 1.

†Brand confectionery coating.

◀ High-Powered Flower

Cookies: Metal Gingerbread Boy Cutter, p. 140; Metal Nesting Blossoms Cutter Set, p. 140; Cookie Sheet, Cooling Grid, p. 160
Tips: 2, 5, 6, 352, p. 136-137
Colors: Rose, Lemon Yellow, Black, Kelly Green, p. 127
Recipes: Royal Icing, p. 111; Roll-Out Cookie, p. 112
Also: Parchment Triangles, p. 134; Meringue Powder, p. 126; cornstarch

Tint a portion of dough green and use gingerbread cutter to cut body. Using second smallest blossom cutter and plain dough, cut flower. Bake and cool cookies. Outline and pipe in petals and face with tip 6 (smooth with finger dipped in cornstarch). Pipe tip 2 mouth, dot nose and cheeks, outline eyebrows. Pipe tip 5 outline arms and legs; add tip 352 leaf hands and feet. Attach flower head to body with icing; support underneath top of flower with another cookie until set. Each serves 1.

◀ What's Your Game?

Pan: Mini Ball, p. 164
Fondant: White Ready-To-Use Rolled Fondant (24 oz. needed), p. 122; Fondant Multi Packs in Natural and Primary Colors, p. 122; Red Brush-On Color™, p. 124; FoodWriter™ in Bold Tip/Primary Colors, p. 124; Cutter/Embosser, Brush Set, Rolling Pin, p. 125
Recipes: Buttercream Icing, p. 111

Bake and cool mini ball cakes; prepare and cover with white or brown fondant (p. 105). For baseball: Use wavy-edge of Embosser to imprint stitching lines. Paint stitches with Brush-On Color. For basketball: Use straight-edge wheel of Embosser to lightly imprint division lines; color in lines with black FoodWriter. Make a ½ in. diameter rope of red fondant for rim; cut to size but do not attach. Roll eight ¼ in. diameter ropes of white fondant for net; crisscross and attach to rim and at intersection points with damp brush. Trim edges. Position rim and net, trimming edges as needed. Each serves 1.

◀ Buzzin' By

Pan: Mini Egg, p. 180
Colors: Lemon Yellow, Golden Yellow, Black, p. 127
Fondant: White Ready-To-Use Rolled Fondant (24 oz. needed), p. 122; Heart Cut-Outs™, p. 123; Cutter/Embosser, Brush Set, Roll & Cut Mat, Rolling Pin, p. 125; FoodWriter™ in Bold Tip/Primary Colors, p. 124
Recipes: Buttercream Icing, p. 111
Also: Cake Board, Fanci-Foil Wrap, p. 217

Ice cakes smooth. The wide end of egg cake will be the front. Tint portions of fondant yellow (combine lemon yellow and golden yellow) and black. Reserve a portion of white. Cover front third of cake with yellow fondant. Cut 2 strips of black fondant and 2 strips of yellow fondant, each ½ in. wide. Position on cake, alternating colors. Cover remaining area of cake with black fondant. For stinger, roll black fondant into a ¾ in. long cone and attach with damp brush. Cut wing using white fondant and large heart Cut-Out; trim 1 in. off pointed end. Imprint dotted lines using ridged wheel from Embosser. Attach wing to cake with damp brush. For eye, roll a small ball of white fondant, flatten and attach. Draw pupil and mouth using black FoodWriter. Each serves 1.

▼ Munchable Moby

Pan: Mini Loaf, p. 160
Color: Royal Blue, p. 127
Candy: Kandy Clay™* Color Packs in Crystal Punch Light Blue, Chocolate Brown, Marshmallow White, p. 145; Scissors/Sculpting Tool Set, p. 144; Apron, p. 144; White Candy Melts®†, p. 146
Also: Piping Gel, p. 126; Disposable Decorating Bags, p. 134

In advance: Make candy plaque (p. 119) in mini loaf pan, using melted white candy.

For whale: Using light blue Kandy Clay, make a large teardrop shape for body. Flatten end and fan out into points for the tail, then curl straight up. Carve smile and tail lines with sculpting tool. Make flat balls for eyes and pupils using white and brown clay; attach with drops of water. Position whale on candy plaque. Pipe water around whale using blue-tinted Piping Gel in cut disposable bag. Each serves 1.

▲ Stuffed to the Gills

Pan: Mini Ball, p. 164
Also: Candy Melts®† in Yellow, Green, p. 146; Disposable Decorating Bags, p. 134; jelly fruit slices, white gumballs, black spice drops, scissors, assorted candies

Make 2 candy shells (p. 119) in mini ball pan for each fish: Pipe dots of melted green candy in pan cavities using cut bag, refrigerate until firm, then fill with melted yellow candy. For eyes, cut gumballs in half. For pupils, cut pieces of spice drops. For top and side fins, cut fruit slices in half. For back fin, cut a piece off fruit slice to even at back. For lips, cut 2 pieces from fruit slice. Attach all features with melted candy. Fill shell with assorted candies. Each serves 1.

▲ Fun Fast Food

Pan: Standard Muffin, p. 160
Candy: Kandy Clay™* Multi-Color Packs in Pastel and Primary Colors (Green Apple Green, Peanut Butter Light Brown, Chocolate Brown, Cherry Red, Lemon Yellow needed), p. 145; Tool Sets: PlayMat/Rolling Pin and Scissors/Sculpting Tools, p. 145
Recipes: Buttercream Icing, p. 111
Also: Assorted Pastel Standard Baking Cups, p. 150; Round Cut-Outs™, p. 123; Decorator Brush Set, p. 147

Ice cupcake tops smooth. Make Kandy Clay taco: Roll out light brown clay and cut shell using largest round Cut-Out. For lettuce, break off small pieces of green clay and attach to edge of shell with drops of water. For meat, roll a ball, flatten and form a half-circle; use sculpting tool to cut random slits. Place meat in shell and fold shell up. For cheese and tomato, break off small pieces of yellow and red; place in shell. Make Kandy Clay hamburger: Roll out and cut light brown bun top and bottom, green lettuce, dark brown meat patty using medium round Cut-Out. Round off bun top and bottom and meat patty with fingers. Use sculpting tool to cut notches in lettuce. Position lettuce and patty on bottom bun. For cheese, roll out yellow clay and cut a square with sculpting tool. For ketchup, break off pieces of red clay. For sesame seeds, roll small teardrop shapes from light brown clay; flatten and attach to top bun with a drop of water. Position cheese, ketchup and top bun. Position taco and hamburger on cupcakes. Each serves 1.

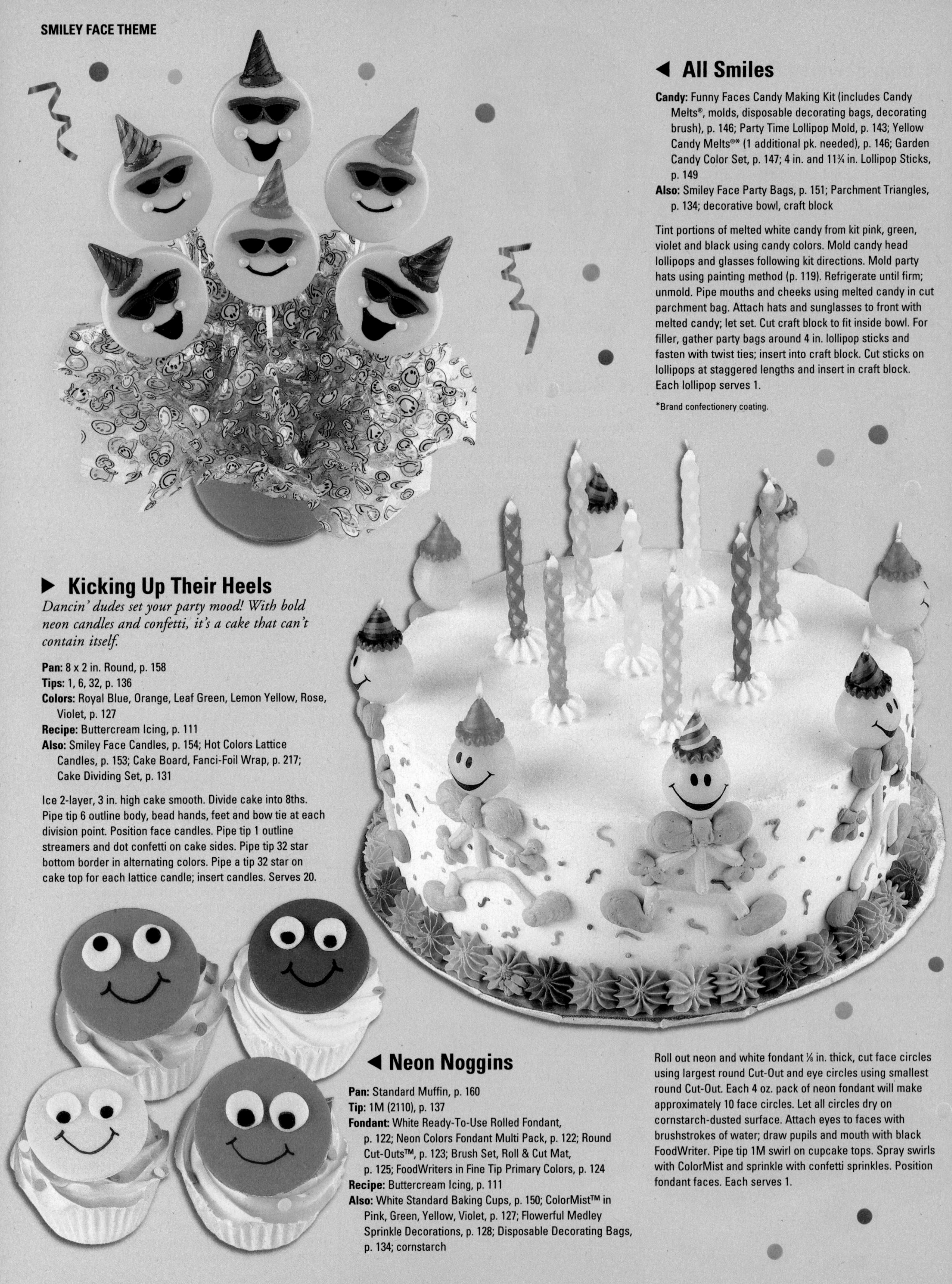

◀ All Smiles

Candy: Funny Faces Candy Making Kit (includes Candy Melts®, molds, disposable decorating bags, decorating brush), p. 146; Party Time Lollipop Mold, p. 143; Yellow Candy Melts®* (1 additional pk. needed), p. 146; Garden Candy Color Set, p. 147; 4 in. and 11¾ in. Lollipop Sticks, p. 149

Also: Smiley Face Party Bags, p. 151; Parchment Triangles, p. 134; decorative bowl, craft block

Tint portions of melted white candy from kit pink, green, violet and black using candy colors. Mold candy head lollipops and glasses following kit directions. Mold party hats using painting method (p. 119). Refrigerate until firm; unmold. Pipe mouths and cheeks using melted candy in cut parchment bag. Attach hats and sunglasses to front with melted candy; let set. Cut craft block to fit inside bowl. For filler, gather party bags around 4 in. lollipop sticks and fasten with twist ties; insert into craft block. Cut sticks on lollipops at staggered lengths and insert in craft block. Each lollipop serves 1.

*Brand confectionery coating.

▶ Kicking Up Their Heels

Dancin' dudes set your party mood! With bold neon candles and confetti, it's a cake that can't contain itself.

Pan: 8 x 2 in. Round, p. 158

Tips: 1, 6, 32, p. 136

Colors: Royal Blue, Orange, Leaf Green, Lemon Yellow, Rose, Violet, p. 127

Recipe: Buttercream Icing, p. 111

Also: Smiley Face Candles, p. 154; Hot Colors Lattice Candles, p. 153; Cake Board, Fanci-Foil Wrap, p. 217; Cake Dividing Set, p. 131

Ice 2-layer, 3 in. high cake smooth. Divide cake into 8ths. Pipe tip 6 outline body, bead hands, feet and bow tie at each division point. Position face candles. Pipe tip 1 outline streamers and dot confetti on cake sides. Pipe tip 32 star bottom border in alternating colors. Pipe a tip 32 star on cake top for each lattice candle; insert candles. Serves 20.

◀ Neon Noggins

Pan: Standard Muffin, p. 160

Tip: 1M (2110), p. 137

Fondant: White Ready-To-Use Rolled Fondant, p. 122; Neon Colors Fondant Multi Pack, p. 122; Round Cut-Outs™, p. 123; Brush Set, Roll & Cut Mat, p. 125; FoodWriters in Fine Tip Primary Colors, p. 124

Recipe: Buttercream Icing, p. 111

Also: White Standard Baking Cups, p. 150; ColorMist™ in Pink, Green, Yellow, Violet, p. 127; Flowerful Medley Sprinkle Decorations, p. 128; Disposable Decorating Bags, p. 134; cornstarch

Roll out neon and white fondant ⅛ in. thick, cut face circles using largest round Cut-Out and eye circles using smallest round Cut-Out. Each 4 oz. pack of neon fondant will make approximately 10 face circles. Let all circles dry on cornstarch-dusted surface. Attach eyes to faces with brushstrokes of water; draw pupils and mouth with black FoodWriter. Pipe tip 1M swirl on cupcake tops. Spray swirls with ColorMist and sprinkle with confetti sprinkles. Position fondant faces. Each serves 1.

◀ More Smiles Per Gallon

Pan: 3-D Cruiser, p. 165
Tips: 12, 16, 21, p. 136
Colors:* Rose, Violet, Lemon Yellow, Leaf Green, Orange, Black, p. 127
Candy: Smiley Face Lollipop Mold, p. 148; Candy Melts®* in Dark Cocoa, Yellow, p. 146; Garden Candy Color Set, p. 147; Decorator Brush Set, p. 147
Recipe: Buttercream Icing, p. 111
Also: Flower and Round Cut-Outs™, p. 123; 8 in. Tapered Spatula, p. 134; Parchment Triangles, p. 134; Cake Board, Fanci-Foil Wrap, p. 217

In advance: Make candy faces. Tint melted cocoa candy black using candy color. Mold faces using painting method for eyes (p. 119); refrigerate until firm, unmold. For mouths, pipe smile line using melted candy in cut parchment bag.

Ice window areas of cake smooth. Randomly imprint cake with medium flower Cut-Out and smallest round Cut-Out for flower centers. Fill in flower areas and cover car body with tip 16 stars; overpipe wheel wells for dimension. Ice smooth yellow tire axles. Pipe tip 21 swirl tires. Add tip 12 band side rails and bumpers. Pipe tip 16 rosette tail lights and swirl headlights. Attach candy faces with dots of buttercream. Add tip 16 star window frame for side windows. Serves 12.

***Note:** Combine Lemon Yellow and Leaf Green for shade shown.

*Brand confectionery coating.

▶ Just For Grins!

What's behind his big smile? An eye-catching fondant-covered cake board, loaded with cut-out fondant gifts, streamers and confetti.

Pan: Soccer Ball, p. 164
Tip: 12, p. 136
Colors: Orange, Lemon Yellow, Rose, Royal Blue, Black, Leaf Green, Violet, p. 127
Fondant: White Ready-To-Use Rolled Fondant (72 oz. needed), p. 122; Square Cut-Outs™, p. 123; Easy-Glide Fondant Smoothers, Brush Set, Cutter/Embosser, p. 125
Recipe: Buttercream Icing, p. 111
Also: 16 in. Cake Circles (2 needed), Fanci-Foil Wrap, p. 217; Piping Gel, p. 126; cellophane tape

Tape two 16 in. cake circles together and cover with foil. Lightly cover board with Piping Gel. Tint 30 oz. of fondant violet, roll out and cover board. Divide 18 oz. of fondant into 6th; tint black, orange, green, blue, rose, leave remainder white. Using medium square Cut-Out, cut 8 spaces for gifts on board. Cut 8 gifts from tinted fondant and inlay into open spaces on board; smooth with Fondant Smoothers. For ribbons and bows on gifts, cut ¼ in. wide strips of white fondant; attach with damp brush. Roll and attach small balls of white fondant for knots. Using various colors of fondant, cut confetti with small end of tip 12 and attach. Cut thin strips for streamers using straight edge wheel of Cutter/Embosser; roll loosely around brush handle, slide off and attach with damp brush.

Tint 24 oz. fondant yellow. Prepare cake and cover with fondant (p. 105). Position cake on board. Roll out and cut white fondant ovals for eyes and black fondant circles for pupils. Roll thin rope of black fondant for mouth. For hat, cut a 4 in. triangle from orange fondant and position. For fringe, cut ½ in. strips of green fondant and cut slits at ends. Attach 2 or 3 rows to bottom of hat with damp brush. For pompom, repeat process but roll from end to end; attach to top of hat with damp brush. Serves 12.

▲ Malt Shoppe Memories

Our fondant soda fountain really takes you back. It's definitely a "conversation cake," thanks to great details like the hand-cut tile floor, lollipop stick stools and cool ice cream treat candles.

Pan: Long Loaf, p. 160
Tips: 1A, 18, 127D, p. 136-137
Colors: Black, Rose, Red-Red, Christmas Red, p. 127
Fondant: White Ready-To-Use Rolled Fondant (48 oz. needed), p. 122; Square Cut-Outs™, p. 123; Roll & Cut Mat, Rolling Pin, p. 125
Recipe: Buttercream Icing, p. 111
Also: 2005 Pattern Book (Backdrop and Easel Back), p. 222; 13 x 19 in. Cake Boards, Silver Fanci-Foil Wrap, p. 217; Ice Cream Candle Set, p. 154; Piping Gel, p. 126; 4 in. Lollipop Sticks, p. 149; Decorator Brush Set, p. 147; large spice drops, mini jawbreakers, colored markers or pencils, glue, cellophane tape

In advance: Prepare floor, countertop and seats. Tint 12 oz. fondant black, 6 oz. gray. To make floor, cut two cake boards to 18½ x 9½ in., tape together and wrap with foil. Roll out 12 oz. black and 12 oz. white fondant ⅛ in. thick and cut tiles using medium square Cut-Out. You will need approximately 30 black and 30 white tiles; cut 4 at a time and attach in alternating fashion to board which has been lightly brushed with Piping Gel.

Make countertop. Cut a cake board to 17 x 5½ in.; wrap with foil. Lightly brush board with Piping Gel and cover with white fondant. Roll out gray fondant and cut ¾ in. wide strips; attach to each countertop edge with Piping Gel. To make seats: For posts, cut 4 lollipop sticks to 2¾ in. long, lightly brush with Piping Gel and cover with gray fondant. For base, cut gray fondant circle with large end of tip 1A . Make a hole in center of base with lollipop stick. For cushions, roll out gray fondant and Red-Red/Christmas Red combination fondant slightly less than ¼ in. thick; cut circles with large end of tip 127D. Stack red circle on gray; shape the rounded top with fingertips. Make a hole in bottom center of seat with lollipop stick. Let all seat pieces dry. Attach seat pieces with gray fondant thinned with water to piping consistency.

Ice 2-layer cake smooth; position on floor. Position countertop on cake top. Using Red-Red color, tint a small amount of fondant pink, roll out and cut napkins using medium square Cut-Out. Cut some squares in half for single-thick napkins and fold others in half for thicker napkins. For spoons, cut a 1 x ¾ in. piece of gray fondant for handle; roll and flatten a small ball for spoon end; attach with piping gel. For extra sundaes, cut rounded end off spice drops, pipe tip 18 rosettes on wide end; position red jawbreakers for cherries. Cut out backdrop pattern and color areas with markers or colored pencils. Attach to cake board, cut to fit. Trace easel back pattern and cut from cake board. Attach with glue to backdrop. Position napkins, spoons, candles and additional sundaes. Position stools and backdrop. Serves 12.

▶ Fiesta Time

Pan: Juggling Clown, p. 162
Tips: 3, 5, 16, 21, p. 136-137
Colors:* Red-Red, Violet, Black, Brown, Creamy Peach, p. 127
Recipe: Buttercream Icing, p. 111
Also: 2005 Pattern Book (Hombre), p. 222; Chocolate Ready-To-Use Decorator Icing, p. 126; Fiesta Candle Set, p. 154; Cake Board, Fanci-Foil Wrap, p. 217; toothpick, cornstarch

Trim tie area off cake. Ice sides and background areas smooth. Lightly ice remainder of cake top and trace pattern with toothpick. Outline shoes, body, head, eyes, mouth and hat with tip 3. Pipe in shoes, shirt, mouth, tongue, whites of eyes, pupils and underside of hat with tip 3 (smooth with finger dipped in cornstarch). Cover pants, jacket, hands and face with tip 16 stars. Pipe tip 3 zigzag "ruffles" on shirt cuffs. Cover sash with tip 5 lines; add tip 3 dot trim on edge. Outline and pipe in bow tie with tip 5, building up to create a puffed look (smooth with finger dipped in cornstarch). Pipe tip 3 outline hair and moustache. Pipe tip 21 shell bottom border. Position candles. Serves 12.

***Note:** Combine Brown and Creamy Peach for skin tone shown. Add Black to Ready-To-Use Chocolate Icing for black shade shown.

◀ How You've Grown

Sometimes it's nice to let fun candles do most of the decorating. Our Farm Candle Set lets you present a great-looking theme cake with ease.

Pan: 8 x 2 in. Round, p. 158
Tips: 3, 14, 44, p. 136-137
Color: Kelly Green, p. 127
Recipe: Buttercream Icing, p. 111
Also: Farm Candle Set, p. 154; Make-Any-Message Letter Press Set, p. 132; Cake Dividing Set, p. 131; Cake Board, Fanci-Foil Wrap, p. 217

Ice 2-layer cake smooth; divide into 10ths. Pipe tip 44 band fence. Add tip 14 pull-out star grass. Imprint message with letter press set; print message with tip 3. Position candles. Serves 20.

◀ Frequent "Flyer"

Pan: Little Hero, p. 165
Tips: 2, 3, 4, 10, 16, 18, 21, 45, 127, p. 136-137
Colors:* Sky Blue, Royal Blue, Brown, Red-Red, Kelly Green, Black, Copper (skin tone), Lemon Yellow, Golden Yellow, p. 127
Cookie: Fish Plastic Cutter, p. 142; Cookie Sheet, Cooling Grid, p. 160
Recipe: Buttercream Icing, p. 111; Roll-Out Cookie, p. 112
Also: Decorator Brush Set, p. 147; Wooden Dowel Rods, p. 214; Cake Board, Fanci-Foil Wrap, p. 217; rolling pin, black shoestring licorice, paper towel.

In advance: Cut and bake fish cookie; let cool. Ice smooth; pipe tip 3 zigzag fins and tail, dot eye. For fishing pole, brush dowel rod with brown icing color thinned with water; wipe off excess with paper towel and let dry.

Trim hose area off cake. Ice sides and background areas smooth. Outline boots, body, head, eyes, mouth and hat with tip 4. Pipe in boots with tip 10 (smooth with finger dipped in cornstarch). Pipe in eyes, inside sleeves, top and underside of hat with tip 4 (smooth with finger dipped in cornstarch). Pipe tip 3 dot pupils (smooth with finger dipped in cornstarch); add tip 3 outline mouth. Cover face, shirt and pants with tip 16 stars; overpipe nose. Cover vest with tip 18 stars. Pipe tip 3 outline ears and vest pockets. Fill in pockets with tip 16 stars and add tip 3 dot buttons. Pipe tip 127 ruffle hat brim; add tip 45 band. Pipe tip 2 zigzag flies on hatband. Pipe tip 3 pull-out hair. Pipe tip 21 C-motion bottom border. For licorice fishing line, cut ½ in. long slits at 2½, 3½ and 8½ in. increments; thread pole through slits. Position pole in hand area, outline hands with tip 3 and overpipe with tip 16 stars. Pipe a tip 3 dot mouth on fish and insert licorice line. Serves 12.

***Note:** Combine Sky Blue and Royal Blue for blue shade shown.

▶ Indy-scribable Excitement!

The country's fastest-growing sport deserves a cake that's built for speed. Cookie pop flags and a sleek candy car rev up the excitement.

Pans: 12 x 2 in. Round, p. 158; Cookie Sheet. Cooling Grid, p. 160
Tips: 3, 5, 7, 13, 14, 21, p. 136-137
Colors: Leaf Green, Lemon Yellow, Violet, Black, p. 127
Candy: Cruisin' Candy Kit (includes Candy Melts®*, molds, bags and brush), p. 146; Candy Melts*† in Red (2 pks.) and White (1 pk.), p. 146; Garden Candy Color Set, p. 147; 4 in. Lollipop Sticks, p. 149
Recipes: Buttercream Icing, p. 111; Roll-Out Cookie, p. 112
Also: 101 Cookie Cutters Set, p. 142; Cake Board, Fanci-Foil Wrap, p. 217

In advance: Tint portion of white candy black using candy color. Using molds from kit and painting method (p. 119), mold car, 4 wheels, spoiler, numbers and lightning bolts. Refrigerate until firm; unmold. Attach wheels, numbers, lightning bolts and spoiler to car with melted candy. Set aside. Roll out cookie dough and use flag cutter from set to cut 2 flags. Cut ball portion off flagpoles; turn one cookie over so each flag faces a different direction. Bake and cool. Attach lollipop sticks to backs of cookies with melted candy; let set. Turn cookies over and cover with tip 14 stars in checkerboard pattern, piping squares of 4 stars each. Pipe tip 7 outline flagpole. Set aside.

Ice 2-layer, 3 in. high cake smooth. Outline road with tip 7. Pipe tip 21 alternating star bottom border. On cake sides, pipe tip 13 star flags with tip 3 outline flagpoles. Write tip 5 message. Position car on top of cake and insert flag cookies. Serves 40.

†**Note:** Candy Melts in kit will not be enough to make car as shown. You will need additional Candy Melts indicated.

*Brand confectionery coating.

▲ Making the Rounds

Our versatile 3-D Cruiser can pull up at any party! On this golf cart, we reshaped the center seat, then added the easy fondant roof, bags and clubs.

Pan: 3-D Cruiser, p. 165
Tips: 3, 4, 16, 21, p. 136-137
Colors: Black, Red-Red, Lemon Yellow, Royal Blue, p. 127
Recipe: Buttercream Icing, p. 111
Also: White Ready-To-Use Rolled Fondant, p. 122; 8 in. Cookie Treat Sticks, p. 143; 4 in. Lollipop Sticks, p. 149; Flower Nail No. 7, p. 134; 13 x 19 in. Cake Boards, Fanci-Foil Wrap, p. 217, 8 in. Straight Spatula, p. 134, craft knife, ruler, cornstarch

Bake and cool cake using firm-textured batter. Trim off passenger area of cake. Cut out a 2¼ in. wide seating area starting 4 in. from front of cake and extending halfway down from top; cut front of seating area at a diagonal. Trim off angled bumper and bottom areas of cake to straighten.

Ice seating area smooth. Pipe tip 4 zigzag bumper, hood trim and running boards (pat smooth with finger dipped in cornstarch). Pipe tip 4 dot axles and tip 21 swirl tires.

Tint a 3 in. ball of fondant light gray. Roll out and cut a 1¾ x 3½ in. seat; attach with icing. Insert 2 lollipop sticks behind seat, 2 in. apart. Cut two 1¼ x 2½ in. seat backs; attach with brushstrokes of water, sandwiching sticks in the center. Reserve remaining gray fondant. Ice section behind seat backs smooth. Cover cart with tip 16 stars. Print tip 3 name.

Tint a small portion of fondant black and cover head of flower nail. Cut away 4 sections to resemble steering wheel and insert nail into cake. For golf bags, tint 2 in. balls of fondant yellow and blue and shape into logs. Flatten one end and indent with finger at other end to form opening for clubs. For pockets, roll and cut small ovals; imprint grooves with spatula edge and attach to side of bag with icing. Cut a ¼ x 2½ in. strap; attach. Using reserved gray fondant, roll ¼ in. balls for club heads; insert on lollipop sticks and shape. Insert clubs in bags.

Insert cookie sticks for roof poles. Cut a 7 x 4½ in. piece of cake board; cover with fondant. Attach roof to sticks with fondant thinned with water. Serves 12.

Celebrate La Quinceañera with Color!

A sweeping display of pretty pastels is the perfect way to capture the excitement of the Quinceañera celebration! Your coordinated party scene begins with a towering multi-tiered cake, surrounded by 8 soft-toned satellite cakes, each topped with a gorgeous rose bouquet. Complete the look with our lovely Celebration Doll, shown below, accompanied by a quintet of doll cakes in pretty pastel fondant gowns.

▼ Court of Honor

Pan: Classic Wonder Mold, p. 161
Tips: 2, 12, 104, 225, p. 136-137
Colors: Creamy Peach, Rose, Kelly Green, Violet, Lemon Yellow, p. 127
Recipes: Buttercream, Royal Icings, p. 111
Also: Teen Doll Pick (5 needed), p. 161; White Ready-To-Use Rolled Fondant (240 oz. needed), p. 122; 12 in. Round Silver Cake Bases (3 pks.), p. 217; Meringue Powder, p. 126; Flower Nail No. 7, p. 134; Cake Dividing Set, p. 131; Decorator Brush Set, p. 147; Celebration Doll, p. 205; ⅜ in. wide white ribbon

In advance: Using royal icing and flower nail, make 100 tip 104 roses with tip 12 bases (20 roses for each cake). Make 175 tip 225 drop flowers with tip 2 dot centers (35 for each cake). Make extras to allow for breakage; let dry.

Ice cakes smooth in buttercream and position on bases. To create folds in dress, using 24 oz. of fondant per cake, roll 8 logs measuring 6 x ¾ in. diameter at one end, tapering to a small point at other end. Divide cake into 8ths and attach 1 fondant log at each division point, positioning wide end at bottom. For various color skirts, tint 24 oz. of fondant for each doll; roll out and cover cake. Insert doll pick. For bodice, cut a 6 x 2 in. wide strip of matching color fondant and attach to pick with damp brush. For straps, bodice trim and waist band, cut ¼ in. wide strips and attach with damp brush. Attach roses at bottom border and drop flowers on skirts with tip 2 dots of buttercream. For held flower, cut 6 in. length of ribbon, fold in half and place in doll's hand; attach rose with buttercream.

At reception, position cakes and Celebration Doll. Each cake serves 12.

▶ Pastel Quinceañera

Pans: 6, 8, 10, 14 x 2 in. Round, p. 159
Tips: 2, 6, 7, 10, 12, 102, 103, 104, 225, 352, p. 136-137
Colors: Lemon Yellow, Creamy Peach, Rose, Violet, Kelly Green, p. 127
Recipes: Buttercream, Royal Icings, p. 111
Also: Crystal Light Separator Ring Set, p. 215; Cake Boards, Fanci-Foil Wrap, p. 217; Meringue Powder, p. 126; White Tulle Circles (2 pks.), p. 210; 6mm White Pearl Beading* (1 pk. needed), p. 210; Hidden Pillars, p. 215; Plastic Dowel Rods, p. 214; Cake Dividing Set, p. 131; ¾ in. deep plywood for base, 6 in. white florist wires (315 needed), white florist tape, needle-nose pliers, waxed paper, cornstarch, 2 in. wide white ribbon (9 ft. needed), hot glue gun

In advance: Prepare plywood base for cake: Position 14 in. separator ring in center of board. Place eight 8 in. cake circles, ⅜ in. apart, around separator ring. Trace around all circles, then cut plywood 1 in. larger around all sides. Wrap board with foil. Attach ribbon to edges of board with hot glue; set aside.

In advance: Using royal icing, make the following flowers: 119 tip 102 roses with tip 7 bases, 116 tip 103 roses with tip 10 bases, 72 tip 104 roses with tip 12 bases and 450 tip 225 drop flowers with tip 2 dot centers. Make extras of all to allow for breakage and let dry.

In advance: Make wired bases for roses and leaves: On 270 white florist wires, use pliers to bend one end for hooks. For 135 roses that will be used in bouquets, using royal icing on waxed paper squares, pipe tip 6 mound bases. Immediately insert hooked end of wire into mound. Let dry overnight. Make 135 tip 352 leaves on wired stems (p. 116). Make extras to allow for breakage; let dry. When dry, attach the following roses to wired bases with tip 6 dots of royal icing: 27 tip 102, 36 tip 103 and 72 tip 104; let dry.

Make 45 tulle puffs. Gather a tulle circle in center and secure with wire. Make 9 bouquets, each with 3 tip 102 roses, 4 tip 103 roses and 8 tip 104 roses. Begin by assembling 5 bunches, each with 3 roses, 2 leaves and 1 tulle puff; wrap each bunch with floral tape. Assemble 5 bunches into a bouquet, add 5 more leaves, then wrap with floral tape. Trim stems of wires to extend 2 in. beyond bottom of bouquet. Set bouquets aside.

Ice smooth 2-layer 6, 10, 14 in. cakes in buttercream and prepare for Plate and Pillar Construction (p. 110). Place eight 1-layer 8 in. cakes on same size cake circles and ice smooth. Place 6 in. cake on 8 in. plate from Separator Set. Divide cake into 5ths; attach 20 tip 102 roses, placing 1 at each division point and 3 in between to form swags. Attach pearl beading for bottom border. Randomly attach 30 drop flowers to sides and top of cake. Cut a hidden pillar to 4 in. long. Insert into top center of cake; remove cake from inside pillar and reposition pillar in cake to hold bouquet at reception. Place 10 in. cake on 12 in. plate from Separator Set and divide into 8ths; attach 32 tip 102 roses in swag formation as above. Attach pearl beading for bottom border*. Randomly attach 55 drop flowers as above. Place 14 in. cake on 16 in. plate from Separator Set and divide in 10ths; repeat swag formation using 40 tip 102 roses. Attach pearl beading for bottom border. Randomly attach 85 drop flowers as above.

Position 14 in. Crystal Light Plate in center of base board. Position 8 in. cakes around plate. Pipe tip 18 shell bottom borders. Attach ten tip 103 roses around outer edge of each cake, forming a continuous rose border. Cut 3 hidden pillars into 2 in. sections. Insert 1 section into center of each cake as on 6 in. cake to hold bouquets. Randomly attach 35 drop flowers as above.

At reception, position large separator ring on 14 in. center plate, then position 14 in. cake. Position 10 in. plate from set on 14 in. cake, topped by medium separator ring, then position 10 in. cake, with 6 in. plate from set on top. Position small separator ring, then 6 in. cake. Insert bouquets in hidden pillars. Serves 263.

***Note:** Remove pearls before cutting and serving.

◀ Fun's a Shore Thing

Your personal stretch of Hawaiian beach is shaded with a candy shell umbrella and adorned with vibrant island flowers.

Pans: 10 x 2 in. Round, p. 158; Sports Ball Set, p. 164
Tips: 1B, 3, 5, 366, p. 136-137
Colors: Orange, Violet, Lemon Yellow, Rose, Leaf Green, Royal Blue, p. 127
Recipes: Buttercream, Royal Icings, p. 111
Also: Beach Sandals Candles, p. 154; Yellow Candy Melts®** (2 pks. needed), p. 146; Cake Board, Fanci-Foil Wrap, p. 217; Meringue Powder, p. 126; Piping Gel, p. 126, granulated brown sugar, waxed paper, candy stick

In advance: On waxed paper-covered board, pipe the following tip 1B swirl flowers in royal icing: 8 each in orange, violet, rose and yellow. Add tip 3 yellow dot centers. Make extras to allow for breakage and let dry.

In advance: Make candy shell (p. 119) umbrella in sports ball pan half, filling to 1 in. below lip. Place in freezer to set, unmold and let come to room temperature. Mark edge of shell in 4ths, then 8ths with dots of royal icing; add two additional dots to each section for a total of 24. Pipe tip 5 lines from edge to top center of shell in royal icing; add a tip 5 ball at center. Let dry, then place ball in freezer for 5 minutes to chill. Attach candy stick to bottom of shell with melted candy.

Ice 2-layer 3 in. high cake smooth with white top and yellow sides. Pipe tip 366 leaf bottom border. Position flowers to form lei. Tint piping gel blue and spread on section of cake top. Cover rest of cake top with brown sugar. Print tip 3 message. Position umbrella and candles. Serves 28.

**Brand confectionery coating.

▶ Be a Bird Watcher

The toucan will be the talk of the party—his layer upon layer of feathers, made with leaf tip 67, create bold texture.

Pan: Partysaurus, p. 162
Tips: 2A, 3, 4, 6, 16, 18, 67, p. 136-137
Colors:* Lemon Yellow, Leaf Green, Violet, Rose, Royal Blue, Brown, Orange, p. 127
Recipe: Buttercream Icing, p. 111
Also: 2005 Pattern Book (Beak, Tail Feathers, Body, Wings), p. 222; Cake Boards, Fanci-Foil Wrap, p. 217; Parchment Triangles, p. 134; cellophane tape, cornstarch, toothpick

Using patterns and cake board, cut out beak and tail feathers. Wrap in Fanci-Foil and secure with tape. Ice sides and background areas of cake smooth. Pipe tip 18 reverse shell bottom border. Attach beak and tail feathers to cake with icing. Lightly ice body and wing areas and trace patterns with toothpick. Ice beak smooth in green. Overpipe yellow area with tip 4. Pipe tip 3 orange beak line. Pipe tip 6 ball eye, add tip 3 dot pupil. Cover head and throat area with tip 16 stars. Randomly drop violet and blue icing into prepared parchment bag. Cover wings and bottom tail feathers with tip 67 violet/blue leaves. Cover body and remaining tail feathers with tip 67 leaves. Pipe tip 2A zigzag perch (smooth with finger dipped in cornstarch). Outline feet with tip 4. Serves 12.

***Note:** Combine Leaf Green and Lemon Yellow for green beak.

▼ Big Fin-ish!

Pans: 8, 12 x 2 in. Round, p. 158; Sports Ball Set, p. 164
Tips: 2, 13, 18, 352, p. 136-137
Colors: Royal Blue, Orange, Leaf Green, Lemon Yellow, Rose, Violet, Brown, p. 127
Candy: Seashells Candy Mold, p. 148; 4 in. Lollipop Sticks, p. 149; Decorator Brush Set, p. 149
Recipe: Buttercream Icing, p. 111
Also: 2005 Pattern Book (Large and Small Top, Back and Side Fins), p. 222; White Ready-To-Use Rolled Fondant, p. 122; Tropical Fish Candle Set, p. 154; Gum-Tex™ Karaya, p. 125; Wooden Dowel Rods, p. 214; 6 in. Plate from Crystal Clear Cake Divider Set, p. 213; Cake Board, Fanci-Foil Wrap, p. 217, granulated brown sugar, sharp knife, ruler, cornstarch

At least 2 days in advance: Make fondant shells, fins and facial features: For shells, tint three 4 oz. portions of fondant light brown, medium orange and rose. Shape into three logs, 3 x ¼ in. Press logs together and gently blend with fingers for a marbled look. Press pieces into shell mold dusted with cornstarch; remove, brush off cornstarch and set aside. For eyes, roll two white balls, 1¼ in. diameter; insert lollipop sticks and set aside. Divide remaining fondant in half and tint violet and green. Roll and flatten two small violet balls for pupils and attach to eyes with damp brush. Roll two 1 x 1 in. violet logs for lips; insert lollipop sticks and set aside. Mix each color of remaining fondant with 1 teaspoon of Gum-Tex for added strength. For fins, roll out green fondant and, using patterns, cut out large top, back and side fins; let dry on cornstarch-dusted surface. Repeat for small top, back and side fins using violet fondant; attach to large fins with damp brush. Let fins dry at least 2 days. When dry, attach to lollipop sticks with fondant thinned with water.

Bake and cool ball cake (using firm-textured batter such as pound cake), 2-layer 8 in. cake and 1-layer 12 in. cake. Ice round cakes smooth and prepare for stacked construction (p. 110). Place ball cake on 6 in. plate and mark 1¾ in. wide sections. Cover sections with tip 18 stars. Insert fins and facial features and position ball cake on stacked round cakes. Pipe tip 352 outline coral on 8 in. cake. Pipe tip 2 dot bubbles. Add tip 13 pull-out star plants on round cakes. Sprinkle brown sugar around cakes and position shells. Position candles. Serves 72.

▶ Hula Dancers

The island experience gets closer for everyone with individual cakes made in the Mini Wonder Mold. With Doll Picks, a drop flower lei and a pull-out star grass skirt, decorating them is a tropical breeze.

Pan: Mini Wonder Mold, p. 161
Tips: 2, 3, 16, 225, p. 136-137
Colors: Golden Yellow, Leaf Green, Violet, Rose, Lemon Yellow, p. 127
Recipes: Buttercream, Royal Icings, p. 111
Also: Mini Doll Picks, p. 161; Meringue Powder, p. 126; Cake Board, Fanci-Foil Wrap, p. 217; waxed paper, cornstarch

In advance: Using royal icing, make 16 tip 225 drop flowers for each dancer (4 each in golden yellow, lemon yellow, violet and rose) with tip 3 lemon yellow dot centers. Make extras to allow for breakage and let dry.

Insert doll picks in cakes. In buttercream, starting at waistline, pipe tip 16 pull-out star grass skirt. Overpipe to build up waist. Pipe in tip 2 suit top and straps (smooth with finger dipped in cornstarch). Attach flowers for waist, lei and hair with dots of buttercream. Each serves 1.

▼ A Blaze of Glory

Get 'em fired up about turning 50! This scene is so much fun, with its frantic firemen and the crowd of candles on the rooftop, that your 50-ish friend won't be put out at all.

Pans: 8, 12 x 2 in. Round, p. 158; 9 x 5 in. Loaf, p. 160
Tips: 1, 2, 3, 7, 18, 129, 352, p. 136-137
Colors:* Lemon Yellow, Copper (skin tone), Brown, Rose, Violet, Kelly Green, Orange, Black, Red-Red, Christmas Red, p. 127

Recipes: Buttercream, Royal Icings, p. 111
Also: 2005 Pattern Book (Window, Door), p. 222; Cake Boards, Fanci-Foil Wrap, p. 217; Icing Sculptor™, p. 131; Cake Dividing Set; Meringue Powder, p. 126; Wooden Dowel Rods, p. 214; Assorted Celebration Candles, p. 152; chocolate sandwich cookies, toothpicks, cornstarch

In advance: Using royal icing, make 60 rose, 50 yellow and 50 violet tip 129 drop flowers with tip 2 white dot centers. Make extras to allow for breakage; let dry. Make 24 tip 18 rosette candleholders; immediately insert candles and set aside.

Prepare 2-layer round cakes for stacked construction (p. 110). Ice smooth in buttercream, icing sides about ½ in. thick, and immediately comb sides with yellow U-shaped blades from Icing Sculptor. Divide 6 in. cake into 6ths and 12 in. cake into 12ths. Using patterns, trace windows and door at division marks with toothpick. Pipe tip 3 zigzag windows, door and door window (smooth with finger dipped in cornstarch). Add tip 3 dot doorknob. Outline windows and door with tip 7; pipe tip 7 zigzag windowsills. Pipe tip 3 zigzag message clouds (smooth with finger dipped in cornstarch). Outline clouds with tip 3; print tip 1 messages. Attach drop flowers to bottom borders with tip 2 dots and add tip 352 leaves.

For fire engine, ice 2-layer loaf cake smooth. Using spatula, build up icing on top of engine cab to approximately 2¼ in. wide. Pipe tip 3 zigzag windows and headlights (smooth with finger dipped in cornstarch). Outline windows and add outline and zigzag details with tip 3. Pipe tip 7 outline ladder. Attach cookie wheels to cake sides with icing; pipe tip 7 dot axles.

On all cakes, pipe tip 7 ball heads with tip 2 dot facial features and string hair. Add tip 3 outline hands; add hats with dot badges on firemen. Position candles. Serves 68.

*Note: Combine Red-Red and Christmas Red for red shade shown.

▶ A Sassy 60

Celebrate 60 with bold oval cakes bordered by colorful streamers. In 30 years, do it again for their 90th!

Pan: Oval Set (10¾ x 7⅞ in. used), p. 159
Tips: 3, 18, 21, 101, p. 136-137
Colors:* Royal Blue, Lemon Yellow, Golden Yellow, Kelly Green, Red-Red, Christmas Red, Violet, p. 127
Recipe: Buttercream Icing, p. 111

Also: 2005 Pattern Book (Number 60), p. 222; Flowerful Medley Sprinkle Decorations, p. 128; Cake Boards, Fanci-Foil Wrap, p. 217; toothpick

Ice 1-layer cakes smooth. Trace number patterns on cake top with toothpick. Outline with tip 3; fill in numbers with tip 18 stars. Pipe tip 21 shell bottom borders. Overpipe shells with tip 101 wavy streamers in assorted colors. Sprinkle bottom border with confetti sprinkles. Each cake serves 20.

*Note: Combine Lemon Yellow and Golden Yellow for yellow shade shown. Combine Red-Red and Christmas Red for red.

◀ Slippery Slope

The pan is slightly askew, but your cake is right on target. Our zigzagging Topsy Turvy design shows that milestone birthdays can really shake you up!

Pan: Topsy Turvy, p. 162
Tips: 2, 3, 7, 12, p. 136-137
Colors: Violet, Red-Red, Black, Copper, Royal Blue, Brown, Lemon Yellow, Kelly Green, p. 127
Recipes: Buttercream, Royal Icings, p. 111
Also: 2005 Pattern Book (Dangling Man, Number 40), p. 222; Cake Board, Fanci-Foil Wrap, p. 217; Flowerful Medley Sprinkle Decorations, p. 128; Meringue Powder, p. 126, 4 in. Lollipop Sticks, p. 149, waxed paper

In advance: Using royal icing and waxed paper-covered patterns, make number 40 and man: Pipe in number using tip 12; let dry. For man, pipe in shirt, sleeves and pants with tip 12. Add tip 12 ball head. Pipe tip 2 pull-out hair, string eyebrows, dot eyes, mouth, hands and fingers. Add tip 7 outline shoes. Let dry. When man and number are dry, turn over and attach lollipop sticks with royal icing; let dry.

Ice cake smooth. Spatula ice fluffy top of each "tier" section; sprinkle with confetti sprinkles. Pipe tip 7 ball borders. Print tip 3 message. Insert man and number 40. Serves 12.

Star Power!

Be ready to take lots of pictures. You'll want to capture all the smiles when the birthday boy or girl sees their very own cake starring their very favorite character. Kids will know this day belongs to them when *Scooby Doo* or the *Fairly OddParents* pop in on a cookie place card or *Spider-Man* swings by on a skyscraper cake. Our ideas make it easy to put on a big production featuring today's biggest names.

Instructions for projects shown on these two pages are on page 32.

HAPPY BIRTHDAY
SCOOBY-DOO!

Perfect *Scooby* Snacks!

Scooby helps you solve the mystery of what to serve! Make quick and easy cupcakes decorated with Scooby toppers and shaped sprinkles.

Pan: Standard Muffin, p. 160
Tip: 1M (2110), p. 136
Recipe: Buttercream Icing, p. 111
Also: *Scooby-Doo!* Party Toppers, Shaped Sprinkles, Baking Cups, p. 191

Pipe tip 1M swirl on cupcake top. Sprinkle with shaped sprinkles. Position topper. Each serves 1.

Scooby is Soaring!

Cookies: 101 Cookie Cutters Set, p. 142; Cookie Sheet, Cooling Grid, p. 160
Tip: 5, p. 136
Colors: *Scooby-Doo!* Icing Color Set (brown, yellow, black, teal), p. 191; Red-Red, p. 127
Recipes: Royal Icing, p. 111; Roll-Out Cookie, p. 112
Also: *Scooby-Doo!* Icing Decorations, p. 191; Meringue Powder, p. 126; black shoestring licorice, waxed paper

Cut cookies using circle cutter from set; bake and cool. Cover cookies with thinned royal icing; let dry. Position cookies on waxed paper. Using full-strength royal icing, pipe tip 5 outline highlight and spiral balloon knot. Immediately insert 3½ in. piece of licorice into knot for string. Attach icing decoration with tip 5 dot of icing. Each serves 1.

A Sucker for Parties

It's nice to see a friendly face at your place! Fun lollipop-filled cups work as centerpieces or favors.

Pan: *Scooby-Doo!* Mini Treat, p. 191
Candy: Party Time Lollipop Mold, p. 148; Candy Melts®† in Light Cocoa, Yellow, Blue, Red, White, p. 146; Garden Candy Color Set, Decorator Brush Set, p. 147; 8 in. Lollipop Sticks, p. 149
Also: Parchment Triangles, p. 134; paper cup, colorful curling ribbon, uncooked pinto beans

Tint portions of melted white candy green, black and pink using candy colors. Mold *Scooby-Doo!* candy plaque (p. 119) ¼ in. deep in pan cavity, using melted candy in cut parchment bag to fill in detail areas. Mold lollipops and birthday hat candy using painting method (p. 119). Refrigerate until firm; unmold. Attach stick to back of candy plaque with additional melted candy.

Fill paper cup with beans and insert lollipops trimmed to staggered heights. Position curling ribbon in cup. Each serves 1.

Scooby Takes The Cake

Scooby won't be the only one excited about this cake! Be sure to have more candy stick "candles" on hand for all the kids to share.

Pan: *Scooby-Doo!*, p. 191
Tips: 2, 3, 4, 6, 12, 16, 21, p. 136-137
Colors: *Scooby-Doo!* Icing Color Set (brown, yellow, black, teal), p. 191; Lemon Yellow, Christmas Red, Creamy Peach, Orange, Violet, p. 127
Recipe: Buttercream Icing, p. 111
Also: 2005 Pattern Book (Tiered Cake), p. 222; Rainbow Jimmies Sprinkle Decorations, p. 128; 8 in. Tapered Spatula, p. 134; Cake Board, Fanci-Foil Wrap, p. 217; candy stick, cornstarch

SCOOBY-DOO!

Ice cake sides and background areas smooth. Position sprinkle decorations on cake sides. Mark tiered cake pattern on cake top. Using tip 3, outline *Scooby-Doo!* and tag. Using tip 4, pipe in whites of eyes; pipe in tip 3 dot pupils and eyebrows. Pipe in mouth, tongue, nose and ears with tip 4 zigzags; smooth with finger dipped in cornstarch. Pipe in tag using tip 4; smooth with finger dipped in cornstarch. Cover *Scooby* and collar with tip 16 stars.

Decorate *Scooby's* cake: Outline and pipe in plate with tip 4 zigzags; smooth with finger dipped in cornstarch. Ice individual tiers smooth with a spatula; add tip 2 stripes, swirls and dots on corresponding tiers. Pipe tip 12 icing swirls on tier tops; smooth slightly with a spatula. Pipe tip 6 pull-out dot flame on candy stick; insert into cake. Pipe tip 21 shell bottom border. Serves 12.

Scooby's Dreams Come True

Pans: 6, 8 x 2 in. Round, p. 159
Tip: 3, p. 136
Colors: Leaf Green, Lemon Yellow, Red-Red, Orange, Violet, Royal Blue, p. 127
Fondant: White Ready-To-Use Rolled Fondant (96 oz. needed), p. 122; Easy-Glide Fondant Smoother, p. 125; Star, Square Cut-Outs™, p. 123
Recipe: Buttercream Icing, p. 111
Also: *Scooby-Doo!* Candle, p. 191; Piping Gel, p. 127; Decorator Brush Set, p. 147; Dowel Rods, p. 214; 12 in. Cake Circles, p. 217

Tint approximately 60 oz. fondant Leaf Green mixed with Lemon Yellow. Tape two 12 in. cake circles together. Spread a thin layer of Piping Gel on circles and cover with fondant; smooth with Easy-Glide Smoother. Prepare 2-layer cakes for stacked construction (p. 110). Prepare cakes for fondant (p. 105); cover and smooth. Tint 16 oz. fondant yellow and 3 oz. each red, orange and violet. From yellow fondant, roll ½ in. diameter balls, attach to bottom borders with damp brush. Roll out red, orange, violet and yellow fondant ⅛ in. thick; cut gifts and stars using medium cut-outs; attach to cake with damp brush. In buttercream, pipe tip 3 swirls and dots on cakes and board. From yellow fondant, roll ⅜ in. diameter ropes for gift ribbons and bows; attach with damp brush. Position candle. Serves 32.

†Brand confectionery coating.

▲ Face-to-Face with *Spidey*

Cookies: *Spider-Man*™ Make-A-Cookie Face Kit (includes face cutter, tube decorating icing and gel, eye icing decorations), p. 190; Cookie Sheet, Cooling Grid, p. 160
Recipe: Roll-Out Cookie, p. 112
Also: *Spider-Man* Treat Bags, p. 190

Bake, ice and decorate cookies following kit instructions. Place in treat bags. Each serves 1.

▲ Web-Spinner's Cupcakes

Pan: Standard Muffin, p.160
Tip: 1, p. 136
Colors: Royal Blue, Violet, Black, p. 127
Recipe: Buttercream Icing, p. 111
Also: *Spider-Man* Icing Decorations, Standard Baking Cups, p. 190

Ice cupcakes smooth. Outline tip 1 web pattern on top of some cupcakes. leave others plain. Position icing decorations. Each serves 1.

▶ Skyscraping Spider

This extra-tall centerpiece sets the tone for a fun birthday. Watch for those jelly candy cars to "drive off" with the kids.

Pans: 6 x 3 in., 12 x 2 in. Round, p. 159
Tips: 2, 3, 4, 7, p. 136
Colors: No-Taste Red, Black, Golden Yellow, Lemon Yellow, Royal Blue, p. 127
Recipes: Buttercream, Color Flow Icings, p. 111
Also: 2005 Pattern Book (Peaked Roof Building, Five sizes of Buildings), p. 222; Color Flow Mix, p. 127; Cake Board, Fanci-Foil Wrap, p. 217; 6 in. Lollipop Sticks, p. 149; *Spider-Man* Candle, p. 190; Dowel Rods, p. 214; Parchment Triangles, p. 134; spice drops, round jelly candies, waxed paper

In advance: Using patterns, make the following Color Flow buildings (p. 118), making half of each size light gray and half darker gray: 2 peaked roof buildings, 4 tallest-size buildings and 6 of each remaining size buildings. Mark patterns on waxed paper and outline with tip 2 using full-strength Color Flow. Fill in with thinned Color Flow in a cut parchment bag; let dry. Pipe windows and doors using tip 4 and full-strength Color Flow; let dry. Attach lollipop sticks to back using full-strength Color Flow; let dry.

Prepare 1-layer 12 in. round (2 in. high) and 2-layer 6 in. round (one 3 in. and one 2 in. high for 5 in. high total). Ice smooth in buttercream and prepare for stacked construction (see p. 110).

Make cars: Slice off opposite sides of a round jelly candy to create a car body shape. Slice a matching color spice drop horizontally in half and attach to top with icing. Using buttercream, pipe tip 3 dot tires, hubcaps and windows.

Pipe tip 2 road lines. Position cars. Insert buildings around 6 in. cake. On 12 in. cake, pipe tip 7 bead bottom border and tip 4 bead top border. Add tip 4 message. Pipe tip 2 spider webs. Position candle. Serves 64.

◀ The Wizard of Webs

The bold fondant-covered web board is a cool way to make your cake look larger and more impressive.

Pan: *Spider-Man*™, p. 190
Tips: 3, 16, 21, p. 136-137
Colors: *Spider-Man* Icing Color Set (light blue, dark blue, red, black), p. 190; Royal Blue, p. 127
Recipe: Buttercream Icing, p. 111
Also: White Ready-To-Use Rolled Fondant (48 oz. needed), p. 122; Color Mist™ Food Color Spray in Yellow, Blue, Violet, p. 126; Cake Dividing Set, p. 131; 101 Cookie Cutters Set, p. 142; Cake Board, Fanci-Foil Wrap, p. 217; Piping Gel, p. 127; Decorator Brush Set, p. 147; 18 in. round heavy cardboard or foam core, cornstarch

Ice cake sides and background areas smooth. Outline tip 3 body and suit web design. Outline and pipe in black and white eye areas with tip 3 (smooth with finger dipped in cornstarch). Cover body, head, arms and hands with tip 16 stars. Set aside.

Brush 18 in. round board with a light layer of Piping Gel; cover with fondant. Spray center area with blue Color Mist and outer area with violet. Using Cake Dividing Set, divide board into 12ths. In buttercream, pipe tip 16 strings from edge to center at each division point; add tip 16 curving lines for web effect. Position cake on board; pipe tip 21 shell bottom border. Using alphabet cutters from set, cut out fondant message; spray letters with yellow Color Mist. Brush backs of letters very lightly with water and attach to board. Serves 12.

◀ *Cosmo* and *Wanda* Wishmaker!

Finally, The Fairly OddParents grant kids exactly what they wish for—cool cookie pops to go with their cake! It's a centerpiece, cake and favor holder all in one!

Pan: Ring Mold, p. 159
Tips: 2, 3, 6, p. 136
Colors: *The Fairly OddParents* Icing Color Set (hot pink and lavender), p. 188; Buttercup Yellow, Black, p. 127
Cookies: 101 Cookie Cutters Set, p. 142; Cookie Sheet, Cooling Grid, p. 160
Recipes: Buttercream Icing, p. 111; Roll-Out Cookie, p. 112
Also: *The Fairly OddParents* Candle, p. 188; 8 in. Lollipop Sticks, p. 149; Cake Board, Fanci-Foil Wrap, p. 217; White Cake Sparkles™, p. 128; White Candy Melts®†, p. 146; craft block, curling ribbon (8 yards needed), cornstarch

In advance: Using medium round and smallest star cutters from set, cut, bake and cool 5 round and 15 star cookies (make extras to allow for breakage). Using tip 3, outline and pipe in cookies (smooth with finger dipped in cornstarch). On star cookies, immediately add Cake Sparkles. On round cookies, overpipe outlines and messages with tip 2. Let dry. Attach lollipop sticks to backs of 5 round cookies and 3 star cookies using melted candy. Let set.

Ice cake smooth. Cut craft block to fit in center of cake. Cover with Fanci-Foil Wrap and position. Using tip 6, pipe ball cloud bottom border and print name on cake side. Insert cookies on sticks into craft block. Attach remaining cookie stars randomly on cake, securing with dots of icing. Cut curling ribbon into 18 in. lengths, curl and arrange on cake top. Position candle. Cake serves 18, cookies each serve 1.

†Brand confectionery coating.

▶ Poof—You're a Year Older!

Pan: *The Fairly OddParents*, p. 188
Tips: 1, 3, 6, 16, p. 136-137
Colors: *The Fairly OddParents* Icing Color Kit (green, hot pink, skin tone, lavender), p. 188; Black, Buttercup Yellow, Sky Blue, Royal Blue, p. 127
Recipe: Buttercream Icing, p. 111
Also: Cake Board, Fanci-Foil Wrap, p. 217; cornstarch

Ice cake sides and background areas smooth. Ice cloud area smooth, and outline with tip 6. Use tip 3 for the following: outline *Cosmo* and *Wanda*, crowns, wings, earring and stars on wands. Outline and pipe in eyes and teeth; smooth with finger dipped in cornstarch. Pipe wand handles, eyebrows, shirt, tie, earring and lipstick. Cover hair, faces, hands, blouse, crowns and stars with tip 16 stars; overpipe nose areas with more stars. Add tip 1 string stars and outline circles randomly on cake top. Pipe tip 3 message inside cloud. Using tip 6, heavy pressure and a circular motion, pipe cloud bottom border. Serves 12.

▼ The Magic Words!

Pan: Standard Muffin, p. 160
Tip: 2, p. 136
Colors: *The Fairly OddParents* Icing Color Set (green), p. 188; Lemon Yellow, Royal Blue, p. 127
Recipe: Buttercream Icing, p. 111
Also: *The Fairly OddParents* Baking Cups, p. 188; White Cake Sparkles™, p. 128

Ice cupcakes smooth. Print tip 2 words and motion lines. Add tip 2 zigzag clouds. Sprinkle tops with Cake Sparkles. Each serves 1.

▼ Jellyfish Party with *SpongeBob*!

A fondant-covered cake circle with stenciled sea scene makes the perfect platter for our SpongeBob mini cake.

Pan: *SpongeBob SquarePants*™ Mini Cake, p. 193
Tips: 1, 2, p. 136
Colors: *SpongeBob SquarePants* Icing Color Kit (yellow, red blue), p. 193; Leaf Green, Black, p. 127
Fondant: White Ready-To-Use Rolled Fondant (24 oz. needed); p. 122; Brush-On Color™ in Yellow and Green, p. 124; Geometric Cake Stamps, p. 123; Color Tray, p. 125
Recipe: Buttercream Icing, p. 111
Also: 2005 Pattern Book (Seaweed Background), p. 222; Piping Gel, p. 127; 6 in. Cake Circle, Fanci-Foil Wrap, p. 217; scissors, waxed paper, cornstarch

A day in advance: Tint 8 oz. fondant lime green (combine Leaf Green and Yellow). Brush cake circle with piping gel. Roll out fondant and cover cake circle. Trace pattern on paper and trim to create seaweed stencil. Combine yellow and green Brush-On Colors in Color Tray to create dark lime green. Position pattern over fondant circle; use round stamp and Brush-On Color to cover seaweed areas.

Ice mini cake smooth. Pipe tip 2 zigzag mouth (pat smooth with finger dipped in cornstarch). Pipe tip 2 teeth and tongue, sponge spots, nose and eyes (shape and pat smooth with finger dipped in cornstarch). Add tip 2 dot pupils and pull-out dot eyelashes. Position cake on fondant circle. Pipe jellyfish with tip 2 oval bodies and tip 1 wavy string legs. Add tip 1 dots. Each serves 1.

▲ Stepping Out with *SpongeBob!*

Pan: *SpongeBob SquarePants*™, p. 193
Tips: 3, 5, 16, 21, p. 136-137
Colors: *SpongeBob SquarePants*™ Icing Color Set (blue, red, yellow and brown), p. 193; Black, p. 127
Recipe: Buttercream Icing, p. 111
Also: Cake Board, Fanci-Foil Wrap, p. 217; cornstarch

Ice sides and background areas smooth. Outline *SpongeBob*, sponge spots, facial features, hands, arms, shirt, button, cummerbund, tie, tuxedo, pants and shoes with tip 3. Pipe in tip 3 sponge spots, whites of eyes, irises, pupils, inside of mouth, tongue, teeth, shirt, cuffs and buttons (smooth with finger dipped in cornstarch). Pipe in tie and cummerbund with tip 5 (smooth with finger dipped in cornstarch). Cover sponge, hands, tuxedo, shoes and pants with tip 16 stars. Pipe tip 21 star bottom border. Serves 12.

▲ Cookie Place Cards

Cookies: Plastic Fish Cutter, Plastic Nesting Teddy Bears Cutter Set, p. 142; Cookie Sheet, Cooling Grid, p. 160
Tips: 1, 2, 5, p. 136
Colors: *The Fairly OddParents* Icing Color Kit (skin tone), p. 188; Black, Buttercup Yellow, Royal Blue, Sky Blue, Violet, p. 127
Recipe: Buttercream Icing, p. 111
Also: White Cake Sparkles™, p. 128; *The Fairly OddParents* Icing Decorations, p. 188; black shoestring licorice

Tint portion of cookie dough violet for bear "people" cookies. Cut one smallest bear, one fish, and two 2 x 2 x 1½ in. triangle easel backs for each cookie place card. Bake and cool. For name cookie, ice fish cookie smooth. Pipe tip 5 ball clouds, immediately sprinkle with Cake Sparkles. Add tip 2 name and lines. For *Wanda and Cosmo*: On bear cookies, pipe tip 2 clothes and outline arms, tip 1 dot left hands. Cut small piece of licorice for wand, position in right hand and overpipe tip 1 dot fingers. Pipe tip 2 wings. Attach star icing decoration to end of wand and face icing decoration to body with dots of icing. Attach cookies together and add easel backs with dots of icing. Each serves 1.

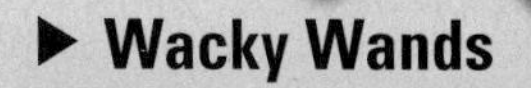

▶ Wacky Wands

Cookies: Plastic Star Cutter, p. 142; Cookie Sheet, Cooling Grid, p. 160
Tip: 3, p. 136
Colors:* Lemon Yellow, Golden Yellow, p. 127
Recipes: Royal Icing, p. 111; Roll-Out Cookie, p. 112
Also: *The Fairly OddParents*™ Icing Decorations, p. 188; Yellow Cake Sparkles™, p. 128; Meringue Powder, p. 126; black licorice twists

Cut, bake and cool cookies. Cover with thinned royal icing (p. 118); immediately sprinkle with Cake Sparkles and let dry. Attach icing decorations and licorice twists with tip 3 and full-strength royal icing. Let dry. Each serves 1.

***Note:** Combine Lemon Yellow and Golden Yellow for shade shown.

▼ Explore with *Dora!*

A Dora Party Topper and a marshmallow "cake" give this simple candy plaque instant celebrity status!

Pan: Mini Loaf, p. 160
Candy: Candy Melts®* in Yellow, Orange, Red, Lavender, p. 146
Also: Parchment Triangles, p. 134; *Dora* Party Toppers, p. 192; marshmallows (regular and mini size)

Mold candy plaque (p. 119) ¼ in. deep in mini loaf pan. Using melted candy, attach regular marshmallow to plaque and mini marshmallow on top. Using melted candy in cut parchment bag, decorate marshmallow "cake" with swags and outlining. Pipe name on plaque. Position topper. Each serves 1.

◀ *Dora* Adores Birthdays!

Pans: *Dora the Explorer*, p. 192; Mini Star, p. 161
Tips: 2, 3, 8, 16, 21, p. 136-137
Colors: *Dora the Explorer* Icing Color Set (red, pink, brown, skin tone), p. 192; Black, Lemon Yellow, Violet, Royal Blue, Red-Red, p. 127
Recipe: Buttercream Icing, p. 111
Also: Cake Sparkles™ in Red, Blue, Yellow, p. 128; 4 in. Lollipop Sticks, p. 149; Cake Board, Fanci-Foil Wrap, p. 217; sugar ice cream cone, curling ribbon (red, yellow and blue)

Ice star cakes smooth. Immediately add Cake Sparkles. Using tip 3, pipe spiral balloon knot. Cut ribbon into approximately 3 ft. lengths and insert one end into same color balloon knot. Set aside.

Ice *Dora* cake sides and background areas smooth. Using tip 3, outline *Dora*; outline and pipe in eyes, pupils, irises, mouth, tongue and bracelet; smooth with finger dipped in cornstarch. Add tip 2 dot eye highlight. Cover *Dora*, clothes, shoes and backpack with tip 16 stars. Pipe tip 2 dots, streamers and lines on background areas and cake sides. Pipe tip 21 star bottom border. Make party hat: Trim sugar cone to 3½ in. long; ice smooth. Pipe tip 8 line, in a spiral from tip to open end. Add tip 3 pull-out fringe at tip and open end. Pipe tip 3 number. Insert lollipop stick at top of head. Position hat over stick. Arrange star balloon cakes around *Dora* cake, gather ribbon and position on *Dora's* hand; overpipe fingers with tip 16 stars to attach. Curl ribbon ends. Serves 15.

▶ *Blue's* Art Adventure

Pan: *Blue's Clues*, p. 199
Tips: 3, 16, 21, p. 136-137
Colors: *Blue's Clues* Icing Color Set (blue, sky blue, dark blue and purple), p. 199; Violet, Brown, p. 127
Fondant: White Ready-To-Use Rolled Fondant (24 oz. needed), p. 122; Brush-On Color™ in Red, Yellow, Blue, Orange, and Green, p. 124; Geometric Cake Stamps, p. 123; Color Tray, Brush Set, Rolling Pin, Roll & Cut Mat, p. 125
Recipe: Buttercream Icing, p. 111
Also: 2005 Pattern Book (Plaque, Beret, Palette), p. 222; Cake Board, Fanci-Foil Wrap, p. 217; Gum Tex™ Karaya, p. 125; Parchment Triangles, p. 134; 6 in. Cookie Treat Sticks, p. 143; cornstarch, large marshmallows, paring knife

In advance: Make fondant palette, beret and plaque. Tint a 1½ in. ball light brown for palette, a 1½ in. ball violet for beret; use a 2½ in. white ball for plaque. Roll out and cut pieces using patterns; let dry. Make paintbrush. For handle, tint a 1 in. ball of fondant brown, roll into a 5½ in. length. For brush end, tint ¾ in. ball of fondant tan, shape into a 1½ in. long teardrop. Score with knife to resemble bristles. With brush, indent hole in large end of teardrop, brush inside with water, insert handle. Let dry. Using round and square stamps and Brush-On Color, imprint balloons and package on plaque. Brush on balloon strings, package ribbon, message and curliques to plaque; add paint to palette. Cut board for cake. Using pan as pattern, extend bottom portion to fit overhang of plaque. Wrap in foil. Ice sides and background areas smooth. Outline *Blue* and facial features with tip 3. Pipe in tip 3 dot eyes and pupils; smooth with finger dipped in cornstarch. Cover *Blue* with tip 16 stars. Add tip 21 shell bottom border.

Position beret, plaque (support with marshmallows), palette (insert cookie sticks angled into cake to support) and paintbrush; secure with dots of icing. Using tip 3, outline paws and overpipe with tip 16 stars. Serves 12.

NICK JR. Blue's Clues

▶ A Day of Bouquets

Pan: *Barbie*™, p. 194
Tips: 21, 349, p. 137
Color: Leaf Green, p. 127
Candy: Candy Melts®* in White (2 pks.), Yellow, p. 146; Garden Candy Colors Set, p. 147; Roses in Bloom Candy Mold, p. 148
Recipe: Buttercream Icing, p. 111
Also: Cake Board, Fanci-Foil Wrap, p. 217

In advance: Make candy: Make 3 flower candy plaques (one at a time) and 1 dress candy plaque (p. 119) filling *Barbie™* pan cavities half full. Refrigerate until firm; unmold. Mold 15 violet and 15 yellow candy roses using mold. Refrigerate until firm; unmold.

Ice cake smooth. If necessary, trim down flower areas of cake for plaques. Position flower and dress plaques. Attach face-maker (included with pan) with icing. Randomly attach candy roses to dress with additional melted candy.

Pipe tip 21 reverse shell bottom border. Attach candy roses with icing. Pipe tip 349 leaves on roses. Serves 12.

*Brand confectionery coating.

▲Your Heart's with *Barbie*™

Cookies: Plastic Heart Cutter, p. 142; Cookie Sheet, Cooling Grid, p. 160
Tip: 2, p. 136
Color: Rose, p. 127
Recipes: Royal Icing, p. 111; Roll-Out Cookie, p. 112
Also: *Barbie*™ Icing Decorations, p. 194; Meringue Powder, p. 126

Cut, bake and cool heart cookies. Cover with thinned royal icing (p. 118); let dry. Using full-strength royal icing, write tip 2 names. Attach icing decorations with dots of icing. Each serves 1.

▶ Gifts From Out of the *Blue!*

Pans: 10½ x 15½ x 1 in. Jelly Roll, Cooling Grid, p. 160
Candy: White Candy Melts®*, p. 146; Garden and Primary Candy Color Sets, p. 147
Also: *Blue's Clues*™ Party Toppers, p. 199; Parchment Triangles, p. 134; waxed paper

Cut cake into 1½ in. squares. Using candy colors, tint melted candy violet, yellow and orange. Cover cakes with violet candy; refrigerate to set. Using yellow and orange candy in cut parchment bags, pipe ribbon and swirls. Refrigerate to set. Position topper. Each serves 1.

▶ Petals In Pink

Pan: Standard Muffin, p. 160
Colors: Rose, Leaf Green, p. 127
Fondant: White Ready-To-Use Rolled Fondant (24 oz. needed), p. 122; Nature Cut-Outs™, p. 123; Roll & Cut Mat, Rolling Pin, Cutter/Embosser, p. 125
Recipe: Buttercream Icing, p. 111
Also: *Barbie*™ Icing Decorations, p. 194

Ice cupcakes smooth. Arrange in flower formation; position *Barbie*™ icing decoration on center cupcake. Tint fondant green. Roll out a 1½ in. ball; cut 2 leaves using cut-out. Using smooth wheel of Cutter/Embosser, imprint veins. For stem, roll a ¼ in. diameter x 8 in. long fondant log. Position between cupcakes in a curved shape; position leaves. Each cupcake serves 1.

◀ Balcony Birdsongs

Pans: *Disney Princess*, p. 196; 12 x 18 x 2 in. Sheet, p. 158; Mini Loaf, p. 160
Tips: 1, 2, 3, 12, 14, 32, 45, p. 136-137
Colors: *Disney Princess* Icing Color Set (Blue, Pink, Yellow used), p. 196; Black, Violet, Brown, p. 127
Candy: White Candy Melts®† (2 pks.), p. 146; Primary Candy Color Set, p. 147
Recipes: Buttercream, Royal Icings, p. 111; Roll-Out Cookie, p. 112
Also: 2005 Pattern Book (Bluebirds, Scrollwork, Window Arch), p. 222; Hidden Pillars (2 pks.), p. 215; Meringue Powder, p. 126; Cake Boards, Fanci-Foil Wrap, p. 217; cornstarch

In advance: Make Candy Plaque (p. 119). Melt white candy, pour to top edge of banner area at bottom section of pan. Refrigerate until firm. Using candy color, tint remaining candy light orange for skin color. Pour into pan to mold face and body. Refrigerate until firm. Decorate plaque using royal icing: Outline banner with tip 3. Cover dress, gloves and headband with tip 14 stars. Pipe in tip 12 hair and tip 3 earrings (smooth with finger dipped in cornstarch). Pipe in tip 2 eyes and mouth (smooth with finger). Add tip 2 dot pupils and outline lips; pipe tip 1 dot eye highlight. Add tip 1 string eyelashes and tip 2 eyebrows. Pipe in tip 3 neckband, pat smooth. Add tip 3 name and tip 2 dots inside banner.

In advance: Make cookies. Trace bluebird patterns with toothpick on rolled cookie dough; cut, bake and cool cookies. Using royal icing, outline and pipe in with tip 3 zigzags (pat smooth with finger dipped in cornstarch). Pipe tip 2 dot eyes; pipe in feet and beak. Overpipe top of beak. Set aside.

Bake and cool 1-layer sheet cake (2 in. high) and 4 mini loaf cakes (1½ in. high). Trace Window Arch pattern (reverse for opposite side) on top end and trim cake at markings. Position mini loaf cakes at opposite end; trim off excess to fit. Ice cake smooth in buttercream. Trace scrollwork pattern on bottom section and down sides of cake. Outline with tip 3. Edge scrollwork with tip 45 bands at top and bottom. Add tip 32 string curtains. Outline window frame with tip 45 bands. Add tip 12 ball curtain tiebacks.

Cut eight hidden pillars to 3½ in. long to support plaque. Insert 6 pillars spaced evenly down center, then insert 2 near bottom where banner will rest. Position plaque and bluebird cookies, securing cookies with dots of icing if necessary. Serves 76.

▶ *Princess* for a Day

Pans: Stand-Up House, p. 163; 10 x 2 in. Square, 6 x 2 in. Round, p. 158
Tips: 2, 3, 6, 32, 45, 47, 225, 349, p. 136-137
Colors: *Disney Princess* Icing Color Set (yellow, blue, pink), p. 196; Lemon Yellow, Red-Red, Kelly Green, Brown, Black, Violet, p. 127
Recipes: Buttercream, Royal Icings, p. 111
Also: 2005 Pattern Book (Castle Door and Windows, Scrolls), p. 222; *Disney Princess* Candle, p. 196; Plastic and Wooden Dowel Rods, p. 214; 13 x 19 in. Cake Boards, Fanci-Foil Wrap, p. 217; 8 in. Lollipop Sticks, p. 149; Meringue Powder, p. 126; ruler, craft block, sugar ice cream cones (3 needed), cornstarch, toothpick

In advance: Using royal icing and tip 225, pipe 50 red and 36 deep pink drop flowers (make extras to allow for breakage) and let dry. Using royal icing, decorate 3 sugar cone Turrets (p. 116).

Bake and cool 1-layer square, 1-layer round and house cakes (use firm-textured batter for house). Cut round cake in half and position at front of square cake (use remaining half for additional slices). Ice base cake smooth in buttercream and prepare for stacked construction (see p. 110). Decorate castle: Position house cake on separate foil-covered board. Trim off eaves. Ice cake smooth. Cut plastic dowel rods: two 7 in. long, one 7½ in. long. Cover rods with tip 47 (smooth side up) lines, leaving 4½ in. uniced at bottom of one 7½ in. and one 7 in. rod (to be inserted in top of roof) and leaving 2 in. uniced at bottom of the second 7 in. rod (to be inserted as side turret). Pat smooth with finger dipped in cornstarch. Insert rods into roof. Cover eaves with tip 45 band; add tip 45 band tiles on roof, beginning at bottom edge and overlapping each row moving up. Add a row of tip 45 band tiles on roof peak. Mark castle door and window pattern on front with toothpick. Pipe in shutters with tip 6, smooth with finger dipped in cornstarch; outline with tip 6. Pipe in tip 3 zigzag upper window and door; smooth with finger dipped in cornstarch. Add tip 3 string drapes. Using tip 6, pipe in area around door, smooth; outline door area with tip 6. Pipe in blue window with tip 3, smooth. Outline and pipe in windowpanes with tip 2. Pipe tip 45 band brickwork on front. Position castle cake on base cake. Insert side turret dowel rod into base cake. Pipe in side turret window with tip 3, smooth with finger, then outline. Remove lollipop sticks from sugar cones. Pipe icing on ends of castle roof rods and position cone turrets. Pipe tip 6 bead bottom border for castle. Decorate base cake: Trace Scroll pattern on front with toothpick. Outline with tip 3. Add tip 45 bands at top and bottom edges. Pipe tip 32 fleur de lis on each side. Pipe tip 2 vines on cake sides and back. Attach drop flowers to fleur de lis and vines with dots of icing. Add tip 349 leaves. Print tip 3 name; position candle. Serves 54.

◀ Royal Treatment

Pans: Non-Stick 6-Cup Regular Muffin, Non-Stick Small Cookie Pan, p. 157
Candy: White Candy Melts®†, p. 146; Primary and Garden Candy Color Sets, p. 147
Also: 2005 Pattern Book (Backdrop), p. 222; *Disney Princess* Party Toppers, p. 196; 101 Cookie Cutters Set, p. 142; Pillow Mints, p. 219; Parchment Triangles, p. 134; waxed paper

Using candy colors, tint portions of melted white candy light blue, dark blue, violet, yellow and pink. Mold candy shell (p. 119) candy dish in muffin pan; refrigerate until firm, unmold. Using melted candy in cut parchment bag, pipe bands around top and bottom edges and scrolls on sides; let set. To make lid, position medium round cookie cutter on cookie pan, fill ⅛ in. deep with melted candy. Refrigerate until firm; unmold. For backdrop, outline and pipe in waxed paper-covered pattern with white melted candy in cut parchment bag; refrigerate until firm. Outline with melted yellow candy; let set. Pipe pink curtains; refrigerate until firm.

Attach topper to lid with melted candy. To make easel back for backdrop, 2 edges of Candy Melts wafer to form a rectangle shape; attach to back with melted candy. Fill dish with pillow mints and position lid. Each serves 1.

▲ Cookies for Her Majesty

Cookies: Plastic Nesting Hearts Cutter Set, p. 142; Cookie Sheet, Cooling Grid, p. 160
Tips: 1, 3, 101s, 349, p. 136-137
Colors: *Disney Princess* Icing Color Set (pink), p. 196; Leaf Green, p. 127
Recipes: Royal Icing, p. 111; Roll-Out Cookie, p. 112
Also: Meringue Powder, p. 126; Flower Nail, p. 134; Disney Princess Icing Decorations, p. 196, waxed paper

In advance: Using flower nail, make 10 tip 101s roses with tip 3 bases for each large heart cookie. Make extras to allow for breakage; let dry.

Using largest and smallest cutters, cut, bake and cool heart cookies. Cover with thinned royal icing (p. 118); let dry. On large hearts, pipe tip 1 vines. Attach roses with dots of icing. Add tip 349 leaves. Attach icing decoration to center with dot of icing. Each serves 1.

▶ *Mickey* Sent Flowers!

Pan: *Minnie Mouse*, p. 197
Tips: 2, 3, 6, 16, 104, 131, 225, 349, 352, p. 136-137
Colors*: *Mickey Mouse* Icing Color Set (black, *Mickey* peach and copper), p. 197; Rose, Violet, Lemon Yellow, Golden Yellow, Leaf Green, p. 127
Recipes: Buttercream, Royal Icings, p. 111; Roll-Out Cookie, p. 112
Also: 2005 Pattern Book (*Minnie's* Purse, Bouquet Background), p. 222; Cake Board, Fanci-Foil Wrap, p. 217; Flower Nail, p. 134; Meringue Powder, p. 126; 6 in. Cookie Treat Sticks, p. 143; waxed paper, toothpick, craft knife, cornstarch

In advance: Using royal icing, make 10 tip 104 Ribbon Roses (p. 115). Make approximately 25 each of tip 131 pink drop flowers and tip 225 purple drop flowers, both with tip 2 yellow dot centers. Make extras of all flowers to allow for breakage; let dry.

Trace purse and bouquet background patterns on cookie dough with toothpick; cut out with knife. Bake and cool. Ice purse cookie smooth with buttercream; outline and add dot button with tip 3. Ice bouquet background smooth; position ribbon roses and add tip 352 leaves. Set aside.

Trim off raised portion of cake top at *Minnie's* left hand. Ice cake sides and background areas smooth. Using tip 3, outline *Minnie*, dress, shoes, bow, gloves and facial features. Pipe in eyes, mouth, tongue and nose, smooth with finger dipped in cornstarch. Cover *Minnie*, bow, dress, shoes and gloves with tip 16 stars. Create closed hand holding flowers using tip 3 outlines and tip 16 stars. Pipe tip 3 outline stems. Position drop flowers on cake sides. Add tip 349 leaves. Pipe tip 6 bead bottom border. Insert cookie sticks in cake sides to support bouquet cookie. Position purse and bouquet cookies on cake top, securing with dots of icing. Pipe tip 3 outline purse handle. Serves 12.

***Note:** Combine Lemon Yellow and Golden Yellow for shade used.

DISNEY
MINNIE MOUSE

†Brand confectionery coating.

▼ A Picnic with *Pooh*

Pans: *Pooh* Stand-Up Set, p. 197; 11 x 15 x 2 in. Sheet, p. 158; Mini Loaf, p. 160
Tips: 2, 3, 4, 8, 16, 224, 352, p. 136-137
Colors: *Pooh* Icing Color Set (Pooh gold, red, royal blue, black), p. 197; Kelly Green, Brown, Violet, Pink, Lemon Yellow, p. 127
Recipes: Buttercream, Royal Icings, p. 111; Roll-Out Cookie, p. 112
Also: 2005 Pattern Book (Large and Small Bushes, Basket Handle), p. 222; Bug Buddies Cutter Set, p. 140; Meringue Powder, p. 126; Cake Boards, Fanci-Foil Wrap, p. 217; Parchment Triangles, p. 134; Plastic Dowel Rods, p. 214; waxed paper, black shoestring licorice, cornstarch, toothpick

In advance: Using royal icing, figure pipe (p. 118) the following: 2 grape bunches using tips 2, 4 and 352; 6 strawberries using tips 2, 8 and 352; 7 bananas using tips 3 and 8; 10 cherries using tips 2 and 8. Let all dry completely. Make basket handle. Cover pattern with waxed paper; using royal icing, pipe tip 3 rope over design; let dry. Turn over handle and repeat on other side; let dry. Using royal icing, make 40 each yellow, pink and violet tip 224 drop flowers with tip 3 white dot centers. Make extras to allow for breakage; let dry.

Using patterns and cookie dough, cut 1 large and 1 small bush; cut 1 butterfly using cutter from set. Bake and cool. Ice bush cookies smooth in buttercream and position drop flowers. Outline and pipe in butterfly with tip 2 (smooth with finger dipped in cornstarch). Pipe tip 3 string body, attach licorice antennae with icing.

Bake and cool *Pooh* cake using firm-textured batter such as pound cake. Place *Pooh* on foil-covered cake board, cut to fit. Ice pads of feet and inside ears smooth. Outline ears, eyebrows, mouth, shirt and hunny pot with tip 3; pipe in nose and eyes with tip 3; smooth with finger dipped in cornstarch. Cover body, shirt and hunny pot with tip 16 stars. Pipe honey and print message with tip 3.

Ice 2-layer (3 in. high) sheet cake smooth. Position dowel rods where Pooh will sit. Mark squares 2½ in. wide x 2¾ in. high on cake top with toothpick; cover with tip 16 stars. Divide front side into thirds, leave back side plain, mark short sides in half. Mark 1¼ in. down from top edge and pipe tip 16 zigzag garlands; attach drop flowers. Pipe tip 16 pull-out grass bottom border.

To make basket, ice mini loaf cake smooth. Using tip 3, pipe basketweave on cake sides and rope bottom border. Attach handle to basket with buttercream and position fruit. Attach butterfly cookie to large bush with buttercream; attach bushes to back of cake. Position *Pooh* and basket. Serves 72.

Disney MICKEY MOUSE

▶ *Mickey's* Wrapped Up in the Fun!

Pans: 10, 14 x 2 in. Square, p. 159; *Mickey* Face, p. 197
Tips: 2, 3, 16, p. 136
Colors: Black, Lemon Yellow, Red-Red, Violet, Kelly Green, Royal Blue, p. 127
Candy: White Candy Melts®† (3 pks. needed), p. 146; Primary Candy Color Set, p. 147; 4 in. Lollipop Sticks, p. 149
Fondant: White Ready-To-Use Rolled Fondant (168 oz. needed), p. 122; Geometric Cake Stamps, p. 123; Brush-On Color™ in Red, Orange, Green, Blue, Yellow, Pink, Purple, p. 124; Easy-Glide Fondant Smoother; Cutter/Embosser, Brush Set; Color Tray, p. 125
Recipes: Buttercream, Royal Icings, p. 111
Also: 2005 Pattern Book (Hands, Tag, Torn Paper), p. 222; Plastic Dowel Rods, p. 214; Flower Former Set, p. 134; Gum-Tex™ Karaya, p. 125; Cake Board, Fanci-Foil Wrap, p. 217; sugar cone, craft knife, plastic drinking straw, waxed paper, rolling pin, cornstarch, scissors

In advance: Make *Mickey* candy plaque (p. 119) in Face pan, using candy tinted flesh tone with orange candy color. Make fondant pieces: Tint fondant as follows: 72 oz. each yellow and violet, 6 oz. each black and red, 3 oz. blue, 1 oz. green. Roll out remaining white fondant; using patterns, cut 2 hands and 1 gift tag. Make hole in tag with straw. Let pieces dry on cornstarch-dusted surface. Remove 10 oz. yellow fondant and mix with 1 teaspoon Gum-Tex. Roll out yellow fondant/Gum-Tex mixture; using pattern, cut 24 torn paper pieces; let dry on large flower formers covered with waxed paper and dusted with cornstarch. Make arms and decorate hands (p. 117).

Prepare three 1-layer 10 in. cakes, each 2 in. high, and 2-layer 14 in. cake, 3 in. high, for stacked construction (p. 110). Prepare cakes for rolled fondant (p. 105); cover and smooth. Using Brush-On Color and Cake Stamps, randomly stamp stars on 10 in. cake and balloon circles on 14 in. cake. Paint streamers and tails on balloons with round brush; paint confetti dots with flat brush. Cut four red fondant ribbons, 8 x 1 in. wide; attach with damp brush. Position 10 in. cake on 14 in. cake. For hat, cover sugar cone with blue fondant. Cut 3/8 x 17 in. long strip of yellow fondant and attach diagonally to cone with damp brush. For pompom, cut 1 x 4 in. long strip of green fondant, roll lengthwise and trim fringe end with scissors; attach to top of cone with damp brush.

Attach lollipop stick to back of head with melted candy, extending 2 in. at top; let set and position hat over stick. For gift tag border, cut 1/4 x 13 in. long strip of blue fondant, cut an 8 in. long strip for hanging ribbon; imprint design with dotted wheel of Embosser. Brush border and ribbon lightly with water and attach to tag. Print tip 2 message. For bottom border, cut 1/2 in. wide strips of red fondant, long enough to surround cake when gathered. Randomly gather strips and attach with damp brush. Before serving, insert candy plaque and arms into cake. Attach lollipop sticks to back of two torn fondant pieces with melted candy, let set and insert under arms. Attach remaining torn pieces with melted candy. Serves 108.

†Brand confectionery coating.

123 SESAME STREET®

▼ Fun in the Sun with *Elmo*

The Elmo cake would be great on its own—but you've sweetened the deal with a sunny cookie scene that makes it irresistible!

Pan: *Elmo*, p. 199; Cookie Sheet, Cooling Grid, p. 160
Tips: 2, 3, 4, 5, 10, 12, 16, 352, p. 136-137
Colors:* No-Taste Red, Christmas Red, Orange, Black, Royal Blue, Lemon Yellow, Kelly Green, Ivory, p. 127
Cookies: 101 Cookie Cutters Set, Plastic Sailboat Cutter, p. 142
Recipes: Buttercream Icing, p. 111; Roll-Out Cookie, p. 112
Also: 2005 Pattern Book (*Elmo's* Sunglasses), p. 222; Cake Board, Fanci-Foil Wrap, p. 217; *Elmo* Icing Decorations, p. 199; cornstarch, granulated brown sugar, small plastic toy shovel

Cut out the following cookies: sunglasses using pattern; sailboat using plastic cutter; letters for message, sun and large round for ball using cutters from set. Bake and cool. Ice sunglasses smooth; outline with tip 12. For sailboat, ice sail smooth, pipe tip 10 boat area. Attach *Elmo* icing decoration with dot of icing. Pipe tip 4 string arms with tip 2 pull-out fingers. For message, ice letters smooth and immediately sprinkle with granulated brown sugar. For beach ball, outline color sections with tip 4; pipe in with tip 5 (smooth with finger dipped in cornstarch). Add tip 4 dot in center (pat smooth). For sun, mound icing slightly in center of cookie and ice smooth. Outline and pipe in tip 2 facial features. Add tip 352 pull-out leaves for sunrays.

For *Elmo* cake, outline and pipe in mouth using tip 3 (smooth with finger dipped in cornstarch). Ice nose and whites of eyes smooth. Pipe in eye centers with tip 3. Cover *Elmo* with tip 16 stars. Position cookie sunglasses, securing with dots of icing if necessary. Position other cookies around cake. Cake serves 12; each cookie serves 1.

***Note:** Combine No-Taste Red and Christmas Red for shade shown.

◀ Flowers, Fruit and Fun

Pans: 6, 8, 10 x 2 in. Round, p. 158
Tips: 3, 352, p. 136-137
Colors: *Strawberry Shortcake*™ Icing Color Set (red, green), p. 189; Rose, Lemon Yellow, p. 127
Fondant: White Ready-To-Use Rolled Fondant (72 oz. needed), p. 122; Round, Flower Cut-Outs™; p. 123; Cutter/Embosser, Roll & Cut Mat, Rolling Pin, p. 125
Recipe: Buttercream Icing, p. 111
Also: *Strawberry Shortcake*™ Candle, p. 189; Plastic Nesting Hearts Cutter Set, p. 142; Wooden Dowel Rods, p. 214; Cake Circles, 12 in. Round Silver Cake Base, p. 217; Decorator Brush Set, p. 147

Tint fondant as follows: 9 oz. red, 7 oz. green, 5 oz. rose, ½ in. ball yellow; reserve remainder white.

Ice 2-layer cakes smooth and prepare for stacked construction (p. 110).

For 10 in. cake: Pipe tip 3 swirls on cake sides. Roll out red fondant and cut 8 strawberries using smallest heart cutter and 7 strawberries using second smallest cutter. Randomly attach to cake sides with icing and add tip 352 leaves. Roll 12 in. circle of white fondant, cut curved edges to resemble dripping icing and position on cake, overlapping sides.

For 8 in. cake: Roll out green, red and rose fondant and cut ¼ in. wide strips; attach to cake sides, ½ in. apart. Cut 9 strawberries using smallest heart cutter and 7 flowers using medium flower cut-out. Randomly attach to cake sides. Roll ¼ in. diameter yellow balls for flower centers; flatten and attach. Pipe tip 3 stems and tip 352 leaves on flowers and berries. Roll 10 in. circle of white fondant, cut and position as for 10 in. cake.

For 6 in. cake: Roll out red fondant; cut dots using smallest round cut-out and randomly attach to cake sides. Roll 8 in. circle of white fondant, cut and position as for other cakes. Assemble cake. Roll ½ in. diameter green, red and rose fondant balls; attach for bottom borders. Position candle. Serves 60.

▶ *Strawberry Shortcake*™ Cupcakes

Pan: Standard Muffin, p. 160
Tips: 2, 352, p. 136-137
Colors*: *Strawberry Shortcake* Icing Color Set (red, green, brown, skin tone), p. 189; Kelly Green, Leaf Green, p. 127
Recipe: Buttercream Icing, p. 111
Also: *Strawberry Shortcake* Icing Decorations, Standard Baking Cups, p. 189

Ice cupcakes smooth. Position icing decorations. Add tip 2 vines and tip 352 leaves to cupcake with strawberry icing decoration. Each serves 1.

*Note: Add red color to white icing for shade shown.

▼ Berry Balloon

Pan: Jumbo Muffin, p. 160
Candy: *Strawberry Shortcake* Lollipop Making Kit (includes mold, red, white, and blue Candy Melts®†, and decorating brush), p. 189; Candy Melts® in White (1 pk. additional needed), Light Cocoa, p. 146; Primary Candy Color Set, p. 147; 6 in. Lollipop Sticks, p. 149
Also: 2005 Pattern Book (Strawberry Top, Stem), p. 222; Parchment Triangles, p. 134; green construction paper, small red balloon, double-stick tape, waxed paper, 24 in. of ⅛ in. wide green satin ribbon, 24 in. of green curling ribbon, scissors

Tint portions of melted white candy light brown using small amounts of melted cocoa candy and yellow candy color. Make a candy shell (p. 119) in muffin pan; refrigerate until firm, unmold. Using melted candy in cut parchment bag, pipe vertical lines; pipe e-motion garlands and bead border trim. Cut 4 lollipop sticks to 5 in. and attach inside basket with melted candy. Set aside.

Tint portions of melted white candy pink (using a small amount of red candy) and green (combine yellow and blue candy color). Mold *Strawberry Shortcake* and strawberry candies from kit using painting method (p. 119); refrigerate until firm, unmold. Using waxed paper and melted candy in cut parchment bag, pipe six ½ in. hearts for small strawberries; pipe pull-out stem. Refrigerate until firm, remove paper. Attach strawberries to basket at garland points with melted candy. Fill basket with remaining candies.

Using pattern, cut strawberry top and stem from construction paper. Curl ends of strawberry top with edge of scissors. Before serving, inflate balloon and attach paper top, stem and curling ribbon with tape. Tie satin ribbons to tops of lollipop sticks in basket and attach with tape if needed. Position balloon in basket. Each serves 1.

†Brand confectionery coating.

▼ *Shortcake's* Harvest House

Kids will get a fun surprise when the birthday cake turns out to be yummy, crispy cereal treats!

Pans: Oval Pan Set (13 x 9⅞ and 7¾ x 5⅝ in. pans used), p. 159
Tips: 1, 2, 3, 4, 5, 14, 224, 349, 352, 366, p. 136-137
Colors: *Strawberry Shortcake* Icing Color Set (red, green), p. 189; Kelly Green, Royal Blue, Golden Yellow, Rose, p. 127
Fondant: White Ready-To-Use Rolled Fondant (24 oz. needed), p. 122; Leaf Cut-Outs™, p. 123; Easy-Glide Fondant Smoother, p. 125
Recipes: Royal Icing, p. 111; Roll-Out Cookie, p. 112; favorite crisped rice cereal treats (double batch needed)
Also: 2005 Pattern Book (Tree, Window, Door), p. 222; *Strawberry Shortcake* Lollipop Making Kit, p. 189; Copper Heart Cutter, p. 141; Wooden Dowel Rods, p. 214; Meringue Powder, p. 126; Parchment Triangles, p. 134; Cake Boards, Fanci-Foil Wrap, p. 217; cornstarch, waxed paper, rolled fudge nougat candy, toothpick

In advance: Mold *Strawberry Shortcake* candies without sticks, following kit directions. Using royal icing, make approximately 35 tip 224 drop flowers with tip 2 dot centers (make extras to allow for breakage) and let dry. Bake and cool cookies: 1 tree (trace pattern and cut), 1 heart (cut off 1 in. of point), 7 large leaves and 4 small leaves (use large and small leaf cut-outs). For leaves, trim lollipop sticks to 3 in. and attach to backs, using melted candy; let set. Ice leaves smooth. Pipe tip 3 vein lines. For tree, trim dowel rod to 7 in. and attach cookie to top 2 in. using melted candy. Spatula ice tree. Pipe tip 4 dot strawberries.

For house, trim dowel rod to 7½ in. and attach to back of heart cookie with melted candy, leaving 1¼ in. of rod exposed at top; let dry. Ice front smooth. Using patterns, mark windows and door with toothpick. Pipe in windows using tip 4, smooth with finger dipped in cornstarch. Add tip 3 outlines. Add tip 14 star flowers with tip 1 dot centers; Pipe tip 349 leaves. Outline and fill in door with tip 5 lines. Pipe in window with tip 3; outline and add panes with tip 2. Add tip 2 dot handle and tip 1 house light. Pipe tip 3 strawberries on windows and door, add tip 349 leaves. Pipe tip 366 leaves on top of house; attach drop flowers with dots of icing. Knead rolled fudge nougat candy until pliable and cover dowel rod stem at top of heart.

Prepare double batch of crisped rice cereal treats and press into prepared oval pans to approximately 1 in. deep. Unmold and stack. Tint 24 oz. fondant Kelly Green and cover "cake"; smooth with Easy-Glide Smoother.

Insert house on tiers. With tip 4, pipe in door mat (smooth with finger dipped in cornstarch), outline, then add strawberry. Insert tree and leaf cookies on sticks. Using tip 1 and buttercream, add bows and collars to candy. Pipe tip 352 leaves on berry candies. Attach candy pieces and drop flowers with melted candy.

Pipe tip 352 leaf bottom border. Attach drop flowers with dots of icing. Serves 24.

▶ Bevy Of Berries!

Pan: *Strawberry Shortcake*™, p. 189; 16 x 2 in. Heart, p. 158
Tips: 3, 16, 67, 129, p. 136-137
Colors: *Strawberry Shortcake* Icing Color Kit (skin tone, red, brown, green), p. 189; Golden Yellow, Rose, p. 127
Recipes: Buttercream, Royal Icings p. 111
Also: Parchment Triangles, p. 134; Cake Board, Fanci-Foil Wrap, p. 217; Plastic Nesting Heart Cutter Set, p. 142; Meringue Powder, p. 126; Wooden Dowel Rods, p. 214, cornstarch

In advance: Using royal icing, make approximately 30 tip 129 white drop flowers with tip 3 yellow dot centers. Let dry.

Position *Strawberry Shortcake* cake on same-size cake board and decorate as follows in buttercream: Ice cake sides, shirt, and background areas smooth. Using tip 3, outline face and facial features, hands, neck, shirt, hat, and bow. Pipe in tip 3 bow (smooth with finger dipped in cornstarch). Pipe tip 3 lines on bow and shirt. Pipe in tip 3 collar. Cover face, neck, hands, hat and strawberry on bow with tip 16 stars. Add tip 3 dots on strawberry and add tip 67 pull-out leaves. Using tip 3, pipe dot nose and line under nose. Pipe tip 16 pull-out star hair. Ice smooth 2-layer (3 in. high) heart cake and prepare for stacked construction (p. 110). Using 2½ in. diameter heart cutter, imprint hearts randomly on cake top and sides. Outline with tip 3, fill in with tip 16 stars. Add tip 3 dot seeds. Pipe tip 67 leaves.

Position *Strawberry Shortcake* cake on heart cake. Add tip 16 shell bottom border. Attach drop flowers with dots of icing. Serves 76.

HOLIDAYS YOUR WAY

Do you take holiday fun seriously? Does your Halloween costume require blueprints? At your house, when the Christmas lights come down, do the Cupid decorations go up? Does the family bring shovels to your Easter egg hunt? We're ready for you, with spectacular haunted houses, jolly Christmas trains and cute bunny houses—the stuff that makes every season worth celebrating.

Instructions for projects shown on these two pages are on page 46.

Good Housecreeping

This old haunt is custom-built with Color Flow windows and doors, gingerbread roof panels and royal icing fences and turrets.

Pans: 6, 8, 10 x 2 in. Square, p. 158
Tips: 2, 3, 4, 45, 47, 55, 57, p. 136-137
Colors: Black, Orange, Golden Yellow, Violet, Brown, Leaf Green, p. 127
Candy: White Candy Melts®*, p. 146; Spooky Ghost Mold, p. 167; Garden Candy Color Set, p. 147
Recipes: Buttercream, Royal, Color Flow Icings, p. 111; Grandma's Gingerbread, p. 112
Also: 2005 Pattern Book (Small and Large Windows; Small and Large Shutters; Door; Fence Pieces; Roof Points; 2nd Floor and 3rd Floor Roof Panels; 2nd Floor and 3rd Floor Braces; 1st Floor Back, Side and Front Roof Panels; 1st Floor Braces), p. 222; 7 in. Grecian Pillars (2 sets needed), p. 215; 7 and 13 in. Square Separator Plates, p. 214; Plastic Dowel Rods, p. 214; Halloween FoodWriter™ Edible Color Markers, p. 166; Violet Color Mist™ Food Color Spray, p. 166; Meringue Powder, p. 126; Color Flow Mix, p. 126; Cake Boards, Fanci-Foil Wrap, p. 217; Decorating Comb, p. 131; Decorator Brush Set, p. 147; Parchment Triangles, p. 134; 20 in. square base (plywood or ½ in. thick foam core), plastic ruler, plastic bag, waxed paper, ten 1 in. diameter purple gum balls, shredded coconut

At least 3 days in advance: Using Color Flow and patterns, outline with tip 2 and then flow in the following using a cut parchment bag (see p. 118): Make 20 small windows, 8 large windows, 2 doors, 20 sets of small shutters, 8 sets of large shutters. Let pieces set for 2 days, then outline detail on doors using tip 2 and full-strength Color Flow. Using royal icing and pattern, make the following tip 57 fence pieces: four 7 in. lengths, two 6 in. lengths and two 4 ½ in. lengths. Pipe 30 tip 4 roof points. Using gingerbread and patterns, cut 2nd floor and 3rd floor roof panels and braces; 1st floor back, side and front roof panels and braces. Also cut four 4 ½ in. squares. Bake all, then immediately re-measure and trim to correct sizes if needed.

A day in advance: Mold candy ghosts; refrigerate until firm and unmold. Tint portion of white candy black using candy color. Using a cut parchment bag, pipe facial features. Draw FoodWriter spider webs and spiders on some windows. Draw lines on shutters. Pipe tip 55 royal icing windowpanes, then outline window frames with tip 57. Set aside. Cover tops of gingerbread roof panels with royal icing and comb swag lines using large-tooth side of decorating comb. Run a spatula along edges to remove excess icing. Let dry. Attach longest edges of braces to backs of roof panels, near top edge of panel; let dry. Thin royal icing and paint pillars. Let dry.

Bake and cool two 10 in. 2-layer tiers, one 8 in. 2-layer tier, and one 6 in. 2-layer tier; ice smooth in buttercream. Assemble and dowel rod the two 10 in. and the 6 in. 2-layer tiers on a same-size cake board. Comb sides of

tiers with small-tooth side of Decorating Comb and spray with Color Mist. Dowel rod all tiers and prepare for stacked construction (p 110). Position 13 in. separator plate on top of 10 in. cake, feet facing up. Leave a 1 in. overhang at back, creating a larger overhang at front of the cake. Center 8 in. tier over 10 in. cake. It will rest on back feet of plate. Position 6 in. tier. Position 7 in. separator plate on top, feet facing down, pressing into cake.

Using royal icing, stack the four gingerbread squares together with icing between each square. Attach to top of cake at center of 7 in. separator plate. Position the cookie roof panels on the stacked squares and join the edges with icing. Outline edges with tip 47. Attach the roof panels to 2nd floor and 1st floor cakes, resting at an angle. Outline edges with tip 47.

Using buttercream icing, outline house corners using tip 45. Divide sides of 6 in. tier in half and sides of 8 in. tier in thirds. Pipe tip 47 stripe down sides at division marks. Attach small window in each section with dots of icing. Pipe tip 57 stripes along side of windows and attach small shutters. On 10 in. tier, attach doors, large windows and large shutters. Using tip 3, pipe shells and dot above doors; pipe fleur de lis and scrolls above large windows.

Attach roof points and gumballs to tops of pillars using royal icing. Ice base board smooth and imprint wood planks using edge of plastic ruler. Position pillars and secure with icing. Attach fence pieces with royal icing, placing two 4½ in. lengths in front, one 7 in. and one 6 in. length on each side and two 7 in. lengths on back. Tint coconut (p. 116) and place around house. Attach candy ghosts with royal icing. Cake serves 88.

*Brand confectionery coating.

Spooky Stew

Stir up the Halloween fun with caramel apples that look like creepy cauldrons.

Candy: Caramel Apple Kit, p. 187; Candy Melts®* in Green, Dark Cocoa, Orange, Yellow, Red, p. 146; Garden Candy Color Set, p. 147; Halloween Gummy Kit, p. 167
Recipe: Candy Clay, p. 112
Also: 6 in. Cake Circle, p. 217; apples, mini marshmallows, pretzel sticks, corn syrup, vegetable shortening, paring knife, waxed paper, cream or evaporated milk

A day in advance, make candy clay using red, orange and yellow candy; set aside.

Insert sticks into apples on an angle and follow kit directions for dipping apples in caramel; let set on waxed paper. Tint melted cocoa candy black with candy color; mix 3 oz. of black candy with 2 tablespoons of corn syrup to make candy clay; set aside. Dip caramel apples into melted black candy; let set. Form cauldron rim at top of apple with black candy clay. Dip ends of pretzel sticks in black candy and position on cake circle to fit around apple; position apple. Marbleize (p. 119) red, orange and yellow candy; roll ⅛ to ¼ in. thick and cut flame shapes with paring knife. Attach to apple with melted candy. Thin melted green candy with 1 tablespoon shortening. Dip mini marshmallows in thinned candy and position individually on apple. Make gummy ghosts and bat following kit directions; attach ghost to stick with candy. Each serves 1.

Poltergeist Pizzas

They're a panic, with crusts handcut using Nesting Ghost cutters.

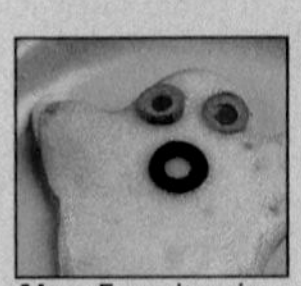

Cookies: Nesting Ghosts Cutter Set, p. 169; Cookie Sheet, p. 160
Also: Favorite pizza dough mix or recipe, pizza sauce, sliced mozzarella cheese, green olives, black olives

Roll out pizza dough and cut out crust with largest ghost cutter. Spread crust with sauce. Cut cheese slice with second largest ghost cutter and position on crust. Position sliced olives for eyes and nose. Bake until cheese is melted. Each serves 1.

▲ See the Fall Colors!

Homemade harvest candies and leaf sprinkles create a dazzling display on simple cupcakes.

Pan: Standard Muffin, p. 160
Color: Lemon Yellow, p. 127
Candy: Candy Melts®* in Red, Orange, Light Cocoa, Dark Cocoa, Green, Yellow, White, p. 146; Harvest Lollipop Mold, p. 137; Decorator Brush Set, p. 147
Recipe: Buttercream Icing, p. 111
Also: Leaves Mix Sprinkle Decorations, p. 187; Harvest Standard Baking Cups, Harvest Party Bags, p. 187

Mold candy using painting method (see p. 119); refrigerate until firm, unmold. Ice cupcakes smooth and top with sprinkles. Position candy. Serve in party bags. Each serves 1.

▶ Fall's Friendly Face

Try this fun fruit snack...a caramel apple scarecrow, decked out in a rolled fondant ruffled collar and cap!

Candy: Caramel Apple Kit, p.187; Peanut Butter Candy Melts®*, p. 146
Colors: Ivory, Brown, Yellow, Red, Black, Kelly Green, Royal Blue, Orange, p. 127
Recipes: Buttercream Icing, p. 111; Color Flow Icing, p. 111
Also: White Ready-To-Use Rolled Fondant, p. 122; fresh apples, cream or evaporated milk

Set aside 2 pieces of caramel from kit. Melt remaining caramel following package directions and dip apples. Tint fondant: Make peanut butter color for ruffle base (combine ivory, brown, yellow, red, black colors), tint white fondant orange for neck ribbon; black for mouth and eye centers, red for cheeks; blue for nose and hat band, green for hat; reserve a small amount white. Melt Candy Melts to attach fondant pieces to apple. Cut out fondant as follows. Ruffle Base: Cut 1 x 16 in. peanut butter-color strip, shape into ruffle and attach to bottom of caramel apple. Neck Ribbon: Cut a ½ x 8 in. orange strip, attach around neck; make two ½ x 2 in. loops and attach; roll a small ball, flatten and attach to center of loops for knot. Mouth: Cut a strip in black, shape and attach. Cheeks: Cut two ¾ in. circles in red, attach to ends of mouth. Nose: Cut a ¾ in. blue triangle and attach. Eyes: Cut two ½ in. white triangles, attach. Cut 2 small black circles, attach to centers of triangles. Hat: Cut a 1 x 12 in. green strip, shape into ruffle and attach for brim. Cut a 5 in. green circle and attach for top of hat. Cut a ⅜ x 7 in. blue strip for hat band, attach. Roll reserved caramels together, shape into pipe bowl. Insert stick into caramel, insert other end of stick into mouth. Each serves 1.

◀ Pilgrim Pair

His and her cakes will look great next to the pumpkin pie on your Thanksgiving table. Try them with your favorite spice cake recipe for a wonderful taste of fall.

Pan: Little Hero, p. 165
Tips: 2, 4, 6, 12, 16, 21, p. 136-137
Colors:* Golden Yellow, Kelly Green, Brown, Black, Copper (skin tone), Red-Red, Royal Blue, Orange, p. 127
Recipe: Buttercream Icing, p. 111
Also: 2005 Pattern Book (Pilgrim Boy and Girl), p. 222; Petite Leaves Icing Decorations (2 pks. needed), p. 187; Cake Board, Fanci-Foil Wrap, p. 217; toothpick, cornstarch

Bake and cool two cakes. Trim off collar area and bottom of hose near feet. Ice sides and lightly ice cake tops smooth, icing background areas more heavily. Trace boy and girl patterns with toothpick. Pipe boy's socks with alternating color tip 4 strings. Outline heads, clothes and gun with tip 4. Pipe tip 4 string mouth and dot eyes; add tip 2 dot pupils. Fill in all outlined areas except gun, collars, cuffs, back hat brims, girl's apron and boy's hat band with tip 16 stars; overpipe noses. Pipe tip 16 pull-out star hair. Add tip 2 string eyelashes. Pipe tip 12 pumpkin, pipe in gun with tip 12, back of hat brims, hat band, collars and cuffs with tip 4 (smooth all with finger dipped in cornstarch). Outline hands with tip 4; fill in with tip 16 stars. Add tip 16 pull-out star pumpkin stem. Pipe tip 6 buckles. Pipe boy's front hat brim with tip 16 stars, build up for dimension. Pipe tip 21 shell bottom borders; position icing decorations around borders. Each cake serves 12.

***Note:** Combine Brown with a little Red-Red for shade shown.

◀ A Bat Puts the Bite on You!

You can build his cookie bag without batting an eyelash! Fill it with creepy treats for everyone at your Halloween bash.

Pan: Just Batty, p. 166; Cookie Sheet, Cooling Grid, p. 160
Tips: 3, 5, 12, 16, 18, 21, p. 136-137
Colors:* Orange, Black, Leaf Green, p. 127
Recipes: Royal, Buttercream, Chocolate Buttercream† Icings, p. 111; Roll-Out Cookie, p. 112
Also: Meringue Powder, p. 126; Cake Board, Fanci-Foil Wrap, p. 217; Decorator Brush Set, p. 147; 8 in. Angled Spatula, p. 134; black twist licorice, assorted Halloween candy, sharp knife, waxed paper, cornstarch

Make cookie bag: Tint dough orange; roll out and cut the following: two 4 x 5 in. pieces for bag front and back, two 1 x 4¾ in. pieces for sides and one 1 x 4 in. piece for bottom. Bake and cool. Position 4 x 5 in. back piece flat on waxed paper. Attach side and bottom pieces upright on edges with royal icing; let dry. Attach 4 x 5 in. front piece with royal icing; let dry. Attach licorice handle to inside of bag with royal icing.

Ice cake sides and background areas smooth. Outline bat with tip 3. Pipe in tip 12 eyes, tip 5 inside mouth and teeth (smooth all areas with finger dipped in cornstarch). Outline mouth with tip 5. Pipe tip 3 dot pupils. Cover remainder of bat with tip 16 stars; add tip 18 star bottom border. Fill cookie bag with candy and position on foil-wrapped board below cake. Pipe tip 21 shell claws holding bag. Print tip 3 message and add tip 3 web on cookie bag. Serves 12.

*Note: Add Black Icing Color to Chocolate Buttercream for black shade shown.

◀ Drac's Blood Suckers

Sink your fangs into a crunchy cookie vampire, decorated with candy in screaming colors.

Cookie: Jack-O-Lantern Cookie Treat Pan, 8 in. Cookie Treat Sticks, p. 169; Cookie Sheet, Cooling Grid, p. 160
Candy: Candy Melts®† in Green, White, p. 146; Primary and Garden Candy Color Sets, p. 147
Recipe: Roll-Out Cookie, p. 112
Also: Parchment Triangles, p. 134, waxed paper

Bake and cool cookies on sticks. Add yellow candy color to melted green candy. Cover cookies with melted candy (p. 118); let set. For ears, pipe 1 in. diameter circles on waxed paper; let set. Tint portions of melted white candy red and black. Pipe hair, eyebrows, nose, eyes, mouth and cheeks using melted candy in cut parchment bags; let set. Add dot pupils; pipe in fangs and tongue. To make ears, cut circles in half and attach to side of cookie with melted candy. Each serves 1.

†Brand confectionery coating.

▲ Cupcakes Raise a Flap!

It's twice the treat, with chocolate cookie wings on a creepy cupcake.

Pan: Standard Muffin, p. 160
Tips: 2, 2A, 3, 352, p. 136-136
Colors:* Leaf Green, Lemon Yellow, Black, p. 127
Recipes: Buttercream, Chocolate Buttercream** Icings, p. 111; Chocolate Roll-Out Cookie, p. 112
Also: Just Batty Baking Cups, p. 167; Leaves and Acorns Nesting Metal Cookie Cutter Set, p. 187

Using smallest oak leaf cutter from set, cut 2 wing cookies for each cupcake; bake and cool. Ice cupcakes smooth. Pipe tip 2A ball head, tip 3 eyeballs and tip 2 dot pupils. Outline mouth with tip 3; add tip 3 pull-out fangs. Pipe tip 352 pull-out ears. Ice wing cookies and position. Each serves 1.

*Note: Combine Leaf Green and Lemon Yellow to achieve color used.

**Or use Chocolate Ready-To-Use Decorator Icing, p. 126

◀ Moonlight Flight

Finger food for the looniest night of the year. Great for party place settings or school costume parties.

Pans: 10½ x 15½ in. x 1 in. Jelly Roll, p. 160; Cooling Grid, p. 160
Color: Golden Yellow, p. 127
Also: Ready-To-Use Decorator Icing, p. 126; Spooky Shapes Cookie Cutter Set, p. 169; Just Batty Icing Decorations, p. 167; Disposable Decorating Bags, p. 134

Bake and cool cake. Using moon cutter from set, cut individual cakes. Tint icing yellow in container; cover cakes with heated icing (p. 118). Let set 30 minutes. Attach icing decoration with dot of icing. Each serves 1.

▶ The Bat Pack and Drac

Frightfully fun lollipops give a simple spider web cake a high profile at your Halloween party.

Pans: 8 x 2 in. Round, p. 158; Cookie Sheet, p. 160
Tips: 1M (2110), 3, p. 136-137
Colors: Violet, Black, p. 127
Candy: Just Batty Lollipop Mold, p. 167; White and Light Cocoa Candy Melts®†, p. 146; Garden and Primary Candy Color Sets, Decorator Brush Set, p. 147; 8 in. Lollipop Sticks, p. 149
Recipe: Buttercream Icing, p. 111
Also: 2005 Pattern Book (Dracula), p. 222; Parchment Triangles, p. 134; Black Colored Sugar, p. 128; 101 Cookie Cutters Set, p. 142; Cake Board, Fanci-Foil Wrap, p. 217; candy corn, toothpick

Tint portions of melted white candy black, violet and green/yellow combination. Mold candy Dracula on cookie sheet, using large boy cutter from set, filling ¼ in. deep with green/yellow candy. Refrigerate until firm; remove cutter. Trace pattern with toothpick. Using melted candy in cut parchment bag, pipe hair, suit, shoes and facial features; refrigerate until firm. Pipe shirt, cuffs and fangs; refrigerate until firm. Pipe bow tie, buttons; refrigerate until firm. Mold bat lollipops: using painting and layering methods (p. 119) refrigerate until firm. Attach lollipop sticks to back of Dracula with melted candy; let set.

Ice 2-layer cake fluffy with spatula. Outline tip 3 spider web and pipe tip 3 dot and string spiders. Add tip 1M rosette bottom border, sprinkle with black sugar and position candy corn at rosette centers. Trim lollipop sticks on bats and Dracula to various lengths and insert in cake. Serves 20.

▼ Enter with Your Skeleton Key!

If you love brownies, here's your dream house! Stack 'em high, top with Sprinkle Sparks, pumpkin decorations and tinted coconut, then position our pre-built cookie castle.

Pan: 9 x 13 x 2 in. Sheet, p. 158
Color: Leaf Green, p. 127
Also: Pre-Assembled Haunted Castle Kit (includes house cookies, icing mixes, candies and ghost icing decorations used), p. 168 ; Halloween Sprinkle Sparks Mix, p, 168; Pumpkin Face Icing Decorations, p. 167; 3 in. Crystal-Look Pillars, p. 215; 8 in. Crystal-Look Plates (2 needed), p. 214; Cake Board, Fanci-Foil Wrap, p. 217; brownie mix (3 to 4 family size mixes, approximately 20 oz. each, needed), shredded coconut, zip-close plastic bag

Tint shredded coconut green (p. 116). Set aside.

Decorate house following kit directions. Prepare brownies according to package directions, top with Sprinkle Sparks, bake and cool. Cut brownies into squares.

Assemble plates and pillars; arrange stacks of brownies around bottom plate to resemble mountain and to hide pillars. Position assembled house on top plate and sprinkle with tinted coconut. Position icing decorations. Each brownie serves 1.

▲ He Takes Off Every Halloween

Our great-tasting fudge recipe cuts easily using the Bat Stencil-A-Cookie™ cutter.

Pan: 11 x 7 x 1½ in. Non-Stick Biscuit/Brownie, p. 157
Recipe: Ready-In-Minutes Cocoa Fudge, p. 112
Also: Bat Stencil-A-Cookie™ Cutter and Stencil Set, p. 168; Dark Cocoa Candy Melts®† (2 pks.), p. 167; Tube Decorating Icings in Chocolate, Orange, White, p. 127; Tip and Nail Set, p. 127; Just Batty Party Bags, p. 167

Prepare fudge recipe and pour into pan. Refrigerate until firm; unmold. Cut bats using cutter from set. Using round tip and tube icings, outline and pipe in ears, eyes and mouth, pipe dot eyes and pupils. Outline and pipe-in wings. Place in party bags. Each serves 1.

▼ The Witch on Watch

Kids will love this friendly face, decorated on a Jack-O-Lantern cake and dressed in a stacked cookie hat.

Pan: Jack-O-Lantern, p. 166
Tips: 1A, 4, 18, p. 136-137
Colors: Violet, Golden Yellow, Orange, Leaf Green, Black, p. 127
Recipes: Buttercream Icing, p. 111; Roll-Out Cookie, p. 112
Also: 2005 Pattern Book (Witch Hat and Face), p. 222; Cake Board, Fanci-Foil Wrap, p. 217, toothpick, cornstarch, paring knife

Using pattern, cut, bake and cool 3 hat cookies. Ice smooth and stack together; set aside.

Trim stem off cake. Ice sides and lightly ice top smooth. Trace face pattern with toothpick. Position stacked cookies above head. Pipe tip 1A large balls for eyeballs; add tip 4 dot pupils. Outline mouth with tip 4. Pipe in tip 4 tooth (smooth with finger dipped in cornstarch). Build up nose area with tip 1A. Cover face with tip 18 stars; overpipe cheeks and eyelids with tip 18 stars. Pipe tip 4 dot warts. Cover hat top and sides, band and buckle with tip 18 stars. Add tip 18 pull-out star wavy hair. Pipe tip 18 star bottom border. Serves 12.

▲ Kolackys from the Crypt

Flaky crusts, cut with our ghoulish Grippy™ cutters, are topped with luscious fruit filling.

Cookie: Halloween Grippy™ Cutter Set, p. 169; Cookie Sheet, Cooling Grid, p. 160
Tip: 2, p. 136
Color: Orange, p. 127
Recipe: Kolackys, p. 112
Also: Tube Decorating Icings in Black, Leaf Green, Orange, p. 127; Coupler Ring Set, p. 127; Disposable Decorating Bags, p. 134; apricot and prune pastry filling (1 can each)

Roll out Kolacky dough and cut out shapes with bat, cat and pumpkin cutters. Tint apricot filling orange. Fill disposable decorating bags with pastry fillings; cut bag and pipe to cover cookies. Bake 18 minutes or until light brown; cool. Fit tube icings with tip 2 and pipe features. Each serves 1.

▶ Hanging on Every Word

This ghost story takes place on an exciting backdrop...a fondant-covered cake board with webs illustrated using FoodWriter Edible Color Markers.

Pans: Step-By-Step Ghost, p. 166; 12½ x 16½ in. Cookie Sheet, p. 143
Tips: 2, 12, p. 136
Colors:* Violet, Black, Orange, Leaf Green, Lemon Yellow, p. 127
Fondant: White Ready-To-Use Rolled Fondant (24 oz. needed), p. 122; Easy-Glide Fondant Smoother, Roll & Cut Mat, Cutter/Embosser, Rolling Pin, p. 125
Recipe: Buttercream Icing, p. 111
Also: 2005 Pattern Book (Book, Eyes), p. 222; 13 x 19 in. Cake Board, p. 217; Gum-Tex® Karaya, p. 125; Halloween Mini Cutter Set, p. 169; 4 in. Lollipop Sticks, p. 149; Decorator Brush Set, p. 147; Halloween FoodWriter™ Edible Color Markers, p. 166; cornstarch, waxed paper, toothpick

In advance: Make fondant pieces. Tint fondant as follows: 16 oz. orange, 4 oz. violet, 1½ oz. green, 1½ oz. black; reserve 1 oz. white. Knead ¼ teaspoon of Gum-Tex into violet fondant; roll out ⅛ in. thick and cut book using pattern. Let dry on cookie sheet dusted with cornstarch. Print tip 2 jagged message. Use cutters to cut ghost, bat, cat and pumpkin from fondant; attach to book with damp brush; pipe tip 2 facial features on all and stem on pumpkin. Roll a ¼ in. diameter rope of purple fondant for spine of book; attach to book pieces with damp brush. Trim edges and press to secure. Let dry.

Bake and cool cake. Cut cake board 1 in. larger than cake pan. Roll out orange fondant, cover board and smooth with Easy-Glide Smoother. Trim "BOO" message area off ghost cake. Ice smooth and position on board. Draw spider webs and spiders on fondant-covered board with black FoodWriter. Using pattern, cut eyes from green fondant; position on cake. Pipe tip 2 dot pupils and string eyebrows.

Cut two lollipop sticks to 3¾ in. and one to 3½ in.; insert sticks in cake to support book, longest stick in center. Position book. Build up tip 12 arms and hands with fingers holding book. Serves 12.

*Note: Add a small amount of yellow color to green fondant for shade shown.

▶ Frank Loosens Up

He may not like parties, but your guests are sure to love him! Have fun building Frank in your laboratory, using mini loaf arms, legs and feet, a Jack-O-Lantern cake head and a biscuit/brownie cake body.

Pans: Stand-Up Jack-O-Lantern, p. 166; 11 x 7 x 1½ in. Non-Stick Biscuit/Brownie, p. 157; Mini Loaf, p. 160
Tips: 2A, 3, 18, 21, p. 136-137
Colors: Violet, Brown, Black, Leaf Green, p. 127
Also: 10 x 14 in. Cake Board, Fanci-Foil Wrap, p. 217; 16 x 24 in. cardboard (2 boards needed), large black spice drops

Bake and cool the following 1-layer cakes: nine mini loaves, one 7 x 11 in. cake and one jack-o-lantern front half; trim stem off jack-o-lantern. Cut double cardboard to fit cakes positioned as follows: 7 x 11 in. body, two vertical mini loaves for each arm (extend board for hands), two perpendicular mini loaves for each leg; the jack-o-lantern head will rest on the body cake and one mini loaf at top edge. Trim to fit as needed. Wrap cardboard with foil and position cakes. Build up eyebrow area, nose, ears and hands with tip 2A. Pipe in tip 2A whites of eyes; add tip 3 pupils. Pipe tip 3 outline mouth and scar. Cover face, ears and hands with tip 18 stars. Beginning at back of head, pipe tip 21 pull-out star hair; overpipe 2 or 3 times to create a squared-off look. Cover legs with tip 18 stars and feet with tip 21 stars. Attach spice drop "bolts" to sides of head. Serves 27.

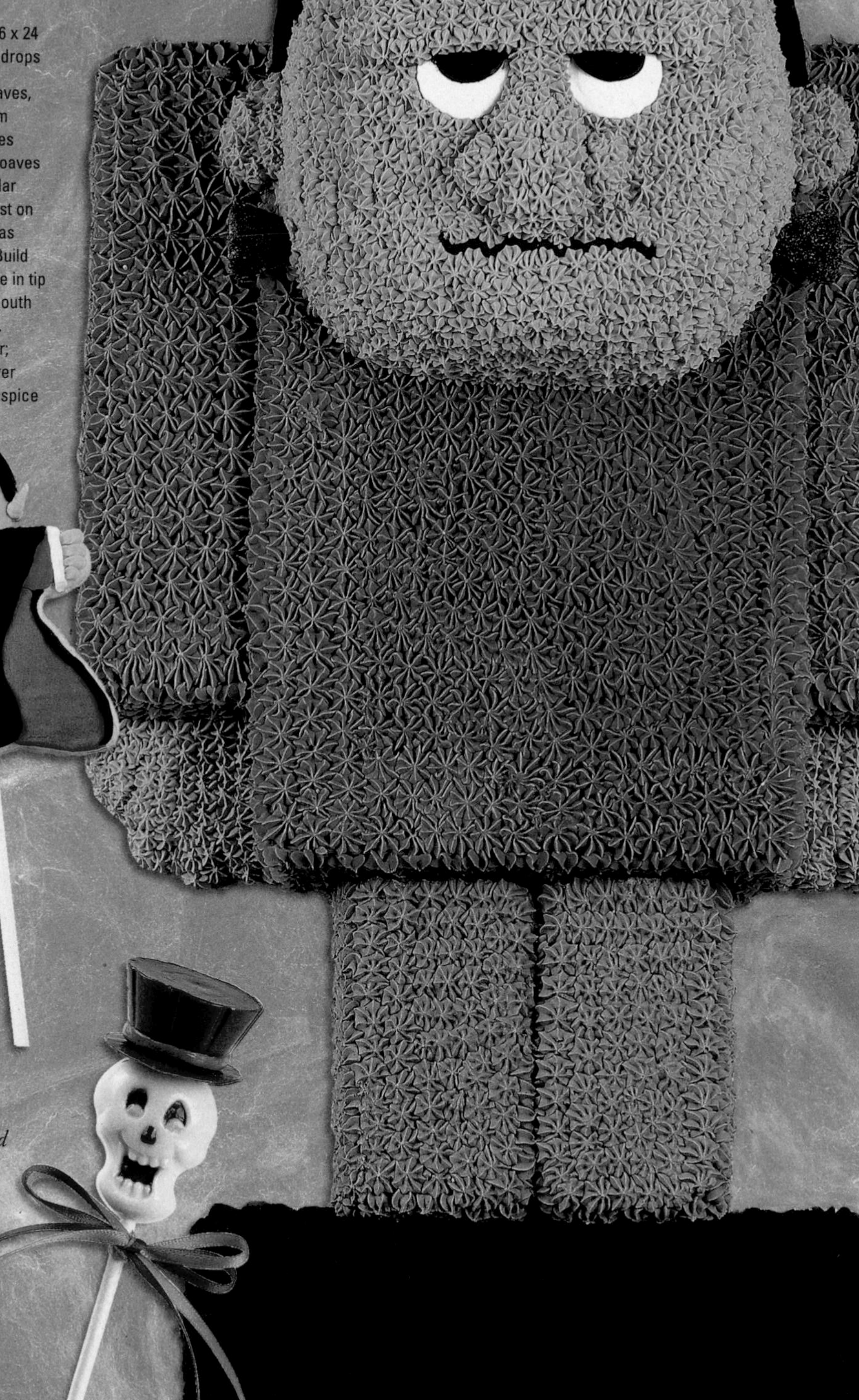

▶ Cape Fear

Because everyone will be in costume for the big day, we've dressed up ghost cookies as vampires on these fun pops.

Cookies: Spooky Shapes Cutter Set, p. 169; Cookie Sheet, Cooling Grid, p. 160
Tip: 3, p. 136
Colors: Black, No-Taste Red, Leaf Green, Violet, p. 127
Recipes: Roll-Out Cookie, p. 112; Royal Icing, p. 111
Also: 8 in. Lollipop Sticks, p. 149; Meringue Powder, p. 126; cornstarch

Cut cookies with ghost cutter from set. Trim off right arm and smooth remaining dough at cut line; bake and cool. Ice face area smooth. Using tip 3, pipe in hair, sleeve, cuff, cape and cape lining (smooth with finger dipped in cornstarch). Pipe tip 3 dot and string facial features, fingers and pull-out ears. Let dry.

Attach stick to back with icing. Each serves 1.

▶ Formerly Formal

Make co-workers smile with an easy treat: lollipops molded with our Halloween Kit and finished with a candy Cordial Cup top hat.

Candy: Halloween Lollipop Kit (includes White, Light Cocoa Candy Melts®†, 8 in. Lollipop Sticks, Candy Mold, Decorator Brush, Disposable Decorating Bags), p. 167; Candy Melts®†—Green, Yellow, p. 146; Cordial Cups Candy Mold, p. 148
Also: waxed paper, orange and purple ribbon

Make a 1½ in. circle pattern in waxed paper for hat brim. Outline and pipe in pattern with melted candy in cut disposable bag. Refrigerate until firm. Mold skeleton head lollipops using painting method (p. 119). Mold solid cordial cups for hats; refrigerate all until firm. Attach hat brim with melted candy; pipe band with green candy in cut bag. Attach hat to head with melted candy. Tie ribbon around stick. Each serves 1.

†Brand confectionery coating.

▼ Snacks on the Tracks

No coal in this Christmas train's cargo! The candy cars are filled with gingerbread boys and seasonal sweets.

Pans: Long Loaf, Mini Locomotive, Petite Loaf, Cookie Sheet, Cooling Grid, p. 160
Tips: 1, 2, 3, 5, 11, 352, p. 136-137
Colors: Kelly Green, Lemon Yellow, p. 127
Cookies: Holiday Mini Cutter Set, p. 173; Metal Nesting Trees Cutter Set, p. 173
Recipes: Buttercream, Chocolate Buttercream, Royal Icings, p. 111; Grandma's Gingerbread, p. 112
Also: Light Cocoa Candy Melts® (2 pks.), p. 146; Wooden Dowel Rods, p. 214; Flowerful Medley, Cinnamon Drops Sprinkle Decorations, p. 128; 13 x 19 in. Cake Board, Fanci-Foil Wrap, p. 217; Meringue Powder, p. 126; Angled Spatula, p. 134; 4 in. Lollipop Sticks, p. 149, scissors, peppermint disks, gumball, mini jawbreakers, hollow-center candy, spice drops, 6 in. candy canes, cornstarch

In advance: Use gingerbread dough and cutters to cut the following cookies: 2 smallest trees, 1 second smallest tree, 2 third smallest trees and 7 gingerbread boys; bake and cool. Using royal icing, pipe tip 352 pull-out leaves on trees; attach confetti sprinkles from Flowerful Medley Assortment with tip 1 dots of icing. Using royal icing, pipe tip 1 dot and outline facial features and buttons on gingerbread boys; let dry. Cut dowel rods to 8 in. long; attach to backs of tree cookies with melted candy, set aside.

Mold candy locomotive, ¼ in. thick, in Mini Locomotive Pan. Mold two candy shell (p. 119) cargo cars in Petite Loaf Pan. Refrigerate until firm; unmold. Using royal icing, decorate all shells: For locomotive, attach cinnamon drop centers to mint wheels and wheels to locomotive with tip 2. Cut candy cane axle to fit between wheel centers and attach. Pipe tip 3 zigzag bands on engine and attach mini jawbreakers. Pipe cowcatcher and "cupcake" smokestack with tip 5 lines; add tip 5 piped snow trim on roof and smokestack; position gumball and mini jawbreakers. Outline and pipe in window with tip 2 (smooth with finger dipped in cornstarch); attach top half of one gingerbread boy. Attach hollow-center candy headlight with tip 2. Attach lollipop stick to back of locomotive with melted candy. For cargo cars: attach gingerbread boys inside cars with tip 3; fill cars with spice drops and pipe tip 3 snow around edges. Attach cinnamon drop wheel centers and mint wheels as for locomotive. Trim candy cane runners to 4¼ in. and attach with tip 2. Set aside.

On foil-covered board, ice long loaf cake sides smooth with chocolate buttercream icing. Ice top with white buttercream. Pipe tip 11 ball snow mounds over edge; blend into top icing with spatula. Print tip 5 message. Insert locomotive and trees; position cars. Pipe tip 11 ball snow mounds around bottom border and position candy. Cake serves 12.

▶ Cookie Confections

Cookies: 101 Cookie Cutters Set, p. 142; Cookie Sheet, Cooling Grid, p. 160
Tip: 3, p. 136
Colors: Violet, Red-Red, Kelly Green, Lemon Yellow, p. 127
Recipes: Roll-Out Cookie, p. 112; Color Flow Icing, p. 111
Also: Color Flow Mix, p. 127; Tapered Spatula, p. 134; waxed paper, granulated sugar, sharp knife

Using cutters from set, cut candy cane, medium circle and bell cookies. Trim off top and bottom from bell to form domed gumdrop shape. Bake and cool all cookies.

Tint portions of Color Flow Icing red, green, yellow and violet; reserve a portion white. Thin all Color Flow, except a small portion of white, following package directions. Cover candy cane and mint disc cookies with white Color Flow (p. 118). Decorate immediately, using tip 3 to pipe stripes on candy canes and outline swirls from center of discs. Let set 2 minutes, then sprinkle with sugar. If needed, trim edges with spatula. Cover gum drop cookies with tinted Color Flow. Let set 2 minutes, then sprinkle with sugar. Trim edges if needed. Move to a waxed paper-covered surface to dry completely. Each cookie serves 1.

▶ A Very Merry-Go-Round

Pans: 6 x 3 in., 10 x 3 in. Round, p. 158; Cookie Sheet, Cooling Grid, p. 160
Tips: 1M (2110), 2, p. 136
Colors: Red-Red, Brown, Kelly Green, p. 127
Recipes: Buttercream, Chocolate Buttercream, Royal Icings, p. 111
Also: Nesting Gingerbread Boys Cutter Set, p. 173; Icing Sculptor™, p. 131; White Ready-To-Use Rolled Fondant (24 oz. needed), p. 122; Meringue Powder, p. 126; Hidden Pillars, p. 215; 8 in. Decorator Preferred® Separator Plate, p. 214; Rainbow Nonpareils Sprinkle Decorations, p. 128; Cake Boards, Fanci-Foil Wrap, p. 217; Decorator Brush Set, p. 147; spice drops, small candy canes, 6 in. candy canes (5 needed), cornstarch, sharp knife

Tint 12 oz. fondant brown and red combination; roll out ⅛ in. thick. Using second smallest cutter from set, cut 14 gingerbread boys; let dry on cookie sheet dusted with cornstarch. Using royal icing, pipe tip 2 dot and string facial features and trim on gingerbread boys. Tint 6 oz. fondant red and reserve 6 oz. white; roll out ⅛ in. thick. Using knife, cut ¼ in. strips of each color and wrap around top half of hidden pillars, attaching with damp brush; set aside.

Prepare 2-layer 6 and 10 in. cakes (3 in. high) for Push-In Pillar Construction (p. 110). Ice cakes smooth in chocolate buttercream, ½ in. thick on sides. Immediately comb sides with Icing Sculptor, using yellow blades with U-shaped edge.

Insert hidden pillars into 10 in. cake, so that fondant strips rest just above cake. Position 6 in. cake on separator plate. Pipe tip 1M rosette top and bottom borders. Cover top tier with tip 1M rosettes, adding a second row in center. Position spice drop and sprinkle nonpareils on each rosette. Position gingerbread boys and small candy canes around cakes. Insert large candy canes. Serves 40.

◀ Sweet Dreams from Santa

Cookies: Copper Holiday Mini Cutter Set, p. 173; Circle Metal Cutter, p. 140; Cookie Sheet, Cooling Grid, p. 160
Candy: White Candy Melts®†, p. 146; 11¾ in. Lollipop Sticks, p. 149; Party Time Lollipop Mold, p. 148; Primary and Garden Candy Color Sets, p. 147
Tips: 1, 2, 3, p. 136
Colors: Copper (skin tone), Red-Red, Brown, Lemon Yellow, Kelly Green, Black, p. 127
Fondant: White Ready-To-Use Rolled Fondant (24 oz. needed), p. 122; Cutter/Embosser, p. 125
Recipes: Roll-Out Cookie, p. 112; Color Flow Icing, p. 111
Also: 2005 Pattern Book (Headboard), p. 222; Color Flow Mix, p. 127; Plastic Dowel Rods, p. 214; Cake Board, Fanci-Foil Wrap, p. 217; Decorator Brush Set, p. 147; 1 in. white gumballs (2 needed), craft block (7 x 7 x 3 in. high), mini candy canes (4 needed), large spice drops, scissors, toothpick

Tint portions of melted candy red, pink and yellow using candy colors. Mold 3 cupcake lollipops using painting method (p. 119). Make cookies: Use circle and mini cutters to cut 4 round heads, 4 gingerbread boys, 3 candy canes and 2 stars. Using pattern, cut headboard. Bake and cool all cookies. Cover all cookies, except headboard, with thinned Color Flow (p. 118). Let dry. Decorate cookies with full-strength Color Flow. For heads, pipe tip 2 mouth, nose, eyes, cheeks and ears. Add tip 13 pull-out hair for girl and tip 2 string hair for boy. For gingerbread boys, pipe tip 1 outline mouth, dot buttons and eyes. For candy canes, pipe tip 2 stripes. For headboard, using tip 2, outline and flow-in design areas with Color Flow (p. 118). Let all pieces dry. Attach lollipop sticks to backs with melted candy. Insert spice drops on other sticks. Set aside.

For bed, wrap craft block with foil. Cut 2 dowel rods to 6 in. long. Mark top area of block 1¾ in. from back edge; insert dowel rod headboard posts at marks. Attach headboard cookie to back of posts and gumballs to top of posts with melted candy. For pillows, cut two ½ in. thick, 2½ in. square pieces of white fondant; pinch corners. For shoulders, roll two ½ in. balls of copper fondant and position below each pillow; push head cookies into shoulders and rest on pillows. For bodies, roll 3 x 1 in. fondant logs; position on bed. Roll four ½ in. diameter fondant balls for feet; attach 2 to bottom of each log. To make blanket, cut a 13 x ¾ in. wide white fondant strip for edging; tint remaining fondant green. Cut 13 x 8 in. wide blanket. Using ridged wheel of Cutter/Embosser, score diagonal lines 1¼ in. apart. Position blanket and attach edging with damp brush.

Create elongated candy canes (approximately 3½ in. long) by cutting curved end off one candy cane and attaching with melted candy to a whole cane. Position candy canes. For hands, roll ¾ in. ovals of copper fondant; shape into ovals and indent fingers with end of spatula. Attach to candy canes with melted candy. Insert cookies, candies and spice drops on sticks in block behind headboard, trimming sticks to various heights as needed. Each lollipop and cookie serves 1.

†Brand confectionery coating.

◀ He's a Ski Mogul

You can almost feel the wind rush around this frosty freestyler. His fondant hat and scarf are curved and extended to catch some big air!

Pan: Stand-Up Snowman, p. 170
Tip: 1A, p. 136
Colors: Christmas Red, Red-Red, Kelly Green, Rose, Black, p. 127
Recipes: Buttercream Icing, p. 111
Also: 2005 Pattern Book (Skis), p. 222; Cake Boards, Fanci-Foil Wrap, p. 217; Wooden Dowel Rods, p. 214; Angled Spatula, p. 134; White Ready-To-Use Rolled Fondant (24 oz. needed), p. 122; Gum-Tex™ Karaya, p. 125; 4 in. Lollipop Sticks, p. 149; Disposable Decorating Bags, p. 134; Decorator Brush Set, p. 147; Flower Former Set, p. 134; ruler, pizza cutter, sharp knife, rolling pin, cornstarch, cotton balls, cellophane tape, waxed paper, aluminum foil

At least one week in advance: Make fondant scarf ends, hat and skis (p. 117). To prepare, add Gum-Tex to fondant following instructions for Extra-Firm Rolled Fondant (p. 112). Tint 6 oz. fondant green, 12 oz. red-red/Christmas red combination; reserve remainder white. After making these decorations, reserve all remaining tinted fondant.

Wrap a double-thick 13 x 7 in. board with foil. Bake and cool snowman cake using firm-textured batter such as pound cake. Trim 1½ in. off bottom of snowman on an angle to create "leaning forward" look. Attach skis to foil-covered board with buttercream; position cake on skis. Spatula ice cake. Tint small amounts of fondant black and rose. Cut black crescent shape for mouth. Roll ½ in. diameter white fondant ball nose and a ¾ in. diameter red ball tongue; indent tongue. Cut ¾ in. white oval eyes. Roll small black ball pupils. Attach pupils to eyes and tongue to mouth with damp brush. Cut ¾ in. diameter rose for circle cheeks. Attach facial features with dots of icing. For flat portion of scarf, cut a 1 x 20 in. long green fondant strip; wrap around neck.

For ski poles, trim wooden dowel rods to 8 in. long and thread red circle baskets over ends. Push poles into sides of cake. Pipe tip 1A outline arms holding poles on each side of body. Position hat. For hatband, cut a 1 in. wide strip of white fondant; attach with a damp brush. For scarf knot, roll a 1 in. diameter green fondant ball; insert scarf ends on lollipop sticks through knot and into cake. Serves 12.

▶ The Blizzard Boys

Pan: Mini Snowman, p. 170
Tips: 2, 3, 14, p. 136
Colors:* Christmas Red, Red-Red, Kelly Green, Royal Blue, Black, Orange, p. 127
Fondant: White Ready-To-Use Rolled Fondant (24 oz. needed), p. 122; Roll & Cut Mat, Rolling Pin, Brush Set, p. 125
Recipe: Buttercream Icing, p. 111
Also: scissors

Ice cakes smooth. Divide fondant into fourths; tint portions green, blue and red, reserve ¼ white. Roll tinted fondant ⅛ in. thick, cut 1½ x 4½ in. pieces and position on snowmen for jackets; trim excess.

Roll logs of fondant, shape into hats and position on heads. For pompoms, roll ¾ in. diameter balls of white fondant. Cut lines in bottom and insert on hats. Decorate blue jacket with ¼ in. diameter balls; decorate red and green jackets with ¼ in. wide strips of white fondant. Attach decorations with damp brush. Pipe tip 14 zigzags on hat brims and jacket edges. Pipe tip 3 pull-out nose, tip 2 dot eyes, cheeks and outline mouth. Each serves 1.

*Note: Combine Christmas Red and Red-Red for shade shown.

◀ One Cool Customer

Pans: Step-By-Step Snowman, p. 170; 12 x 2 in. Round, p. 158
Colors:* Kelly Green, Christmas Red, Red-Red, Orange, p. 127
Recipe: Buttercream Icing, p. 111
Also: 6 in. Cookie Treat Sticks, p. 143; Silver Fanci-Foil Wrap, p. 217; Straight Spatula, p. 134; Disposable Decorating Bags, p. 134; ½ in. thick foam-core or sturdy board (approximately 25 x 13 in.), 1 in. diameter jelly candy disks, round wafer candies, candy-coated chocolates, black shoestring licorice, sugar cone, rolled fruit snack, jelly spearmint leaves, jumbo candy cane, toasted coconut-covered marshmallow, scissors

For nose, cut cone to 2½ in., ice smooth with orange icing; set aside. Ice face area of snowman cake smooth with spatula; position wafer candy eyes and cheeks, licorice mouth; position nose. Attach candy-coated chocolate pupils with buttercream. To ice hat area, place icing in a disposable bag cut with a ½ in. opening. Cover hat area; ice smooth with spatula. For hatband, cut fruit snack into ¾ in. wide strips; attach with white buttercream. For holly, cut jelly leaves in half with scissors; attach leaves and candy-coated chocolate berries with buttercream.

For body, spatula ice 1-layer round cake. Ice and smooth jacket area following procedure for hat area. Score jacket seam with spatula edge; attach jelly disk buttons and candy-coated chocolate trim with buttercream. For bow tie, press two 7 in. lengths of rolled fruit snacks together at one end to form longer ribbon. Fold ends into center to form loops and crimp at center. Wrap a 2 in. strip of rolled fruit around center and attach for knot with icing; position on cake. For pipe, trim cookie stick to 4 in.; insert marshmallow on one end, insert other end in mouth area. Position candy cane. Serves 52.

***Note:** Combine Christmas Red and Red-Red for shade shown.

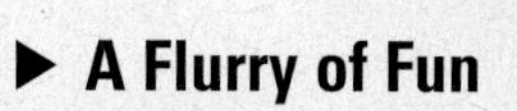

▶ A Flurry of Fun

Pan: 8 x 2 in. Round, p. 158; Cookie Sheet, Cooling Grid, p. 160
Tips: 1, 2, 3, 4, 5, p. 136
Colors:* Kelly Green, Lemon Yellow, Royal Blue, Red-Red, Christmas Red, Orange, Black, Violet, Rose, p. 127
Cookies: White Ice-A-Cookie™, p. 172; Snowman Copper Cookie Cutter, Colorful Holiday Cutter Set, p. 173
Recipes: Buttercream, Royal Icings, p. 111; Roll-Out Cookie, p. 112
Also: Cake Board, Fanci-Foil Wrap, p. 217; 6 in. Lollipop Sticks, p. 149; Meringue Powder, p. 126; shredded coconut, small candy canes, large candy cane, cornstarch

Using copper snowman cutter, cut 1 large snowman. Using colorful holiday cutter, cut 10 small snowmen, reversing 5. Bake and cool all cookies. Following package directions, cover cookies in Ice-A-Cookie, let dry. Using royal icing, decorate with tip 2 string mouths, tip 2 dot eyes and cheeks, tip 3 pull-out dot noses. For large snowman, also pipe in vest using tip 5, pat smooth with finger dipped in cornstarch. Pipe in tip 3 bow tie with dot knots and tip 4 hat, pat smooth with finger dipped in cornstarch; add tip 4 string hatband. For small snowmen, pipe in tip 4 vests and scarves, pat smooth with finger dipped in cornstarch. Add tip 1 string fringe to scarves. Pipe in tip 5 hats. Using tip 3, pipe zigzag fur on hats and add dot pompom. Let all dry. Attach candy canes; let dry. Attach lollipop sticks to backs of large snowman and one small snowman cookie. Let dry.

Ice 2-layer 8 in. round cake smooth in buttercream; cover in shredded coconut. Insert cookies on sticks in top of cake. Position remaining cookies around cake, securing with dots of icing. Serves 20.

***Note:** Combine Christmas Red and Red-Red for shade shown.

▲ Miracle of the Manger

The meaning of the season is brought home beautifully in this joyful manger scene. A unique way to decorate for church celebrations or family gatherings.

Pans: Mini Wonder Mold, p. 161; Petite Loaf, p. 160; Cookie Sheet, Cooling Grid, p. 160
Tips: 1, 2, 3, 5, 7, 12, 47, 352, p. 136-137
Colors: Brown, Black, Red-Red, Copper (skin tone), Lemon Yellow, Orange, Rose, Royal Blue, Kelly Green, Violet, p. 127
Recipes: Buttercream, Royal Icings, p. 111; Roll-Out Cookie, p. 112
Also: White Ready-To-Use Rolled Fondant (24 oz. needed), p. 122; 4 in. Lollipop Sticks, p. 149; 101 Cookie Cutter Set, p. 142; Meringue Powder, p. 126; Plastic Dowel Rods, p. 214; 13 x 19 in. Cake Board, Fanci-Foil Wrap, p. 217; shredded wheat cereal, cornstarch, rolling pin, waxed paper, sharp knife

In advance: Make cookie heads. Cut 7 circle cookies using smallest round cutter from set; bake and cool. Place on cooling grid and cover with thinned royal icing (p. 118); let dry. Position cookies on waxed paper and pipe tip 1 dot eyes and string mouths; tip 2 dot noses and cheeks. Add tip 3 zigzag or outline hair, beards and moustaches. Pipe tip 3 outline and pipe in crown, then overpipe. Pipe tip 3 spiral turban with outline and pipe-in jewel. Let all cookies dry. Attach lollipop sticks to backs with royal icing; let dry.

Also in advance: Make fondant pieces. For halo and star, tint 1 in. ball of fondant yellow, roll out and cut with smallest round and smallest star cutters. For Joseph's staff, tint 2 in. ball of fondant brown, roll into 7 in. log and curl end. For wings, roll out white fondant and cut using heart cutter; cut heart vertically in half. Let all pieces dry several days on cornstarch-dusted surface. Using royal icing, pipe tip 352 pull-out feathers on wings. Attach lollipop stick to back of star with royal icing.

Make 2 resting lambs (p. 118) (the held lamb will be made directly on cake). Bake and cool 7 Mini Wonder Mold cakes and 1 Petite Loaf cake. Trim loaf horizontally on an angle to make slanted manger; ice smooth in buttercream. For Baby, pipe tip 5 ball head and body; add tip 1 facial features. Cover body with tip 47 band wrap; add tip 2 pull-out straw. Ice mini cakes smooth in buttercream; use spatula edge to form folds in robes for angel and Mary. Pipe tip 12 pull-out arms (except for angel). Pipe tip 2 dot, zigzag, swirl and pull-out fur trim on robes; add tip 2 outline cuffs for Mary. Insert cookie heads into cakes. Make and position fondant sash and headpieces (p. 117). Pipe tip 3 outline headbands; add tip 3 pipe-in and dot button to red headpiece. Position Joseph's staff. Decorate held lamb (p. 118) on cake. Outline and pipe in tip 2 gifts. Add tip 2 bead hands and fingers. Trim dowel rods to 3 in. and insert into angel cake for arms; ice smooth. Fill dowel rod with icing and insert star on stick. Pipe tip 2 bead hands and fingers; attach wings to cake and halo to head with icing. Position figures and lambs on foil-wrapped 13 x 19 in. board; sprinkle board with crushed shredded wheat. Each cake serves 1.

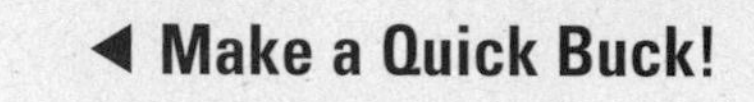

◀ Make a Quick Buck!

Pans: Animal Crackers, p. 162, Cookie Sheet,
Cooling Grid, p. 160
Tips: 3, 8, 18, p. 136
Colors: Brown, Red-Red, Black, Rose, p. 127
Recipes: Buttercream Icing, p. 111; Roll-Out Cookie, p. 112
Also: 2005 Pattern Book (Antlers), p. 222; 8 in. Angled
Spatula, p. 134; Cake Board, Fanci-Foil Wrap, p. 217;
sharp knife, cornstarch, toothpick

With toothpick; trace antlers pattern on rolled-out dough. Cut antlers with knife. Make extras to allow for breakage; bake and cool.

Build up ears to a point with icing and spatula. Pipe inside of ears, eyes and nose with tip 3 (smooth with finger dipped in cornstarch). Cut off tongue portion of cake and extend mouth area with icing. Outline mouth and center of muzzle with tip 3; pipe in tip 3 mouth and tongue (smooth with finger dipped in cornstarch). Cover cake with tip 18 stars. Cover tops of antler cookies with tip 8 (smooth with finger dipped in cornstarch). Insert antlers into cake. Serves 12.

▶ He's Elf-Employed!

No one brings more holiday cheer than this guy! Dressed in the season's favorite colors, he's easy to decorate on our Jolly Santa pan.

Pan: Jolly Santa, p. 170
Tips: 3, 4, 5, 16, 21, 366, p. 136
Colors:* Kelly Green, Christmas Red, Red-Red, Black,
Golden Yellow, Copper (skin tone), Royal Blue, p. 127
Recipe: Buttercream Icing, p. 111
Also: Cake Board, Fanci-Foil Wrap, p. 217; Angled Spatula,
p. 134; cornstarch, small paring knife

Trim down leg area on cake with knife. Ice sides and background areas smooth with spatula. Build up face area with icing, using spatula to level with beard and moustache area of cake. Outline elf with tip 4. Outline and pipe in eyes and mouth with tip 4 (pat smooth with fingers dipped in cornstarch). Pipe tip 3 bead tongue (smooth with finger dipped in cornstarch). Cover hat, face, hands, jacket and shoes with tip 16 stars; overpipe nose with tip 16 stars. Add tip 366 pull-out ears and leaf collar. Pipe tip 5 lines for leggings; add tip 5 outline belt and buckle. Pipe tip 5 zigzag fur on hat, cuffs and shoes. Add tip16 pull-out star hair. Add tip 5 balls at collar and jacket points and on tips of shoes and hat. Pipe tip 21 star bottom border. Serves 12.

***Note:** Combine Christmas Red and Red-Red for shade shown.

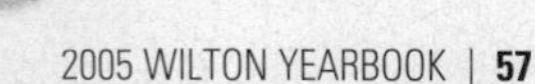

◀ Santa's Sweet Sedan

It's a gingerbread sled that seats lots of package pops and one jolly Santa cookie!

Cookies: Gingerbread Boy Stencil-A-Cookie™ Cutter & Stencil Set, p. 172; Cookie Sheet, Cooling Grid, p. 160
Tips: 1, 2, 4, 5, 10, 349, p. 136-137
Candy: Candy Melts®† in Red, Green, Lavender, Yellow, Blue, White, p. 146; 4 in., 6 in. Lollipop Sticks, p. 149; Gifts Galore Lollipop Mold, p. 171
Colors:* Red-Red, Christmas Red, Kelly Green, Brown, p. 127
Recipe: Royal Icing, p. 111; Grandma's Gingerbread, p. 112
Also: 2005 Pattern Book (Sleigh Sides, Back, Bottom, Front), p. 222; Cake Board, White Fanci-Foil Wrap, p. 217; White Nonpareils Sprinkle Decorations, p. 128; Meringue Powder, p. 126; Decorator Brush Set, p. 147, craft block (5 in. long x 2½ in. wide x 2 in. high), cornstarch, 2 giant candy canes, cellophane tape, toothpick, waxed paper

In advance: Mold gift lollipops on 4 in. and 6 in. lollipop sticks, using painting method (p. 119).

Also in advance: Make cookies. Trace sleigh patterns in gingerbread dough. Cut 2 Sleigh Sides (reverse pattern to cut opposite side), and 1 each Sleigh Back, Front and Bottom. Use gingerbread boy cutter from set to cut 1 cookie for Santa. Bake and cool all cookies. Working one sleigh cookie piece at a time, using softened royal icing, pipe a tip 10 heavy outline on top edges of sleigh pieces; immediately cover with nonpareils. On sleigh sides, pipe tip 2 wavy lines and tip 1 dot berries; add tip 349 leaves. Let sleigh pieces completely dry.

Outline and pipe in Santa's suit and face with tip 4 (smooth with finger dipped in cornstarch). Pipe tip 2 pull-out beard, dot eyes and pipe-in mouth. Outline moustache and eyebrows with tip 2. Pipe tip 4 string belt and buckle. Add tip 13 zigzag fur to suit and hat. Attach 6 in. lollipop stick to back with melted candy.

Assemble sleigh using royal icing. lay one sleigh side flat and attach bottom, front and back pieces with tip 5; let set at least 1 hour. When set, carefully attach other sleigh side with tip 5 and stand up on waxed paper-covered board. Reinforce inside seams with tip 5 lines if needed. Let dry completely. Attach candy cane runners with tip 5; let set. Trim craft block to fit inside sleigh. Wrap with Fanci-Foil. Position craft block in sleigh; insert lollipops and Santa at staggered heights. Each lollipop serves 1.

***Note:** Combine Christmas Red and Red-Red for red shade shown; combine Brown and a small amount of Red-Red for brown shade shown.

†Brand confectionery coating.

▶ Santa's Helpers

Pan: 8 x 2 in. Square, p. 158
Colors: Red-Red, Kelly Green, Black, Rose, Copper (skin tone), p. 127
Fondant: White Ready-To-Use Rolled Fondant (48 oz. needed), Fondant Multi Packs in Primary Colors (2 pks. needed), 122; Romance Cake Stamps, p. 123; FoodWriter™ Edible Color Markers in Bold Tip Primary Colors, Red Brush-On Color™, p. 124; Brush Set, Easy-Glide Fondant Smoother, Color Tray, p. 125
Recipe: Buttercream Icing, p. 111
Also: 2005 Pattern Book (Gift Tag), p. 222; Cake Board, Fanci-Foil Wrap, p. 217; 4 in. Lollipop Sticks, p. 149; wooden skewers, waxed paper, ruler, 1 in. high craft block, sharp knife, cornstarch

At least 5 days in advance: Make fondant elves (p. 117) and gift tag. For gift tag, roll out white fondant and cut out tag using pattern. Let dry on cornstarch-dusted surface. Decorate tag and write message using FoodWriter markers.

Prepare 2-layer square cake for rolled fondant (p. 105) and cover cake with 36 oz. of white fondant; smooth with Easy-Glide Smoother. Make fondant ribbon and bow using red from Multi Pack: Cut ⅞ in. wide strips as follows—For ribbon, cut four 8 in. long strips, attach across cake top with damp brush. For bow loops, cut two 7 in. strips and fold in half, pinch ends and attach with damp brush. For bow center, cut one 2 in. long strip, wrap around center of bow. For streamer, cut one 4½ in. strip, notch one end; attach to bow with damp brush. Using swirl Cake Stamp and Brush-On Color, imprint designs randomly on cake. Remove skewers from elves. Position marker in large elf's hands and stamp in small elf's hands. Position elves and tag. Serves 20.

▼ Sack Time for Santa

Cookies: Christmas Collection Cutter Set, p. 173; Cookie Sheet, Cooling Grid, p. 160
Tips: 1, 2, p. 136
Colors:* Red-Red, Christmas Red, Copper (skin tone), Black, Lemon Yellow, Golden Yellow, Kelly Green, p. 127
Recipes: Royal Icing, p. 111; Roll-Out Cookie, p. 112
Also: White Ready-To-Use Rolled Fondant (24 oz. needed), p. 122; Gifts Galore Icing Decorations, p. 171; Meringue Powder, p. 126, sharp knife

Using Santa cutter from set, cut cookie. Using knife, cut a 1 x 2 in. rectangle cookie support. Bake and cool all cookies. Outline and pipe in face, hat, suit, shoes and belt with tip 2 (smooth with finger dipped in cornstarch). Pipe in tip 2 outline buckle. Add tip 2 e-motion hair, beard and fur trim. Pipe tip 2 dot nose, gloves and pompom on hat. Pipe tip 1 dot eyes and mouth; add tip 2 pull-out eyebrows and moustache. Attach cookie support to back with icing.

For sack, roll a 1½ in. diameter ball of green-tinted fondant; shape into bag and indent center area with thumb to create space for icing decoration; position decoration. Serves 1.

*Note: Combine Christmas Red and Red-Red for red shade shown. Combine Lemon Yellow and Golden Yellow for yellow shade shown.

▶ Cookies with Bows On!

These gifted goodies are brightly wrapped in Color Flow icing, and packaged in our merry Gifts Galore party bags.

Cookies: Gifts Galore Stencil-A-Cookie™ Cutter & Stencil Set, p. 172; Cookie Sheet, Cooling Grid, p. 160
Tip: 2, p. 136
Colors:* Red-Red, Christmas Red, Royal Blue, Kelly Green, Violet, Lemon Yellow, Golden Yellow, p. 127
Recipe: Color Flow Icing, p. 111
Also: Tapered Spatula, p. 134; Color Flow Mix, p. 129; Gifts Galore Party Bags, p. 171

Cut, bake and cool cookies. Outline and flow-in with tip 2 and Color Flow (p. 118); let dry.

Position stencil and ice over openings with full-strength Color Flow. Smooth out icing and remove stencil. Place cookies in bags. Each serves 1.

*Note: Combine Christmas Red and Red-Red for red shade shown. Combine Lemon Yellow and Golden Yellow for yellow shade shown.

▶ The Gifts Stack Up!

Pan: 12 x 2 in. Round, p. 158
Tip: 1, p. 136
Colors: Kelly Green, p. 127
Fondant: White Ready-To-Use Rolled Fondant, (48 oz. needed), Fondant Multi Packs in Primary and Neon Colors, p. 122; Icing Writer™ in Red, Yellow, Blue, Green, Violet, p. 124; Square Cut-Outs™, p. 123; Roll & Cut Mat, Rolling Pin, Easy-Glide Fondant Smoother, p. 125
Recipes: Buttercream, Royal Icings, p. 111
Also: Cookie Tree Kit, p. 175; Gum Paste Mix (2 cans needed), p, 125; Meringue Powder, p. 126; Plastic Dowel Rods, p. 214; Decorator Brush Set, p. 147; cornstarch, ruler

One week in advance: Prepare gum paste following package directions and tint green. Roll out gum paste ⅛ in. thick and prepare the following (make extras to allow for breakage): **Ring Spacers (to raise tree branches):** Cut ¼ in. wide strips, wrap around plastic dowel rods, trim ends evenly and let dry. **Star Branches:** Using all cutters except the smallest, cut 2 stars of each size. Using a plastic dowel rod, cut out center holes. Lay stars on cornstarch-dusted surface to dry several days. Tint a small amount of fondant yellow and cut out one star using smallest star cutter. Lay on cornstarch-dusted surface to dry. Using royal icing, pipe tip 1 lines on star branches. Let dry.

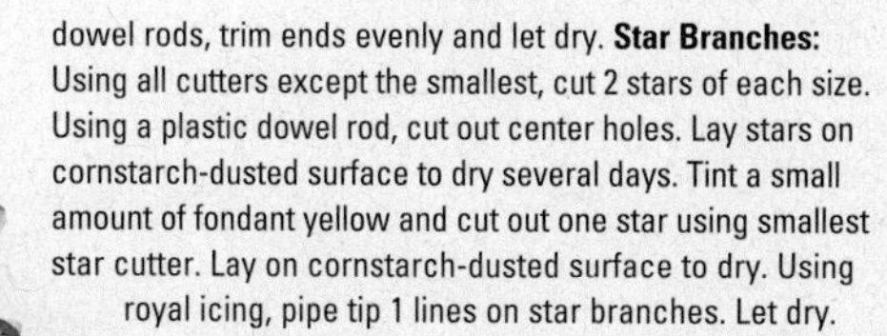

Prepare and cover 2-layer round cake with rolled fondant (p. 105). Cut 1 in. off end of plastic dowel rod and insert rod into center of cake. Thread gum paste ring spacers and star branches alternately onto rod, stacking stars from largest to smallest. Attach yellow star to top with royal icing. Using medium Cut-Out, cut square gifts from primary and neon fondant. Attach to cake using damp brush. Pipe dots and string ribbons and bows on squares using Icing Writer. Cut ½ in. wide strips of white fondant. Attach in loose folds to bottom border with damp brush. Roll small balls of fondant and attach randomly onto cake with damp brush. Serves 40.

▶ Evergreen Everest

Bring color back to winter! See how beautiful snow-frosted trees look against a mountain of richly-tinted fondant tiers.

Pan: 6, 8, 10 x 2 in. Round, p. 158
Tips: 1, 5, p. 136
Colors: Violet, Royal Blue, Kelly Green, p. 127
Cookies: Copper Christmas Tree Cutter, Metal Nesting Trees Cutter Set, p. 173; Plastic Nesting Stars Cutter Set, p. 142
Recipes: Buttercream, Royal Icings, p. 111
Also: White Ready-To-Use Rolled Fondant (120 oz. needed), p. 122; Easy-Glide Fondant Smoother, p. 125; Meringue Powder, p. 126; Wooden Dowel Rods, p. 214; Cake Dividing Set, p. 131; Piping Gel, p. 126; 14 in. Round Silver Cake Base, p. 217; craft knife, cornstarch

At least 1 to 2 days in advance: Make fondant trees and star, using 24 oz. of white fondant. Roll fondant ⅛ in. thick. Using copper tree cutter, cut 3 trees for 6 in. cake top; with knife, cut 2 trees vertically in half. Using two smallest metal tree cutters, cut 12 of each size tree (24 total); cut trees vertically in half. Cut 1 star with smallest cutter from set. Position all pieces on cornstarch-dusted surface to dry. When dry, using royal icing, pipe tip 1 outline branches on trees and rays on star.

Roll 24 oz. of white fondant into a 14 in. circle. Using craft knife, cut wavy design around edge and position on cake base.

Tint 36 oz. fondant blue, 24 oz. green, 12 oz. violet; reserve remaining white fondant for additional trees. Prepare 2-layer cakes for stacked construction (p. 110). Prepare and cover cakes with fondant (p. 105); smooth. Position cakes on base. Divide 6 in. cake into 6ths, 8 in. cake into 8ths and 10 in. cake into 10ths. Roll white fondant ⅛ in. thick and use two smallest metal tree cutters to cut another set of 12 of each size tree (24 total), one at a time. Use Piping Gel to alternately attach larger and smaller trees to cake sides at division points. Pipe tip 1 branches with royal icing. (Note: There will be a space between trees where balls will be piped.) With tip 1 and royal icing, attach dried fondant tree halves to corresponding-size trees on cake sides, positioning in a "wing" fashion. Repeat process to attach tree halves for 6 in. cake top to whole cake top tree. Attach tree and star with royal icing. Pipe tip 1 snowflakes and dots on cake sides and tip 5 balls between trees with royal icing. Serves 60.

◀ Personal Pine

A blossom cookie makes a tasty tree stand for this pretty pine of swirling whipped icing.

Pan: 11 x 7 x 1½ in. Non-Stick Biscuit/Brownie, p. 157
Tip: 1M (2110), p. 136
Color: Kelly Green, p. 127
Cookies: 101 Cookie Cutters Set, p. 142; Nesting Blossoms Metal Cutter Set, p. 140
Candy: Candy Melts®* in Yellow, White, Red, p. 146; Mini Gingerbread Candy Mold, p. 171
Also: Vanilla Whipped Icing Mix, p. 126; Parchment Triangles, p. 134; Rainbow Nonpareils Sprinkle Decorations, p. 128

In advance: Make candy blossoms. Place largest blossom cutter in pan, pour in melted candy, ¼ in. thick. Tap pan to remove bubbles and refrigerate until firm; unmold. Using melted candy in cut parchment bag, edge blossom with zigzag; let set. Using Mini Gingerbread Mold, make a star; refrigerate until firm, then unmold.

Bake and cool 1 in. high cake. Use smallest and second smallest round cutters from set to cut cakes. Stack cake on candy blossom and cover with tip 1M swirl of whipped icing. Sprinkle with nonpareils; position candy star on top. Each serves 1.

▼ Menorah Markers

Set everyone's place for the Hanukkah feast with easy-to-mold candy place cards.

Pan: Mini Loaf, p. 160
Candy: White Candy Melts®, p. 146; Hanukkah Lollipop Mold, p. 176; Primary Candy Color Set, p. 147
Also: Decorator Brush Set, p. 147; Parchment Triangles, p. 134

Mold candy plaques (p. 119), filling pan cavities ¼ in. deep with melted white candy. Refrigerate until firm; unmold. Tint a portion of white candy yellow and blue. Mold menorah candies using painting method (p. 119) and filling molds ½ full; refrigerate until firm then unmold. Attach menorah to plaque with melted candy. Write name and add dots using melted candy in parchment bag cut with a tiny opening. Each serves 1.

▶ The Lights of Hanukkah

Even if your menorah candles burn too quickly, you'll have the bright lights of this cake to admire throughout the celebration. For the spiral design, just wind strips of tinted fondant around dowel rods.

Pans: Petal Set (15 in. used), p. 159; 6 x 2 in. Round, p. 158
Tips: 1A, 2, 2A, 4, 5, 12, 14, p. 136
Colors: Orange, Violet, Lemon Yellow, Kelly Green, Royal Blue, p. 127
Fondant: Ready-To-Use Rolled Fondant (96 oz. needed), p. 122; Easy-Glide Fondant Smoothers, Roll & Cut Mat, Cutter/Embosser, Brush Set, p. 125
Recipe: Buttercream Icing, p. 111
Also: Hanukkah Cookie Cutter Set, p. 175; Plastic Dowel Rods (3 pks. needed), p. 214; Cake Boards, Fanci-Foil Wrap, p. 217; black shoestring licorice, 19 in. square double-thick cardboard or ½ in. thick foam core for base

Prepare 2-layer 15 in. petal and 1-layer 6 in. round cakes for rolled fondant (p. 105) and stacked construction (p. 110).

Tint fondant as follows: 78 oz. blue, plus 4 oz. each of yellow, orange, violet and green. Reserve 2 oz. white. Cover cakes with blue fondant; smooth with Easy-Glide Smoother. Roll out tinted fondant ⅛ in. thick and use menorah cutter from set to cut 2 menorahs in each color. Attach to petal sides near top edge with damp brush. Pipe tip 5 outline menorah branches, tip 4 outline candles and tip 2 outline candleholders on fondant menorahs. Add tip 14 pull-out star flames.

Cut assorted fondant dots using narrow end of tip 12; attach to sides of round cake with damp brush.

For large candles, cut 8 plastic dowel rods to 8 in. long and one to 7 in. long. Cut assorted color fondant strips, ¼ x 15 in. Wind and attach strips around dowel rods with a damp brush, placing strips around 5 in. of the dowel rod. Wrap 7 in. candle in blue and 2 each in other colors. Attach white fondant balls to tops of rods to resemble dripping wax. Insert a ¾ in. piece of black shoestring licorice for wick; insert wick in a teardrop-shaped yellow fondant flame. For candleholders, roll out fondant ¼ in. thick; cut large circle using wide end of tip 1A and small circle with wide end of tip 2A. Attach small circle to large with damp brush. Push candles into fondant circles up to beginning of spirals. Set aside.

For round cake bottom border, roll a ¼ in. diameter x 21 in. long blue fondant rope; attach with damp brush. For petal cake bottom border, roll fondant 1/16 to ⅛ in. thick and cut eight 4½ x 7 in. rectangles. Gather each rectangle into 3 folds and attach to petal sections with damp brush; trim as needed. Roll ½ in. fondant balls and attach with damp brush at meeting points of each drape. Insert candles into cake just below candle rings, placing 7 in. candle in round cake. Serves 54.

▼ Brightest Stars

Cookies: Hanukkah Cutter Set, p. 175; Cookie Sheet, Cooling Grid, p. 160
Candy: Hanukkah Lollipop Mold, p. 175; White Candy Melts®*, p. 146; Primary Candy Color Set, Decorator Brush Set, p. 147
Tip: 2, p. 136
Color: Royal Blue, p. 127
Recipes: Color Flow Icing, p. 111; Roll-Out Cookie, p. 112
Also: Color Flow Mix, p. 126; Parchment Triangles, p. 134

Cut cookies using star cutter from set; bake and cool. Outline and flow-in with tip 2 and Color Flow (p. 118); let dry overnight. Tint portion of melted candy yellow. Mold message candies using painting method (p. 119) and filling molds ½ full. Refrigerate until firm; unmold. Attach candies to cookie with melted candy. Each serves 1.

▼ A Gift of Gelt

Candy: Hanukkah Candy Making Kit (includes Light Cocoa Candy Melts®*, mold, disposable decorating bags, foil squares, mesh coin bags and twist ties), p. 175

Follow directions in kit to make candy Hanukkah coins. Refrigerate until firm; unmold. Wrap candy in foil squares and place in mesh bag; secure with twist tie. Each bag serves 1.

*Brand confectionery coating.

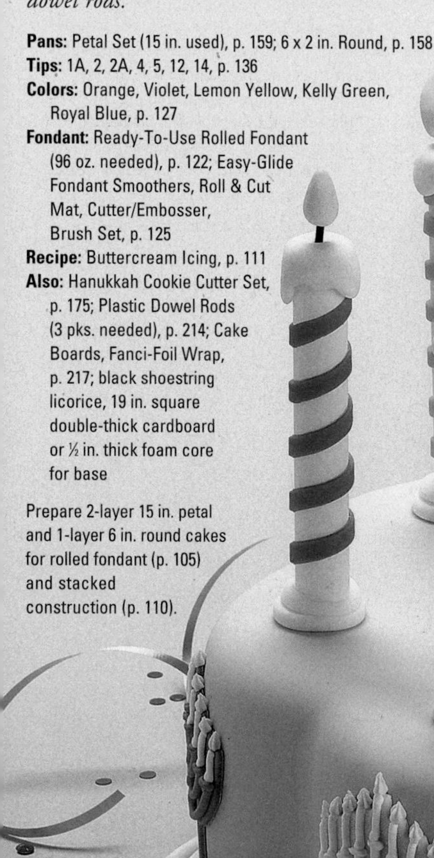

◀ Making Hearts Flutter!

Pans: Butterfly, p. 162; Cookie Sheet, Cooling Grid, p. 160
Tips: 2, 3, 5, 8, 18, p. 136-137
Colors:* Rose, Red-Red, Christmas Red, Black, p. 127
Recipes: Buttercream Icing, p. 111; Roll-Out Cookie, p. 112
Also: 2005 Pattern Book (Love Bug's Body), p. 222; Plastic Nesting Hearts Cutter Set, p. 179; Cake Board, Fanci-Foil Wrap, p. 217; White Candy Melts®*, p. 146; black twist and shoestring licorice, red jelly hearts, paring knife

In advance: Make cookie body and hearts. Cut body using pattern and knife, cut one cookie each using 2nd and 3rd smallest heart cutters. Cut 2nd smallest heart in half to create feet. Bake and cool all cookies. Ice smooth and set aside.

Ice smooth cake sides and top areas where hearts will appear. Imprint bottom corners of wings with smallest heart cutter. Imprint top corners with 4th smallest cutter then imprint 2nd smallest cutter inside. Outline wings with tip 5; fill in with tip 18 stars; randomly pipe tip 3 dots. Pipe tip 8 ball bottom border.

Cover body cookie with tip 18 stars. Pipe in tip 3 mouth, dot cheeks and bead tongue; add tip 5 ball eyes with tip 3 dot pupils and string eyebrows. Position body on cake. For arms, insert 3½ in. pieces of twist licorice in cake under cookie and bend to a slight curve (cut a slit if needed to curve). Position cookie heart under arms; add tip 3 dot hands, outline cuffs and tip 2 message. For legs, attach cookie feet to two full lengths of twist licorice with melted candy. Insert into cake under body. For antennae, insert ¾ in. pieces of black shoestring licorice into jelly hearts and insert into head. Serves 12.

*Note: Combine Red-Red and Christmas Red for darkest red color shown.

▶ Nutty Guy

Our cute stand-up squirrel makes this classic heart cake stand out. We added a bushy cookie tail to the Mini Stand-Up Bear cake to create an irresistible combination.

Pans: SweetHeart, p. 159; Mini Stand-Up Bear Set, p. 163; Cookie Sheet, Cooling Grid, p. 160
Tips: 1M (2010), 2, 3, 6, 13, 14, p. 136-137
Colors: Rose, Brown, Black, p. 127
Recipes: Buttercream, Poured Cookie Icings, p. 111; Roll-Out Cookie, p. 112
Also: 2005 Pattern Book (Squirrel Tail), p. 222; White Candy Melts®†, 4 in. Lollipop Sticks, p. 149; Valentine Sprinkle Sparks, p. 178; Hearts Remembered Petite Icing Decorations, p. 177; Nesting Hearts Cutter Set, p. 179; Cake Board, Fanci-Foil Wrap, p. 217; Angled Spatula, p. 134

In advance: Cut, bake and cool one tail cookie using pattern and one heart cookie using second smallest cutter. Cover heart cookie with poured cookie icing (p. 118); let set. Attach tail to lollipop sticks with melted candy.

Ice 2-layer heart cake (3 in. high) with spatula. Pipe tip 1M rosette bottom border; add Sprinkle Sparks and position heart icing decorations.

Trim ears and hands off mini bear cake. Build up cheeks, forehead, nose and feet areas with tip 6. Cover cake with tip 14 stars. Pipe tip 3 dot eyes, tip 2 pupils and nose. Attach heart cookie with dots of icing. Pipe tip 14 zigzag arms and ears; overpipe with tip 14 stars. Position squirrel cake on heart cake. Insert cookie tail; cover tail with tip 13 pull-out stars. Add tip 2 message. Serves 16.

†Brand confectionery coating.

◀ Sweetheart's Sandwich

Give lunch a loving touch—sandwiches made easy with our Stencil-A-Cookie Set and Color Mist Food Color Spray.

Cookies: Valentine Stencil-A-Cookie™ Cutter and Stencil Set, p. 178
Also: Pink Color Mist™ Food Color Spray, p. 176; bread, ham, cheese, lettuce

Cut two bread hearts for each sandwich. Position stencil and spray top heart with Color Mist. Cut ham and cheese hearts; build sandwich. Each serves 1.

◀ A Perfect Fit

No need to puzzle over the way these fondant pieces fit together. Position some of the hearts, then use your cookie cutter to remove overlapping areas in an inlay fashion.

Pans: 10 x 2 in. Heart, p. 158
Colors: Kelly Green, Rose, Violet, Lemon Yellow, Creamy Peach, p. 127
Recipe: Buttercream Icing, p. 111
Also: Valentine FoodWriter™ Edible Color Markers, p. 176; Plastic Nesting Hearts Cutter Set, p. 179; White Ready-To-Use Rolled Fondant (60 oz. needed), p. 122; Easy-Glide Fondant Smoother, p. 125; Decorator Brush Set, p. 147

Prepare 2-layer cake for fondant (p. 105); cover with approximately 36 oz. of fondant; smooth with Easy-Glide Smoother. Divide 24 oz. of fondant into 5 portions; tint green, rose, violet, yellow and peach. Roll out each color fondant ⅛ in. thick. Using 3rd largest heart cutter, cut 3 or 4 hearts at a time in various colors. Position on cake to determine overlapping areas. Remove from cake and cut out overlapping portions to form an inlay pattern. Attach inlay hearts on cake with brush dipped in water; smooth edges with fingers. Repeat to cover entire cake and smooth with Easy-Glide Smoother. Let set for 2 to 4 hours. Print messages with FoodWriter. Serves 24.

▶ What the Heart Wants

Love is a many-textured thing. This heart cake combines pretty stand-up fondant hearts on a rosette-covered top, neatly-combed sides and a shell and zigzag bottom border.

Pans: 8 x 2 in. Heart, p. 158
Tips: 1M (2110), 18, p. 137
Colors: Rose, p. 127
Fondant: White Ready-To-Use Rolled Fondant (24 oz. needed), p. 122; Heart Cut-Outs™, p. 123; Roll & Cut Mat, p. 125
Also: Vanilla Whipped Icing Mix (2 pks), p. 126; Icing Sculptor™, p. 131; Pink Cake Sparkles™, p. 128; Straight Spatula, p. 134; Cake Boards, Fanci-Foil Wrap, p. 217; cornstarch

Two days in advance: Roll out pink-tinted fondant and cut 13-15 hearts using second smallest cut-out. Let pieces dry on cornstarch-dusted surface.

Ice smooth 2-layer cake (bake two 1½ in. layers to form 3 in. high cake); ice sides at least ½ in. thick. Comb cake sides with Icing Sculptor, using ivory ("W"-shaped) blades. Pipe tip 1M rosettes on cake top; sprinkle with Cake Sparkles and position fondant hearts. Pipe tip 18 shell bottom border; overpipe with tip 18 zigzags. Serves 18.

▼ Love Match

Cookies: 101 Cookie Cutters Set, p. 142; Cookie Sheet, Cooling Grid, p. 160
Tip: 2, p. 137
Colors: Royal Blue, Brown, Copper (skin tone), Black, Red-Red, Lemon Yellow, p. 127
Recipes: Roll-Out Cookie, p. 112; Color Flow Icing, p. 111
Also: Color Flow Mix, p. 127; FoodWriter™ Edible Color Markers in Fine Tip Primary and Neon, p. 124

A day in advance: Cut cookies using large boy cutter from set, bake and cool. Outline and flow in with Color Flow icing and tip 2 (p. 118). Let dry overnight. Pipe tip 2 dot noses, pull-out hair on boy and curly hair on girl with full-strength Color Flow. Use FoodWriter markers to draw eyes and mouths, kiss marks and messages. Each serves 1.

◀ Stamp of Approval

A great-looking Valentine cookie can still be easy when you cover it with rolled fondant and decorate with FoodWriter Edible Color Markers.

Cookie: Copper Heart Cutter, p. 141; Cookie Sheet, Cooling Grid, p. 160
Recipes: Roll-Out Cookie, p. 112
Also: White Ready-To-Use Rolled Fondant (3 oz. needed for each cookie), p. 122; FoodWriter™ Edible Color Markers in Fine Tip Primary and Neon, p. 124; Decorator Brush Set, p. 147; plastic ruler

Cut, bake and cool heart cookies. Roll out fondant and cut fondant heart; attach to cookie with damp brush. Cut 1 in. fondant square for stamp. Use handle end of brush to pull out jagged edge effect on stamp; attach with damp brush. Use FoodWriters to draw heart, cancel marks and message. Each serves 1.

▶ Aiming for Love

Cookie Cupids hit the cookie heart target every time—blame it on love, and Wilton Cookie Cutters!

Cookie: Gingerbread Boy Metal Cutter, p. 140; Plastic Nesting Heart Cutter Set, p. 179; Cookie Sheet, Cooling Grid, p. 160
Tips: 2, 3, 5, 352, p. 136-137
Colors: Rose, Black, Lemon Yellow, Copper (skin tone), Christmas Red, p. 127
Recipes: Roll-Out Cookie, p. 112; Color Flow Icing, p. 111
Also: Fanci-Foil Wrap, p. 217; 11¾ in. Lollipop Sticks, p. 149; Color Flow Mix, p. 126; 3 x 2 in. deep round craft block, 6 x 3 in. deep round glass bowl, pink curling ribbon, pink, red and white candy-coated chocolate dots

Make cookies in advance: Tint one fourth of cookie dough copper and cut out 3 cupids using gingerbread boy cutter. Using remaining dough and cutters, cut one of largest heart and three of second smallest hearts. Bake and cool. Pour Color Flow icing over smaller hearts and let dry. Decorate Cupids with tip 2 dot and string facial features and hair, tip 5 diapers, tip 5 bows and arrowheads, tip 2 strings and arrows. Add tip 352 pull-out wings. Outline large heart with Color Flow icing and tip 3, then thin down icing and flow in each section (p. 118). Let dry overnight, then pipe tip 2 message. When completely dry, attach lollipop sticks to backs of cookies using full-strength Color Flow icing.

Cover craft block with Fanci-Foil Wrap; position in bowl, securing with Color Flow icing. Trim ends of lollipop sticks to various heights and insert lollipop sticks into block to arrange cookies. Add candy-coated chocolate dots to bowl. Curl ribbon and arrange on top. Each cookie serves 1.

▶ A Bear in the Air!

Here's proof that you can shape Candy Clay into just about anything. The balloon basket is made of Candy Clay ropes woven through lollipop sticks, giving this cookie gift a special lift.

Pans: 6 x 2 in. Round, p. 158; Cookie Sheet, Cooling Grid, p. 160
Tips: 2, 3, p. 136
Colors: Kelly Green, Rose, Lemon Yellow, Violet, Brown, Black, p. 127
Cookie: Heart Solid Copper Cutter, p. 179; Plastic Nesting Teddy Bears Cutter Set, p. 142; Valentine Colored Metal Cutter Set, p. 179
Recipes: Color Flow Icing, p. 111; Roll-Out Cookie, p. 112; Candy Clay, p. 112
Also: Color Flow Mix, p. 127; White Candy Melts®† (2 pks.), p. 146; 4 in. Lollipop Sticks, p. 149; Wooden Dowel Rods, p. 214; Cake Circles, Fanci-Foil Wrap, p. 217; two 5 x 1 in. deep round craft blocks, light corn syrup, waxed paper, white curling ribbon, cellophane tape

A day in advance: Prepare balloon basket. Cut 12 lollipop sticks to 3 in. long. Dip sticks into ½ pk. of melted Candy Melts, tap to remove excess and let dry approximately 30 minutes on waxed paper. Remelt remaining candy and pour ¼ in. deep in pan; insert 12 sticks evenly around edge. Refrigerate to set overnight. Roll Candy Clay ropes, 24 in. long and ½ in. diameter. Weave rope pieces around sticks, blending ends and trimming off excess in each row and making new rows to reach basket top. For top, twist 2 ropes together and insert on sticks.

Double cookie dough recipe. Cut, bake and cool the following cookies: 3 hearts using copper cutter, 1 bear using largest bear cutter, 4 of each Valentine shape using colored cutters. Multiply Color Flow recipe by 5; tint 3 cups pink, 1 cup brown, 1½ cups each green, yellow and violet, ½ cup each black, bright pink; reserve ½ cup white. Using Color Flow instructions (p. 118) and tips 2 and 3, flow in and decorate all cookies.

Cut one dowel rod to 12 in. and two to 9 in. long; wrap with curling ribbon. Trim one craft block to fit basket. Cut second block in half and form a moon shape; line up with back of first block and wrap 2 layers with foil. Attach block inside basket, dowel rods to heart balloon cookies and lollipop stick to bear cookie with melted candy. Make holes in craft block with lollipop stick; insert cookies on sticks. Arrange remaining cookies in basket. Each serves 1.

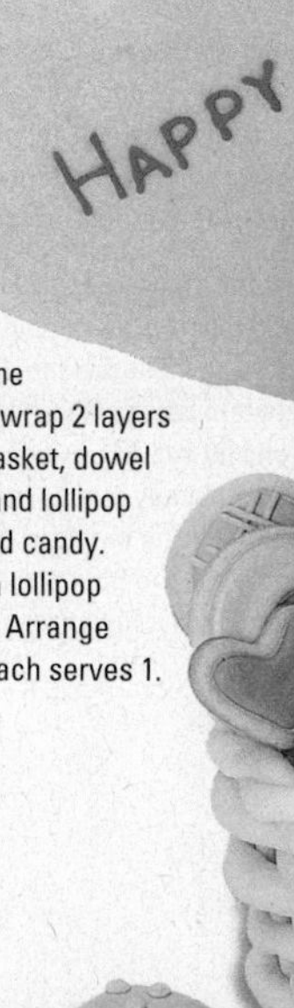

◀ Heartbeat Treats

Pan: Standard Muffin, p. 160
Tips: 1M (2110), p. 137
Color: Rose, p. 127
Cookie: From The Heart Nesting Cutter Set, p. 179; Cookie Sheet, Cooling Grid, p. 160
Recipes: Buttercream Icing, p. 111; Roll-Out Cookie, p. 112
Also: Hearts Remembered Icing Decorations, p. 177; Hearts Remembered Baking Cups, p. 177; Pink Colored Sugars, p. 128

Tint cookie dough rose and cut 1 cookie using smallest crinkle cutter for each treat needed. Sprinkle with pink sugar, bake and cool. Pipe tip 1M swirl on cupcakes. Attach icing decoration to cookie with icing; insert cookie into cupcake. Each serves 1.

◀ Facial Expressions

When you and the kids put your heads together, you'll have a great time making Valentine pops with personality! Molding is easy with our Funny Faces Kit and the Heart Cookie Treat pan.

Cookie: Heart Cookie Treat Pan, p. 143; 8 in. Cookie Treat Sticks, p. 143
Candy: Funny Faces Candy Making Kit (includes mold and Red & White Candy Melts®† used), Candy Melts®† in White, Red (for additional candies), p. 146; Garden Candy Color Kit, p. 147

Using candy color, tint portion of melted white candy pink. Mold heart pops in pan; refrigerate until firm, unmold. Make facial features using layering method (p. 119); refrigerate until firm, unmold. Attach facial features to heart pops with melted candy. Each serves 1.

†Brand confectionery coating.

▲ Fondant Goes Vibrant!

It's as much fun to decorate egg cookies as it is to color Easter eggs! Let everyone paint and stamp designs in their favorite colors, using Brush-On-Color, Cake Stamps and Brushes.

Pans: Cookie Sheet, Cooling Grid, p. 160
Fondant: White Ready-To-Use Rolled Fondant (24 oz. needed), p. 122; Brush-On-Color™ in Violet, Green, Pink, Yellow, Blue, p. 124; Funny Flower Cake Stamps, p. 123; Rolling Pin, Brush Set, Color Tray, Roll & Cut Mat, Cutter/Embosser, p. 125
Recipe: Roll-Out Cookie, p. 112
Also: 9 Pc. Easter Colored Metal Cutter Set, p. 183; Piping Gel, p. 126, Tapered Spatula, p. 134

Cut ¼ in. thick cookies using egg cutter; bake and cool. Roll out fondant and cut egg shapes with cutter. Position fondant on cookies covered lightly with Piping Gel. Using round-tip brush and flower stamps, decorate cookies with Brush-On-Color designs. Each serves 1.

▶ Bunny Bungalow

A happy cookie hutch at every place setting will make your Easter brunch bunch feel welcome.

Pans: Mini Loaf, p. 160; Cookie Sheet, Cooling Grid, p. 160
Candy: White Candy Melts®†, p. 146; Garden Candy Color Set, p. 147; Easter Lollipop Kit, p. 151
Recipe: Roll-Out Cookie, p. 112
Also: House Stencil-A-Cookie™ Cutter and Stencil Set, p. 141; Parchment Triangles, p. 134; Straight Spatula, p. 134

In advance: Make candy. Tint portions of melted white candy violet, black and green using candy colors. Mold 1 bunny for each cookie using painting method (p. 119). Mold 1 white candy plaque (p. 119) for each cookie using Mini Loaf pan. Refrigerate all until firm; unmold.

Bake and cool house cookies. Position stencil on cookie and pipe zigzag curtains and panes for lower windows using melted white and yellow candy in cut parchment bag; remove stencil, smooth with spatula and let set. Reposition stencil and pipe violet door, chimney and eaves; smooth. Pipe upper window, pink shutters, flowers, door knob and window. Attach house and bunny to plaque with melted candy. Pipe green grass. Each serves 1.

◀ Baskets All Around!

Pans: Petal Set (15 in. used), p. 159; 6 x 2 in. Round, p. 158; Mini Loaf, p. 160; Non-Stick Cookie Sheet, p. 157
Tips: 2, 16, p. 136-137
Colors: Rose, Lemon Yellow, Royal Blue, Kelly Green, Violet, p. 127
Cookie: Bunny Copper Cutter, p. 183
Candy: White Candy Melts®† (1 pk. needed), p. 146; 6 in. Lollipop Sticks, p. 149
Recipes: Buttercream, Royal Icings, p. 111
Also: 2005 Pattern Book (Basket Handle), p. 222; Cake Boards, Fanci-Foil Wrap, p. 217; Meringue Powder, p. 126; Angled Spatula, p. 134; Plastic Dowel Rods, p. 214; ⅜ in. wide pink satin ribbon (12 in. needed), shredded coconut, zip-close plastic bag, waxed paper, pastel candy-coated chocolates with nuts

At least 2 to 3 days in advance: Make basket handles (p. 116). **A day in advance:** Make candy bunny and base plaque. For base plaque, fill one mini loaf pan cavity ¼ in. deep with melted candy. Refrigerate until firm and unmold. For bunny, place cutter on cookie sheet and fill with remaining candy. Refrigerate until firm and remove from cutter. Attach bunny to base plaque with melted candy.

Ice 2-layer 15 in. petal cake (bake two 1½ in. layers to form 3 in. high cake) and 1-layer 6 in. round cake smooth. Position dowel rod where bunny will sit on 6 in. cake. Pipe tip 16 shell bottom border on 6 in. cake. On petal cake, pipe tip 16 basketweave on sides; add tip 16 rope top and bottom borders. Add tip 16 rope on cake top for back side of baskets. Insert basket handles into cake. With buttercream, pipe tip 2 dot eyes and nose on bunny; pipe in inside ears with tip 2. Make small bow and attach with icing. Tint coconut green (p. 116). Position tinted coconut, candy-coated chocolates and bunny on cake. Serves 54.

†Brand confectionery coating.

▶ He Paints in Pastels

The same pan you use to create a traditional Easter lamb cake works beautifully for this artistic bunny.

Pan: Stand-Up Lamb, p. 180
Tips: 4, 12, 16, 18, 21, 47, 233, p. 136-137
Colors:* Rose, Sky Blue, Leaf Green, Lemon Yellow, Violet, Black, p. 127
Cookie: 9-Pc. Easter Colored Metal Cutter Set, p. 183; Cookie Sheet, Cooling Grid, p. 160
Recipes: Buttercream Icing, p. 111; Roll-Out Cookie, p. 112
Also: 2005 Pattern Book (Cookie Basket Handle, Ears, Feet), p. 222; Cake Board, Fanci-Foil Wrap, p. 217; 4 in. Lollipop Sticks, p. 149; White Candy Melts®†, p. 146; large marshmallows, black shoestring licorice, cornstarch, toothpick, sharp knife, shredded coconut, zip-close plastic bag

Roll out cookie dough and trace patterns with toothpick. Using knife, cut two ears and feet, one basket handle. Cut 6 eggs using cutter from set. Bake and cool cookies. Trim lollipop sticks to 3 in. long and attach with melted candy to backs of cookies, leaving 2 in. extending to insert in cake; let set. Ice cookies smooth. Cover basket handle with tip 21 rope.

Bake and cool lamb cake. Trim off ears. Ice body smooth, building up areas as needed. Build up cheeks with tip 12. Ice mouth smooth (smooth with finger dipped in cornstarch). Build up foot cookies with tip 12 and position in front of cake. Cover bunny with tip 16 stars. Insert ears; outline with tip 16 stars. Pipe in tip 4 eyes and nose (smooth with finger dipped in cornstarch). Position cookie egg on bunny. Pipe tip 12 pull-out arms and hands holding egg; overpipe with tip 16 stars. For paintbrush, cut lollipop stick to 2½ in. and insert in hand; add tip 4 pull-out bristles on end. Cut licorice 2 in. long and insert for whiskers. Cover basket with tip 47 basketweave; pipe tip 18 rope top and bottom borders. Pipe tip 233 pull-out grass in basket. Insert handle and egg cookies in basket. Tint coconut green (p. 116) and position around cake. For paint cans, pipe tip 4 icing drips on marshmallows (smooth with palm of hand dipped in cornstarch); position around bunny. Serves 12.

***Note:** Combine violet with a small amount of rose for lilac shade shown.

▶ Look Who's Hatched!

Pull off a neat rabbit trick—unwrap the sugar-dusted fondant bow to reveal a sweet surprise inside.

Pans: Mini Egg, p. 180; Mini Muffin, p. 160
Tip: 12, p. 137
Color: Kelly Green, p. 127
Candy: White Candy Melts®†, p. 146; Primary Candy Color Set, p. 147; Bunnies 'n Carrots Mold, p. 181; Decorator Brush Set, p. 147
Fondant: White Ready-To-Use Rolled Fondant (24 oz.), p. 122; Cutter/Embosser, Roll & Cut Mat, p. 125
Also: Soft Pink Sugar, p. 182; Mini Eggs Icing Decorations, p. 181; White Mini Baking Cups, p. 150; Parchment Triangles, p. 134; shredded coconut, zip-close plastic bag

Using candy colors, tint portions of melted white candy yellow, pink (use a little red), green, blue and orange. Mold one bunny using painting method (p. 119), one candy shell (p. 119) in baking cup and and two candy shells in mini egg pan for each treat needed. Refrigerate until firm, unmold. Tint coconut (p. 116). Attach bunny, icing decorations and a small amount of coconut inside back egg shell with melted candy. Slide egg bottoms over warming tray to flatten edges; immediately attach halves with melted candy. Position egg in muffin candy shell. Roll fondant thin, brush lightly with water and sprinkle with pink sugar. Using small end of tip 12, cut dots and attach to egg with water. Cut ¼ x 1½ in. strips for 6 loops and 2 streamers; attach loop ends. Attach bow pieces to egg with candy. Each serves 1.

▶ Going Back to His Roots

Pans: 3-D Bunny, p. 180
Tips: 3, 67, 233, p. 136-137
Colors:* Rose, Orange, Kelly Green, Leaf Green, p. 127
Cookie: 9-Pc. Easter Colored Metal Cutter Set, p. 183; Cookie Sheet, Cooling Grid, p. 160
Recipes: Buttercream Icing, p. 111; Large Batch Roll-Out Cookie, p. 112; Color Flow Icing, p. 111
Also: Color Flow Mix, p. 127; Cake Board, Fanci-Foil Wrap, p. 217; blue candy-coated chocolates, pink jelly bean, shredded coconut, zip-close plastic bag, waxed paper

Bake bunny cake from firm-textured batter such as pound cake and position on foil-wrapped board. Ice inside of ears smooth with spatula. Cover cake with tip 233 pull-out fur. Position candy-coated chocolate eyes and jelly bean nose.

Cut cookies with carrot cutter; bake and cool. Outline and flow in with Color Flow icing and tip 3 (p. 118); let dry. Pipe tip 67 pull-out leaf greenery in buttercream.

Tint shredded coconut green (p. 116). Sprinkle coconut around bunny and position cookies. Cake serves 8; each cookie serves 1.

*Note: Combine Kelly Green and Leaf Green for green shade shown.

▶ Hybrid Car

Pan: Mini Egg, p. 180
Tips: 5, 7, 18, p. 136-137
Colors:* Orange, Kelly Green, Leaf Green, p. 127
Fondant: White Ready-To-Use Rolled Fondant, p. 122; Rolling Pin, Roll & Cut Mat, p. 125
Recipe: Buttercream Icing, p. 111
Also: Easter Mini Cutter Set, p. 183; Straight Spatula, p. 134; Cake Board, Fanci-Foil Wrap, p. 217; hollow-centered candy discs, candy-coated chocolates, cornstarch

In advance: Make bunny head. Roll out fondant ¼ in. thick and cut head using bunny cutter. Let dry overnight on cornstarch-dusted board. When dry, draw facial features and inside ears with FoodWriters.

Position cake on board, flat side down. Spatula ice cake to create a banded carrot look, moving from left wheel side to right. For wheels, using tip 5 dots of icing, attach candy-coated chocolates to discs and discs to cake. For bunny body, pipe tip 7 mound for chest, tip 5 mound for neck. Insert fondant head. Attach candy disc steering wheel with icing. Pipe tip 5 outline arms, attaching right arm to steering wheel. Add tip 18 pull-out star greenery. Each serves 1.

*Note: Combine Kelly Green and Leaf Green for shade shown.

▼ Soft Shades of Spring

Gentle reminders of your favorite time of year... cupcakes topped with 3 pastel sugars and a cute spring decoration.

Pan: Standard Muffin, p. 160
Recipe: Buttercream Icing, p. 111
Also: Soft Sugars in Pink, Lavender, Yellow and Green, p. 182; Easter Patchwork Baking Cups, p. 181; Springtime Icing Decorations, p. 181, Straight Spatula, p. 134

Ice cupcakes smooth. Sprinkle 3 colors of sugar on each; position icing decoration. Each serves 1.

▶ Eggsclusive Neighborhood

The dimensional look on the roof shingles, front door and shutters, imprinted with the Cutter/Embosser, helps give this egg house curb appeal.

Pan: Decorated Egg, p. 180
Tips: 2, 352, p. 136-137
Colors:* Violet, Rose, Lemon Yellow, Kelly Green, Leaf Green, p. 127
Fondant: White Ready-To-Use Rolled Fondant (48 oz. needed), p. 122; Cutter/Embosser, Roll & Cut Mat, Rolling Pin, Easy-Glide Fondant Smoother, p. 125
Recipes: Buttercream, Royal Icings, p. 111
Also: 2005 Pattern Book (Stairs, Roof, Door, Windows, Eaves, Shutter, Fence), p. 222; Floral Collection Flower Making Set, p. 134; Meringue Powder, p. 126; Decorator Brush Set, p. 147; Cake Board, Fanci-Foil Wrap, p. 217; cornstarch, ruler

Several days in advance: Make fondant roof and shutter pieces. Tint 8 oz. fondant violet, 6 oz. rose. Roll fondant ⅛ in. thick. Cut 1 front and 2 side roof pieces. Using straight-edge wheel of embosser, mark shingle shapes. Cut 4 shutters, reversing pattern on 2; using wavy-edge wheel of embosser, mark lattice pattern. To make fondant flowers, tint 18 oz. fondant yellow. Using cutters from set, cut 48 forget-me-nots and 48 apple blossoms—16 each in, rose, violet and yellow. Cup centers with stick number 2 from floral collection set. Let all pieces dry on thick foam. Reserve remaining fondant.

Prepare egg cake for rolled fondant (p. 105); cover cake and smooth. Attach roof pieces with royal icing. Using patterns, cut door, door window, door eaves, 2 fences, top, middle and bottom stairs (roll fondant ¼ in. thick for bottom stair, ⅜ in. thick for middle stair, ⅛ in. thick for top stair). Using wavy-edge wheel of embosser, mark lattice on door. Attach door and door window with damp brush. Roll ¼ in. diameter ropes and position around door and at roof seams. Roll additional ¼ in. diameter ropes and use side window patterns as a guide for positioning window frames; attach with water. Roll and attach a ⅜ in. diameter door window frame with ⅛ in. diameter panes; attach a ¼ in. diameter ball for doorknob. Cut fondant bricks, ¾ x 1¼ in., and attach. Attach shutters, fence pieces, stairs, eaves and a 1½ in. diameter ball for roof peak with buttercream. Pipe tip 2 royal icing centers on all flowers. Attach flowers with buttercream; add tip 352 buttercream leaves. Serves 12.

***Note:** Combine Kelly Green and Leaf Green for green shade shown.

◀ He Brings Us Spring!

Pan: 3-D Egg Pan, p. 180
Color: Rose, p. 127
Fondant: Ready-To-Use Rolled Fondant in White, Pastel Blue, Pastel Green (24 oz. each), p. 122; Brush-On-Color™ in Pink, Violet, Yellow, p. 124; Flower Cake Stamps, Alphabet/Number Cut-Outs™, p. 123; Brush Set, Roll & Cut Mat, Cutter/Embosser, Color Tray, Easy-Glide Fondant Smoother, p. 125
Recipe: Buttercream Icing, p. 111
Also: Bunnies Nesting Metal Cutter Set, p. 183; Cake Board, Fanci-Foil Wrap, p. 217; rolling pin

Prepare egg cake, baked in one pan half, for rolled fondant (p. 105). Roll out blue fondant to fit top ⅔ of cake; use Cutter/Embosser to make wavy bottom edge and position on cake. Roll out green fondant to fit bottom ⅓ of cake, cut a matching wavy top edge and position. Smooth seam and trim off excess fondant.

For bunny, roll out white fondant ⅛ in. thick. Cut body using second largest cutter, trim off ears for feet. Cut head using smallest cutter, attach to body with damp brush. Cut another smallest bunny, trim off ears for arms. Roll small balls of fondant for toes and fingers. Attach arms, feet, fingers and toes with damp brush. Position bunny on cake. Using round-tip brush and Brush-On-Color, paint details on bunny. Stamp flower designs with Brush-On-Color. Tint 6 oz. fondant rose; roll out and cut message; attach with damp brush. Roll two ¼ in. diameter ropes, one green and one blue; twist together to form rope bottom border. Serves 6.

◀ Send Flowers to Mom

A bouquet will make her day and there's none sweeter than this arrangement of cookie faces in a pound cake pot, baked in the Wonder Mold.

Pan: Classic Wonder Mold, p. 161
Tips: 1, 2, 3, 8, 18, p. 136
Colors: Royal Blue, Kelly Green, Lemon Yellow, Rose, Violet, Orange, Black, p. 127
Fondant: White Ready-To-Use Rolled Fondant (24 oz. needed), p. 122; Heart and Leaf Cut-Outs™, p. 123; Rolling Pin, Roll & Cut Mat, p. 125
Cookie: 6-Pc. Nesting Blossoms Cutter Set, p. 140; 8 in. Cookie Treat Sticks, p. 143; Cookie Sheet, Cooling Grid, p. 160
Recipes: Roll-Out Cookie, p. 112; Royal, Buttercream Icings, p. 111, favorite pound cake
Also: Gum-Tex™, p. 125; Meringue Powder, p. 126; Decorator Brush Set, p. 147; Parchment Paper, p. 129; Candy Melts®†, p. 146; floral tape; 18 gauge floral wire (three 18 in. lengths needed); ¼ in. wide ribbon (6 in. needed); waxed paper, chocolate cookie crumbs, cornstarch

Cut blossom cookies—1 using 2nd largest cutter and 3 using 4th largest; make extras to allow for breakage. Bake and cool. Divide fondant and tint as follows: 2 in. balls in orange, violet and yellow, 3 in. ball in rose, reserve 2 in. ball white, tint remaining fondant green. Knead 3 teaspoons Gum-Tex into green fondant. Roll out green fondant and cut 2 large leaves and 38 medium leaves using Cut-Outs. Place on cornstarch-dusted cookie sheet to dry. Using tip 3 and royal icing, pipe vein line on leaves. Let dry. Roll out fondant in various colors; using blossom cutters, cut out same-size fondant blossoms to cover cookies; attach with damp brush. On parchment, draw 2 in., 1⅛ in. and 1 in. diameter circles for flower center patterns. Trace and cut yellow fondant centers and attach with brushstrokes of water. On all, using royal icing, outline petals with tip 3, pipe tip 1 facial features, pipe tip 2 swirl for hair. Let dry.

Wrap wire lengths in floral tape and cut wire into six 3 in. lengths and two 6 in. lengths. Attach 6 medium leaves to 3 in. lengths of wire and the 2 large leaves to the 6 in. lengths of wire with melted candy. Let dry on waxed paper. Attach cookies to sticks with melted candy. When dry, wrap cookie sticks with floral tape and attach leaves (leave bottom portion of stick unwrapped). Cut a 3 x 1½ in. tag from white fondant. Cut out hole using small end of tip 8. Add tip 1 royal icing message and let dry.

Using Classic Wonder Mold, bake pound cake, filling pan halfway. Cool and level. Trim ¾ in. off the narrow end to create a wider base. Ice cake smooth in buttercream and position on foil-wrapped board, wide side up. Pipe tip 2 swirls and tip 3 dots. Using smallest heart Cut-Out, cut shapes from rose and yellow fondant. Attach to cake sides using dots of buttercream. Pipe tip 18 rope bottom border.

Insert cookie blossoms into cake. Tie tag onto stem of one cookie blossom using ribbon length. Cover cake top with chocolate cookie crumbs. Insert and arrange leaves around edge of cake top, securing with buttercream icing. Cake serves 8; each cookie serves 1.

†Brand confectionery coating.

▶ Kids Put Their Hearts in It!

Here's the ideal first cake for kids, easy to ice and fun to decorate with cut-out fondant hearts and letters.

Pan: 8 x 3 in. Round, p. 158
Color: Rose, p. 127
Fondant: White Ready-To-Use Rolled Fondant (24 oz. needed), p. 122; Heart, Alphabet/Number Cut-Outs™, p. 123; Rolling Pin, Roll & Cut Mat, p. 125
Recipe: Buttercream Icing, p. 111
Also: Decorator Brush Set, p. 147; Cake Board, Fanci-Foil Wrap, p. 217; Angled Spatula, p. 134

Ice 1-layer cake fluffy with spatula. Tint 8 oz. fondant dark rose and a 2 in. ball of fondant light rose. Roll fondant ⅛ in. thick. Cut out message and assorted sizes of hearts. Attach smaller hearts to larger hearts with damp brush. Position hearts and message on cake. For bottom border, roll ⅝ in. diameter balls of dark rose fondant; attach with damp brush. Serves 20.

▶ Treating Dad Right!

The kids will have a blast cutting the colorful fondant shapes to top Dad's favorite brownies. Our new fondant Cut-Outs and pre-colored Rolled Fondant make it a snap!

Pan: 9 x 13 x 2 in. Sheet, p. 158
Fondant: Primary & Natural Fondant Multi-Packs, p. 122; Cut-Outs™ in Alphabet/Numbers, People and Star; p. 123; Roll & Cut Mat, Rolling Pin, Cutter/Embosser, p. 125
Also: Chocolate Ready-To-Use Decorator Icing, p. 126; Flowerful Medley Sprinkle Decorations, p. 128; FoodWriter™ Edible Color Markers in Fine Tip Primary Colors, p. 124; Angled Spatula, p. 134; favorite brownie recipe

Ice brownies smooth in pan with chocolate icing. Combine red and yellow fondant from Primary Multi-Pack to make orange. Roll out fondant colors needed. Cut out heads, hands, legs, clothes, stars and message using Cut-Outs; position on cake. Draw facial features with black FoodWriter. Add confetti sprinkles. Serves 45.

◀ Surveying His Kingdom

Spending his day his way! Dad will wish his robe looked as cozy as this multicolored design.

Pan: Little Hero, p. 165
Tips: 1, 3, 4, 6, 16, 18, 21, 47, p. 136-137
Colors: Kelly Green, Red-Red, Royal Blue, Brown, Black, Golden Yellow, Copper (skin tone), p. 127
Recipes: Buttercream, Royal Icings, p. 111
Also: 2005 Pattern Book (Dad & Crown), p. 222; 13 x 19 in. Cake Board, Fanci-Foil Wrap, p. 217; Angled Spatula, p. 134; Parchment Paper, p. 129; cellophane tape, scissors, toothpick, knife, cornstarch

Using pattern, cut crown from board; wrap with foil. Trim off hose areas of cake around hands and feet with sharp knife. Ice sides, background and trimmed areas smooth with spatula. Trace pattern with toothpick. Outline dad, robe, lapels and slippers with tip 3. Fill in head, chest, legs and slippers with tip 16 stars; overpipe nose. Pipe tip 3 outline mouth, tip 4 dot eyes and pupils with tip 1 dot eye highlight. Pipe in lapels, shirt and shorts with tip 4 (pat smooth with finger dipped in cornstarch). Add tip 4 outline coffee and back rim for mug. Pipe tip 4 zigzag mug front (smooth with finger dipped in cornstarch). Outline hands with tip 3; fill in with tip 16 stars. Cover robe with tip 18 stars in random colors. Add tip 47 smooth side up robe ties. Insert crown in cake. Pipe tip 6 puffy zigzags for fur; add tip 1 lines in fur. Pipe tip 16 pull-out hair and tip 1 pull-out chest hair. Using light pressure, pipe tip 1 stubble on face. Add tip 1 message. Pipe tip 21 shell bottom border. Serves 12.

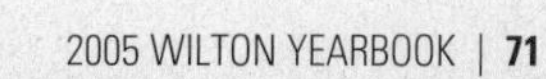

Proudest Moments

It's the day they've been waiting for and your cake says it all! Capture the joy of Christening in an adorable fondant carriage. Express the glee of Graduation as our candy plaque grad opens his locker for the last time. Share the fun of life's biggest thrill—Parenthood—on our Stork Airlines shower cake. Enjoy every moment!

Instructions for projects shown on these two pages are on page 74.

Bless the Child

Pans: Petal Set (9 x 2 in., 15 x 2 in. used), p. 159
Tips: 2, 6, p. 136
Fondant: White Ready-To-Use Rolled Fondant (120 oz. needed), p. 122; Round Cut-Outs™, p. 123; Easy-Glide Smoother, Cutter/Embosser, p. 125
Recipes: Buttercream, Royal Icings, p. 111
Also: 2005 Pattern Book (Carriage, Bow, Handle), p. 222; Gum-Tex™ Karaya, p. 125; Cake Boards, Fanci-Foil Wrap, p. 217; 8 in. Lollipop Sticks, p. 149; Decorator Brush Set, p. 147; White Cake Sparkles™, p. 128, tea strainer, waxed paper, cornstarch, craft knife

In advance: Prepare and decorate fondant carriage, bow and handle (p. 117). Attach lollipop sticks to back with royal icing.

Prepare 2-layer 9 in. and 15 in. cakes for rolled fondant (p. 105) and stacked construction (p. 110). Cover with fondant and smooth. Cut 80 fondant circles using smallest round Cut-Out. Lightly brush top of circles with damp brush and cover with Cake Sparkles crushed through tea strainer. Brush backs with water and attach ten to alternating petal divisions. For each remaining division, roll out fondant thin and cut a 4 x 6½ in. rectangle. Using Cutter/Embosser with ridged wheel and plastic ruler, imprint criss-cross diagonal lines ½ in. apart. Attach to cake with water, trimming to fit as needed.

For bottom borders, roll 2 fondant ropes approximately ¼ in. diameter and twist together. Trim to lengths needed and attach separately to petal sections with water. Roll 1 in. diameter fondant balls and attach to border at petal divisions. Insert carriage. Serves 62.

Carriage Cookies

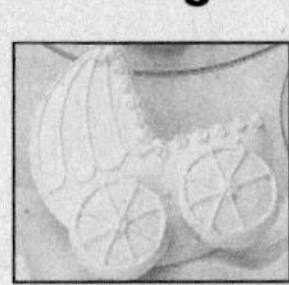

Cookie: Comfort Grip™ Round Cutter, p. 140; Cookie Sheet, Cooling Grid, p. 160
Tips: 1, 13, p. 136-137
Recipes: Royal, Poured Cookie Icings, p. 111; Roll-Out Cookie, p. 112
Also: Round and Square Cut-Outs™, p. 123; Clear Party Bags, p. 151; Meringue Powder, p. 126

One day in advance: Using white royal icing, make 17 tip 13 drop flowers with tip 1 dot centers for each cookie. Make extras to allow for breakage and let dry. Cut cookie dough with Comfort Grip cutter, then cut opening with large square Cut-Out. Cut 2 wheels with medium round Cut-Out. Bake and cool all cookies. Cover with poured icing (p. 118). Let cookies dry at least 3 hours or overnight.

Using royal icing, pipe tip 1 lines, scallops and dots on carriage and wheels. Attach flowers and wheels to carriage with tip 1 dots of icing. Let dry; place in party bag. Each serves 1.

Cloud Cuddling

Pan: Standard Muffin, p. 160
Tip: 1A, p., 136
Fondant: White Ready-To-Use Rolled Fondant (24 oz. needed), p. 122; Star Cut-Outs™, p. 123; Brush Set, p. 125
Recipe: Buttercream Icing, p. 111
Also: Sleeping Angels Set, p. 219; White Cake Sparkles™, p. 128

One day in advance: Make 2 fondant stars for each cupcake. Roll out fondant and cut using medium Cut-Out. Brush lightly with water; cover with Cake Sparkles. Let dry.

Ice cupcake top and sides. Cover with large tip 1A swirls in alternating directions. Position angel and stars. Each serves 1.

▲ Beginning Her Devotion

White roses and apple blossoms define the day's pure spirit. The delicately-piped fondant Cross cookies below are the perfect accompaniment to either communion cake here.

Pans: Petal Set (15 x 2 in. used), 6 x 2 in. Round, p. 159
Tips: 1, 3, 4, 10, 101, 103, p. 136-137
Recipes: Buttercream, Royal Icings, p. 111
Also: Romantic Heart Base, p. 202; Communion Girl, p. 155; Wooden Dowel Rods, p. 214; 16 in. Cake Circles, Fanci-Foil Wrap, p. 217; Flower Nail No. 7, p. 134; Meringue Powder, p. 126; waxed paper

In advance: Using royal icing and flower nail, make 56 tip 103 roses with tip 10 bases. Make 95 tip 101 apple blossoms with tip 1 dot centers. Make extras to allow for breakage; let dry.

Ice smooth 2-layer round cake (3 in. high) and 2-layer petal cake (4 in. high); prepare for stacked construction (p. 110). Attach roses on top sides of both cakes. Pipe tip 4 bead bottom borders; position apple blossoms over beads. Using tips 3 and 4, pipe dot bead garland, 1½ in. deep, and cross on petal sections (use tip 4 for larger dots). Position base on cake; position girl topper. Serves 60.

◀ First Communion Cookies

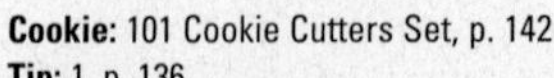

Cookie: 101 Cookie Cutters Set, p. 142
Tip: 1, p. 136
Fondant: White Ready-to-Use Rolled Fondant, p. 122; Heart and Round Cut-Outs™, p. 123
Recipes: Roll-Out Cookie, p. 112; Buttercream Icing, p. 111
Also: Decorator Brush Set, p. 147

Cut out cookies using cross cutter; bake and cool. Roll out fondant and cut cross shape to cover top of cookie. Brush back lightly with water and position on cookie. Cut fondant hearts and circles using medium-size Cut-Outs; brush with water and attach. Add tip 1 dots, leaves, strings, outlines and printing. Each serves 1.

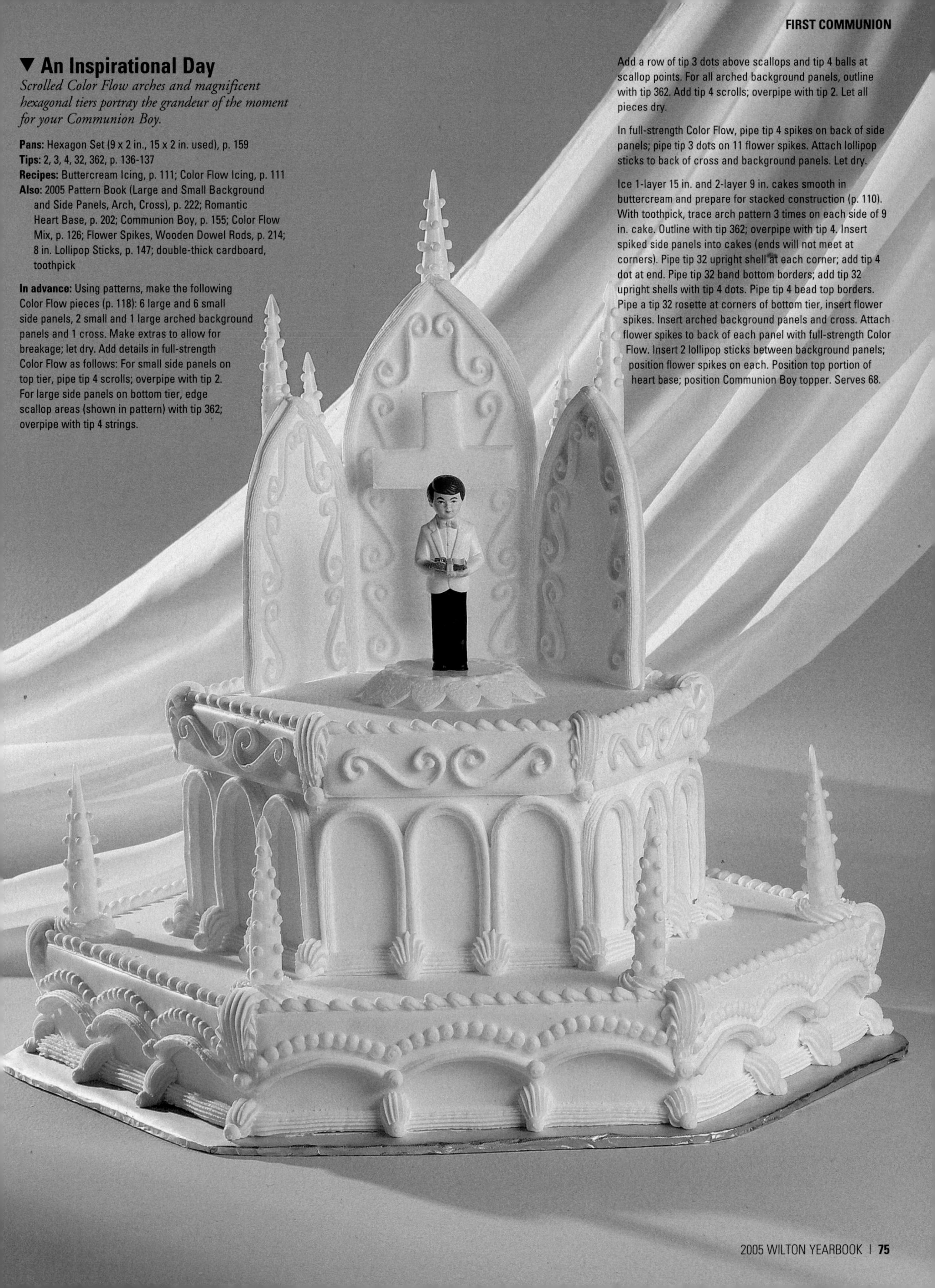

▼ An Inspirational Day

Scrolled Color Flow arches and magnificent hexagonal tiers portray the grandeur of the moment for your Communion Boy.

Pans: Hexagon Set (9 x 2 in., 15 x 2 in. used), p. 159
Tips: 2, 3, 4, 32, 362, p. 136-137
Recipes: Buttercream Icing, p. 111; Color Flow Icing, p. 111
Also: 2005 Pattern Book (Large and Small Background and Side Panels, Arch, Cross), p. 222; Romantic Heart Base, p. 202; Communion Boy, p. 155; Color Flow Mix, p. 126; Flower Spikes, Wooden Dowel Rods, p. 214; 8 in. Lollipop Sticks, p. 147; double-thick cardboard, toothpick

In advance: Using patterns, make the following Color Flow pieces (p. 118): 6 large and 6 small side panels, 2 small and 1 large arched background panels and 1 cross. Make extras to allow for breakage; let dry. Add details in full-strength Color Flow as follows: For small side panels on top tier, pipe tip 4 scrolls; overpipe with tip 2. For large side panels on bottom tier, edge scallop areas (shown in pattern) with tip 362; overpipe with tip 4 strings. Add a row of tip 3 dots above scallops and tip 4 balls at scallop points. For all arched background panels, outline with tip 362. Add tip 4 scrolls; overpipe with tip 2. Let all pieces dry.

In full-strength Color Flow, pipe tip 4 spikes on back of side panels; pipe tip 3 dots on 11 flower spikes. Attach lollipop sticks to back of cross and background panels. Let dry.

Ice 1-layer 15 in. and 2-layer 9 in. cakes smooth in buttercream and prepare for stacked construction (p. 110). With toothpick, trace arch pattern 3 times on each side of 9 in. cake. Outline with tip 362; overpipe with tip 4. Insert spiked side panels into cakes (ends will not meet at corners). Pipe tip 32 upright shell at each corner; add tip 4 dot at end. Pipe tip 32 band bottom borders; add tip 32 upright shells with tip 4 dots. Pipe tip 4 bead top borders. Pipe a tip 32 rosette at corners of bottom tier, insert flower spikes. Insert arched background panels and cross. Attach flower spikes to back of each panel with full-strength Color Flow. Insert 2 lollipop sticks between background panels; position flower spikes on each. Position top portion of heart base; position Communion Boy topper. Serves 68.

◀ One Cool Commencement!

On hot graduation days, it's a pleasure to serve this creamy gelatin grad surrounded by colorful gelatin stars.

Pans: Smiley Grad, p. 186; 6 x 2 in. Round or Square (5 needed), p. 158
Tips: 5, 6, 18, p. 136-137
Colors: Golden Yellow, Black, Royal Blue, p. 127
Recipes: Wilton Gelatin Treats, Creamy Gelatin, p. 112
Also: Nesting Stars Metal Cutter Set, p. 140; Vanilla Whipped Icing Mix, p. 126, non-stick vegetable pan spray

A day in advance: Prepare all gelatin. Spray grad pan, fill with Creamy Gelatin. Spray round or square pans and fill ½ in. high with 5 flavors of Gelatin Treats. Chill all overnight.

Unmold grad gelatin onto serving plate. Trim off background area at bottom of cap. Prepare whipped icing and tint 2 cups blue and ½ cup each black and yellow. Pipe tip 18 stars on cap; add tip 5 string tassel, dot button and knot. Pipe in tip 6 eyes and mouth. Cut out gelatin treats using 3 smallest star cutters. Position on plate. Creamy gelatin serves 12; each star serves 1.

▶ Unlocking His Potential

Pans: 16 x 2 in. Square, p. 159; Graduate, p. 186
Tips: 2, 8, p. 136
Colors:* Royal Blue, Black, p. 127
Candy: Candy Melts®†—White, Light Cocoa, Red, Yellow, p. 146
Recipes: Buttercream, Royal Icings, p. 111
Also: 2005 Pattern Book (Small and Large Locker Vents, Lock and Locker Handle), p. 222; Color Flow Mix, p. 126; Meringue Powder, p. 126; 6 in. Cookie Treat Sticks, p. 143; Cake Board, Fanci-Foil Wrap, p. 217; Parchment Triangles, p. 134; Flowerful Medley Sprinkle Decorations, p. 128; Tapered Spatula, p. 134; Graduation Candle Set, p. 180; 17 in. square cardboard (3 needed), curling ribbon (yellow, red, green, blue), waxed paper, sharp knife

In advance: Mold candy plaque graduate in pan (p. 119). Mold to just below diploma (no need to make full body as it will be covered by locker door). Using patterns and tip 2, make 3 large and 3 small Color Flow locker vents (p. 118). Make extras to allow for breakage; let dry. Make open locker door. Wrap 5¼ in. x 16 in. cardboard piece with foil and ice smooth with royal icing; let dry.

In advance: Make 3 locks and locker handles using pattern, tip 8 and royal icing. Tape pattern to board and cover with waxed paper. Outline locker handle and lock ring with tip 8; pipe in combination circle and dot knob with tip 8. Immediately use spatula or sharp knife to make combination indentations on lock. Make extras to allow for breakage and let dry.

Ice 2-layer cake (bake two 1½ in. layers to form 3 in. high cake) smooth in buttercream. Position candy plaque. Trim cookie treat sticks for door support and insert upright in cake. Position open locker door resting on sticks.

Position vents and locks on cake. Pipe tip 2 numbers and tip 8 door hinges in buttercream. Position confetti sprinkles from Flowerful Medley, candles and curling ribbon. Serves 80.

*Note: Add a small amount of black to white royal icing to achieve gray shade used for locks.

†Brand confectionery coating.

◀ Success Is in Her Grasp

See how our Cuddly Bear cake can become the image of your favorite student—right down to her proud smile.

Pan: Stand-Up Cuddly Bear Set, p. 163
Tips: 3, 12, 16, p. 136-137
Colors: Kelly Green, Rose, Black, Brown, p. 127
Recipes: Buttercream Icing, p. 111
Also: Plastic Dowel Rods, p. 214; Petite Romantic Heart Base, p. 202; Cake Circle, Fanci-Foil Wrap, p. 217; ⅛ in. wide yellow curling ribbon (2 yards), hot glue gun, cornstarch

For mortarboard, cut a 5 in. square from cake circle. Wrap square and the bottom portion of heart base with foil, tucking ends under rim. Hot glue base to underside of square. Cover with tip 16 stars.

Bake and cool bear cake using firm-textured batter such as pound cake. Trim off right hand and forearm, muzzle, ears and area on chest where diploma will rest; fill in eye area with icing. Using dowel rod cut to 6 in. long as a guide, build up tip 12 arms. Pipe in tip 3 mouth and collar; smooth with finger dipped in cornstarch. Ice shoe bottoms smooth with spatula. Build up lower body with tip 12. Cover face and body with tip 16 stars; overpipe nose. Add tip 3 outline eyes, lashes and bead tongue. Attach dowel rod diploma with dots of icing; pipe tip 16 star hands. Add tip 16 swirl hair. Cut four 12 in. lengths of ribbon; fold three lengths in half and knot around the fourth. Attach to mortarboard with tip 16 rosette. Position mortarboard. Serves 12.

▶ Tomorrow's Stars!

Pans: 8, 12, 16 x 2 in. Round, p. 159
Tips: 1, 2, 2B, 3, 4, 18, 21, p. 136-137
Colors: Lemon Yellow, Royal Blue, Kelly Green, Christmas Red, Red-Red, Black, Copper (skin tone), Brown, p. 127
Cookie: 101 Cookie Cutters Set, A-B-C and 1-2-3 Cutter Set, p. 142
Recipes: Buttercream, Royal Icings, p. 111
Also: 2005 Pattern Book (Graduation Cap), p. 222; White Ready-To-Use Rolled Fondant (24 oz. needed), p. 122; Gum-Tex™ Karaya, p. 125; Fine Tip Primary FoodWriter™ Edible Color Markers, p. 124; Cake Sparkles™ in Red, Yellow, Blue, Green, p. 128; Cake Dividing Set, p. 131; 8 in. Lollipop Sticks, p. 149; Meringue Powder, p. 126; Decorator Brush Set, p. 147; Wooden Dowel Rods, p. 214; 18 in. Round Silver Cake Base, p. 217; cornstarch, waxed paper, craft knife, white curling ribbon

Several days in advance: Make fondant pieces. Add 2 teaspoons of Gum-Tex™ to fondant, knead and divide as follows: Tint ¼ blue and ⅛ each copper (skin tone), light brown (for ethnic skintone), black, yellow, green and Christmas Red/Red-Red combination. Make 14 graduates and caps (p. 117). Using numeral cutters, cut red "2", yellow "0", blue "0" and green "5". Brush with water and sprinkle with Cake Sparkles. Using medium and small star cutters from 101-cutter set, cut stars in various colors. Let all pieces dry several days on cornstarch-dusted surface.

A day in advance: Using royal icing, make 14 hanging cap tassels. Using tip 1, pipe dot with five ½ in. strings on waxed paper. Make extras to allow for breakage; let dry. Attach lollipop sticks to backs of fondant numbers and stars with tip 4 dots of royal icing; let dry.

Ice 2-layer 8 in. and 12 in. cakes and 1-layer 16 in. cake smooth with buttercream. Prepare for stacked construction (p. 110). Using Cake Dividing Set, divide 8 in. cake into 6ths, 12 in. cake into 8ths and 16 in. cake into 16ths. On 8 in. and 12 in. cakes, pipe tip 4 bead bottom borders. Add tip 2B vertical band columns at division points. Pipe tip 18 scrolls at top and bottom of columns. On 16 in. cake, pipe tip 18 zigzag garland, 1 in. deep, between division points; add tip 21 shell bottom border. Draw facial features with black FoodWriter and position graduates on cake between pillars. Attach hanging tassels with tip 1. Curl ribbon and position on cake; tie ribbon on sticks for tallest stars. Insert numbers and stars at staggered heights on cake top. Serves 137.

◀ Ride with Pride!

Baby-soft pastels and a charming Color Flow scene are sure to earn "oohs" and "aahs" from every guest!

Pans: 9 x 2 in. Round Set, p. 159
Tips: 1, 2, 3, 352, p. 136-137
Colors: Rose, Lemon Yellow, Violet, Royal Blue, Kelly Green, Buttercup Yellow, Copper (skin tone), Brown, p. 127
Recipes: Buttercream Icing, p. 111, Color Flow Icing, p. 111
Also: 2005 Pattern Book (Mother and Carriage), p. 222; Color Flow Mix, p. 126; Floral Collection Flower Making Set, Confectionery Tool Set, p. 124; White Ready-To-Use Rolled Fondant (48 oz. needed), p. 122; Easy-Glide Smoother, p. 125; Parchment Triangles, p. 134; Cake Circles, Fanci-Foil Wrap, p. 217, 6 in. Lollipop Sticks, p. 149; paring knife, waxed paper

In advance: Make Color Flow Mother and carriage pieces (p. 118) on waxed paper using patterns. When dry, attach lollipop stick to Mother and carriage with full-strength Color Flow; let dry.

Also in advance: Make fondant flowers. Tint 4 oz. portions of fondant rose, lemon yellow, violet and green. Using cutters from set, cut 16 pansies, 30 apple blossoms and 5 forget-me-nots in various colors. Use ball tool to cup flowers on thick foam; let dry. Add tip 2 dot centers in full-strength Color Flow; let dry.

For cake, tint 30 oz. fondant buttercup yellow and 6 oz. green. Prepare 2-layer cake for rolled fondant (p. 105), cover and smooth with Easy-Glide Smoother. In buttercream, pipe tip 3 stems on cake sides; attach pansies and apple blossoms and pipe tip 352 leaves. For grass border, roll out fondant ⅛ in. thick on cornstarch-dusted surface. Cut into strips ¾ in. wide. Using paring knife, cut ⅛ in. wide x ½ in. deep slits for grass effect. Brush base of cake lightly with water and attach strips. Repeat as needed to form grass border, adding 2 or 3 layers for a full look.

Attach forget-me-nots to Mother's hat with full-strength Color Flow. Roll out green fondant ⅛ in. thick and cut a free-form oval; attach to cake top. Attach fondant grass and flowers. Insert Mother and carriage pieces in cake. Serves 24.

▶ Teddy Rocks the Block!

Make your shower a block party with individual squares of candy-coated cake. Don't worry about an unsteady Teddy—lollipop sticks attached on his back keep him from falling!

Pans: 10 x 2 in. Square, p. 159; Mini Bear, Mini Locomotive, p. 161; Mini Ball, p. 164; Cooling Grid, p. 160
Candy: Candy Melts®† in White (5 pks.) and Light Cocoa, p. 146; Primary and Garden Candy Color Sets, p. 147; Alphabet Mold, p. 148, Decorator Brush Set, p. 147; 4 in. Lollipop Sticks, p. 149
Recipe: Buttercream Icing, p. 111
Also: Disposable Decorating Bags, p. 134; Parchment Triangles, p. 134; Spatula, p. 134; 16 in. Round Silver Cake Base, p. 217; waxed paper

In advance: Mold candies. Using candy colors, tint portions of melted white candy blue, yellow, pink and green; lighten portions of melted cocoa candy with white. Mold bear, train and ball using painting method (p. 119), filling ball 1 in., bear and train ½ in. deep. Mold 100 letters, filling mold halfway. Refrigerate all candy until firm; unmold.

Bake and cool 1-layer square cake using firm-textured batter such as pound cake. Cut into 25 squares, 2 x 2 in. Lightly ice cakes and place on cooling grid over drip pan; cover with melted white candy; let set. Outline blocks with melted candy using cut parchment bag decorate 6 in each color. Attach letters to blocks with melted candy. Position cakes, approximately 12 on bottom, 10 in center and 2 on top. Position train and ball. Attach lollipop sticks to bear with melted candy, extending 1½ in. and insert in top of cakes. Each block serves 1.

†Brand confectionery coating.

▼ They Deliver for You

Prepare the figure-piped storks for take-off 3 days ahead. The easy-to-decorate stand-up house and cake base runway ensure on-time arrival at the shower.

Pan: Stand-Up House, p. 163
Tips: 2, 2A, 3, 5, 8, 12, 55, 233, p. 136-137
Colors: Lemon Yellow, Royal Blue, Kelly Green, Rose, Brown, p. 127
Fondant: White Ready-To-Use Rolled Fondant (24 oz. needed), p. 122; Easy-Glide Smoother, p. 125
Recipes: Buttercream, Royal Icings, p. 111
Also: Plastic Dowel Rods, p. 214; 8 in. Lollipop Sticks, p. 149; Newborn Baby Figurines, p. 219; Rubber Ducky Icing Decorations (2 pks.), p. 150; Cake Board, Fanci-Foil Wrap, p. 217; Meringue Powder, p. 126; Angled Spatula, p. 134; Decorator Brush Set, p. 147; 10 x 16 x 1 in. craft block, ¾ in. wide white ribbon (5 ft. needed), ⅞ in. wide pink and blue wired ribbon (12 in. of each), waxed paper, cornstarch

At least 3 days in advance: Make storks (p. 116). Prepare cake base. Attach a cake board to bottom of craft block with icing and wrap with foil. Tint 8 oz. fondant blue, 8 oz. green, reserve 8 oz. white. Roll fondant ⅛ in. thick and cut 4 x 16 in. blue runway strip and 6 x 16 in. grass strip. Brush backs with water and attach to cake base; smooth strips together. Attach white ribbon to base of craft block and icing decorations to ribbon with royal icing; let dry. To make baby conveyor belt, roll out and cut 4 x ¾ in. strip of white fondant; let dry on waxed paper board covered with cornstarch. Keep prepared base away from light to prevent fading.

Trim off front and bottom of house cake to level. Attach house to cake base with icing. Ice smooth; spatula ice roof fluffy. Pipe tip 12 band eaves. Mark door and window areas with toothpick as follows: Front windows ¾ x 1½ in. high; door 1¾ x 3½ in. high, side windows 1¼ x 1½ in. high. Pipe in areas with tip 3; smooth with finger dipped in cornstarch. Outline doors and windows with tip 55; add tip 2 dots and message. Pipe tip 233 pull-out grass around house. Insert storks into cake. Using royal icing, cover legs with tip 5; pipe tip 3 outline feet. Pipe tip 3 center lines on runway.

Insert two 2 in. lengths of dowel rods into cake base for conveyor belt base, positioning at height of side window ledge. Position fondant conveyor belt. Tie babies with ribbon; position on conveyor belt and on beaks of storks. Serves 12.

◀ Wake Up, Sleepy Head!

Pan: Round Cookie Treat, p. 143
Colors: Royal Blue, Pink, p. 127
Also: Candy Melts®† in White, Pink, Light Cocoa, p. 146; White Ready-To-Use Rolled Fondant (24 oz. needed), p. 122; 8 in. Cookie Treat Sticks, p. 143; Parchment Triangles, p. 134; Decorator Brush Set, p. 147

Lighten melted pink and cocoa candy by adding white. Mold candy plaque (p. 119) heads in Cookie Treat Pan; refrigerate until firm. Using melted candy in cut bag, pipe dot cheeks and noses. Pipe eyes and mouths. Divide fondant and tint blue and pink; reserve some white. Shape fondant into nightcaps and attach to candy plaques with melted candy. Roll white fondant into balls and attach to end of caps with brush strokes of water.

Attach sticks to back of candy plaques with melted candy. Let set. Each serves 1.

◀ How Sheep Get to Sleep

His fondant blanket looks extra cuddly with the textured look of quilted stitch lines done with the Cutter/Embosser tool.

Pan: Cuddly Lamb, p. 163
Tips: 4, 16, p. 136
Colors:* Lemon Yellow, Rose, Royal Blue, Brown, Red-Red, p. 127
Recipes: Buttercream Icing, p. 111
Also: White Ready-To-Use Rolled Fondant (24 oz. needed), p. 122; Heart and Flower Cut-Outs™, p. 123; Roll & Cut Mat, Cutter/Embosser, p. 125; Newborn Baby Figurines, p. 219; Decorator Brush Set, p. 147; Cake Board, Fanci-Foil Wrap, p. 217, Spatula, p. 134; plastic ruler

Ice inside ears and hooves smooth with spatula. Outline sheep with tip 4; cover head and body with tip 16 stars. Pipe fur and tail with tip 16 rosettes (tail is needed for dimension under blanket). Pipe tip 4 eyes, mouth and nose. Tint 8 oz. fondant yellow; roll out ⅛ in. thick and cut to fit blanket area of cake, approximately 11 x 9 in. Using Cutter/Embosser (straight-edge wheel) and ruler, mark diagonal stitching lines on blanket, spacing 1 in. apart. Tint 1½ in. balls of fondant pink and blue. Roll out ⅛ in. thick, and using smallest Cut-Outs, cut hearts and flowers. Lightly brush backs with water and attach to blanket.

Position blanket; trim to size needed. Roll out additional yellow fondant; cut two ½ x 18 in. strips for blanket binding. Attach with water. Roll out white fondant ¼ in. thick and form rounded cloud shape with hands. Position above sheep; roll small fondant balls and position next to cloud. Attach babies with icing; pipe tip 4 numbers and dots. Serves 12.

*Combine Brown and Red-Red for shade used. You may also substitute Brown Tube Decorating Icing (p. 127).

▶ Under Her Wing

This love nest is a wonderful shower showcase, featuring beautiful dimensional birds made in our Rubber Ducky and Mini Ball pans.

Pans: 3-D Rubber Ducky, p. 163; Mini Ball, p. 164
Tips: 1, 3, 7, 18, 104, p. 136-137
Colors: Lemon Yellow, Black, Orange, Brown, p. 127
Recipe: Buttercream Icing, p. 111
Also: Baby Bottles Favor Containers, p. 218; Baby Blocks Set, p. 218; Shower Rattles, p. 219; Scrolls (2 needed), Wooden Dowel Rods; p. 214; 6 in. Lollipop Sticks, p. 149; Spatula, p. 134; shredded coconut (two 14 oz. bags needed), large marshmallows, zip-close bag, cornstarch, milk

Bake and cool Rubber Ducky cake and 2 mini ball cakes using firm-textured batter such as pound cake. Assemble baby bird (p. 116). Pipe in tip 7 beak (smooth with finger dipped in cornstarch). Pipe tip 3 dot eyes with tip 1 dot highlights. Cover body with tip 18 stars. Add tip 18 pull-out wings and tip 104 ruffle bonnet.

To make mother bird: Slice Rubber Ducky cake across neck and turn head to face baby; insert dowel rod and ice to hold head in place. Trim bill to a pointed beak; ice smooth with spatula (smooth with finger). Pipe tip 3 dot eyes with tip 1 dot highlight. Cover body with tip 18 stars. Position cakes on plate. Cut lollipop sticks in half. Insert sticks into sides of mother bird to support wings (Note: the mother's right wing will rest on baby). Insert scrolls into icing, resting on top of sticks. Cover scrolls with tip 18 pull-out feathers. Tint coconut brown (p. 116); position around birds for nest.

Fill baby bottle with powdered milk. Position, bottle, blocks and rattle. Serves 10.

◀ Baby Bear

The new Animal Crackers pan is perfect for decorating critters in close-up—so guests can focus on that cute baby face.

Pan: Animal Crackers, p. 162
Tips: 4, 18, p. 136-137
Colors: Brown, Rose, Royal Blue, p. 127
Fondant: White Ready-To-Use Rolled Fondant (24 oz. needed), p. 122; Round Cut-Outs™, p. 123; Cutter/Embosser, p. 125
Recipe: Buttercream Icing, p. 111
Also: 2005 Pattern Book (Bonnet), p. 222; Cake Board, Fanci-Foil Wrap, p. 217; Decorator Brush Set, p. 147; cornstarch, craft knife, ruler, cornstarch

In advance: Make fondant bonnet and bow. Roll out fondant ⅛ in. thick; using pattern and craft knife, cut bonnet. Using ridged Cutter/Embosser wheel and ruler, mark ½ in. wide criss-cross design on bonnet. Roll ¼ in. diameter fondant rope and attach with water to trim bonnet edge; roll and attach ¼ in. diameter balls to bonnet front. Cut two 1 x 6 in. bow loops and two 3 in. streamers. Attach loop ends together with water and stand on side to dry. Roll 1 in. round ball for knot. Use Embosser to mark criss-cross design on bow and knot as on bonnet. To make pacifier: Tint a 1 in. fondant ball blue. Use medium round Cut-Out and blue tinted fondant to make base; roll small ball for handle and attach to base with water. Let all fondant pieces dry on cornstarch-dusted surface.

Ice inside of ears smooth. Cover face and muzzle with tip 18 stars. Pipe in tip 4 nose and eyes (smooth with finger dipped in cornstarch). Pipe tip 18 swirls for hair. Position pacifier, bow and streamers. Serves 12.

▼ Save 'Em for a Rainy Day

Decorate every table with these adorable candy cups filled with mints.

Pans: Standard Muffin, p. 160; Non-Stick Cookie Sheet, p. 157
Tip: 14, p. 137
Color: Rose, p. 127
Candy: Candy Melts®† in White, Blue, Orange, Yellow, Green, p. 146; Springtime Treats Lollipop Mold, p. 148; Decorator Brush Set, p. 147; Mint Drops, p. 219
Recipes: Royal Icing, p. 111
Also: 101 Cookie Cutters Set, p. 142; White Standard Baking Cups, p. 150; Meringue Powder, p. 126; Parchment Triangles, p. 134; Angled Spatula, p. 134

In advance: Using royal icing, make 4 tip 14 rose-colored drop flowers for each favor needed. Make extras to allow for breakage; let dry.

Make candy shell in baking cup (p. 119), painting white candy up side of cup. Make a candy plaque lid (p. 119), using medium round cookie cutter. Using painting method (p. 119), mold baby duck with umbrella. Refrigerate until firm; unmold. Trim two sides of a Candy Melts wafer to form easel. Attach to back of chicks with melted candy.

Lighten green candy with a little white; spatula ice "grass" on top of lid; position drop flowers on top. Attach duck to lid and flower to umbrella with melted candy; let set. Fill cup with Mint Drops. Each serves 1.

†Brand confectionery coating.

▶ Bouncing Baby Baskets

Another fuss-free favor! Easy baby face cookies go right in our Flower Baskets on a bed of pillow mints.

Cookie: 101 Cookie Cutters Set, p. 142
Tips: 2, 7, p. 136
Colors: Copper (skin tone), Brown, p. 127
Recipes: Roll-Out Cookie, p. 112; Royal Icing, p. 111
Also: White Flower Basket, p. 209; Pillow Mints, p. 219; Meringue Powder, p. 126; Cooling Grid, p. 160; ⅛ in. wide white curling ribbon (18 in. needed for each basket), small helium balloons, toothpick

Cut one cookie for each basket using smallest round cutter; bake and cool. Cover cookies with thinned royal icing (p. 118) in copper or brown; let set. Fill baskets with mints. Using full-strength royal icing, pipe tip 2 facial features and hair curl. Position faces in basket against mints. Pipe tip 7 ball hands; indent with toothpick for fingers. Tie helium balloon to basket with curling ribbon. Each serves 1.

Visions of Love

When wedding cakes were just round and white, your choice was easy. Now you have so many fresh colors at your disposal, from golden yellow to garden green. New shapes are open to you as well, with ovals, hexagons and hearts as prevalent as rounds and squares. Today, choosing your wedding cake can be a thrill, especially when you coordinate the look with the perfect favors, shower cakes and reception accents. Let the excitement begin!

Instructions for projects shown on these two pages are are on page 84.

A Diamond Day

Fondant diamonds in gentle yellow create glamorous texture on this tiered cake and its matching shower cakes.

Pans: 8, 12, 16 x 2 in. Round, p. 158
Tips: 3, 6, p. 136
Colors: Lemon Yellow, Golden Yellow, p. 127
Fondant: White Ready-To-Use Rolled Fondant (216 oz. needed), p. 122; Square Cut-Outs™, p. 123; Easy-Glide Fondant Smoothers, Rolling Pin, Roll & Cut Mat, Brush Set, p. 125
Ornament: Bianca, p. 200
Recipe: Buttercream Icing, p. 111
Also: 9, 17 in. Scrollwork Cake Stands (includes Crystal-Look Plates), p. 212; Hidden Pillars, p. 215; 13 in. Crystal-Look Plates, p. 214; Crystal-Look Bowl, p. 216; Plastic Dowel Rods, p. 214; Cake Boards, Fanci-Foil Wrap, p. 217; 6, 14 in. Grease-Proof White Doilies, p. 216; fresh and silk flowers, 12 in. wide non-skid mat

Prepare 2-layer cakes for rolled fondant (p. 105); prepare 12 in. cake for stacked construction (p. 110). Cover cakes with rolled fondant, reserving 24 oz.; smooth with Easy-Glide Smoother. Tint reserved fondant Lemon Yellow with a little Golden Yellow. Roll out and cut approximately 104 squares using medium Cut-Out. Attach squares to cake sides, point-to-point in 2 rows, using damp brush. Pipe tip 3 dots at meeting points. Add tip 6 ball bottom borders to all cakes.

At reception: Assemble cake. Position 16 in. cake on 17 in. plate and stand. Insert four hidden pillars. Cut 14 in. doily to fit and place on cake top. Position 12 in. cake on 13 in. plate. Position the second 13 in. plate, feet up, on 12 in. cake, securing with buttercream. Trim non-skid mat to fit inside plate. Position mat and 9 in. stand on plate; position 8 in. cake on stand. Cut four dowel rods to 5½ in. long and insert in center of 8 in. cake for ornament support. Cut 6 in. doily to fit and position on cake top. Attach top only of Crystal-Look Base to dowel rods with buttercream; position ornament, securing with buttercream. Pipe mounds of buttercream on cake tops and position flowers. Serves 156.*

The perfect accents: *Find the Fluted Toasting Glasses and the Cake Knife and Server Set on p. 204.*

***Note:** The smallest tier is often saved for the first anniversary. The number of servings given does not include the smallest tier.

A Budding Romance

Pan: 12 x 18 in. Jelly Roll, p. 160
Tips: 3, 6, p. 136
Colors: Lemon Yellow, Golden Yellow, p. 127
Fondant: White Ready-To-Use Rolled Fondant (24 oz. covers 3 cakes), p. 122; Square Cut-Outs™, p. 123; Rolling Pin, Easy-Glide Fondant Smoother, Roll and Cut Mat, Brush Set, p. 125
Recipe: Buttercream Icing, p. 111
Also: Round Comfort Grip™ Cutter, p. 140; Flower Spikes, p. 216; Cake Board, Fanci-Foil Wrap, p. 217; fresh flowers

Tint ⅓ of each 24 oz. of fondant using Lemon Yellow with a little Golden Yellow. Bake and cool jelly roll cake using firm-textured batter such as pound cake. Using Comfort Grip cutter, cut out 2 circles for each cake; stack, ice and cover with fondant. Roll out fondant and cut approximately 28 squares for each cake using smallest Cut-Out. Attach squares to cake sides in diamond fashion, starting on top and trimming bottom diamond as needed. Pipe tip 3 dots at meeting points and add tip 6 ball bottom border. Insert flower spike at an angle in cake top and position flower just before serving. Each serves 1.

The perfect favor: *Graceful Champagne Flutes (p. 209), filled with Pillow Mints (p. 211) and finished with a bow made with ¼ in. wide satin ribbon.*

Capture the Feeling

Elegant choices for anniversaries or showers, each cake shown here carries design elements from the wedding cakes that follow.

▲ Promised Forever

The soft green color echoes the Lush Layers wedding cake on p. 87.

Pans: Oval Set (13 x 9⅞ in. and 16½ x 12⅜ in. used), p. 159
Tips: 2, 3, 4, 7, p. 136
Colors: Kelly Green, Moss Green, Violet, Rose, p. 127
Ornament: Devotion, p. 201
Recipes: Buttercream Icing, Gum Paste, p. 111
Also: White Ready-To-Use Rolled Fondant (120 oz. needed), p. 122; Gum Paste Mix, p. 125; Decorator Brush Set, p. 147; Stepsaving Rose Bouquet Flower Cutter Set, p. 134; Confectionery Tool Set, p. 134; Decorator Favorites Pattern Press Set, p. 132; Candy Melting Plate, p. 147; Cake Board, p. 217; non-toxic pastel chalks, fine mesh strainer, ⅛ in. thin foam squares, sharp knife, rolling pin, aluminum foil or bubble wrap, cornstarch, double-thick cardboard or ½ in. thick foam core board

In advance: Make 75 gum paste flowers (25 in each color) and 40 gum paste leaves (p. 117).

Tint 96 oz. fondant Kelly Green; reserve 24 oz. white. Prepare 2-layer 13 x 9⅞ in. cake for rolled fondant (p. 105), cover and smooth with Easy-Glide Smoother. Cut foam core or double-thick cardboard 2½ in. larger than cake; cover with green fondant; smooth. Position cake. For overlay, roll out white fondant and use 16½ x 12⅜ in. pan, upside down, for pattern. Carefully cut with sharp knife. Cut scalloped edge using large C-scroll from press set, cutting as close to edge as possible; trim off excess. Position overlay on cake. Pipe tip 7 scroll design on edges. Pipe tip 3 alternating single and double drop strings beneath overlay scallops; add tip 2 dots at string points. Pipe tip 7 bead bottom border and position flowers and leaves. Write tip 4 message and position ornament, flowers and leaves. Serves 30.

◀ Cupcake Corsages

Pretty cupcakes, displayed in our fun new dessert stand, are the perfect companion to the Floral Flair wedding cake on p. 86.

Pan: Standard Muffin, p. 160
Fondant: White Ready-To-Use Rolled Fondant, p. 122; Fondant Multi Packs in Neon and Pastel, p. 122; Leaf and Funny Flower Cut-Outs™, p. 123; Cutter/Embosser, Rolling Pin, Roll & Cut Mat, Brush Set, p. 125
Recipe: Buttercream Icing, p. 111
Also: Cupcakes 'N More Dessert Stand, p. 130; White Sparkling Sugars, p. 128; Assorted Pastel Baking Cups, p. 150

In advance: Make fondant flowers and leaves. Combine 2 oz. white fondant with 2 oz. violet fondant; combine 2 oz. white with 2 oz. orange. Roll out various colors 1/16 in. thick and cut 22 large and 22 medium flowers using Cut-Outs. Attach medium flowers to large with damp brush. Roll pea-size balls of fondant in various colors; attach with water for flower centers. Brush medium flowers with water and sprinkle with sparkling sugar. Let dry. Roll out green fondant and cut 22 leaves using large Cut-Out. Imprint veins using straight-edge wheel of Cutter/Embosser; let dry.

Ice 22 cupcakes smooth. Position flowers and leaves and place on stand. Each serves 1.

▶ Heart's Treasure

The elegant swags on this shower cake are also found on The Moment Endures on p. 90.

Pans: 10, 12 x 2 in. Heart, p. 158
Tips: 2 (used for blossom centers), 4, p. 136
Color: Creamy Peach, p. 127
Fondant: White Ready-To-Use Rolled Fondant (24 oz. needed), p. 122; Cutter/Embosser, Roll & Cut Mat, Rolling Pin, p. 125
Recipes: Buttercream Icing, p. 111; Candy Clay, p. 112
Also: 2005 Pattern Book (Lettering), p. 222; White Candy Melts®* (5 pks. needed), p. 146; Floral Collection Flower Making Set, p. 124; Flower Former Set, p. 134; Confectionery Tool Set, p. 125; Cake Board, Fanci-Foil Wrap, p. 217; wooden skewers, cornstarch, waxed paper

In advance: Make candy plaque heart (p. 119) in 12 in. heart pan. Make 20 Candy Clay roses (p. 119) using 1 candy clay recipe. Make Candy Clay blossoms (p. 119) using a second Candy Clay recipe combined with 12 oz. fondant.

Ice 2-layer 10 in. cake smooth. Using remaining candy clay/fondant mixture, roll out and cut 20 strips, 3/4 x 4 in.; use straight-edge wheel of Cutter/Embosser to imprint lattice lines 3/8 in. apart. Position strips 3/4 in. apart on cake sides. Position candy plaque on cake top. For bottom swags, cut candy clay/fondant mixture into 1½ in. squares. Form drapes by placing one skewer under bottom edge of square and one on top, next to the first skewer. Repeat with more skewers to form three folds; remove skewers and gather fondant at each end; trim as needed. Attach swags between strips with melted candy; use veining tool to define folds if needed. For top swags, cut candy clay/fondant mixture into 2½ in. squares and repeat draping process used for bottom swags; attach to candy plaque with melted candy. Attach blossoms at swag points with melted candy.

Trace lettering pattern on waxed paper. Using melted candy, pipe tip 4 monogram; refrigerate until firm. Position monogram. Attach roses to cake top with melted candy. Serves 24.

*Brand confectionery coating.

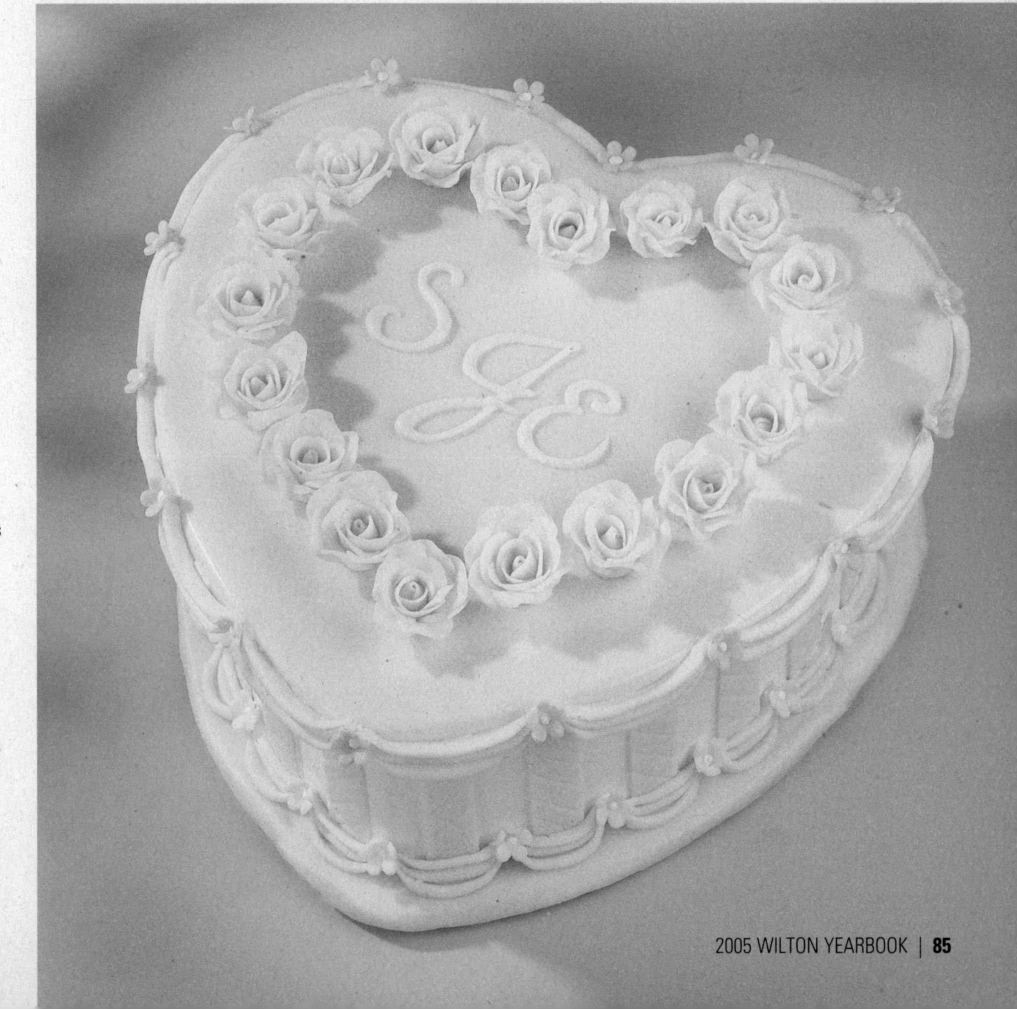

Floral Flair

Sugared fondant blossoms add a sweet touch of color to classic white rounds.

Pans: 6, 10, 14 x 2 in. Round, p. 158
Tips: 3, 5, 7, 9, p. 136
Colors: Rose, Violet, Kelly Green, Lemon Yellow, Golden Yellow, p. 127
Fondant: White Ready-To-Use Rolled Fondant (48 oz. needed), p. 122; Fun Flowers, Leaves Cut-Outs™, p. 123; Rolling Pin, Brush Set, p. 125
Ornament: Devotion, p. 201
Recipes: Buttercream, Royal Icings, p. 111
Also: Round Floating Tiers Cake Stand Set (includes 8, 12, 16 in. Separator Plates), p. 212; Plastic Dowel Rods, p. 214; White Sparkling Sugar, p. 128; Meringue Powder, p. 126; Gum-Tex™ Karaya, p. 125; white florist tape, 20-gauge white cloth-covered wires (23 needed), 22-gauge white cloth-covered wires (9 in. lengths, 62 needed), craft block, 6 in. wide white tulle (7½ yds. needed), cornstarch, waxed paper

In advance: Make flowers and leaves for bouquets. Add 2 teaspoons of Gum-Tex to 24 oz. of fondant and divide into 4 sections; tint lemon yellow/golden yellow combination, rose, violet/rose combination and green. Cut the following fondant flowers in assorted colors, using Cut-Outs indicated: 23 medium flowers, 23 small flowers, 16 large leaves and 20 small leaves (make extras of each to allow for breakage). Brush tops with water and sprinkle with sparkling sugar. Using royal icing, pipe tip 3 dot centers on small flowers and tip 7 dot centers on medium flowers. Let dry. Attach flowers and leaves to wire stems (p. 116), using 20-gauge wire and tip 9 royal icing bases for medium flowers and 22-gauge wire and tip 5 royal icing bases for small flowers and all leaves. Let dry in craft block. To assemble large spray (on 14 in. cake), combine 10 medium flowers, 9 small flowers, 9 large leaves and 5 small leaves. Gather 3 yards of tulle, folding into five 4 in. loops; twist together with 22-gauge wire and wrap together with flowers and leaves with floral tape. For medium spray (on 10 in. cake), combine 8 medium flowers, 6 small flowers, 4 large leaves and 6 small leaves. Gather and loop 2½ yards of tulle as above and wrap spray with floral tape. For small spray (on 6 in. cake), combine 5 medium flowers, 8 small flowers, 3 large leaves and 9 small leaves. Gather and loop 2 yards of tulle as above and wrap. Set aside.

Ice 2-layer cakes smooth in buttercream. Using remaining tinted fondant, cut the following fondant flowers in assorted colors, using Cut-Outs indicated: 53 medium flowers, 33 small flowers and 68 small leaves. Brush tops with water, sprinkle with sugar. Randomly attach flowers and leaves to cake sides with buttercream; add tip 3 vines and dot accents. Pipe tip 3 dot centers on small flowers and tip 7 dot centers on medium flowers. Roll ¼ in. diameter fondant logs; twist together to make ropes and attach at bottom borders with buttercream.

At reception: Position cakes on stand. Cut hidden pillars 3 in. long for each bouquet and insert into cake; insert bouquets in pillars. Position ornament.* Serves 116.**

***Note:** Always place a separator plate or cake board cut to fit, on the cake before you position any figurine or ornament. This protects both the cake and your keepsake. For extra stability, secure your figurine to the plate with double-stick craft tape.

The perfect favor: *Flower Shape Baskets (p. 209) filled with Jordan Almonds (p. 211) and a bouquet to match the cake. For each favor, make 1 small and 3 medium flowers, and 3 leaves on 3½ in. wires; insert in craft block and position in basket before adding almonds.*

The perfect accent: *Find the Cake Knife and Server Set on p. 204.*

Lush Layers

It's only natural that your cake should support your garden theme with some green of its own.

Pans: 6, 14 x 2 in. Round, 18 x 3 in. Half Round, p. 158
Tip: 3, p. 136
Color: Kelly Green, p. 127
Fondant: White Ready-To-Use Rolled Fondant (264 oz. needed), p. 122; Easy-Glide Fondant Smoothers, Roll & Cut Mat, Rolling Pin, Brush Set, p. 125
Recipe: Buttercream Icing, p. 111
Also: 2005 Pattern Book (Oval and Lettering), p. 222; Tiered Floral Centerpiece, p. 207; 8 in. Separator Plate from Crystal-Clear Cake Divider Set, p. 213; Plastic Dowel Rods, p. 214; Cake Circles, 20 in. Round Silver Cake Base, p. 217; ruler, waxed paper, toothpick, silk flowers

Tint 36 oz. fondant green, set aside. Prepare 2-layer cakes for rolled fondant (p. 105); you will combine four 18 in. half rounds, each 2 in. high, to make a 4 in. high cake. Prepare all cakes for stacked construction (p. 110). Cover cakes with white fondant; smooth with Easy-Glide Smoother. Position two bottom tiers.

Roll out green fondant 1/8 in. thick and cut 1/2 x 4 in. strips; attach to cake sides, 1 in. apart, with damp brush. Trim ends of strips even with cake tops. Trace oval pattern on waxed paper; using toothpick, trace oval area on 14 in. cake. Trim off portions of strips where oval monogram will be positioned. Roll out white fondant 1/8 in. thick and cut oval using pattern. Using toothpick, trace lettering patterns; pipe letters with tip 3. Attach oval to cake with damp brush. Edge oval with tip 3 beads. Roll 1/2 in. diameter balls of green fondant and attach for bottom borders with damp brush.

At reception: Assemble cakes with centerpiece set, placing 8 in. plate on 14 in. cake and a cake circle cut to 5 in. diameter on 6 in. cake for centerpiece to rest on. Position silk flowers. Serves 370.**

The perfect accent: *From This Day Unity Candle (p. 206) is beautifully displayed with the Hydrangea Lighted Bridal Garland Set and Candle Holder Set (p. 206).*

****Note:** The top tier is often saved for the first anniversary. The number of servings given does not include top tier.

Five-Star Sophistication

Formally attired hexagons feature a contrast of delicate white dotted flowers with pinpoints of black on the scrolled cake tops.

Pans: Hexagon Set (9, 12, 15 x 2 in. used), p. 159
Tips: 1, 2, 3, 4, 5, 7, p. 136
Color: Black, p. 127
Fondant: White Ready-To-Use Rolled Fondant (332 oz. needed), p. 122; Easy-Glide Fondant Smoother, Brush Set, Roll & Cut Mat, Rolling Pin, p. 125
Ornament: Floral Topper, p. 200
Recipes: Buttercream, Royal Icings, p. 111
Also: 2005 Pattern Book (Swag, Panels A & B), p. 222; Decorator Favorites Pattern Press Set, p. 132; Cake Circles, Fanci-Foil Wrap, p. 217; Decorator Preferred™ 10 in. Hexagon Separator Plate, p. 214; 7 in. Grecian Spiked Pillars (2 pks. needed), p. 215; Wooden Dowel Rods, p. 214; Gum-Tex™ Karaya, p. 125; Meringue Powder, p. 126; 4 in. Lollipop Sticks, p. 149; Decorating Comb, p. 131; two sheets of ½ in. thick foam core board or plywood for base, waxed paper, transparent tape, cornstarch

In advance: Make fantasy flowers using royal icing. On waxed paper squares, make 54 star flower frames using tip 3, first piping five ½ in. long lines in a star formation, then piping five ¼ in. long lines in between. On waxed paper, using thinned royal icing and tip 3, pipe fifty-four ¾ in. diameter dots and five hundred forty ¼ in. diameter dots for flower petals. Make extras of all to allow for breakage and let dry.

Assemble flowers: Using tip 2 and royal icing, attach one large dot to each star center. Attach 10 small dots to the ends of star lines; let dry. Remove flowers from waxed paper and reinforce backs using tip 2; let dry. Attach 16 flowers to lollipop sticks, using royal icing and tip 3. Set remaining flowers aside.

Mix 2 teaspoons of Gum-Tex into 24 oz. rolled fondant. Roll fondant ⅛ in. thick and cut three each of panels A and B using patterns. Let dry on cornstarch-dusted surface. Ice panels with thinned royal icing. Immediately comb with large-tooth edge of decorating comb. Trim excess icing from edges and let dry.

Prepare cake base using double-thick foam core or plywood: Using 15 in. hexagon pan as pattern, mark 2¾ in. larger than pan on all sides. Cut out boards, tape together and wrap with foil. Cover with rolled fondant (about 80 oz.); smooth with Easy-Glide Smoother.

Prepare 2-layer 9 in. and 12 in. cakes (4 in. high) and 15 in. cake (5 in. high) for Push-In Pillar and Stacked Construction (p. 110). Prepare for rolled fondant and cover (use 36 oz. for 9 in., 48 oz. for 12 in. and 96 oz. for 15 in.); smooth with Easy-Glide Smoother. Dowel rod 15 in. cake and position on prepared base.

Decorate 15 in. cake. Pipe a tip 5 line of royal icing 2 in. from bottom. Alternately attach panels A and B to cake sides. Roll out 48 oz. of fondant ⅛ in. thick. Using pattern, cut out 6 swags and attach to cake with damp brush, positioning swag peaks at corners, ½ in. from top of cake. Using buttercream, outline scallop on bottom edge of swags with tip 5. Add tip 5 beads at swag seams. Pipe tip 1 black dots.

Mark top of 12 in. cake with separator plate for positioning of pillars. Attach 9 in. cake to 10 in. plate. Stack 12 and 15 in. cakes. Decorate 9 and 12 in. cakes: Imprint vine from press set on sides and tops. Outline with tip 5 in buttercream. Add tip 1 black dots. Pipe tip 7 bead bottom borders.

Attach fantasy flowers. On 15 in. cake, use a lollipop stick to make holes in cake top for placement of flowers at corners and at center of each side. Insert flowers on sticks. Using royal icing, attach remaining flowers in sets of three, in swag formation on cake sides, between flowers on sticks.

At reception: Insert pillars in 12 in. cake; assemble cakes. Position topper. Serves 110.*

***Note:** The top tier is often saved for the first anniversary. The number of servings given does not include the top tier.

The perfect favor: *Place Wedding Message Hearts (p. 211) in champagne goblets flowing with tulle and ribbon. Create the goblets using our Goblet Favor Making Kit (p. 208).*

The perfect accent: *Surround the richly-beaded From This Day Unity Candle with the delicate French Rose Candle Holder (both p. 206).*

Rose Resonance

A bed of pure white icing roses creates a rich, textured effect on our oval cake tower.

Pan: Oval Set, p. 159
Tips: 6, 10, 104, p. 136-137
Color: Royal Blue, p. 127
Ornament: Elegance, p. 200
Recipes: Buttercream, Royal Icings, p. 111
Also: Oval Separator Plates (8½, 11½, 14 in. needed), p. 214; Flower Nail No. 7, p. 134; 7 in. Crystal-Look Spiked Pillars (3 pks. needed), p. 215; 8 oz. Meringue Powder (2 cans needed), p. 126; Silver Fanci-Foil Wrap, p. 217; 1½ in. waxed paper squares, triple thick cardboard or ½ in. foam core board

Several days in advance: Using royal icing, make 450 tip 104 roses with tip 10 bases (make bases only ½ to ¾ in. high). Make extras to allow for breakage; let dry.

Prepare cake board and wrap with foil. Ice 2-layer 7¾ x 5⅝ in., 10¾ x 7⅝ in., 13 x 9⅞ in. and 16½ x 12⅜ in. cakes smooth and prepare for Push-In Pillar Construction (p. 110). Attach roses to cake sides with tip 6 dots of icing.

At reception: Assemble cakes and position ornament** on top. Serves 141*.

Note: Always place a separator plate or cake board cut to fit, on the cake before you position any figurine or ornament. This protects both the cake and your keepsake. For extra stability, secure your figurine to the plate with double-stick craft tape.

The perfect accent: *Add the sophisticated style of our Pearl Toasting Glasses Set and Cake Knife and Server Set from p. 204.*

The Moment Endures

Candy plaque cake tops with fondant swags add a sculpted grandeur to square tiers. Candy favors tie the look together.

Pans: 6, 8, 10, 12, 14, 16 x 2 in. Square, 12 x 18 x 2 in. Sheet, p. 159; Petite Loaf, p. 160
Tip: 3, p. 136
Color: Creamy Peach, p. 127
Fondant: White Ready-To-Use Rolled Fondant (96 oz. needed), p. 122; Cutter/Embosser, Easy-Glide Fondant Smoother, Roll & Cut Mat, p. 125
Ornament: Forever In Your Eyes, p. 200
Recipes: Buttercream Icing, p. 111; Candy Clay, p. 112
Also: Tall Tier Cake Stand Basic Set, Cake Corer Tube, p. 213; Plastic Dowel Rods, p. 214; Flower Former Set, p. 134; Floral Collection Flower Making Set, p. 124; Confectionery Tool Set, p. 125; Piping Gel, p. 126; White Candy Melts®† (27 pks. needed), p. 146; Disposable Decorating Bags, p. 134; Wedding Bells Candy Favor Kit, p. 211; Cake Boards, p. 217; wooden skewers, 20 in. square foam core board

A day in advance: Prepare 6 recipes of candy clay; let set at room temperature. Make the following candy plaque (p. 119) cake tops in square pans: one 8 in. (uses 1 pk. Candy Melts) four 10 in., (each uses 2 pks.), one 12 in. (uses 3 pks.) and one 16 in. (uses 8 pks.). Refrigerate until firm and set aside. Also make candy favors. Make candy plaque name cards in Petite Loaf Pan and candy bells using directions in Favor Kit. Refrigerate until firm. Write message using melted candy in cut disposable bag. To make easel back for each favor, cut a Candy Melts wafer rectangle. Attach easel backs and bells to name cards with melted candy and set aside. Make fondant flowers. Tint 12 oz. fondant peach. Using apple blossom cutter from Floral Collection Set, cut 80 peach and 120 white fondant flowers. Place flowers on thick foam and cup centers with small end of ball tool; let dry on small flower formers. Add tip 3 dot icing centers.

Ice smooth 2-layer 6, 10 and 14 in. cakes and prepare for Center Column Construction (p. 110). For bottom tier, bake and cool three 12 x 18 in. cakes. Cut one cake in half to create two 6 x 18 in. cakes; position half cakes next to whole cakes, stacked, to create a 2-layer 18 in. square cake. Ice smooth and insert dowel rods for support.

Knead 12 oz. fondant for each of the 6 prepared candy clay recipes. Cut cake boards 2 in. larger than cakes. Cut holes in center of board to accommodate center column. Roll out candy clay/fondant and cut 4 in. wide strips for edges of boards. Attach strips with Piping Gel, wrapping so that 2 in. of strip is on top and 2 in. on underside of board. Smooth with Easy-Glide Smoother. Make 140 candy clay/fondant strips for sides of cakes. Roll out candy clay/fondant 1/16 in. thick and cut 140 strips, 3/4 x 4 in. Score strips with lattice design, making lines 3/8 in. apart with straight-edge wheel of Cutter/Embosser. Strips can be made about 2 hours before attaching; store on cookie sheet covered with plastic wrap. Attach to cake sides, about 3/4 in. apart.

Using sharp knife, cut holes in center of all candy plaque cake tops except 10 in. plaques, to accommodate center column. For four 10 in. plaques, position side by side to form a 20 in. square; trace center column where corners meet and cut out traced area. Position candy plaque cake tops as follows: 8 in. plaque on 6 in. cake, 12 in. plaque on 10 in. cake, 16 in. plaque on 14 in. cake and four 10 in. plaques on 18 in. cake. Make bottom swags. Cut candy clay/fondant mixture into 1½ in. squares. Form drapes by placing one skewer under bottom edge of square and one on top, next to the first skewer. Repeat with more skewers to form three folds; remove skewers and gather fondant at each end. Trim as needed. Position swags between strips with dots of icing; use veining tool to define folds if needed. For top swags, roll out mixture 1/8 in. thick and cut 3 x 2 in. strips. Repeat draping process used for bottom swags; attach to candy plaque with melted candy. Attach flowers at swag points with melted candy.

At reception: Assemble cake following Center Column instructions (p. 110). Position ornament and favors. Serves 490.*

The perfect accent: *Drink to a glowing future with the Pearl Toasting Glasses Set (p. 204).*

Truffle Tower

A rich chocolate wedding cake feels even more indulgent when topped with three types of dipped truffles.

Pans: 6, 8, 10, 12, 14, 16 x 2 in. Round, p. 158; Sports Ball Set, p. 164
Tip: 789, p. 136
Color: Royal Blue, p. 127
Recipes: Chocolate Buttercream Icing, p. 111; Truffles (22 recipes needed), p. 112
Also: Candy Melts®† in White (1 pk. needed) and Light Cocoa (50 pks. needed), p. 146; Icing Sculptor™, p. 131; Cake Circles: 6 in. (2 needed), 8 in. (5 needed), 10 in. (17 needed), 14 in. (1 needed), 16 in. (3 needed), p. 217; Gold Fanci-Foil Wrap, p. 217; Parchment Triangles, p. 134; Professional Turntable, p. 131; Straight Spatula, p. 134; 16 in. Featherweight Decorating Bag, p. 134; Plastic Dowel Rods, p. 214; 16 in. plywood circle, 8 x 5 in. craft block, chopped walnuts, whipping cream, fresh red roses

In advance: Make the following chocolate-dipped truffles: 149 plain, 175 rolled in chopped walnuts and 202 topped with a swirl using melted white candy in cut parchment bag. Make ⅜ in. thick candy plaques (p. 119) in round pans: one each 8, 12 and 16 in., plus five 10 in. Refrigerate until firm, unmold. Make candy shell (p. 119) bowl ⅜ in. thick, in ball pan half. Refrigerate until firm; unmold.

Ice 2-layer 6, 10 and 14 in. cakes and five 8 in. cakes using Featherweight bag fitted with tip 789. Immediately use Icing Sculptor with U-shaped yellow blade to comb cake sides. Position 6 and 10 in. cakes on same-size foil-wrapped circles; position 14 in. cake on 16 in. foil-wrapped plywood circle and position 8 in. cakes on triple-thick 10 in. foil-wrapped circles. Ice edges of circles around 8 and 14 in. cakes. Prepare cakes for Stacked Construction (p. 110)

At reception: Top each 8 in. satellite cake with an 8 in. cake circle and a 10 in. candy plaque. Position satellite cakes around center craft block. Position 16 in. plywood circle and 14 in. cake on craft block; add 16 in. candy plaque on 14 in. circle, position 10 in. cake on 16 in. plaque, add 12 in. plaque on 10 in. circle, position 6 in. cake on 12 in. plaque, add 8 in. plaque on 6 in. cake, position candy shell bowl on 8 in. plaque. Fill bowl with assorted truffles and position additional truffles on all satellite cake tops and around tiers. Position fresh roses between satellite cakes. Serves 236.*

†Brand confectionery coating.

***Note:** The smallest tier is often saved for the first anniversary. The number of servings given does not include the smallest tier.

FONDANT FUN!

The scrapbooking craze comes to cakes! Why not use fondant, the most versatile icing, the way scrapbookers decorate with paper? With fondant, you can do it all to embellish your cake—cut fun shapes, write messages, stamp fun designs and much more. Just like scrapbooking, anyone can create a special design that makes an amazing memory.

So go ahead and play! We've made it easy for you with some great new products. Pre-colored fondant in a rainbow of shades from neon to natural—you'll never have to add color by hand again! Special icings for writing and drawing. Cool tools like Cut-Outs™ and Cake Stamps™, plus the Cutter/Embosser and Rolling Pin. Find them all on pages 122-125, and look here for the most exciting fondant cakes you've ever seen. Who knew fondant could be so much fun!

A Wild Scene

The normally-conservative sheet cake screams "party!" when you add dazzling fondant designs.

Pan: 12 x 18 x 2 in. Sheet, p. 158
Fondant: White Ready-To-Use Rolled Fondant (48 oz. needed); Primary Multi Pack, p. 122; Round, Square and Alphabet/Number Cut-Outs™, p. 123; Brush-On Color™ in Red, Yellow, Blue and Green, p. 124; Brush Set, Color Tray, Easy-Glide Fondant Smoothers, p. 125
Recipe: Buttercream Icing, p. 111
Also: Cake Board, Fanci-Foil Wrap, p. 217; ruler, toothpicks

Cover 1-layer cake with fondant (p. 105). Roll fondant into a ⅜ in. diameter rope; attach to bottom border with damp brush. Using large and medium Cut-Outs, cut balloons and packages. Using alphabet Cut-Outs, cut message. Attach pieces with damp brush, layering and overlapping some of the shapes to add dimension. Use the Cutter/Embosser to cut strips for the ribbons, cake, candle, icing and cake stand. Cut flame by overlapping two medium circle Cut-Outs and removing the overlap. Mark sides in 3 in. divisions. Wrap 6 x ¼ in. strips around a brush handle to curl; attach strips and ½ in. fondant balls at division points with damp brush. Paint package designs, balloon strings, streamers and confetti with round brush and Brush-On Color. Serves 72.

Candlepower

Our pre-tinted fondant Multi Packs let you go crazy with color without cutting into your decorating time! We've used the Primary and Neon collections to create candles in a host of fun combinations.

Pan: 6, 10 x 2 in. Round, p. 158

Fondant: Ready-To-Use Rolled Fondant in White (24 oz. needed), Pastel Blue (48 oz. needed), Primary and Neon Multi Packs, p. 122; Romantic Cake Stamps, Leaf Cut-Outs™, p. 123; Yellow Brush-On Color™, p. 124; Brush Set, Rolling Pin, Color Tray, Roll & Cut Mat, Easy-Glide Fondant Smoother, p. 125

Recipe: Buttercream Icing, p. 111

Also: Plastic Dowel Rods, p. 214; Cake Board, Fanci-Foil Wrap, p. 217; Rainbow Twist Candles, p. 153; Cake Dividing Set, p. 131; confectioner's sugar, paring knife, black shoestring licorice

Prepare 2-layer cakes for stacked construction (p. 110) and cover with fondant (p. 105). Imprint swirls using Brush-On Color and swirl design Cake Stamp. Divide 10 in. cake in 16ths and 6 in. cake in 10ths. For candles, cut 26 strips, ¾ x 2¼ to 2¾ in. high; trim some tops at an angle and attach with damp brush at division points. Cut shoestring licorice wicks and attach with tip 2 and fondant thinned with water to piping consistency. Cut 26 flames using leaf Cut-Out; attach. Cut strips and tip 8 dots for candle trims; attach. Roll 26 logs for candle bases and 26 balls, ½ in. diameter, for between bases; attach. Roll a ½ in. diameter ball for candle bases on cake top; flatten and insert candles. Serves 40.

Do The Locomotion!

It's the little train that could make any kid's birthday unforgettable! Fondant makes it easy to create the great 3-D mountain effect.

Pan: 10 x 2 in. Round, p. 158

Fondant: Ready-To-Use Rolled Fondant in White (24 oz. needed) and Pastel Blue (48 oz. needed), Multi Packs in Natural and Primary, p. 122; Round, Square and Alphabet/Number Cut-Outs™, p. 123; Bold Tip Primary FoodWriters™, p. 124; Brush Set, Cutter/Embosser, p. 125

Recipe: Buttercream Icing, p. 111

Also: Piping Gel, p. 126; Cake Board, Fanci-Foil Wrap, p. 217; Rainbow Lattice Candles, p. 153

Wrap a 12 in. cake circle in foil and trace a 10 in. circle in the center. Brush outside the circle with Piping Gel and cover brushed area with light brown fondant. Draw tracks ½ in apart with black FoodWriter. Cover 2-layer cake with fondant (p. 105). Add a little white fondant to green; cut fondant mountains with straight-edge wheel of Cutter/Embosser and attach with damp brush. Cut fondant cars with square Cut-Outs—2 large for engine, 1 medium for center and back cars. Trim ¾ in. off engine squares and ⅜ in. off center car. Attach all with damp brush, 1 in. apart, with center and back cars ½ in. from bottom. Cut strips for axles, train linkage, stripes, roof and floors; attach. For cowcatcher and smokestack, cut squares using smallest Cut-Out and cut triangle shapes; attach. Cut windows with smallest square Cut-Out (trim as needed) and wheels with small and medium round Cut-Outs; attach. Roll small balls for wheel centers and candleholders; attach. Roll various size balls for smoke clouds; flatten and attach. Cut message using alphabet Cut-Outs; attach. Position candles. Serves 28.

◀ Guarding The Garden

Nothing sets a scene like flexible fondant! Look at the dimension here, as flowers and leaves tumble over the sides and a neatly cut grass border trims the base.

Pans: 12 x 3 in. Round, p. 158
Tip: 3, p. 136
Fondant:* Ready-To-Use Fondant in White and Pastel Yellow (24 oz. each); Multi Packs in Primary, Natural and Neon, p. 122; Brush-On Color™ in Yellow, Pink and Green, p. 124; Cut-Outs™ in Round, Leaf and Flower, p. 123; Easy-Glide Fondant Smoother, Brush Set, Rolling Pin, Roll & Cut Mat, p. 125
Recipe: Buttercream Icing, p. 111
Also: Cake Board, Fanci-Foil Wrap, p. 217; shoestring licorice.

Cover 3 in. high cake with fondant (p. 105); reserve leftover fondant. Cut ladybugs using round Cut-Outs—large for bodies, medium for heads. Cut ½ in. from body and attach body and head to cake with damp brush. Cut spots using small round Cut-Out; attach. Pipe tip 3 dot eyes in buttercream. Position small fondant balls for pupils. Insert shoestring licorice antennae. Cut 5 large, 9 medium and 9 small fondant flowers using Cut-Outs. Paint large and medium flower centers with lines of Brush-On Color. Roll small balls for centers and attach with damp brush. Attach flowers to cake. Cut fondant leaves using medium and small cut-outs. Paint veins with Brush-On Color and attach next to large and medium flowers. For grass, cut ¾ in. wide strips with ½ in. deep thin slits; dampen uncut edge and attach. Roll logs for letters and attach. Serves 40.

***Note:** Mix 2 oz. neon yellow and ¼ oz. primary yellow with pastel yellow for covering cake; combine 2 oz. of mixture with 1 oz. neon yellow for yellow flowers and 2 oz. of mixture with 1 oz. primary green for leaves.

▶ Always Adored

Flowers she'll remember forever...wide-open fondant blossoms in vibrant colors.

Pan: 8 x 2 in. Square, p. 158
Tip: 3, p. 136
Fondant: White Ready-To-Use Rolled Fondant, Multi Packs in Neon and Primary, p. 122; Geometric Cake Stamps, Funny Flower and Leaf Cut-Outs™, p. 123; Yellow Brush-On Color™, Fine Tip Neon FoodWriters™, p. 124; Brush Set, Cutter/Embosser, p. 125
Recipe: Buttercream Icing, p. 111
Also: Flower Former Set, p. 134; Cake Board, Fanci-Foil Wrap, p. 217

In advance, cut 13 each orange, neon pink, and violet flowers using medium Cut-Out. Roll ¼ in. white ball centers and attach with damp brush. Cut 53 green leaves using smallest leaf Cut-Out. Imprint veins using straight-edge wheel of Cutter/Embosser. Let flowers and leaves dry on flower formers dusted with cornstarch. Cover 3 in. high cake (bake two 1½ in. layers) with rolled fondant (p. 105). Imprint checkerboard pattern using square stamp and Brush-On Color. Roll ½ in. diameter fondant balls and attach to bottom border with damp brush. Attach flowers and leaves using buttercream and tip 3. Write "Mom" using purple FoodWriter. Serves 20.

Tulip Tourists

These irresistible fondant bugs, shaped on sticks, have a birds-eye view of the pretty tulip-stamped cake below.

Pan: 8 x 2 in. Round, p. 158

Fondant:* Ready-To-Use Rolled Fondant in White and Pastel Yellow (24 oz. each), Primary and Neon Multi Packs, p. 122; Nature Cake Stamps, Heart and Leaf Cut-Outs™, p. 123; Brush-On Color™ in Violet and Pink, Bold Tip Primary FoodWriters™, p. 124; Rolling Pin, Brush Set, Color Tray, Cutter/Embosser, Easy-Glide Fondant Smoother, p. 125

Recipe: Buttercream Icing, p. 111

Also: 6 in. Lollipop Sticks, p. 149; Cake Dividing Set, p. 131; black shoestring licorice, cornstarch

In advance: Make insects. For butterfly bodies, roll fondant in an oblong shape and insert on 6 in. lollipop sticks. Insert shoestring licorice antennae on butterflies. For dragonfly body and all insect heads, roll fondant balls and insert on lollipop stick. For outer and inner wings, cut and overlap two hearts using small, medium and large heart Cut-Outs; press centers together. Let insects and wings dry at least 2 days.

Cover 2-layer cake with rolled fondant (p. 105). Divide cake into 16ths using Cake Divider. Imprint tulip at each division point using Cake Stamp and Brush-On Color. Draw stems, leaves, wing details and insect facial features with FoodWriters. Roll out fondant and cut 80 leaves for bottom border and 35 leaves for cake top using small leaf Cut-Out; imprint veins with straight-edge wheel from Cutter/ Embosser. Attach wings to bodies, brushing with fondant which has been thinned with water to piping consistency. Insert insects and position leaves. Serves 20.

***Note:** Combine 2 oz. white fondant with 4 oz. green for leaves, combine 1 oz. white with 2 oz. neon pink and 1 oz. white with 2 oz. violet for insects.

Star Spectrum

An electrifying backdrop of colorful swirls helps these fondant stars shine! Just stamp them on your cake using Romantic Cake Stamps and Yellow Brush-On Color.

Pan: Star, p. 164

Fondant: White Ready-To-Use Rolled Fondant, Primary and Neon Multi Packs, p. 122; Romantic Cake Stamps, Star Cut-Outs™, p. 123; Yellow Brush-On Color™, Bold Tip Primary FoodWriters™, p. 124; Brush Set, Color Tray, Easy-Glide Fondant Smoother, Rolling Pin, p. 125

Recipe: Buttercream Icing, p. 111

Also: 2005 Pattern Book (Center Star), p. 222; Cake Board, Fanci-Foil Wrap, p. 217; confectioner's sugar, paring knife

Combine 4 oz. violet fondant with 20 oz. white fondant and cover cake (p. 105). Imprint swirls using Brush-On Color and swirl design from the Romantic Cake Stamp Set. Using pattern, roll and cut center star; attach with water. Cut out primary color stars using large star Cut-Out; trim portions of some stars to fit around center stars and attach with damp brush. Write message with red FoodWriter. Serves 12.

◀ Pizza Party

A true dessert pizza, with the works...fondant veggies, icing cheese and strawberry preserve sauce on a cake crust.

Pan: 14 x 2 in. Round, p. 158
Color: Orange, p. 127
Fondant: White Ready-To-Use Rolled Fondant (24 oz. needed), Primary and Natural Multi Packs, p. 122; Round Cut-Outs™, p. 123; White Icing Writer™, p. 124; Rolling Pin, Roll & Cut Mat, p. 125
Recipe: Buttercream Icing, p. 111
Also: strawberry preserves

Ice 1 in. high cake smooth. Tint fondant for crust and rim; mix 4 oz. light brown with 45 oz. white (reserve 3 oz. white). For rim, roll a ⅜ in. diameter rope and position on iced cake edge. Cover cake with rolled fondant (p. 105). Add a little orange icing color to strawberry preserves and spread to edge of rim. For sausage, form uneven balls of dark brown fondant. For onions and peppers, cut white and green fondant with large round Cut-Out; cut center with medium round Cut-Out and remove. Cut green rings into 8ths. Position toppings. For cheese, cut a small hole in Icing Writer tip and drizzle over cake. Serves 12.

▶ Life In a Fishbowl

A great example of the way easy-to-make fondant shapes can make a conventional round cake something special.

Pan: 10 x 2 in. Round, p. 158
Fondant:* Ready-To-Use Rolled Fondant in White and Pastel Blue (24 oz. each), Primary and Neon Multi Packs, p. 122; Round and Heart Cut-Outs™, p. 123; Bold Tip Primary FoodWriters™, p. 124; Cutter/Embosser, Rolling Pin, Easy-Glide Fondant Smoother, Roll & Cut Mat, p. 125
Recipe: Buttercream Icing, p. 111
Also: Rainbow Nonpareils Sprinkle Decorations, p. 128; Cake Board, Fanci-Foil Wrap, p. 217

Cut off 1½ in. from the top of 1-layer cake. Cover cake with fondant (p. 105). Brush area for rocks with water. Immediately sprinkle with Rainbow Nonpareils. Cut fish parts using Cut-Outs: large round for body, small heart for side fin and mouth, medium heart for top and back fins and small round for eye. Trim hearts to fit. Also cut ¼ in. wide strips for stripes. Imprint lines on top and back fins with straight-edge wheel from Cutter/Embosser. Attach all parts with damp brush. Draw pupil with black FoodWriter. For seaweed, cut free-form waves and imprint center veins with straight-edge wheel from Cutter/Embosser. Cut again to conform to shapes of fish, using heart and round Cut-Outs and attach to cake with damp brush. For coral, roll ⅛ in. thin ropes of fondant and attach in branch fashion. Roll 8½ in. long x ½ in. diameter rope and attach for top rim. Roll small balls for bubbles and attach. Serves 20.

***Note:** Combine small amounts of neon pink with white fondant for pink seaweed shown.

◀ Scrapbook Mania!

With fondant, it's easy to personalize the perfect birthday cake, scrapbook style.

Pan: 2-Mix Book, p. 163
Fondant: White Ready-To-Use Rolled Fondant (48 oz. needed), Fondant Multi Packs in Primary, Natural and Neon, p. 122; Cut-Outs™ in Star, Square, Round and People, p. 123; Fine Tip Neon FoodWriters™, p. 124; Cutter/Embosser, Rolling Pin, Roll & Cut Mat, p. 125
Recipe: Buttercream Icing, p. 111
Also: Decorating Comb, p. 131; Cake Board, Fanci-Foil Wrap, p. 217; ruler, straight pin

Ice cake smooth (ice sides thick) and comb with decorating comb. Cover top with rolled fondant (p. 105). Lighten blue, green, pink and purple fondant with a little white. Using Cutter/Embosser, cut out various size photo spaces from cake top; cut out and position same-size fondant rectangles in various colors. For photo borders and top cake border, use wavy-edge wheel of Cutter/Embosser to cut ¼ in. wide strips and attach with water. Cut faces and clothes using people Cut-Outs; attach with damp brush. Cut thin strips for hair, wind around toothpick and attach. Cut squares to fit for cake and gifts in pictures; add strips for icing, candle and flame; attach. Cut balloons, stars and remaining gifts using small round, star and square Cut-Outs. Attach small strips for bows. Using FoodWriters, print messages and draw confetti and balloon strings. For bottom border, roll a ½ in. diameter rope and position around cake. Serves 24.

▶ Meet Your Goal!

Honor your team with a cake featuring their true uniform colors, using the many fondant shades available in our Primary, Natural and Neon Multi Packs.

Pans: 12 x 18 x 2 in. Sheet, p. 158
Fondant: Ready-To-Use Rolled Fondant in White (24 oz. needed) and Pastel Green (48 oz. needed), Fondant Multi Packs in Primary (2 pks. needed), Natural and Neon, p. 122; People and Alphabet/Number Cut-Outs™, p. 123; Bold Tip Primary FoodWriters™, p. 124; Brush Set, Rolling Pin, Roll & Cut Mat, Easy-Glide Fondant Smoother, p. 125
Recipe: Buttercream Icing, p. 111
Also: Soccer Balls Candles (2 pks.),p. 154; 101 Cookie Cutters, p. 142; 13 x 19 in. Cake Boards, Fanci-Foil Wrap, p. 217; craft knife, ruler

Cover cake with rolled fondant (p. 105). Cut ½ in. wide strips for field markings and attach with water. Cut center circle using large round Cut-Out; cut open center with medium round Cut-Out; attach with damp brush. Using people Cut-Outs, cut heads and clothes; use foot cutter to cut strips for hands, socks and legs, trimming as needed. For curly hair, cut 1/16 x ½ in. strips and wrap around a toothpick to curl; attach. For straight hair, cut tiny strips and imprint strands with straight-edge wheel of Cutter/Embosser. Attach players with damp brush. For grass, cut 2 x ¾ in. wide strips, then cut fringed ends, ¼ in. deep, leaving bottom edge uncut. Attach around bottom border. Cut letters using Cut-Outs; attach. Position candles. Serves 72.

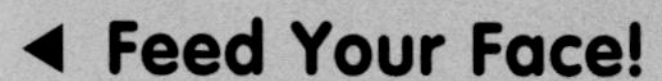

◄ Feed Your Face!

Serving kids personalized cupcakes that look like them? Priceless! And they look even cooler sitting on our new Cupcakes 'N More Dessert Stand.

Pan: Standard Muffin, p. 160
Fondant: Neon and Natural Multi Packs, p. 122; Round Cut-Outs™, p. 123; Fine Tip Neon FoodWriters, p. 124; Rolling Pin, Roll & Cut Mat, Brush Set, Cutter/Embosser, p. 125
Recipe: Buttercream Icing, p. 111
Also: White Standard Baking Cups, p. 150; Cupcakes 'N More™ Dessert Stand, p. 130; paring knife, cornstarch

In advance: Make fondant faces and hair. Cut faces using pink fondant from Natural Multi Pack and large and medium round Cut-Outs. For curly hair, cut ⅛ in. strips of fondant and wrap around brush handle; attach to head with damp brush. For spiky hair, cut ½ in. to 1 in. high fondant strips; cut fringed ends with paring knife, leaving bottom edge uncut; attach. Cut straight hair using paring knife; attach. Roll small balls. Let dry overnight on cornstarch-dusted surface. Draw facial features with black and pink FoodWriters. Ice cupcakes smooth in buttercream. Position heads. Each serves 1.

► Headed For A Party!

It's a portrait on a plate! Every kid at the party can see their face in their cake...with fondant, it's easy to add personal touches like glasses, bows and curly hair.

Pan: Mini Ball, p. 164
Fondant:* White Ready-To-Use Rolled Fondant (24 oz. needed), Neon, Natural and Primary Multi Packs, p. 122; Round and Star Cut-Outs™, p. 123; Brush Set, Rolling Pin, Roll & Cut Mat, Cutter/Embosser, p. 125
Recipe: Buttercream Icing, p. 111
Also: Cake Board, Fanci-Foil Wrap, p. 217, craft knife, ruler

Cover cakes with rolled fondant (p. 105). For mouths and lips, use medium round Cut-Out to cut a circle and then an arc from the circle; imprint lips with Cutter/Embosser. For tongues, press together two small balls to form a heart shape. Cut eyes and cheeks with small round Cut-Out. Roll small balls for noses, pupils and freckles. For ears, roll balls; shape edge and press inner ear flat with brush handle. For hair, cut strips with straight-edge wheel of Cutter/Embosser; for curly hair, wrap strips around brush handle. For glasses, roll 1 in. diameter ropes and form round frames and strips for ear pieces and bridge. For bow, cut 1 x 5 in. strip, join ends and pinch at center. Wrap around a ½ in. wide strip for knot. For sunglasses, cut black lenses and orange frames with medium star Cut-Out. Cut center of frames with small Cut-Out. Cut strips for earpieces and bridge. Attach all pieces with damp brush. Each serves 1.

***Note:** Combine white fondant with neon pink for shade shown on tongues, lips and cheeks.

◀ Mini Heart Art

Express yourself on cakes with different colors and designs for every guest. Twisted strips, quilted textures, flowing bows and pretty flowers are just some of the exciting styles you can choose.

Pan: Mini Heart, p. 176

Fondant: White Ready-To-Use Rolled Fondant (24 oz. needed), Pastel and Neon Multi Packs (3 oz. needed to cover each cake; you may need individual 24 oz. pks. of pastel fondant to cover desired number of cakes), p. 122; Heart, Leaf and Funny Flower Cut-Outs™, p. 123; Icing Writer™ in Pink and Yellow, p. 124; Brush Set, Cutter/Embosser, p. 125

Recipe: Buttercream Icing, p. 111

Also: Colored Sugars in Pink, Orange and Green, White Cake Sparkles™, p. 128

Cover Mini Heart cakes with various colors of pastel fondant. For pink heart, immediately imprint diagonal lines using ridged wheel of Cutter/Embosser. For the bow heart cut ⅜ in. wide strips to make ribbon, loops and streamers; cut V-shape in streamers. Roll a small ball for knot and attach all pieces with damp brush. For other cake centers, cut fondant pieces using small, medium and large heart and flower Cut-Outs. Most designs use stacked shapes, for light blue cake, cut a large white heart with a medium size open center and position over a medium green heart. After cutting some shapes, immediately brush with water and sprinkle with Cake Sparkles or Colored Sugars. Cut ¼ in. wide strips for sides of some designs; twist strips on light blue heart. Roll fondant balls for bottom borders. Attach all pieces with damp brush. Add dot flower centers with Icing Writer. Each serves 1.

▶ Cute Quilt

The quilt cake gets its puffed texture from our Cutter/Embosser—just roll diagonally across each square.

Pan: 12 x 2 in. Square, p. 159

Fondant: White Ready-To-Use Rolled Fondant (48 oz. needed); Pastel Multi Packs (2 pks. needed), p. 122; Square Cut-Outs™, Baby Cake Stamps, p. 123; Brush-On Color™ in Yellow, Pink and Blue, p. 124; Cutter/Embosser, Rolling Pin, Roll & Cut Mat, Brush Set, Color Tray, Easy-Glide Fondant Smoother, p. 125

Recipe: Buttercream Icing, p. 111

Also: ruler

Ice 1-layer cake smooth. Cover top with a 12 in. white fondant square. Cut nine 4 in. quilt squares: 2 each in blue, pink and green, 3 in yellow. Attach to cake top with damp brush. Immediately imprint stitching lines, ¾ in. apart, with ridged wheel of Cutter/Embosser. Cut white squares for each section using large square Cut-Out; attach. Stamp designs using Baby Cake Stamps and Brush-On Color. For top border, cut ¾ in. wide strips in all pastel colors; cut ½ in. slits for fringe; cut 1 in. pieces of each color and attach. For bottom border, twist two ¼ in. diameter ropes and attach. Serves 48.

Floral Dimensions

Here's a showstopping way to present a floral cake—stack coordinating pastel petals to create blossoms with incredible texture. It's easy to do with our new Cut-Out cutters.

Pans: 6, 10 x 2 in. Round, p. 158; Mini Ball, p. 164

Fondant: Ready-To-Use Rolled Fondant in White, Pastel Yellow and Pastel Pink (24 oz. each needed), Pastel and Neon Multi Packs, p. 122; Flower and Leaf Cut-Outs™, p. 123; Cutter/Embosser, Rolling Pin, Roll & Cut Mat, Easy-Glide Fondant Smoother, p. 125

Recipe: Buttercream Icing, p. 111

Also: Plastic Dowel Rods, p. 214; Flower Former Set, p. 134; 12 in. Round Silver Cake Base, p. 217, cornstarch

In advance: Make pastel flowers for cake topper: cut 20 each using medium and small Flower Cut-Outs. With damp brush, attach small flowers to center of medium flowers. Roll small balls for centers and attach. Let dry in small flower formers dusted with cornstarch. Prepare 2-layer round cakes for Stacked Construction (p. 110) and position on cake base. Cover round cakes and a mini ball cake for topper with rolled fondant (p. 105). For cake sides, cut flowers with Cut-Outs: 15 large white, 35 medium white, 15 medium colored, 50 small colored. Attach flowers to cake as each is made, attaching smaller size flowers to centers of each flower. Roll small balls for centers and attach. Cut 200 leaves using small Leaf Cut-Out; imprint veins with straight-edge wheel from Cutter/Embosser. Attach topper flowers and all leaves with buttercream. Serves 41.

Step-By-Step

Decorating Guide

Decorating help is here. Whatever cake you want to make from this Yearbook, you'll find out how to make it happen on the following pages. Whether you're creating a cake for the first time, or need a quick brush-up on a technique, it's easy to use this handy guide as you decorate.

Want to learn more?

For up-close, in depth instructions on decorating, register on-line for Wilton Cake Decorating classes in your area or at the Wilton School at **www.wilton.com.** Our website is also a great place to see decorating techniques, find recipes and chat with other decorators. Visit us regularly!

Cake Preparation

Think of your cake as the canvas on which you will create beautiful icing decorations. To achieve the masterpiece you want, it is essential that your canvas be smooth and free of crumbs. These steps for preparing and icing your cake will result in the perfectly smooth decorating surface essential for your work of art.

BAKING THE CAKE

Follow recipe directions for specific baking instructions and recommended batter amounts for the pan size you choose.
HINT: To help cakes rise high, add 1 to 2 Tablespoons Meringue Powder (p. 126) to each boxed two-layer cake mix.

Prepare the pan by generously greasing the inside using a pastry brush or paper towel and solid vegetable shortening. For best results, do not use butter, margarine or liquid vegetable oil. Spread the shortening so that all indentations are covered. Sprinkle about 2 Tablespoons of flour inside the pan and shake so that the flour covers all greased surfaces. Turn pan upside down and tap lightly to remove excess flour. If any uncovered spots remain, touch up with shortening and flour. Or use Bake Easy™ Non-Stick Spray or Cake Release (p. 129) to coat the pan—no grease or flour needed. Pour batter into pan and place in pre-heated oven.

After cake has baked the specified time, remove it from the oven and let it cool in the pan on a cake rack for 10 minutes. Run a thin knife between the cake and side of the pan. Unmold from pan by placing cooling rack against cake and turning both cooling rack and pan over. Lift pan off carefully. Cool at least one hour and brush off loose crumbs prior to icing.

CUTTING AND WRAPPING THE CAKE BOARD

For round, square and sheet cakes, you don't need to cut the cake board. Simply use a board that is 2 in. larger than your cake. (For example, if the cake is 8 in. diameter, buy a 10 in. round board.) For shaped cakes, cut a board to fit: Turn the pan upside down and trace onto your cake board, leaving 1 in. extra around the edges. Cut board with a craft knife.

Next, trace the cut board onto Fanci-Foil Wrap, making the outline 3-4 in. larger than the board. Cut Fanci-Foil along the outline. Place your board, white side down, on top of your cut foil. Cut deep slits at several points along foil edge, creating tabs of foil to wrap neatly around the board. Secure foil tabs to the board with tape.

LEVELING THE CAKE

After the cake has cooled at least one hour, you'll need to level the top of the cake. This can be done in one of two ways.

Using a Serrated Knife

Place the cake on a cake board, then place the board on a Trim 'n Turn Cake Stand (p. 131). While slowly rotating the stand, move the knife back and forth across the top of cake in a sawing motion to remove the crown. Try to keep knife level as you cut.

Using the Wilton Cake Leveler

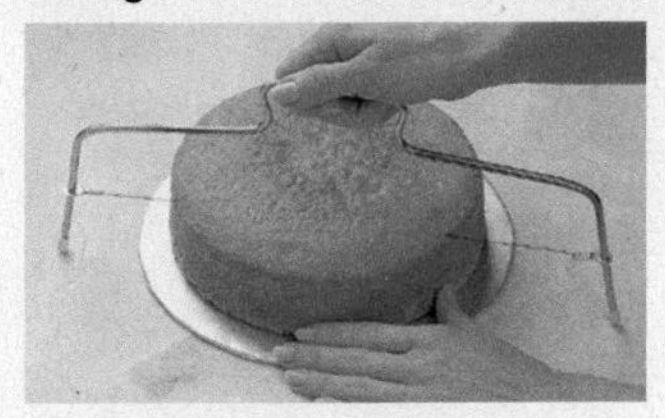

Position the ends of the cutting wire (or feet on large leveler) into the notches at the desired height. With legs standing on the work surface, cut into the crusted edge using an easy sawing motion, then proceed by gently gliding through the cake.

TORTING THE CAKE

A serrated knife or the Cake Leveler (p. 129) also may be used to cut a cake into multiple layers. Torting adds extra height, drama and taste to the cake when the layers are filled with icing, pudding or fruit filling.

Using a Serrated Knife

Measure cake sides and mark with dots of icing or toothpicks all around. Place one hand on top of the cake to hold it steady and rotate the stand. While slowly turning the cake, move the knife back and forth to cut the cake along the measured marks. Repeat for each additional layer.

Using the Cake Leveler

Torting is easily accomplished with the Cake Leveler. Simply follow the same directions as for leveling.

Separating the Layers

Carefully slide the top torted layer onto a cake board to keep it rigid and safe from breakage. Repeat for each additional layer to bottom.

FILLING THE LAYERS

Fill a decorating bag with medium consistency icing and use a large round tip, like tip 12. Or simply use the coupler without mounting a tip.

Starting with the bottom layer, leveled side up, create a dam of icing just inside the edge of the cake (about ¾ in. high and ¼ inch from the outside edge). Fill with icing, preserves or pudding. Place next layer on top, level; repeat. Finish with top layer leveled side down.

ICING THE CAKE

Using a Spatula

The trick to keeping crumbs out of your icing is gliding your spatula on the icing—never allow it to touch the surface of the cake. Place a large amount of thin consistency icing on the center of the cake top. Spread across the top, pushing toward edges.

Smooth the top using the edge of the spatula. Sweep the edge of the spatula from the rim of the cake to its center. Then lift it off and remove excess icing.

Cover the sides with icing. Smooth sides first by holding the spatula upright with the edge against the side, slowly spinning the turntable without lifting the spatula from the cake's surface. Return excess icing to the bowl and repeat until sides are smooth.

Rotate the cake slightly and repeat the procedure, starting from a new point on the rim until you have covered the entire top surface. Smooth the center of the cake by leveling the icing with the edge of your spatula. For easier smoothing, it may help to dip the spatula into hot water, wipe dry and glide it across the entire surface. Set the cake aside and allow the icing to crust over for at least 15 minutes before decorating. At this point you may also lay Non-Stick Parchment Paper (p. 129) on the iced cake top and gently smooth with the palm of your hand.

Using a Decorating Tip

Trim a 16 in. Featherweight bag to fit tip 789. Fill bag half full with icing. Hold bag at 45° angle and lightly press tip against cake. Squeeze a ribbon of icing in a continuous spiral motion to cover cake top, with last ribbon forcing icing over edge of cake top.

To ice the sides, squeeze icing as you turn the cake slowly. Repeat the process until the entire cake side is covered.

Smooth sides and top with spatula, same as above.

Using Rolled Fondant

The dough-like consistency of fondant makes it the perfect medium for creating ruffles and braids, stately molded accents, distinctive borders, fun trims and beautiful flowers. Decorators agree that fondant is an icing that is truly easy to work with. It's even easier with Wilton Ready-To-Use Rolled Fondant—no mixing, no mess!

COVERING THE CAKE

First determine the diameter you need to cover your cake. Measure opposite sides and top of cake across center; roll out fondant to that size, ¼ inch thick. For example, an 8 in., two-layer cake, with two sides each 4 in., equals 16 in. diameter. For simple, accurate measuring, roll out the fondant on top of Cake Dividing Wheel included in Cake Dividing Set (p. 131). (Fondant shown below has been tinted with Icing Colors.)

1. Prepare cake by lightly covering with buttercream icing.

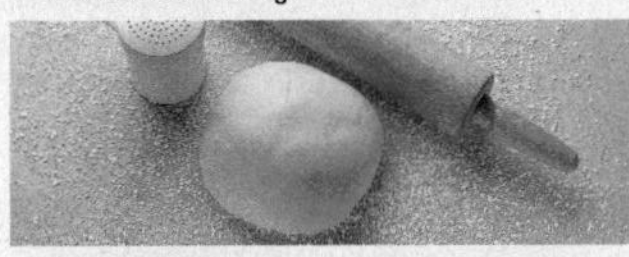

2. Before rolling out fondant, knead until it is a workable consistency. If fondant is sticky, knead in a little confectioner's sugar. Lightly dust smooth work surface and rolling pin with confectioner's sugar to prevent sticking.

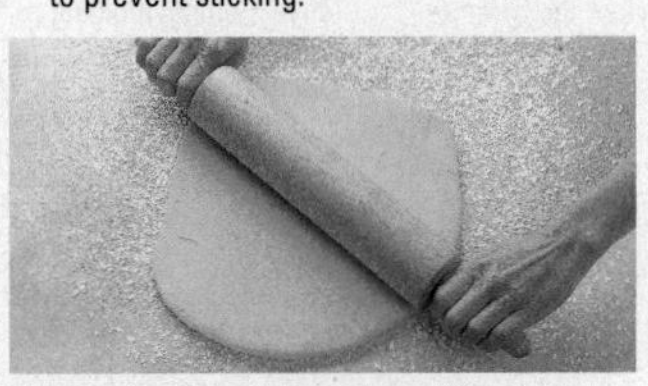

3. Roll out fondant sized to your cake (see amounts at right). Roll fondant with rolling pin, lifting and moving as you roll. Add more confectioner's sugar if necessary.

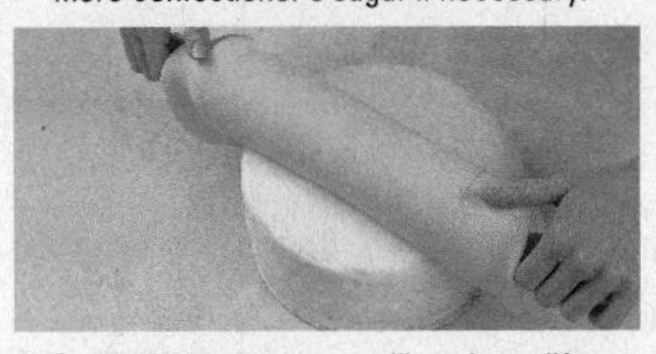

4. Gently lift fondant over rolling pin, or lift with the support of both hands, taking care not to tear it with your fingernails. Position on cake. If tear develops, pinch together.

5. Smooth and shape fondant on cake using Easy-Glide Smoother (p. 125). Beginning in the middle of the cake top, move the smoother outward and down the sides to smooth and shape fondant to cake and remove air bubbles. If an air bubble appears, pop it with a pin and smooth area again.

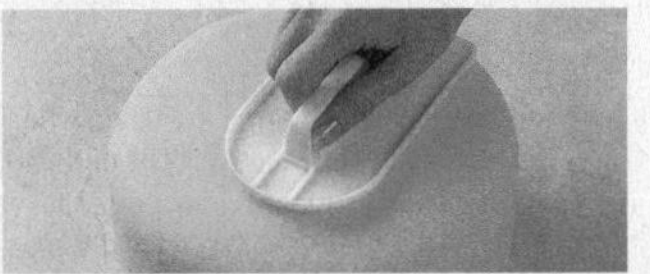

COVERING LARGE CAKES

In most cases, the smaller your cake, the easier it will be to cover with rolled fondant. However, there is an easy way to position and smooth fondant on cakes that are 12 in. diameter or larger. Follow the steps below to lift fondant onto the cake without tearing.

1. Cover cake lightly with buttercream icing. Roll out fondant sized to fit your cake.

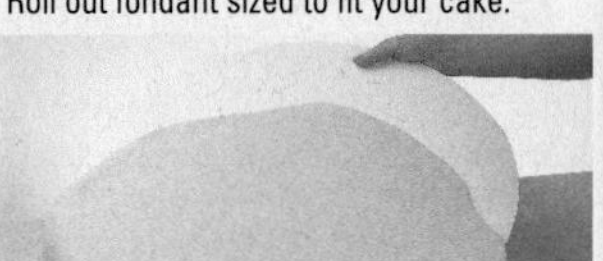

2. Slide a large cake board that has been dusted with confectioner's sugar under the rolled fondant. Lift the board and the fondant and position over cake. Gently shake the board to slide the fondant off and into position on the cake. Smooth and trim as described at left.

FONDANT AMOUNTS

Use this chart to determine how much Ready-To-Use Rolled Fondant to buy. Wilton Fondant is available in 24 oz. (1 lb. 8 oz.) or 80 oz. (5 lb.) packages. Amounts listed do not include decorations.

Cake size:		Use this amount:
Rounds 4 in. high	6 in.	18 oz.
	8 in.	24 oz.
	10 in.	36 oz.
	12 in.	48 oz.
	14 in.	72 oz.
	16 in.	108 oz.
Rounds 3 in. high	6 in.	14 oz.
	8 in.	18 oz.
	10 in.	24 oz.
	12 in.	36 oz.
	14 in.	48 oz.
	16 in.	72 oz.
Ovals 4 in. high	7 in.	24 oz.
	13 x 9 in.	48 oz.
	10 x 7 in.	48 oz.
	16 x 12 in.	72 oz.
Hearts 4 in. high	6 in.	18 oz.
	8 in.	24 oz.
	9 in.	34 oz.
	10 in.	36 oz.
	12 in.	48 oz.
	14 in.	72 oz.
	15 in.	72 oz.
	16 in.	96 oz.
Petals 4 in. high	6 in.	18 oz.
	9 in.	30 oz.
	12 in.	48 oz.
	15 in.	72 oz.
Squares 4 in. high	6 in.	24 oz.
	8 in.	36 oz.
	10 in.	48 oz.
	12 in.	72 oz.
	14 in.	96 oz.
	16 in.	120 oz.
Hexagons 4 in. high	6 in.	18 oz.
	9 in.	36 oz.
	12 in.	48 oz.
	15 in.	84 oz.

HOW TO COLOR AND FLAVOR FONDANT

Wilton Ready-To-Use Rolled Fondant is now available in favorite colors. You may also easily tint our White fondant or the Rolled Fondant recipe (p. 111) using Wilton Icing Colors (p. 127). Add icing color, using toothpick, a little at a time and knead into fondant until color is evenly blended. Wilton Ready-to-Use Rolled Fondant has a mellow flavor which can be enhanced using Wilton Butter Flavor, Clear Vanilla Extract or Almond Extract (p. 126). Knead flavor into icing until well blended.

Icing Basics

In this section, we've listed general descriptions of icings, their uses, qualities and consistencies. Use this information to determine the right icing for your cake. Refer to our recipes for homemade icings on page 111, along with color instructions below, to create the look and taste you want.

ICING USAGE GUIDE

Icing Type	Flavor/Description	Consistency	Best Used For...	Coloring	Storage/Freshness	Special Information
Buttercream (Wilton Mix or homemade)	Sweet, buttery flavor. Tastes/looks great for most decorating.	Thin-to-stiff depending on amount of corn syrup or sugar added (sugar stiffens).	Icing cakes smooth. Borders, writing, flowers, decorations.	Yields all colors. Most deepen upon setting. Let set 2-3 hours for deep color. Some may fade in bright light.	Can be refrigerated in airtight container for 2 weeks. Iced cake—stored at room temperature for 2-3 days.	Flowers remain soft enough to be cut with a knife.
Snow-White Buttercream (homemade)	Sweet, almond flavor. Ideal for wedding cakes.	Thin-to-stiff depending on amount of corn syrup or sugar added (sugar stiffens).	Icing cakes smooth. Borders, writing, flowers, decorations.	Yields truer colors due to pure white base color. Creates deep colors. Most colors deepen upon setting.	Can be refrigerated in airtight container for 2 weeks. Iced cake—stored at room temperature for 2-3 days.	Air-dried flowers have translucent look. Flowers remain soft enough to be cut with knife.
Wilton Ready-to-Use Decorator White	Sweet, vanilla flavor. Convenient, ready-to-spread icing. Pure white color ideal for tinting.	Medium-to-stiff. Make roses right from the can.	Shells, stars, flowers—use from container. Icing cakes, writing, leaves—thin with milk, water or corn syrup.	Yields truer colors due to pure white base color. Creates deep colors. Most colors deepen upon setting.	Leftover icing can be refrigerated for 2 weeks. Iced cake—stored at room temperature for 2-3 days.	Available for purchase through Wilton Yearbook or any authorized Wilton retailer.
Wilton Ready-to-Use Decorator Chocolate	Sweet chocolate flavor. Convenient ready-to-spread icing.	Medium-to-stiff. Make roses right from the can.	Shells, stars, flowers—use from container. Icing cakes, writing, leaves—thin with milk, water or corn syrup.	Recommended when black or brown icing is needed. Add a little black icing color to chocolate for a better tasting black icing.	Leftover icing can be refrigerated for 2 weeks. Iced cake—stored at room temperature for 2-3 days.	Available for purchase through Wilton Yearbook or any authorized Wilton retailer.
Royal (Made with Wilton Meringue Powder)	Very sweet flavor. Dries candy-hard for lasting decorations.	Thin-to-stiff, depending on the amount of water added.	Flower-making, figure piping, making flowers on wires. Decorating cookies and gingerbread houses.	Yields deep colors. Some colors may fade sitting in bright light. Requires more icing color than buttercream to achieve the same intensity.	Icing can be stored in airtight, grease-free container at room temperature for 2 weeks. Air-dried decorations last for months.	Bowls/utensils must be grease-free. Cover icing with damp cloth to prevent crusting.
Rolled Fondant (Wilton Ready-to-Use or homemade Rolled Fondant)	Covers cakes with a perfectly smooth, satiny iced surface. Easy and fast to use. Knead in flavor of your choice.	Dough-like. Is rolled out before applying to cake. Stays semi-soft on cakes.	Any firm pound or fruit cake. Cutting, molding and modeling decorations.	White yields pastels to deep colors. Wilton pre-colored fondant is also available in favorite pastel shades and in Multi-Packs for fondant decorations in a variety of colors.	Excess can be stored 2 months in an airtight container. Do not refrigerate or freeze. Iced cake—stored at room temperature for 3-4 days.	Prior to applying fondant, cake must be lightly covered in a glaze and/or buttercream icing to seal in freshness and moisture.
Whipped Icing Mix (Wilton Mix)	Light, delicate vanilla flavor. Holds shape like no other mix. **For chocolate icing**, add ½ cup of sifted cocoa powder.	Velvety, perfect for stars, roses, borders, garlands and writing	Icing cakes. Most decorations. Toppings on pies, puddings, tarts and more.	Yields any color.	Can be refrigerated in airtight container. Iced cake—stored at room temperature for 2-3 days.	Exclusive Wilton formula. Available for purchase through Wilton Yearbook or Wilton retailer.
Fluffy Boiled Icing (homemade)	Marshmallow-like flavor. 100% fat-free.	Very fluffy. Sets quickly.	Icing cakes smooth and fluffy. Borders, figure piping, writing, stringwork.	Yields pastels to deep colors.	Use immediately. Iced cake can be stored at room temperature.	Serve within 24 hours.
Stabilized Whipped Cream (homemade)	Creamy, delicate sweetness.	Light, thin-to-medium.	All cakes but especially those decorated with fruits. Borders, large tip work, writing.	Yields pastels only.	Use immediately. Iced cake must be refrigerated.	Texture remains soft on decorated cake.
Ice Cream Mix	Rich, creamy taste	Perfect texture for spreading and decorating right after mixing. Holds its shape for borders or decorations.	Icing and filling cakes. Star and rosette borders, lattice. Great for layer cakes, cake rolls, ice cream sandwiches and pies.	Pure white color. Yields any color. Add color during whipping.	Can be stored up to 30 days in freezer in an airtight container.	Available for purchase through Wilton Yearbook or any authorized Wilton dealer.

COLORING ICING

Using Colors

Choosing appropriate colors for your cake will help you capture the mood you want for the occasion. When planning your cake, think about color. Gather inspiration from the theme of your celebration. The icing colors you choose will carry that theme and personalize your decorating. Look around, notice everyday objects—from a garden in bloom, to the clothes people wear. Which colors appeal to you? Use your favorite colors in your decorating. Don't be afraid to try something different. Have fun using rich, bright colors or different color combinations. Begin by making a monochromatic cake, decorated all in white or in a single, pale color. Try using color decorations in contrast to an all-white cake background. Decorate using all pastels or all primary colors. Experimenting with color will help you decide which colors work to make your cake designs spectacular!

Mixing Colors

Begin with white icing and use concentrated Icing Colors (p. 127) which will not affect your icing consistency. Using standard food colors can thin your icing and affect your ability to pipe certain decorations. If you are tinting icing dark brown or black, begin with chocolate icing—your icing will not have the aftertaste that large amounts of icing color may produce. If you are tinting a large area red, use No-Taste Red.

Dip a toothpick into the color, then swirl it into the icing. Add color a little at a time until you achieve the shade you desire. Always use a new toothpick each time you add color; you want to avoid getting icing into your jar of color. Blend the icing well with a spatula.

Consider the type of icing you are using when mixing color. Icing colors intensify or darken in buttercream icing about 1-2 hours after mixing. Royal icing requires more color than buttercream icing to achieve the same color intensity.

Always mix enough of each icing color to complete your entire cake. For example, if you are going to decorate a cake with pink flowers and borders, color enough icing for both. It is difficult to duplicate an exact shade of any color, an important fact if you want to keep colors consistent on your cake.

Bag Striping Effects:

You can easily pipe two-tone decorations just by adding a different color inside the bag before you put in your tinted icing. This is how you pipe flowers with natural light and dark tones or make a rainbow-colored clown suit to brighten up the party.

Brush Striping

Produces more intense multiple colors because it is done with straight icing color brushed into the bag. Apply one or more stripes of icing color with a decorating brush, then fill the bag with white or pastel-colored icing. As the icing is squeezed past the color, decorations will come out striped.

Spatula Striping

Produces two-tone and realistic pastel tones in flowers and figure piping. It is done with pastel-colored icing, striped inside the decorating bag with a spatula. After striping, fill the bag with white icing or another shade of the same color as the striping. Squeeze out decorations with soft contrasts.

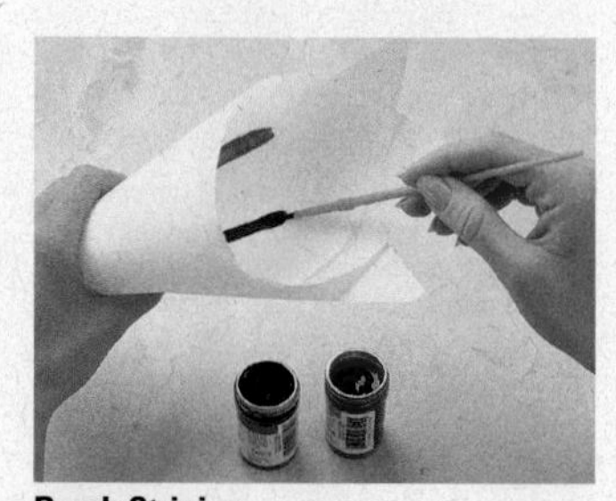

Brush Striping

Spatula Striping

The 3 Essentials of Cake Decorating

Every decoration you make is the result of three things working together: the consistency of your icing, the position of the bag (that is, the way you are holding it) and the amount and type of pressure you apply to the bag. You'll know when you have everything right because you'll get perfect results time after time. This will take practice. The more you concentrate on perfecting these three essentials, the sooner you will achieve perfect results.

ICING CONSISTENCY

If the consistency of your icing is not right, your decorations will not be right either. Just a few drops of liquid can make a great deal of difference in your decorating results. Many factors can affect icing consistency, such as humidity, temperature, ingredients and equipment. You may try using different icing consistencies when decorating to determine what works for you. As a general guideline, if you are having trouble creating the decorations you want and you feel your icing is too thin, add a little more confectioner's sugar; if you feel your icing is too thick, add a little more liquid. In royal icing recipes, if adding more than ½ cup confectioner's sugar to thicken icing, also add 1-2 additional teaspoons of Meringue Powder.

Stiff icing is used for decorations such as flowers with upright petals, like roses, carnations and sweet peas. Stiff icing also creates figure piping and stringwork. If icing is not stiff enough, flower petals will droop. If icing cracks when piped out, icing is probably too stiff. Add light corn syrup to icing used for stringwork to give strings greater elasticity so they will not break.

Medium icing is used for decorations such as stars, borders and flowers with flat petals. If the icing is too stiff or too thin, you will not get the uniformity that characterizes these decorations.

Thin icing is used for decorations such as printing and writing, vines and leaves. Leaves will be pointier, vines will not break and writing will flow easily if you add 1-2 teaspoons light corn syrup to each cup of icing. Thin icing is used to ice cakes smooth. Begin with your prepared icing recipe, then add small amounts of the same liquid used in the recipe (usually milk or water) until the proper spreading consistency is reached.

CORRECT BAG POSITION

The way your decorations curl, point and lie depends not only on icing consistency but also on the way you hold the bag and the way you move it. Bag positions are described in terms of both angle and direction.

Angle

Angle refers to the position of the bag relative to the work surface. There are two basic angle positions, 90° (straight up) and 45° (halfway between vertical and horizontal).

90° angle
or straight up, perpendicular to the surface.

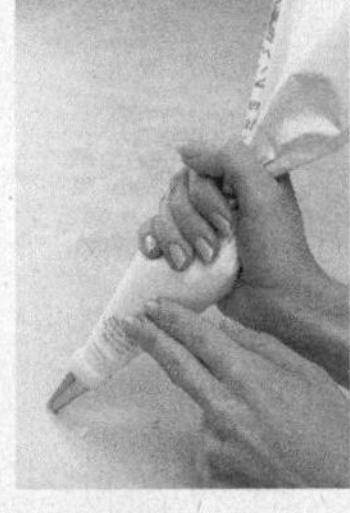

45° angle
or halfway between vertical and horizontal.

Direction

The angle in relation to the work surface is only half the story on bag position. The other half is the direction in which the back of the bag is pointed.

Correct bag direction is easiest to learn when you think of the back of the bag as the hour hand of a clock. When you hold the bag at a 45° angle to the surface, you can sweep out a circle with the back end of the bag by rolling your wrist and holding the end of the tip in the same spot. Pretend the circle you formed in the air is a clock face. The hours on the clock face correspond to the direction you point the back end of the bag.

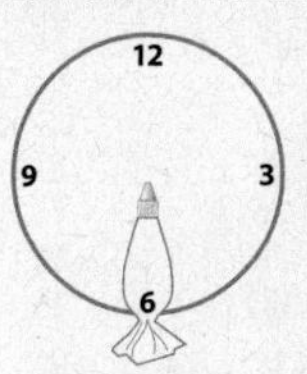

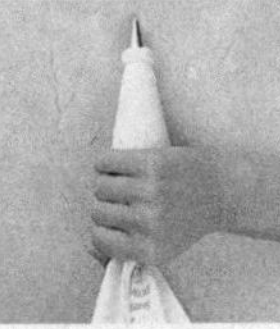

Back of bag at 6:00

Back of bag at 3:00

The technique instructions in this Decorating Guide will list the correct direction for holding the bag. When the bag direction differs for left-handed decorators, that direction will be listed in parentheses. For example, when a bag is to be held at 3:00 for a right-handed decorator, it should be held at 9:00 for a left-handed decorator.

One more thing: since most decorating tip openings are the same shape all the way around, there's no right side and wrong side up when you're squeezing icing out of them. However, some tips, such as petal, ruffle, basketweave and leaf have irregularly shaped openings. For those you must watch your tip position as well as your bag position. If the tip opening must be in a special position, the instructions will tell you.

PRESSURE CONTROL

In addition to having the proper icing consistency and the correct bag position, you'll need to master three types of pressure control: heavy, medium and light. The size and uniformity of your icing design are affected by the amount of pressure you apply to the bag and the steadiness of that pressure. (In other words, how you squeeze and relax your grip on the decorating bag). Your goal is to learn to apply pressure so consistently that you can move the bag in a free and easy glide while just the right amount of icing flows through the tip. Practice will help you achieve this control.

Heavy Pressure **Medium Pressure** **Light Pressure**

Storing Cakes

Take some final precautions and store your cake the best way possible. After all, your time, effort and creativity have made it very special! Beware of the following factors, which can affect the look of your decorated cake:

Sunlight will alter icing colors. Keep your cake stored in a covered box and out of direct sunlight.

Humidity can soften royal icing and gum paste decorations. If you live in a climate with high humidity, prepare your royal icing using only pure cane confectioner's sugar (not beet sugar or dextrose), add less liquid and add 1 more teaspoon Meringue Powder (p. 126) to the recipe.

Heat can melt icing and cause decorations to droop. Keep your decorated cake as cool as possible and stabilize buttercream icing by adding 2 teaspoons Meringue Powder (p. 126) per recipe. Protect your cake by placing it in a clean, covered cake box. Avoid using foil or plastic wrap to cover a decorated cake—these materials can stick to icing and crush delicate decorations. The icing that covers your cake determines how it should be stored—in the refrigerator, at cool room temperature, or frozen, if storing for longer than 3 days. If you want to store your iced cake in a different way than noted, make a small test cake.

Icing type determines care. See chart on p. 106 for storage information.

NOTE: Cakes with thoroughly-dried royal icing decorations should be stored according to the type of icing they are covered with. However, if royal icing decorations are to be put on a cake that will be frozen, it is recommended that icing decorations be placed on the cakes after thawing, so that colored decorations won't bleed from condensation or royal icing decorations become soft.

Transporting Cakes

Moving a tiered cake from one location to another does not have to be difficult. Following some simple guidelines ensures that your cake will arrive safely—whether you are traveling hundreds of miles or just a few.

Be certain the cake is constructed on a sturdy base made of three or more thicknesses of corrugated cardboard. Base tiers of very heavy cakes should be placed on a fiberboard or plywood base, ½ in. thick.

Cakes on pillars must be transported unassembled. Toppers, candles and ornaments should be removed from cakes when they are being moved.

For stacked cakes, move the entire assembled cake. Or, for a larger quantity of tiers, transport unassembled and assemble at the reception. Be sure to have with you the equipment and icings you will need to finish any decorating needed after assembly at the final destination.

For a combination cake (pillar and stacked), take tiers apart, keeping stacked tiers as units. Boxing the cake makes transportation easier. Not only does it protect the tiers from damage, but it keeps the tiers clean—free from dirt, dust and bugs. Place the boxes on carpet foam or a non-skid mat on a level surface in the vehicle to prevent shifting. Keep the boxes flat; never place on a slanted car seat. Boxed cakes can also be transported in the trunk of the car, except in hot weather, because air conditioning will not reach the trunk area.

At the destination, request a cart on wheels to move the cake into the reception area. This is easier and safer than carrying by hand. Remove the cakes from the boxes on the reception table by cutting the sides of the boxes and sliding the cakes out. Bring along a repair kit—extra icing, prepared decorating bags and tips, flowers, spatulas—just in case it is necessary to make any repairs.

In Pan

Take tiers apart if constructed in Center Column or Push-in Leg method. Position the plates on crumpled foil or in shallow pans if they do not sit level. Remove pillars from tier plates; plates stay in position.

In Box

Place the cakes in clean, covered, sturdy boxes that are sized to the base board of each cake. This will prevent the cake from shifting within the box and possibly crushing the sides of the cake. If the box is too big, roll pieces of masking tape sticky side out and attach to the inside bottom of the box. Position the cake base on top of the tape. The tape will hold the base in place within the box. For boxes which must hold taller decorations, prop up top and sides and secure with masking tape.

Look for strong Wilton Cake Boxes in a great selection of sizes on p. 217

On Foam

If tiers cannot be boxed, they can be transported on large pieces of non-slip foam. Place the foam on the floor of the vehicle, then carefully place the tiers centered on each piece of foam.

Cake Baking and Serving Guides

These charts show baking information and serving amounts for 2-in. and 3-in. deep pans. The figures for 2-in. pans are based on a 2-layer or 4-in. high cake; fill pans ½ to ⅔ full. The figures for 3-in. pans are based on a 1-layer cake which is torted and filled to reach 3-in. high; fill pans ½ full. For large cakes, always check for doneness after they have baked for one hour. The serving amounts are based on party-sized portions of 1½ x 2 in., or wedding-sized portions that are cut smaller, approximately 1 x 2 in. Even though there is a difference in height, 1 and 2-layer cakes follow the same pattern of cutting, yielding the same number of servings. Some decorators prefer calculating the number of servings using the formula of ½ cup batter equaling 1 serving. However, when cutting the actual cake into serving pieces, that number is sometimes difficult to achieve. Number of servings are intended as a guide only. Icing amounts are very general and will vary with consistency, thickness applied and tips used. These amounts allow for top and bottom borders.

PARTY CAKES (2 in. Deep Pans)

PAN SHAPE	SIZE	NUMBER SERVINGS 2 LAYER	CUPS BATTER 1 LAYER, 2 IN.	BAKING TEMP.	BAKING TIME MINUTES	APPROX. CUPS ICING TO ICE AND DECORATE 2 LAYER CAKE
Round	6"	12	2	350°	25-30	3
	7"	16	2½	350°	30-35	3½
	8"	20	3	350°	30-35	4
	9"	24	5½	350°	30-35	4½
	10"	28	6	350°	35-40	5
	12"	40	7½	350°	35-40	6
	14"	63	10	325°	50-55	7½
	16"	77	15	325°	55-60	9
Sheet	7 x 11"	28	5½	350°	30-35	5
	9 x 13"	45	7	350°	35-40	6
	11 x 15"	60	11	325°	35-40	8
	12 x 18"	72	14	325°	45-50	10
Square	6"	12	2	350°	25-30	3½
	8"	20	4	350°	35-40	4½
	10"	30	6	350°	35-40	6
	12"	48	10	350°	40-45	7½
	14"	63	13½	325°	45-50	9½
	16"	80	15½	325°	50-55	11
Heart	6"	8	1½	350°	25-30	3½
	8"	18	3½	350°	30-35	4½
	9"	20	4	350°	30-35	6
	10"	24	5	350°	30-35	8½
	12"	34	8	325°	45-50	9
	14"	48	10	325°	45-50	10
	15"	50	11	325°	40-45	11
	16"	64	12½	325°	40-45	12
Petal	6"	6	1½	350°	25-30	4
	9"	14	3½	350°	35-40	6
	12"	38	7	350°	35-40	9
	15"	48	12	325°	50-55	11
Hexagon	6"	10	1¾	350°	30-35	3
	9"	20	3½	350°	35-40	5
	12"	34	6	350°	40-45	6
	15"	48	11	325°	40-45	9
Oval	7¾ x 5⅝"	9	2½	350°	25-30	3
	10¾ x 7⅞"	20	5	350°	25-30	4
	13½ x 9¾"	30	8	350°	35-40	5½
	16½ x 12⅜"	44	11	325°	40-45	7½

WEDDING CAKES (2 in. Deep Pans)

PAN SHAPE	SIZE	NUMBER SERVINGS 2 LAYER	CUPS BATTER 1 LAYER, 2 IN.	BAKING TEMP.	BAKING TIME MINUTES	APPROX. CUPS ICING TO ICE AND DECORATE 2 LAYER CAKE
Oval	7¾ x 5⅝"	13	2½	350°	25-30	3
	10¾ x 7⅞"	26	5	350°	25-30	4
	13½ x 9¾"	45	8	350°	35-40	5½
	16½ x 12⅜"	70	11	325°	40-45	7½
Round	6"	12	2	350°	25-30	3
	8"	24	3	350°	30-35	4
	9"	32	5½	350°	30-35	4½
	10"	38	6	350°	35-40	5
	12"	56	7½	350°	35-40	6
	14"	78	10	325°	50-55	7½
	16"	100	15	325°	55-60	9
Square	6"	18	2	350°	25-30	3½
	8"	32	4	350°	35-40	4½
	10"	50	6	350°	35-40	6
	12"	72	10	350°	40-45	7½
	14"	98	13½	325°	45-50	9½
	16"	128	15½	325°	50-55	11
	18"	162	18	325°	60-65	13
Heart	6"	14	1½	350°	25-30	3½
	8"	22	3½	350°	30-35	4½
	9"	28	4	350°	30-35	6
	10"	38	5	350°	30-35	8½
	12"	56	8	325°	45-50	9
	14"	72	10	325°	45-50	10
	15"	74	11	325°	40-45	11
	16"	94	12½	325°	40-45	12
Petal	6"	8	1½	350°	25-30	4
	9"	18	3½	350°	35-40	6
	12"	40	7	350°	35-40	9
	15"	64	12	325°	50-55	11
Hexagon	6"	12	1¾	350°	30-35	3
	9"	26	3½	350°	35-40	5
	12"	40	6	350°	40-45	6
	15"	70	11	325°	40-45	9

PARTY CAKES (3 in. Deep Pans)

PAN SHAPE	SIZE	NUMBER SERVINGS 1 LAYER, 3 IN.	CUPS BATTER 1 LAYER, 3 IN.	BAKING TEMP.	BAKING TIME MINUTES	APPROX. CUPS ICING TO ICE AND DECORATE 1 LAYER, 3 IN. CAKE
Round	6"	12	3	350°	35-40	3
	8"	20	5	350°	55-60	4
	10"	28	8	325°	65-75	5
	12"	40	10½	325°	60-65	6
	14"	63	15	325°	75-85	8
	16"	77	18	325°	75-85	9
	18" Half	55	12	325°	60-65	10½
Sheet	9 x 13"	45	11½	325°	70-75	5
	11 x 15"	60	16	325°	80-85	6½
	12 x 18"	72	20	325°	85-90	8
Square	8"	20	6½	350°	60-65	4½
	10"	30	9	325°	65-75	6
	12"	48	14	325°	65-75	7½
	14"	63	19	325°	65-75	9½
Contour	7"	6	3½	350°	45-50	2
	9"	11	5½	350°	45-50	2½
	11"	16	8	325°	80-85	3
	13"	22	13	325°	75-80	4
	15"	32	16	325°	75-80	5

For pans 10 in. and larger, we recommend using a heating core to insure even baking. Use 2 cores for 18-in. pans.

WEDDING CAKES (3 in. Deep Pans)

PAN SHAPE	SIZE	NUMBER SERVINGS 1 LAYER, 3 IN.	CUPS BATTER 1 LAYER, 3 IN.	BAKING TEMP.	BAKING TIME MINUTES	APPROX. CUPS ICING TO ICE AND DECORATE 1 LAYER, 3 IN. CAKE
Round	6"	12	3	350°	35-40	3
	8"	24	5	350°	55-60	4
	10"	38	8	325°	65-75	5
	12"	56	10½	325°	60-65	6
	14"	78	15	325°	75-85	8
	16"	100	18	325°	75-85	9
18" Half	2"layer	146*	9**	325°	60-65	10½
Round	3"layer	146*	12**	325°	60-65	10½
Sheet	9 x 13"	65	11½	325°	70-75	5
	11 x 15"	90	16	325°	80-85	6½
	12 x 18"	108	20	325°	85-90	8
Square	8"	32	6½	350°	60-65	4½
	10"	50	9	325°	65-75	6
	12"	72	14	325°	65-75	7½
	14"	98	19	325°	65-75	9½
Contour	7"	11	3½	350°	45-50	2
	9"	17	5½	350°	45-50	2½
	11"	24	8	325°	80-85	3
	13"	39	13	325°	75-80	4
	15"	48	16	325°	75-80	5

*Two half rounds **For each round pan

For additional pan information, check out www.wilton.com

Cake Cutting Guides

It's important to know approximately how many servings your decorated cake will yield. That's why we have provided an estimated number of servings with the instructions for each cake design in this book. It also helps to have a plan when you are cutting the cake. This will help you serve attractive, uniform pieces while reaching your targeted number of servings.

WEDDING CAKES—1 X 2 IN.

This guide shows how to cut popular shaped wedding tiers into pieces approximately 1 x 2 in. and 2 layers high (about 4 in.). Even if a larger serving size is desired, the order of cutting is still the same. The first step in cutting is to remove the top tier, and then begin the cutting with the 2nd tier followed by the 3rd, 4th and so on. The top tier is usually saved for the first anniversary, so it is not calculated into our stated serving amounts.

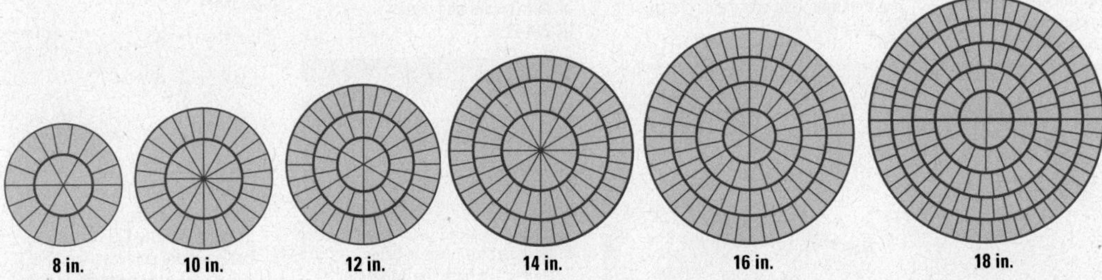

8 in. | 10 in. | 12 in. | 14 in. | 16 in. | 18 in.

Round Tiers:

Move in 2 in. from the tier's outer edge and cut a circle. Slice and serve 1 in. pieces from around the circle. Now move in another 2 in. and cut another circle. Repeat process until the tier is completely cut. The center core of each tier and the small top tier can be cut into 4ths, 6ths, or more, depending on size.

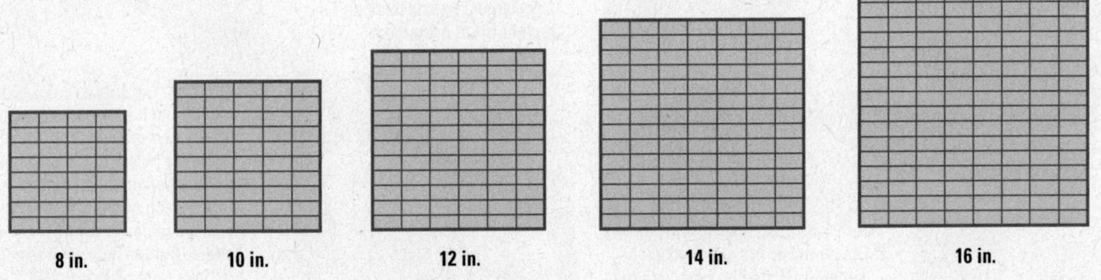

8 in. | 10 in. | 12 in. | 14 in. | 16 in.

Square Tiers:

Move in 2 in. from the outer edge and cut across. Slice and serve 1 in. pieces of cake. Now move in another 2 in. and repeat process until the entire tier is cut.

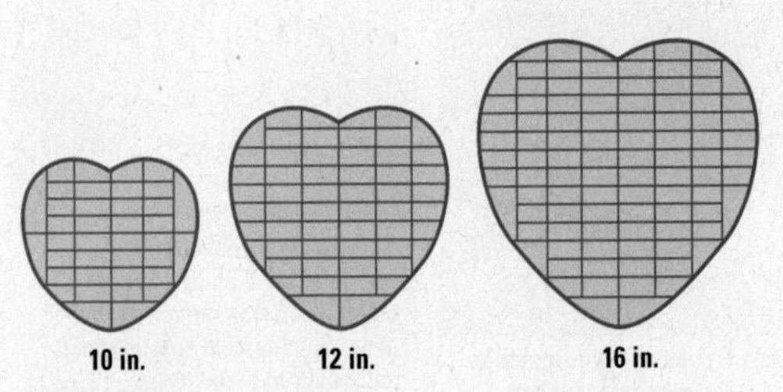

10 in. | 12 in. | 16 in.

Heart Tiers:

Divide the tiers vertically into halves, 4ths, 6ths or 8ths. Within rows, slice and serve 1 in. pieces of cake.

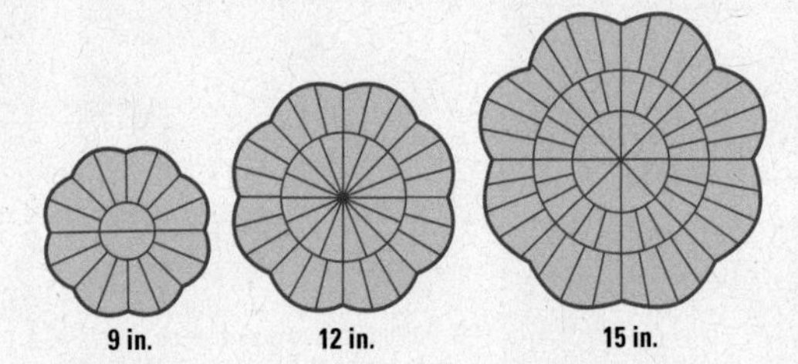

9 in. | 12 in. | 15 in.

Petal Tiers:

Cut similar to round tiers as diagram shows.

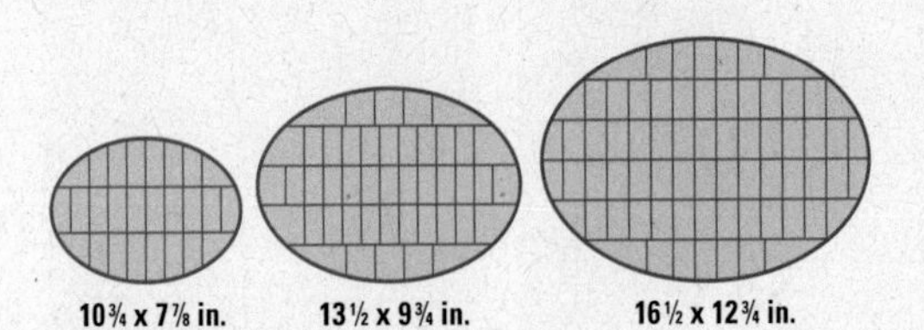

10¾ x 7⅞ in. | 13½ x 9¾ in. | 16½ x 12¾ in.

Oval Tiers:

Move in 2 in. from the outer edge and cut across. Slice and serve 1 in. pieces of cake. Now move in another 2 in., repeat process until the entire tier is cut.

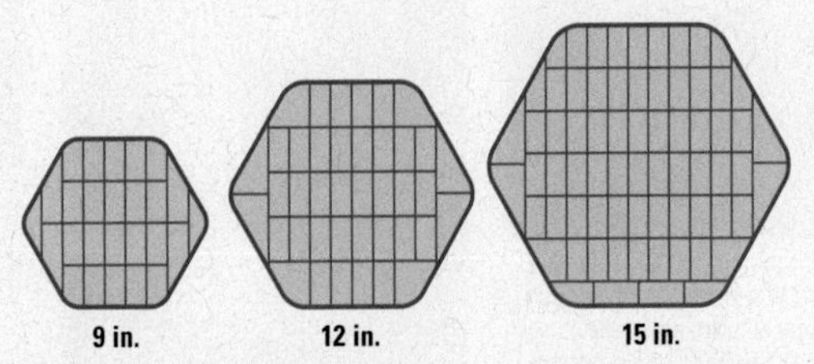

9 in. | 12 in. | 15 in.

Hexagon Tiers:

Move in 2 in. from the outer edge and cut across. Slice and serve 1 in. pieces of cake. Now move in another 2 in., repeat process until the entire tier is cut.

PARTY CAKES—1½ X 2 IN. SLICES

The diagrams shown represent the cutting plan for specific pan shapes. You will use the same general technique to cut each size cake in that shape.

Rounds:

To cut round cakes, move in two inches from the cake's outer edge; cut a circle and then slice approximately 1½ in. pieces within the circle. Now move in another 2 inches, cut another circle, slice approximately 1½ in. pieces and so on until the cake is completely cut. **Note:** 6 in. diameter cakes should be cut in wedges, without a center circle. Cut Petal and Hexagon cakes similar to round tiers.

Squares:

To cut square cakes, move in 2 inches from the outer edge and cut across. Then slice approximately 1½ in. pieces of cake. Now move in another 2 inches and slice again until the entire cake is cut.

Sheets:

Cut sheet cakes similar to square cakes.

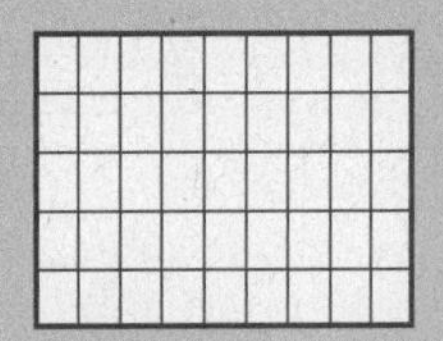

9 x 13 in. Sheet

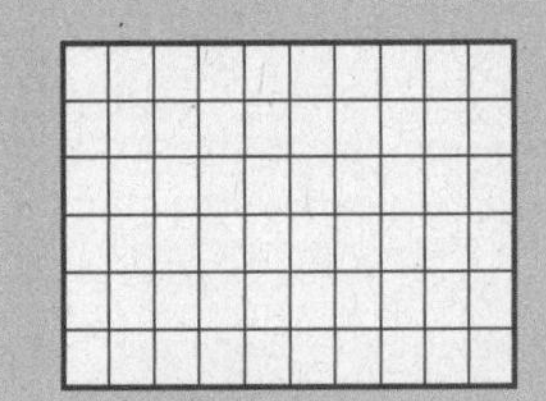

11 x 15 in. Sheet

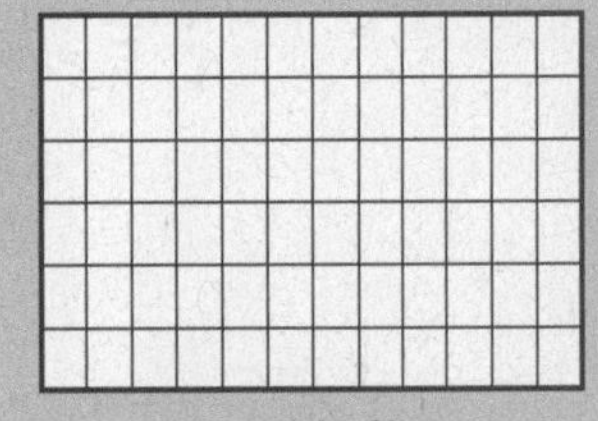

12 x 18 in. Sheet

Tiered Cake Construction

There are many methods of constructing tiered cakes. Here are some of the ones used in this book. Visit www.wedding.wilton.com for more construction methods.

TO PREPARE CAKE FOR ASSEMBLY

Place base tier on a sturdy base plate of 3 or more thicknesses of corrugated cardboard. For heavy cakes, use masonite or plywood. Base can be covered with Fanci-Foil Wrap and trimmed with Tuk 'N Ruffle or use Ruffle Boards® (p. 217). Each tier of your cake must be on a cake circle or board cut to fit. Place a few strokes of icing on boards to secure cake. Fill and ice layers before assembly.

Adding Dowel Rods to Tiered Cakes

Use the upper tier for size reference when determining dowel rod placement. All the dowel rods must be placed within the area you will mark (see steps below) to provide adequate support.

1. Center a cake board the same size as the tier above it on base tier and press it gently into icing to imprint an outline. Remove. Use this outline to guide the insertion of the dowel rods.

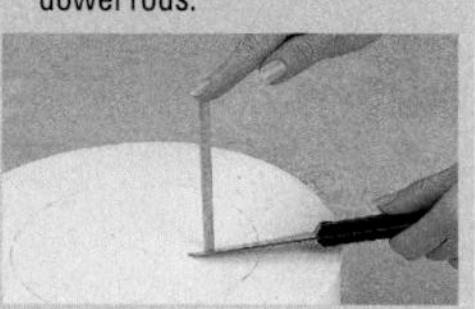

2. Insert one dowel rod into cake straight down to the cake board. Make a knife scratch on the rod to mark the exact height. Pull dowel rod out.

3. Cut the suggested number of rods the exact same length, using the mark on the first one as a guide.

4. Now, insert rods into tier, spacing evenly 1½ inches in from the imprinted outline. Push straight down until each touches the cake board. Repeat this procedure for every stacked or pillared tier on the cake.

NOTE: The larger and more numerous the tiers, the more dowels needed. If the tier above is 10 in. or less, use six ¼ in. wooden dowels. Use 8 dowel rods for 16 in. and 18 in. cakes; on these larger tiers, use ¾ in. plastic dowel rods in the base tier. When using white plastic dowel rods that are wider and provide more support, the number needed may be less.

Stacked Construction

Stacking is the most architectural method of tiered cake construction. Tiers are placed directly on top of one another and pillars are not used. Cakes are supported and stabilized by dowel rods and cake boards.

1. Dowel rod all tiers except top tier.

2.* Position the middle tier on the base tier, centering exactly.

3. Repeat with the top tier.

4. To stabilize tiers further, sharpen one end of a dowel rod and push it through all tiers and cake boards to the base of the bottom tier. To decorate, start at the top and work down.

***TIP:** Finely shredded coconut or confectioner's sugar, placed under cake circles or plastic plates, helps prevent frosting on the cake from sticking.

2-Plate and Pillar Construction

This most dramatic method features 2, 3 or more single cakes towered together. Use separator plates and pillars.

1. Set cake tiers on separator plates 2 in. larger in diameter than cakes.

2. Dowel rod cakes and position separator plates on tiers with feet up. (**NOTE:** Connect only same size separator plates with pillars.)

3. Position pillars over feet on separator plates.

4. Carefully set cake plate on pillars. Continue adding tiers this way.

Push-In Pillar Construction

Simple assembly–no dowel rods needed! Use any type of Wilton push-in pillars and plates (p. 214-215).

1. Mark tier for push-in pillar placement. Use the separator plate for the next tier above, gently pressing it onto the tier, feet down, making sure it is centered. Lift plate away. The feet will leave marks on the icing to guide the position of pillars when you assemble the tier. Repeat this process for each tier, working from largest to smallest tier. The top tier is left unmarked.

2. Place each tier on its separator plate, securing with icing.

3. Position push-in pillars at marks, and insert into tiers. Push straight down until pillars touch the cake plate.

4. To assemble, start with the tier above the base tier. Place the feet of the separator plate on the pillar openings. Continue adding tiers in the same way until the cake is completely assembled.

Center Column Construction

1. Use boards the same size as tiers, or if tiers are shaped, cut boards to fit. Make a waxed paper pattern for each tier except the top tier in order to find the exact center for the columns. Fold the pattern in quarters. Snip the point to make a center hole. Test the hole for size by slipping it over a column, adjust size if necessary. Trace hole pattern on prepared cake board and cut out. Also cut a hole in the top tier board to allow for the column cap nut. Save patterns for marking cake tops later.

2. The base tier of the cake will rest on a 12, 14, 16 or 18 in. plate. (18 in. plate is footed. Do not use a bottom plate smaller than 12 in.). To add legs to this plate, turn it upside down. Using extra strength glue designed for plastic, attach the six legs, positioning the legs over each of the ribs on the plate.

3. Prepare and ice tiers and position on prepared cake boards. Make the center holes for the columns in all tiers except the top tier. Mark the top of the cakes with corresponding waxed paper pattern. Cut the hole by pressing the Cake Corer Tube (p. 213) through the tier right down to the bottom. Hold the corer upright, remove cake corer and push the upper part down to eject the cake center.

4. Screw in a column to the prepared base plate and bottom column bolt from underneath the plate. Slip the next size tier on its plate over the column.

5. At the reception, add a second column and position the next size tier on its plate, slipping it over the column. Finally, add on the top plate only, securing the top column nut. Place the top tier on the plate and decorate bottom border.

Recipes

The cakes, cookies and other desserts in this Yearbook were made using our favorite kitchen-tested recipes. Follow the instructions for decorated desserts that look and taste their best!

ICING RECIPES

Buttercream Icing

½ cup solid vegetable shortening
½ cup butter or margarine[1]
1 teaspoon Clear Vanilla Extract (p. 126)
4 cups sifted confectioner's sugar (approx. 1 lb.)
2 Tablespoons milk[2]

Cream butter and shortening with electric mixer. Add vanilla. Gradually add sugar, one cup at a time, beating well on medium speed. Scrape sides and bottom of bowl often. When all sugar has been mixed in, icing will appear dry. Add milk and beat at medium speed until light and fluffy. Keep bowl covered with a damp cloth until ready to use. For best results, keep icing bowl in refrigerator when not in use. Refrigerated in an airtight container, this icing can be stored 2 weeks. Rewhip before using.
YIELD: 3 cups.

[1] Substitute all-vegetable shortening and ½ teaspoon Wilton No-Color Butter Flavor (p. 126) for pure white icing and stiffer consistency.

[2] Add 3-4 Tablespoons light corn syrup per recipe to thin for icing cake.

Chocolate Buttercream Icing

Add ¾ cup cocoa (or three 1 oz. unsweetened chocolate squares, melted), and an additional 1 to 2 Tablespoons milk to Buttercream Icing recipe. Mix until well blended. For a unique change of pace, add ⅛ to ¼ teaspoon Wilton Candy Flavors (p. 147), in place of vanilla extract.

Chocolate Mocha Icing: substitute freshly brewed strong coffee for milk in recipe.

Darker Chocolate Icing: add 4 more unsweetened chocolate squares (or ¼ cup sifted cocoa powder), and 1 more Tablespoon of milk to Chocolate Buttercream.

Snow-White Buttercream Icing

⅔ cup water
4 Tablespoons Meringue Powder (p. 126)
12 cups sifted confectioner's sugar (approx. 3 lbs.)
1¼ cups solid vegetable shortening
¾ teaspoon salt
¾ teaspoon No-Color Almond Extract (p. 126)
¾ teaspoon Clear Vanilla Extract (p. 126)
½ teaspoon No-Color Butter Flavor (p. 126)

Combine water and meringue powder; whip at high speed until peaks form. Add 4 cups sugar, one cup at a time, beating at low speed after each addition. Alternately add shortening and remainder of sugar. Add salt and flavorings; beat at low speed until smooth.
YIELD: 7 cups.

NOTE: Recipe may be doubled or halved. If halved, yield is 3½ cups.

Heated Wilton Ready-To-Use Decorator Icing

Open icing container, remove foil. Microwave on 50% power for 1 minute; stir. Continue to microwave at 30 second intervals until ready to pour. If a microwave is unavailable, icing container can be heated on a warming tray or in a pan of hot water on a stove.

Royal Icing

3 Tablespoons Meringue Powder (p. 126)
4 cups sifted confectioner's sugar (approx. 1 lb.)
6 Tablespoons water[3]

Beat all ingredients at low speed for 7-10 minutes (10-12 minutes at high speed for portable mixer) until icing forms peaks.
YIELD: 3 cups.

[3] When using large countertop mixer or for stiffer icing, use 1 Tablespoon less water.

Stabilized Whipped Cream Icing

½ pint (1 cup) heavy whipping cream
2 Tablespoons confectioner's sugar
2 Tablespoons Piping Gel (p. 126)
½ teaspoon Clear Vanilla Extract (p. 126)

Combine whipping cream and sugar in mixing bowl. Whip to soft peak stage. Add Piping Gel and vanilla, then continue to whip until stiff peaks form. Do not overbeat.
YIELD: 1½ to 2 cups.

As an alternative, you can use frozen Non-Dairy Whipped Topping or Packaged Topping Mix. Thaw frozen whipped topping in refrigerator before coloring or using for decorating. Use packaged topping mix immediately after preparing. Do not allow either to stay at room temperature, as it becomes too soft for decorating. Store decorated cake in refrigerator until ready to serve.

Classic Whipped Cream for Wilton Dessert Whipper Pro™

(p. 132)

1 pint heavy whipping cream
1 Tablespoon confectioner's sugar

Fill Dessert Whipper Pro™ with well-chilled heavy whipping cream and add confectioner's sugar. Use according to instructions.
YIELD: about 8 cups.

Fluffy Boiled Icing

MERINGUE:

3 Tablespoons Meringue Powder (p. 126)
½ cup cold water

SYRUP:

2 cups granulated sugar
¼ cup corn syrup
½ cup water

Beat meringue powder and cold water until stiff, about 4 minutes. In large microwave-safe measuring cup, stir sugar, corn syrup and water. In microwave oven, bring syrup mixture to a boil (approximately 5 minutes). Cool slightly. Slowly add syrup to meringue mixture while beating on low. Beat on HIGH for 4 minutes until stiff and glossy.
YIELD: 8 cups.

For top of range: Mix sugar, corn syrup and water in 2 quart saucepan. Bring to a boil; cool slightly and follow directions above.

Confectioner's Sugar Glaze

1¼ cups confectioner's sugar
3 Tablespoons milk
½ teaspoon Clear Vanilla Extract (p. 126)

Stir milk into sugar. Drizzle on dessert cakes, muffins and cookies. May be thickened with confectioner's sugar or thinned with milk or other flavored liquids.
YIELD: ½ cup.

Color Flow Icing Recipe (Full-Strength for Outlining)

¼ cup + 1 teaspoon water
4 cups sifted confectioner's sugar (approx. 1 lb.)
2 Tablespoons Color Flow Icing Mix

In an electric mixer, using grease-free utensils, blend all ingredients on low speed for 5 minutes. If using hand mixer, use high speed. Color Flow icing "crusts" quickly, so keep bowl covered with a damp cloth while using. Stir in desired icing color. In order to fill an outlined area, this recipe must be thinned with ½ teaspoon of water per ¼ cup of icing (just a few drops at a time as you near proper consistency). Color Flow is ready for filling in outlines when a small amount dropped into the mixture takes a count of ten to disappear. Use grease-free spoon or spatula to stir slowly. Makes approx. 2 cups + 2 Tablespoons full-strength Color Flow icing.

NOTE: Color Flow designs take a long time to dry, so plan to do your Color Flow piece up to 1 week in advance.

Poured Cookie Icing

This icing dries to a shiny, hard finish. Great to use as icing or to outline and fill in with tip 2 or 3.

1 cup sifted confectioner's sugar
2 teaspoons milk
2 teaspoons light corn syrup

Place sugar and milk in bowl. Stir until mixed thoroughly. Add corn syrup and mix well. For filling in areas, use thinned icing (add small amounts of light corn syrup until desired consistency is reached).

ROLLED FONDANT AND GUM PASTE RECIPES

Fondant is rolled out and used as a covering for a pound or fruit cake, which is traditionally first covered with a layer of marzipan to seal in flavor and moistness of the cake. A light layer of buttercream or apricot glaze may also be used. Cakes covered with rolled fondant can be decorated with royal or buttercream icing. Wilton also has convenient, Ready-to-Use Rolled Fondant (p. 122) for easy-to-handle fondant with no mixing.

Rolled Fondant

1 Tablespoon unflavored gelatin
¼ cup cold water
½ cup Wilton Glucose (p. 125)
1 Tablespoon Wilton Glycerin (p. 125)
2 Tablespoons solid vegetable shortening
2 lbs. sifted confectioner's sugar
2-3 drops liquid food color and flavoring, as desired

Combine gelatin and cold water; let stand until thick. Place gelatin mixture in top of double boiler and heat until dissolved. Add glucose and glycerin, mix well. Stir in shortening and just before completely melted, remove from heat, add flavoring and color. Cool until lukewarm. Next, place 1 lb. confectioner's sugar in a bowl and make a well. Pour the lukewarm gelatin mixture into the well and stir with a wooden spoon, mixing in sugar and adding more, a little at a time, until stickiness disappears. Knead in remaining sugar. Knead until the fondant is smooth, pliable and does not stick to your hands. If fondant is too soft, add more sugar; if too stiff, add water (a drop at a time). Use fondant immediately or store in airtight container in a cool, dry place. Do not refrigerate or freeze. When ready to use, knead again until soft. This recipe yields approx. 36 oz., enough to cover a 10 x 4 in. high cake.

For instructions on preparing and covering cakes with rolled fondant, see p.105.

Extra-Firm Rolled Fondant

Use this recipe for a fondant with the extra body and pliability ideal for making drapes, swags, woven and elaborate decorations.

1 to 2 teaspoons Gum-Tex™ (p. 125)
24 oz. Wilton Ready-To-Use Rolled Fondant (p. 122)

Knead Gum-Tex™ into fondant until smooth. Store in an airtight container or tightly wrapped in plastic.

Apricot Glaze

Ideal for preparing a cake for fondant or for crumb-coating cakes before icing.

1 cup apricot preserves

Heat preserves to boiling, strain. Brush on cake while still hot. Let dry. Glaze will dry to a hard finish in 15 minutes or less.
YIELD: Covers a 10 x 4 in. cake.

Gum Paste

Its clay-like texture means gum paste can be rolled thinner than fondant for finer detail—ideal for flowers and greenery. Gum paste dries hard and is meant more for decoration than consumption.

1 heaping Tablespoon Glucose (p. 125)
3 Tablespoons warm water
1 Tablespoon Gum-Tex™ (p. 125)
4 cups sifted confectioner's sugar (approx. 1 lb.) or more

Heat glucose and water until just warm. Mix Gum-Tex™ with one cup of the confectioner's sugar and add to glucose mixture. Mix well. Gradually knead in enough confectioner's sugar until you have used about ¾ lb.

Recipes

COOKIE RECIPES

Roll-Out Cookies

1 cup unsalted butter, softened
1 ½ cups granulated sugar
1 egg
1 ½ teaspoons Clear Vanilla Extract (p. 126)
½ teaspoon No-Color Almond Extract (p. 126)
2¾ cups all-purpose flour
2 teaspoons baking powder
1 teaspoon salt

Preheat oven to 400°F. In mixing bowl, cream butter with sugar until light and fluffy. Beat in egg and extracts. Mix flour, baking powder and salt; add to butter mixture 1 cup at a time, mixing after each addition. Do not chill dough. Divide dough into 2 balls. On a floured surface, roll each ball into a circle approximately 12 in. wide and ⅛ in. thick. Dip cookie cutter in flour before each use. Bake cookies on ungreased cookie sheet 6-7 minutes or until cookies are lightly browned.
Makes about 3 dozen cookies.

Large Batch Roll-Out Cookies

2 cups unsalted butter, softened
3 cups granulated sugar
2 eggs
1 tablespoon Clear Vanilla Extract (p. 126)
1 teaspoon No-Color Almond Extract (p. 126)
5½ cups all-purpose flour
4 teaspoons baking powder
2 teaspoons salt

Preheat oven to 400°F. In mixing bowl, cream butter with sugar until light and fluffy. Beat in egg and extracts. Mix flour, baking powder and salt; add to butter mixture 1 cup at a time, mixing after each addition. Do not chill dough. Divide dough into 4 balls. On a floured surface, roll each ball into a circle approximately 12 in. wide and ⅛ inch thick. Dip cookie cutter in flour before each use. Bake cookies on ungreased cookie sheet 6-7 minutes or until cookies are lightly browned.
Makes about 6 dozen cookies.

Chocolate Roll-Out Cookies

¾ cup butter or margarine, softened
1 cup granulated sugar
2 eggs
1 teaspoon vanilla
3 squares (3 oz.) unsweetened chocolate, melted and cooled
3 cups all-purpose flour
1 teaspoon baking powder

Preheat oven to 375°F. In large mixing bowl, beat together butter and sugar with mixer until light and fluffy. Add eggs and vanilla; mix well. Blend in chocolate. Combine flour and baking powder; gradually add to butter mixture, beating until smooth. Cover and chill until firm, about 1 hour.

Roll dough approximately ⅛ in. thick. Dip cutters in flour, cut and transfer cookies to cookie sheet. Bake 8-10 minutes. Remove to rack and cool thoroughly.
Makes 2-2½ dozen cookies.

Grandma's Gingerbread

5 to 5½ cups all-purpose flour
1 teaspoon baking soda
1 teaspoon salt
2 teaspoons powdered ginger
2 teaspoons ground cinnamon
1 teaspoon nutmeg
1 teaspoon ground cloves
1 cup solid vegetable shortening
1 cup granulated sugar
1¼ cups unsulphured molasses[4]
2 eggs, beaten

Preheat oven to 375°F. Thoroughly mix flour, soda, salt and spices. Melt shortening in large saucepan. Cool slightly. Add sugar, molasses and eggs; mix well. Add 4 cups dry ingredients and mix well.

Turn mixture onto lightly floured surface. Knead in remaining dry ingredients by hand. Add a little more flour, if necessary, to make firm dough. Roll out on a lightly floured surface to ⅛ in. thickness for cutout cookies. Bake on ungreased cookie sheet. Small and medium-sized cookies for 6-10 minutes, large cookies for 10-15 minutes.

Makes 40 medium-sized cookies.

NOTE: If you're not going to use your gingerbread dough right away, wrap in plastic and refrigerate. Refrigerated dough will keep for a week. Remove 3 hours before using so it softens and is workable.

[4] Substitute 1¼ cups light corn syrup for molasses to make Blonde Gingerbread.

SPECIALTY RECIPES

Creamy Gelatin

See One Cool Commencement, p. 76.

2 (6 oz.) pks. and 1 (3 oz.) pk. lemon gelatin
4 envelopes unflavored gelatin
5 cups boiling water
4 (8 oz.) pks. cream cheese, softened
3 cups cold water
12 oz. non-dairy whipped topping, thawed

Dissolve in 5 cups boiling water, mix until clear. Beat cream cheese; gradually blend in hot gelatin mixture. Blend completely until smooth, then slowly add 3 cups cold water. Chill until slightly thickened. Stir in whipped topping. Pour into pan sprayed with vegetable oil pan spray. Refrigerate overnight. To unmold, dip pan in warm water for 10 seconds; invert onto plate.

Wilton Gelatin Treats

See One Cool Commencement , p. 76.

2 small (3 oz.) pks. gelatin mix
1¼ cups boiling water

This recipe yields a firmer gelatin, recommended for molding and cutting shapes. Completely dissolve gelatin in boiling water. Lightly spray pan with vegetable pan spray. Slowly pour gelatin into pans. Refrigerate until set, at least 3 hours. Unmold.

Cone Cupcakes

See Birthday Whirligig, p. 13.

Preheat oven to 350°F. Prepare cake mix following package directions. Wrap bases of cones with aluminum foil and position straight up in ungreased muffin pan. Fill cones approximately ½ full with cake batter (about ¼ cup each). Do not overfill. Let batter settle before placing in oven. Bake filled cones 25-30 minutes. Let cool completely.

Kolackys

See Kolackys from the Crypt, p. 50.

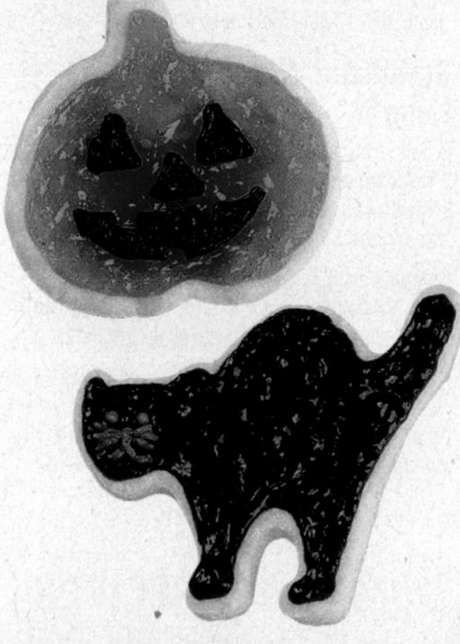

3 cups all-purpose flour
1½ cups butter or margarine
½ cup sour cream
¼ cup confectioner's sugar
Pastry filling of your choice

Using a pastry blender, cut butter or margarine into flour and confectioner's sugar. Add sour cream and blend. Refrigerate to chill thoroughly. Preheat oven to 375°F. Divide dough into 2 portions. On a lightly floured board, roll one portion at a time to ⅛ in. thick. Roll out Kolacky dough and cut out shapes with bat, cat and pumpkin cutters. Fill disposable decorating bags with pastry fillings; cut bag and pipe to cover cookies. Bake 18 minutes or until light brown; cool. Fit tube icings with tip 2 and pipe features.

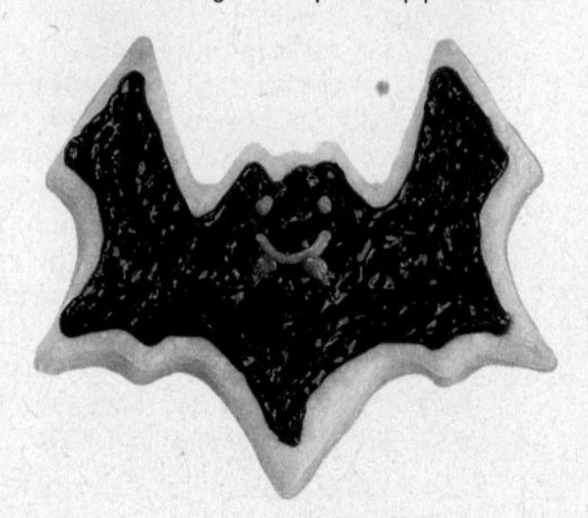

CANDY RECIPES

Basic Ganache and Truffles

14 oz. Candy Melts®*
½ cup heavy whipping cream

Chop Candy Melts®* (you can use a food processor). Heat whipping cream in saucepan just to boiling point. Do not boil. Remove from heat and add chopped Candy Melts®*, stir until smooth and glossy.

Ganache Glaze: If mixture is too thick, add 1 to 2 Tablespoons whipping cream. Position cake on wire rack over drip pan. Pour glaze onto center and work out toward edges.

NOTE: Cake may be iced first in buttercream. Let icing set, then pour on ganache glaze. If cake has a perfect surface, no other icing is needed.

Whipped Ganache: Follow recipe above, using 1 cup whipping cream. Allow mixture to set and cool to room temperature (mixture will have the consistency of pudding, this may take 1-2 hours.) Whip on high speed with an electric mixer until light and soft peaks form.

Truffles: Add 1 Tablespoon liqueur for flavor, if desired. Stir until smooth and creamy. Refrigerate until firm. Roll into 1 in. diameter balls. Can be used as center for dipped candies, served plain or rolled in nuts, coconut or cocoa powder. Store truffles in refrigerator up to 3 weeks.
YIELD: About 2 dozen 1 in. diameter balls.

Candy "Clay"

14 oz. package of Candy Melts®*
⅓ cup light corn syrup

Melt Candy Melts®* following package directions. Add corn syrup and stir to blend. Turn out mixture onto waxed paper and let set at room temperature to dry. Wrap well and store at room temperature until needed. Candy Clay handles best if hardened overnight.

To Use

Candy Clay will be very hard at the start; knead a small portion at a time until workable. If Candy Clay gets too soft, set aside at room temperature or refrigerate briefly. When rolling out Candy Clay, sprinkle work surface with cornstarch or cocoa (for cocoa clay) to prevent sticking; roll to approximately ⅛ in. thick.

To Tint

White Candy Clay may be tinted using Candy Color or Icing Color. Knead in color until well blended.

To Store

Prepared Candy Clay will last for several weeks at room temperature in an airtight container.

Ready-In-Minutes Cocoa Fudge

20 oz. (approximately 4½ cups) Dark Cocoa Candy Melts®*
1 (14 oz.) can condensed milk (not evaporated)

Melt Candy Melts®* on low power in microwave-safe container. Add milk; stir until blended. Microwave an additional 2 to 3 minutes on medium power; stir until fudge develops a sheen. Pour mixture into buttered 7 x 11 in. sheet pan and refrigerate until firm.

*Brand confectionery coating.

Tip Techniques

Your icing turned out great—now you're ready to learn to pipe beautiful shapes on your cake. Stars, shells, dots, lines and other techniques are the foundation of your decorating knowledge. We'll tell you step-by-step how to pipe each one, including the angle, pressure and movement to use for a uniform look. With practice, you can build on these basics to create many other impressive designs and borders.

ROUND TIPS

Dot

Pipe dots for flower centers, faces, figure piping and border effects. When making large dots, lift the tip as you squeeze to allow icing to fill out completely.

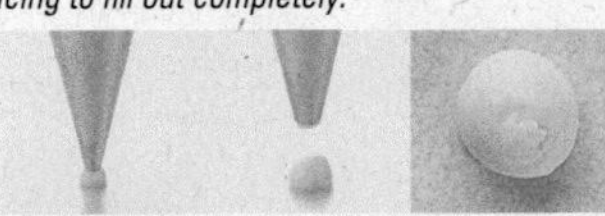

Practice With: Tip 3
Icing Consistency: Medium
Bag Position: 90°
Hold Tip: Slightly above surface

1. Hold the bag straight up with the tip slightly above the surface. Squeeze the bag and keep point of the tip in icing until the dot is the size you want.
2. Stop squeezing the bag completely before you lift the tip from the dot.
3. Lift tip up and pull away from piped dot.

Ball

An important technique to master, the ball shape makes bold borders, and is a first step technique to figure piping. Vary the basic look by adding stars, dots or spirals on the ball shapes.

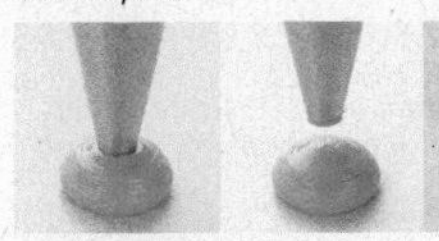

Practice With: Tip 9
Icing Consistency: Medium
Bag Position: 90°
Hold Tip: Slightly above surface

1. Squeeze the bag, applying a steady even pressure. As the icing begins to build up, raise the tip with it, but keep the tip end buried in the icing.
2. Stop squeezing as you bring the end of the tip to the surface.
3. Lift the tip up and pull away from your piped ball. Use the edge of the tip to shave any point so that your ball is nicely rounded.

Bead

If you can pipe a shell, you can pipe a bead—the movements are similar. To pipe a bead heart, simply pipe one bead, then a second, joining the tails. Smooth together using a decorator's brush.

Practice With: Tip 5
Icing Consistency: Medium
Bag Position: 45° at 3:00 (9:00)
Hold Tip: Slightly above surface

1. Squeeze as you lift tip slightly so that icing fans out.
2. Relax pressure as you draw the tip down and bring the bead to a point.
3. To make a bead border, start the end of your next bead so that the fanned end covers the tail of the preceding bead to form an even chain.

Cornelli Lace

The lacy design of this free-hand technique depends on continuous curving strings that do not overlap or touch.

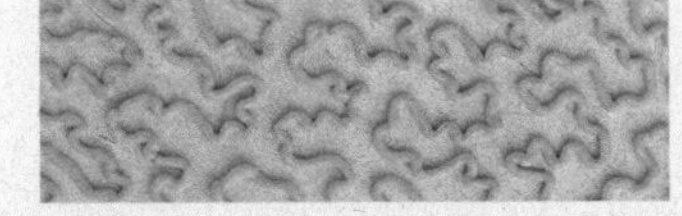

Practice With: Tip 1 or 2
Icing Consistency: Thin
Bag Position: 90°
Hold Tip: Close to cake so icing attaches without scraping cake with tip and without flattening icing strings

Beginning and ending at edges, pipe a continuous string of icing, curve it up, down and around until area is covered. Make certain strings never touch or cross. Don't leave any loose ends! Stop pressure; pull tip away.

Sotas

The lacy texture of sotas looks magnificent on borders, outlined areas and as a background for flowers.

Practice With: Tip 1
Icing Consistency: Thin
Bag Position: 90°
Hold Tip: Slightly above surface

Squeeze bag and allow icing to drop randomly in a series of overlapping loops. Cover area edge-to-edge. Use a small amount of thinned icing in your bag—this puts less pressure on your hands.

Printing

Practice With: Tip 3 with message press
Icing Consistency: Thin
Bag Position: 45° at 3:00
Hold Tip: Slightly touching surface

You may pipe letters freehand, pipe over a pattern traced with a toothpick, or pipe after imprinting letters with a pattern press. If you are using a pattern press, let icing crust slightly, then imprint the message. With a steady, even pressure, squeeze out a straight line, lifting the tip off the surface to let icing string drop. To prevent tails from forming, be careful to stop squeezing before you touch tip to surface and pull away. Be sure the end of the tip is clean before you go on to another line.

Writing

Practice With: Tip 5
Icing Consistency: Thin
Bag Position: 45° at 3:00
Hold Tip: Slightly touching surface

You may pipe letters freehand, pipe over a pattern traced with a toothpick, or pipe after imprinting letters with a pattern press. If you are using a pattern press, let icing crust slightly, then imprint the message. Steadily squeeze, gliding along the surface in a smooth, continuous motion. Use your arm, not your fingers, to form each line, letter or word. Keep your wrist straight, moving your entire forearm in a single unit. After you begin to master the curves and swings of the letters, lift the tip up slightly as you write. You'll find you have more control if you let the icing draw out slightly over the surface as you write.

Outline

Characters or designs are often outlined first, then piped in with stars or zigzags. Outlines are used for facial features, too. Color Flow plaques are also outlined before icing is flowed into the shape.

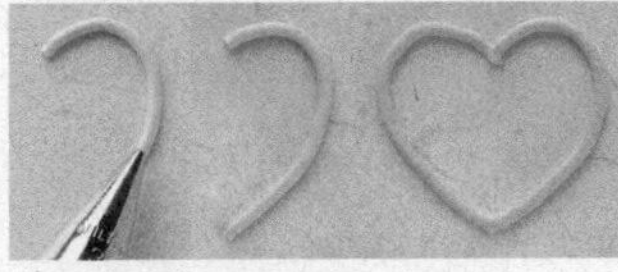

Practice With: Tip 3
Icing Consistency: Thin
Bag Position: 45° at 3:00 (9:00)
Hold Tip: Slightly above surface

1. Touch tip to surface. Raise the tip slightly and continue to squeeze.
2. The icing will flow out of the tip while you direct it along the surface.
3. To end, stop squeezing, touch tip to surface and pull away.

Drop Strings

These flowing strings are a beautiful way to adorn the sides of a cake. The trick to making drop strings is to pull the bag toward you as the string drapes down. If you "draw" the string with the tip, you won't achieve a pretty curve and your strings will tend to break. Pipe at eye level to your cake so that strings line up evenly. The Cake Divider Set (p. 131) is a great help in accurately dividing and marking your cake for even drop strings.

Single Drop Strings

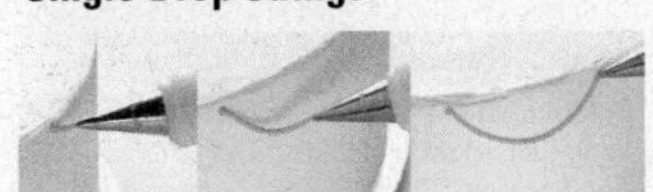

Practice With: Tip 3
Icing Consistency: Stiff
Bag Position: Shoulder level at 4:30 (7:30)
Hold Tip: Lightly touching surface to attach

1. With a toothpick, mark horizontal divisions on cake in the width you desire. Touch tip to first mark and squeeze, pausing momentarily so that icing sticks to surface.
2. While squeezing, pull the bag toward you. Continue squeezing to allow the icing to drape naturally into an arc. Icing will drop by itself—do not move the tip down with the string. The end of the tip should be the same distance from the surface as the width from point to point on your cake.
3. Stop pressure before you touch tip to second mark to end string. Repeat, keeping drop strings uniform in length and width.

Multiple Drop Strings

Try a different color for each row of multiple drop strings—put holiday colors together to really dress up your cake.

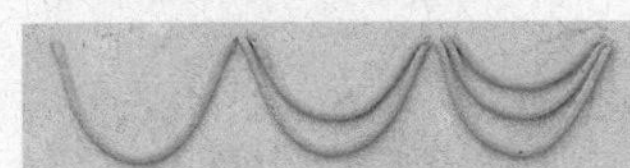

To add multiple rows of strings, mark the cake for the deepest row and pipe that row. Return to the first drop string point, squeeze the bag, and drop a string with a slightly shorter arc than in the first row. Join the end of this string to the end of the corresponding string in the first row. Repeat the process for a third row of drop strings above the second.

STAR TIPS

Star

Practice With: Tip 16
Icing Consistency: Medium
Bag Position: 90°
Hold Tip: Between 1/8 and 1/4 in. above surface

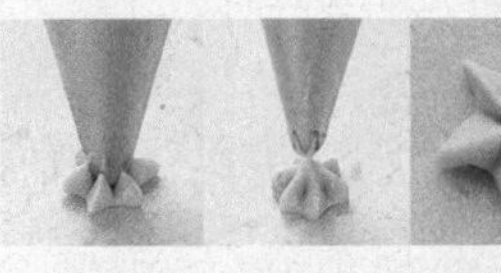

1. Hold the decorating bag straight up, with the tip between 1/8 and 1/4 in. above the surface, while using your other hand to hold the tip steady. Squeeze the bag to form a star. Increasing or decreasing the pressure changes the size of the star.
2. Stop squeezing the bag completely before you lift the tip from the star.
3. Lift the tip up and pull away from piped star.

Pull-out stars add even more dimension to your cake. To make them, hold bag at a 45° angle to surface. As you squeeze out icing, pull tip up and away from cake. When your mound is high enough, stop pressure and pull tip away. Work from bottom to top of area to be covered with pull-out stars.

Star Fill In

Because these close-together stars require so much piping from the same bag, it's a good idea to keep replenishing the icing. Replenish icing when it gets soft or stars will be poorly defined.

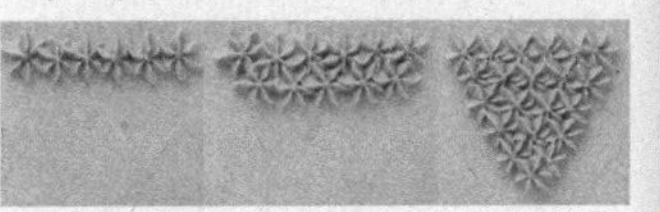

Practice With: Tip 16
Icing Consistency: Medium
Bag Position: 90° (straight up)
Hold Tip: 1/4 in. above surface

1. Pipe a row of stars evenly and close together, adjusting the tip position slightly each time so that the points of the stars interlock and cover the area without gaps.
2. Pipe a row of stars beneath the first, again adjusting tip position to close any gaps.
3. Continue to fill in entire area.

Zigzag

Popular way to fill in outlined areas, perfect for ribbed sweater and cuff effects. You can also use tight zigzags to cover the entire side of your cake—they look great!

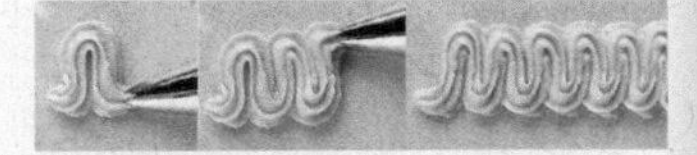

Practice With: Tip 16
Icing Consistency: Medium
Bag Position: 45° at 3:00 (9:00)
Hold Tip: Lightly touching surface

1. Steadily squeeze and move your hand in a tight up and down motion.
2. Continue piping up and down with steady pressure. To end, stop pressure and pull tip away. For more elongated zigzags, move your hand to the desired height while maintaining a steady pressure. For a more relaxed look, just increase the width as you move the bag along.
3. Repeat as you move in a straight line with consistent up/down motion.

Tip Techniques cont.

Zigzag Puff

This is the fluffy look you want for making clouds or smoke and to add dimension as a side border.

Practice With: Tip 17
Icing Consistency: Medium
Bag Position: 45° at 3:00 (9:00)
Hold Tip: Lightly touching surface

1. Begin to pipe with a light pressure, then use heavier pressure toward the center of the puff, then return gradually to a light pressure to form the tapered end.
2. To end each puff, stop pressure and pull tip away.
3. Repeat as you move in a straight line to form a row of puffs.

Shell

Most popular icing technique of all, the shell is the basis for many borders. Lift tip slightly when piping shells to avoid a bumpy look.

Practice With: Tip 21
Icing Consistency: Medium
Bag Position: 45° at 6:00
Hold Tip: Slightly above surface

1. Hold the bag in the 6:00 position so that you can pull the bag toward you. The tip should be slightly above the surface.
2. Squeeze hard, letting the icing fan out generously as it lifts the tip—do not lift the bag. Gradually relax your pressure as you lower the tip until it touches the surface.
3. Stop pressure and pull the tip away, without lifting it off the surface, to draw the shell to a point.
4. To make a shell border, start the end of your next shell so that the fanned end covers the tail of the preceding shell to form an even chain.

Reverse Shell

Opposite-facing shells look spectacular as top and bottom borders and as framed areas on your cake—they add a wonderful motion effect. The look is even fancier finished with a dot or a star at the center of each shell curve.

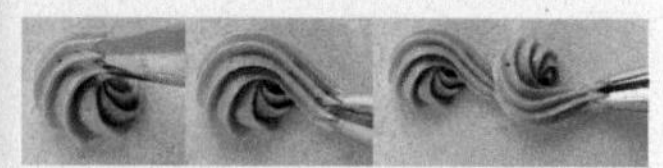

Practice With: Tip 21
Icing Consistency: Medium
Bag Position: 45° at 6:00
Hold Tip: Slightly above surface

1. As you begin to form a shell, squeeze hard, letting the icing fan out.
2. Form a curve, moving the tip from 9:00 (3:00) to 12:00 to 6:00. Relax pressure and lower the tip, pulling straight toward you at 6:00 to form a tail.
3. Repeat with another shell, curving from 3:00 (9:00) to 12:00 to 6:00.
4. To make a reverse shell border, pipe a chain of swirling reverse shells, with the fan end of each new shell covering the tail of the previous shell. If you are making the border on a round cake, turn the cake as you go so that the back of the bag is at 6:00 and you are working toward yourself.

Rope

Finish your piped baskets with pretty edging and handles. Excellent for western or nautical themed cakes. You can make a great-looking rope with star or round tips (or basketweave tips, ridged or smooth side up).

Practice With: Tip 21
Icing Consistency: Medium
Bag Position: 45° at 4:30 (7:30)
Hold Tip: Lightly touching surface

1. Using a steady, even pressure, move the tip in a gentle sideways "S" curve. Stop pressure and pull tip away.
2. Insert tip under the bottom curve of the "S" shape.
3. Squeeze the bag with steady pressure as you pull down, then lift the tip. Move up and over the tail of the "S" as you continue to squeeze and form a hook.
4. Keep spacing as even as possible and "S" curves uniform in thickness, length and overall size. Be sure to tuck the tip into the bottom curve of the previous "S" before you begin squeezing to insure the clean, continuous look of a rope.

e-Motion

These continuous e-shaped loops work best on a bottom border, or as a western lariat. If you have to stop on your border to change positions, push in your tip at the end of the "e" and continue piping to keep a smooth look.

Practice With: Tip 16
Icing Consistency: Medium
Bag Position: 45° at 3:00 (9:00)
Hold Tip: Slightly above surface

1. Starting with bag at a 45° angle, and at bottom edge, squeeze out icing with even pressure, moving tip up to the right…
2. …and around as if writing the letter "e".
3. Repeat to complete the border, using a steady, even pressure. To end, stop pressure, pull tip away. You can vary the look of the "e" motion border by making tight e's or stretched e's.

BASKETWEAVE TIPS

Try using different tips to vary the woven effects.

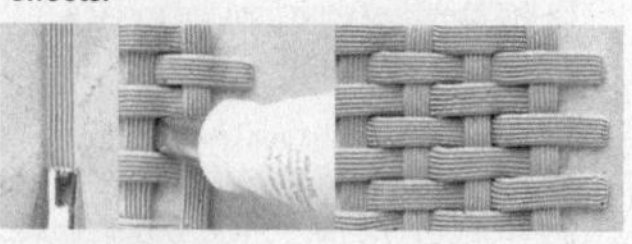

Practice With: Tip 47
Icing Consistency: Medium
Bag Position: 45° at 6:00 for vertical stripes; at 3:00 (9:00) for horizontal bars
Hold Tip: Lightly touching surface, serrated side up

1. Squeeze out a vertical stripe of icing from top to bottom (shown ridged side up).
2. Squeeze out short horizontal stripes of icing across the vertical stripe starting at the top. Spacing between stripes should be the same as the width of the tip opening. Squeeze next vertical stripe over ends of horizontal stripes. Start next set of horizontal stripes by burying the tip under the first vertical stripe.
3. Repeat vertical lines then horizontal lines until you achieve basketweave effect. Each new set should fit between the previous set.

MULTIPLE TIPS

Swirl Drop Flower

The swirled look adds a nice motion effect to the cake. You must squeeze and turn at the same time.

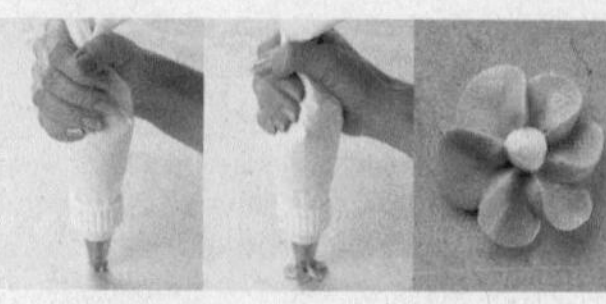

Practice With: Tips 2D, 3; Use Large Coupler
Icing Consistency: Use royal icing: medium for flower, thin for center
Bag Position: 90°
Hold Tip: Slightly above surface

1. Turn your wrist in toward you before piping. Hold bag straight up, just touching the surface. You will turn wrist a full twist. Starting with the flat of your knuckles at 9:00 (3:00), as you squeeze out the icing, slowly turn your hand, with knuckles ending at 12:00.
2. Stop squeezing and lift the tip away.
3. Make a tip 3 dot flower center, holding your bag straight up and keeping the tip buried as you squeeze. Stop squeezing, then pull your tip up and away.

Star Drop Flower

Pipe them in buttercream when you want to add pretty flowers instantly, right on your cake. Use royal icing if you want to make them in advance.

Practice With: Tips 2D, 3; Use Large Coupler
Icing Consistency: Use royal icing: medium for flower, thin for center
Bag Position: 90°
Hold Tip: Slightly above surface

1. Hold the bag straight up, with the end of drop flower tip 2D just touching surface.
2. Squeeze, letting the icing build up to make the flower. Stop squeezing, then lift tip away.
3. Make a tip 3 dot flower center, holding your bag straight up and keeping the tip buried as you squeeze. Stop squeezing, then pull your tip up and away.

Crown Border

Majestic upright shells actually "crown" the top edges and sides of your cake. You can embellish the shell points with dots, stars or strings.

Practice With: Tip 32 or 4B for shell, 4 for dot
Icing Consistency: Medium
Bag Position: Slightly less than 90° at 6:00
Hold Tip: Slightly above surface

1. Start each shell at the top edge of the cake; apply pressure to let the shell build up and curve over the edge of the tier.
2. Relax pressure and move down to draw the shell to a point. Continue piping a row of side-by-side shells over the top edge of your cake.
3. Pipe a tip 4 dot at the end of each shell. Optional: Use tip 3 to pipe double drop strings on shell ends, then pipe tip 4 dots at shell points.

PETAL TIPS

Ruffle

Everyone loves a ruffle's graceful motion—ruffles always add interest to your cake. Use them as a top border, to frame a plaque or to trim doll dresses and baby bonnets.

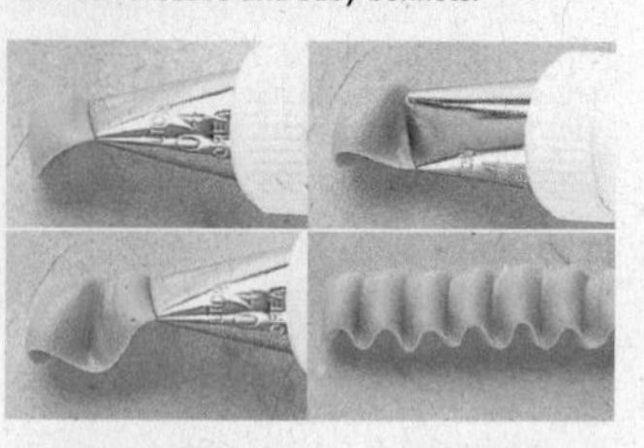

Practice With: Tip 104
Icing Consistency: Medium
Bag Position: 45° at 3:00 (9:00)
Hold Tip: Wide end lightly touching surface with narrow end facing down and away from surface

1. Keep the wide end of your tip touching the cake with the narrow end down. Move wrist up to pull up icing.
2. Move wrist down to complete one curl of the ruffle.
3. Repeat up and down motion.
4. Raise and lower the narrow end as you move around the cake. Repeat this motion for the entire ruffle.

Bow

The bow has many uses. Create a different look each time you use a different tip: round, star and petal will work.

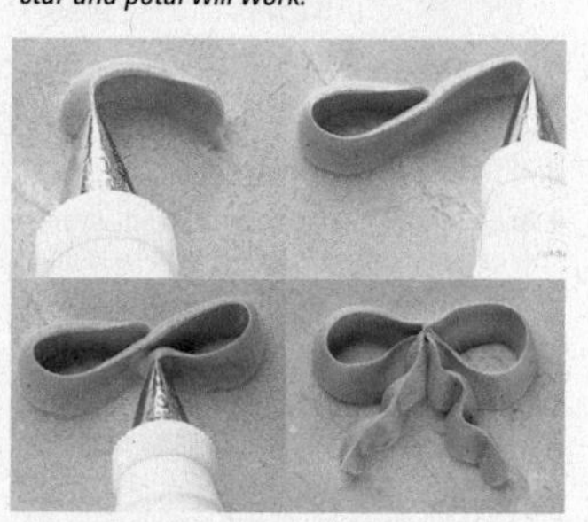

Practice With: Tip 104
Icing Consistency: Medium
Bag Position: 45° at 6:00
Hold Tip: Wide end touching surface, narrow end straight up

1. With narrow end of tip pointing straight up, squeeze, moving the tip up and around to the left and back to the starting point.
2. Continue around, making a second loop on the right.
3. The two loops will form a figure 8.
4. While holding bag in the same position, return to the center and squeeze out two streamers.

Flower Making Techniques

Explore beautiful flowers like the sweet pea or carnation, which add lovely color to your cake design. Create the magnificent rose—the most popular icing flower of all—then progress to the grandest bell-shaped lilies. With practice, your flowers will have the just-picked look of real garden flowers.

FLOWER NAIL FLOWERS

Using a Flower Nail

The nail is a revolving platform you hold in your hand to conveniently build roses and other flowers. It allows you to work close up, to turn for easy piping and to remove your completed flowers without damage, ready to dry.

The key to making the flower on the nail is to coordinate the turning of the nail with the formation of each petal.

Attach a square of waxed paper on the flat surface of the flower nail using a dot of icing. Pipe your flower directly on the waxed paper. Hold the flower nail between the thumb and forefinger of your left (right) hand (use other fingers to support nail) and roll it slowly counterclockwise as you press out icing with the decorating bag held in the right (left) hand. Your right (left) hand moves in and out, or up and down, as it holds the decorating bag and tip at just the right angle (in most cases 45°) and keeps the icing flowing at an even speed. After piping, slide the waxed paper with flower off the nail to dry.

Wilton Rose

***NOTE:** If you are going to be placing your roses on your cake immediately, waxed paper squares are not needed. To remove finished roses, use the Flower Lifter (p. 134). Slide flower from lifter onto cake, using a spatula.*

Practice With: Tips 104, 12
Icing Consistency: royal or stiff buttercream icing
Bag Position: Base, 90° (straight up); petals, 45° at 4:30 (7:30)
Hold Tip: For base, slightly above nail; for petals, wide end touching base
Flower Nail: #7 (larger roses) or #9 (smaller roses)

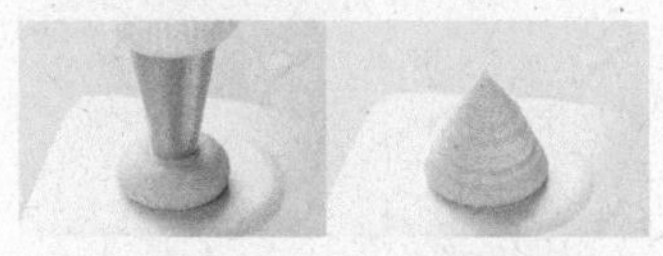

1. Make the rose base, using tip 12 and flower nail 7. Hold the bag straight up, the end of tip 12 slightly above the center of your waxed paper-covered flower nail, which is held in your other hand. Using heavy pressure, build up a base, remembering to keep your tip buried as you squeeze. Start to lift the tip higher, gradually raise the tip, and decrease the pressure.
2. Stop pressure, pull up and lift away. The rose base should be 1½ times as high as the rose tip opening.

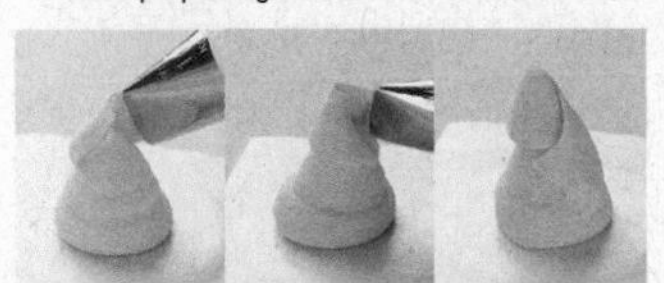

3. Make the center bud, using tip 104. Hold nail containing base in your left (right) hand and bag with rose tip 104 in right (left) hand. Bag should be at a 45° angle to the flat surface of the nail and in the 4:30 (7:30) position. The wide end of the tip should touch the cone of the icing base at or slightly below the midpoint, and the narrow end of the tip should point up and angled in over top of base.
4. Now you must do 3 things at the same time: squeeze the bag, move the tip and rotate the nail. As you squeeze the bag, move the tip up from the base, forming a ribbon of icing. Slowly turn the nail counterclockwise (clockwise for lefties) to bring the ribbon of icing around to overlap at the top of the mound, then back down to starting point. Move your tip straight up and down only; do not loop it around the base.
5. Now you have a finished center bud.

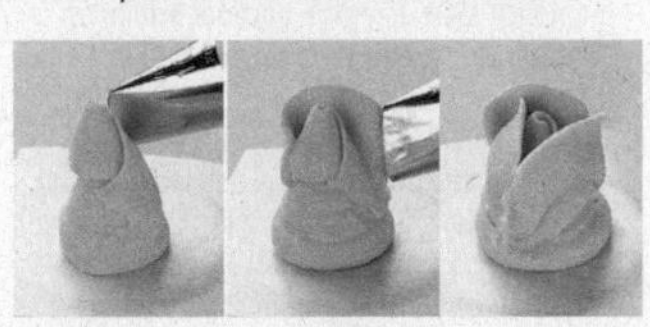

6. Make the top row of 3 petals. Touch the wide end of tip to the midpoint of bud base, narrow end straight up.
7. Turn nail, keeping wide end of tip on base so that petal will attach. Move tip up and back down to the midpoint of mound, forming the first petal.
8. Start again, slightly behind end of first petal, and squeeze out second petal. Repeat for the third petal, ending by overlapping the starting point of the first petal. Rotate the nail ⅓ turn for each petal.

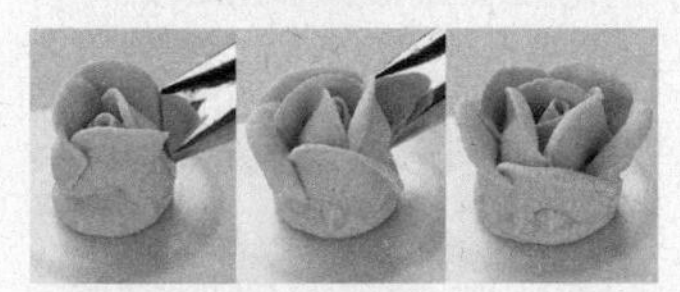

9. Make the middle row of 5 petals. Touch the wide end of tip slightly below center of a petal in the top row. Angle the narrow end of tip out slightly more than you did for the top row of petals. Squeeze bag and turn nail, moving tip up, then down to form first petal.
10. Repeat for a total of 5 petals, rotating the nail ⅕ turn for each petal.
11. The last petal end should overlap the first's starting point.

12. Make the bottom row of 7 petals. Touch the wide end of tip below the center of a middle row petal, again angling the narrow end of tip out a little more. Squeeze bag and turn nail to end of fingers, moving tip up, then down to form first petal.
13. Repeat for a total of 7 petals, rotating the nail ⅐ turn for each petal.

14. The seventh petal end should overlap the first's starting point. Slip waxed paper and completed rose from nail.
15. This is the completed Wilton rose.

Rosebud

Finish your petits fours or cupcakes with one pretty rosebud. Made in buttercream, this flat flower can be piped directly on the cake.

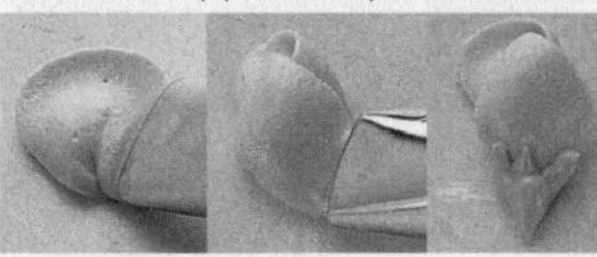

Practice With: Tips 104, 3
Icing Consistency: Stiff consistency buttercream for petals, thin consistency for sepals and calyx
Bag Position: 45° at 4:30 (7:30) for petals; 45° at 6:00 for sepals and calyx

1. Using tip 104, make the base petal. Keep the narrow end of the tip raised up and slightly to the right (left for lefties). While squeezing, move the tip along the surface away from you in a straight line about ¼ in. long. Pause, then continue squeezing as the icing fans out. Returning the tip to the original position and halfway back, start to release pressure, move tip to starting point, stop pressure and pull tip away.
2. Using tip 104, make the overlapping petal. Touch the wide end of the tip to the outside edge of completed petal. The bag is positioned as for the base petal, at 4:30 (7:30); hold it steady in this position until the second petal is completed. As you continue squeezing, the icing will catch the edge of the base petal and roll it over naturally. When the second petal looks complete, stop pressure completely, touch the tip back down to the surface and pull tip away.
3. Using tip 3, make the sepals and calyx. Form the middle sepal first by squeezing and letting icing build up. Lift the bag up and away from the flower. Stop pressure as you pull away to form the point of the sepal. Repeat, making a sepal on the left and right sides. For the calyx, insert tip into the base of the center sepal. Squeeze, letting the icing build up. Slowly draw the tip toward you, relaxing pressure as you move away from the flower. Stop pressure, pull away. You may want to blend the calyx into the stem using a damp brush.

Sweet Pea

One of the fastest, easiest-to-make flowers; works beautifully as part of a floral cascade. Try piping them in variegated shades.

Practice With: Tips 104, 3
Icing Consistency: Buttercream—stiff for petals, thin for calyx
Bag Position: For center petal and calyx, 45° at 6:00; for left petal, 45° at 4:30; for right petal, 45° at 7:30.
Hold Tip: Wide end touching surface; narrow end straight up

1. Make the center petal. Squeeze the bag and lift the tip slightly off the surface (about ¼ in.) as the icing moves forward and curls. Continue to squeeze without changing position. Relax pressure and return the tip to the surface. Stop squeezing, pull tip away.
2. Make the side petals. Position your bag slightly to the left of the center petal. Follow the same procedure as you did for the center petal—squeeze, and while the petal curls, lift the tip, relaxing your pressure and lowering the tip back to the surface. Stop squeezing and pull away. Repeat for the right side petal, holding the tip to the right of the center petal.
3. Make the calyx with tip 3.

Wild Rose

A pretty year-round flower piped about the size of nail head #7. If you prefer a more cupped shape, increase the angle you hold the tip. Dry in flower formers (p. 134) to keep the curved shape.

Practice With: Tips 103, 1
Icing Consistency: Medium royal icing
Bag Position: For petals, 45° at 3:00 (9:00); for center, 90°
Hold Tip: For petals, wide end lightly touching center of nail, narrow end pointing out and raised ⅛ in. above nail surface; for centers, slightly above flower
Flower Nail: #7

1. Use tip 103 at a 45° angle. Touch nail with wide end of tip, keeping narrow end just slightly above nail surface. Begin at center of flower nail and squeeze out first petal, turning nail ⅕ turn as you move tip out toward edge of nail. Relax pressure as you return to center of nail, curving tip slightly upward to create a cupped shape. Stop squeezing as wide end touches center of nail and lift up.
2. Repeat step 4 more times.
3. Pull out tiny stamens with tip 1.

Apple Blossom

This springtime flower is virtually the same as the wild rose, but uses a smaller tip. Pipe apple blossoms about the size of a penny and dry them on flower formers.

Practice With: Tips 101, 1
Icing Consistency: Stiff royal icing
Bag Position: 45° for petals; 90° for dots
Hold Tip: Wide end touching surface, with narrow end pointed out.
Flower Nail: #7

1. Use tip 101 and hold bag at a 45° angle to flower nail with wide end of tip touching nail center, narrow end pointed out ⅛ in. away from nail surface.
2. Squeeze bag and turn nail as you move tip ⅛ in. out from nail center and back, relaxing pressure as you return to starting point.
3. Repeat procedure to make 4 more petals. Add 5 tip 1 dots for center.

Ribbon Roses

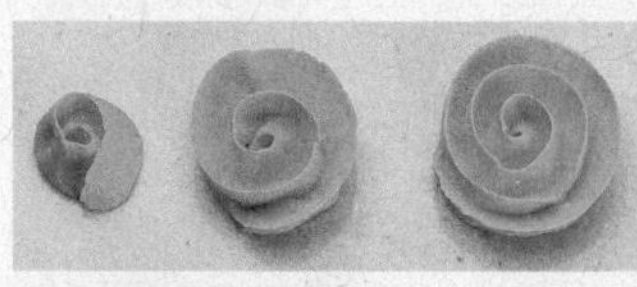

Practice With: Tip 104
Icing Consistency: Stiff royal icing
Bag Position: 90° at 6:00
Hold Tip: Wide end touching center of flower nail
Flower Nail: #7

1. Use tip 104 and hold bag at a 90° angle with wide end of tip touching center of flower nail.
2. Turn nail counterclockwise and, using even pressure, squeeze out a ribbon of icing, wrapping it around to form a rose.

FLORAL GREENERY

Leaves

Practice With: Tips 352, 67, 366
Icing Consistency: Buttercream thinned with corn syrup
Bag Position: 45° at 6:00
Hold Tip: Lightly touching surface; wide opening parallel to surface

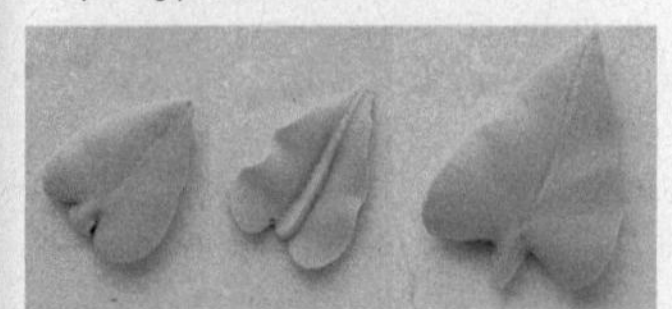

Basic Leaf Tip #352	**Veined Leaf Tip #67**	**Large Leaf Tip #366** Use large coupler

These three leaves are all made following the same sequence.

1. Squeeze hard to build up the base and, at the same time, lift the tip slightly.
2. Relax pressure as you pull the tip toward you, drawing the leaf to a point.
3. Stop squeezing and lift away.

Vines

Practice With: Tip 3
Icing Consistency: Thin
Bag Position: 45° at 3:00 (9:00)
Hold Tip: Lightly touching surface

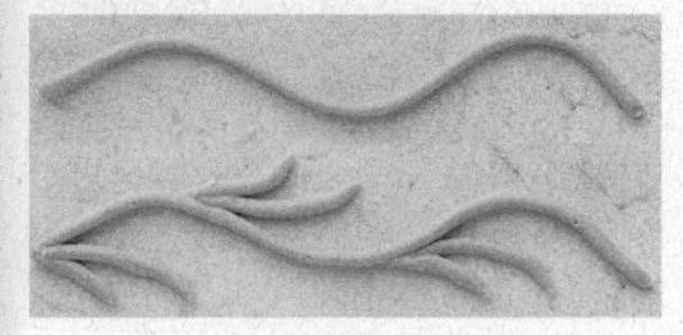

1. Touch your tip lightly to the surface as you start to squeeze, then lift slightly above the surface as you draw out the stem.
2. Move tip gently up and down to form "hills and valleys." To end the line, stop squeezing and pull the tip along the surface.
3. Add secondary curved stems, starting at main stem, stopping pressure as you pull to a point.

Attaching Bases or Flowers to Wire Stems

On waxed paper square, using royal icing, pipe a dot base with tip 3. Make ⅛ in. hook on end of 4 in. florist wire and insert hook into base. With slightly moistened decorator brush, smooth and taper the icing around the wire. Push other end of wire into a piece of craft block and let dry. Remove waxed paper and attach flower with dots of icing.

Attaching Leaves to Wire Stems

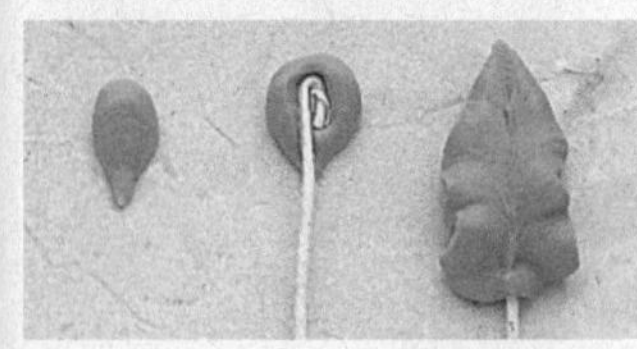

On waxed paper square, using royal icing, pipe a dot base with tip 4. Make ⅛ in. hook on end of florist wire and insert hook into the dot base. Use tip 352 and pipe a leaf directly on top of wire. Push the other end of the wire into a craft block and let dry. Remove waxed paper square when dry.

Other Decorating Techniques

Combing

Practice with: Icing Sculptor™, Decorating Comb or Triangle (p. 131)
Icing Consistency: Medium-to-thin buttercream

Cover the cake with a slightly thicker coating of icing so the comb's ridges will not touch the cake. Comb immediately after icing cake, while icing is soft. Using a turntable helps to keep the movement smooth. Use the Icing Sculptor™, Decorating Comb or Decorating Triangle to add different contoured effects to your iced cake. Choose the type of effect you want—wide or narrow—then run that edge around your cake to form ridges. Ridges will be deep or shallow depending on the Icing Sculptor™ blade or the side of Decorating Comb or Triangle you use.

Icing Sculptor™ *(p. 131)*
Select the sculpting blades you want and slide into holder. Press sculptor into iced cake as you rotate cake on turntable. The 64 blades included can create hundreds of different effects! Mix and match between the 14 edge designs to achieve the perfect look for your cake.

Combed Garland
To create a garland, hold comb so that about 4 teeth from the edge are touching the cake at the beginning of garland. Run comb in a curve, positioning so that about 6 teeth are touching cake at the bottom of the garland, then curve back with 4 teeth touching to finish garland. It's important to keep the comb level with the cake surface, so that the ridges created are uniform.

Pattern Press

The trick to uniform designs and steady writing and printing is using a pattern press! Simply imprint the press onto all types of icing, including fondant! Use the vine pattern press on cake sides for a beautiful botanical effect.

Practice With: Tips 3; 16
Icing Consistency: Medium
Bag Position: 45° at 3:00
Hold Tip: Slightly above surface

1. Lightly press pattern onto your iced cake to imprint the design.
2. Outline the imprinted design with icing, using the tip of your choice. Change the tip to change the look of each pattern.

Tinting Shredded Coconut

Place desired amount of coconut in plastic bag, add a few drops of color and knead until color is evenly blended. Dry on waxed paper.

Tower Turrets

See Princess for a Day, p. 38.

1. Moisten bottom edge of cone with water. Trim cone to 3¾ in. Pipe a small amount of icing into cone and insert lollipop stick to hold cone when decorating. Using tip 47 (smooth side up), pipe vertical bricks at bottom edge; overpipe tip 47 band bottom border.
2. Pipe tip 6 vertical shells to cover cone, row-by-row, beginning at bottom edge. Flatten shells with finger dipped in cornstarch.
3. Overlap each row, and continue all the way to point. Insert sticks into craft block and set aside to dry.

Basket Handles

See Baskets All Around, p. 66.

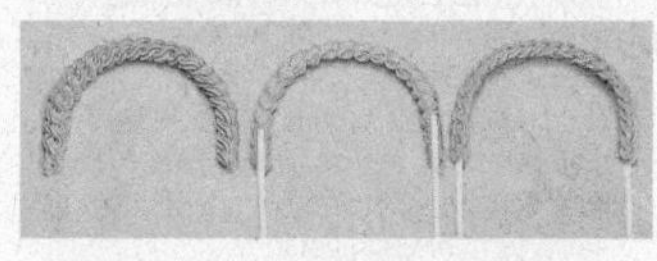

1. Tape pattern on board and cover with waxed paper. Pipe tip 16 rope over pattern with royal icing, making 2 handles each in rose, yellow, blue and violet. Make extras to allow for breakage and let dry overnight.
2. Carefully release handle from waxed paper with spatula and turn over. Cut 8 lollipop sticks in half; attach one half to each end of handle with royal icing, leaving 2¼ in. extending to insert into cake.
3. Overpipe tip 16 rope on top side. Let dry.

Wedding Fantasy Flowers

See Five-Star Sophistication, p. 88.

1. Use tip 3 and royal icing to pipe ½ in. dots for flower center and ¼ in. dots for flower sides on waxed paper. Let dry.
2. Use tip 3 and royal icing to pipe star shape on waxed paper. Let dry.
3. Attach dots to star with tip 3 and royal icing. Let set.

Baby Bird Assembly

See Under Her Wing, p. 80.

Ice 2 mini ball halves together, base to base; trim bottom so that cake sits level. Cut lollipop stick to 3 in. and insert in marshmallow; insert in top of cake for head. With spatula, ice marshmallow into rounded shape. Refer to p. 80 for directions on finishing your baby bird.

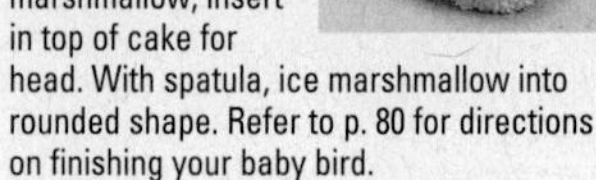

Storks

See They Deliver For You, p. 79.

1. For Standing Storks, secure lollipop stick on waxed paper-covered surface with tip 3 dot of royal icing. Using royal icing, pipe tip 12 ball head and tip 2A body. Position 1 in. length of lollipop stick for beak into head. Pipe tip 5 outline pull-out wings. Let dry overnight.
2. Use spatula to release stork from waxed paper; turn over and repeat same process on other side to create a full 3-D figure; let dry. Pipe tip 3 pull-out tail.

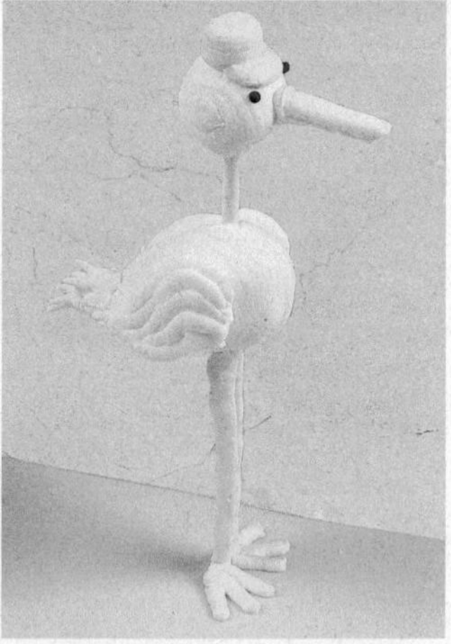

3. Use tip 12 to pipe ball hat with tip 3 brim. Add tip 2 dot eyes. Insert lollipop stick "beak" into bag fitted with tip 8; squeeze icing and pull out. Cover legs with tip 5; add tip 3 outline feet.

For Stork in "take-off" position (shown on p. 79), follow Standing Stork directions, except use tip 5 to pipe pull-out wings separately on waxed paper and let dry overnight. Attach wings to body with royal icing; hold in position with tissue or foam and let dry.

DECORATING WILTON SHAPED CAKES STEP-BY-STEP

When decorating a cake that's simply covered with stars, here are the easy steps involved.

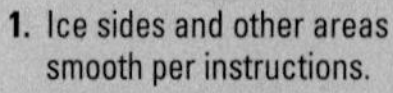

1. Ice sides and other areas smooth per instructions.

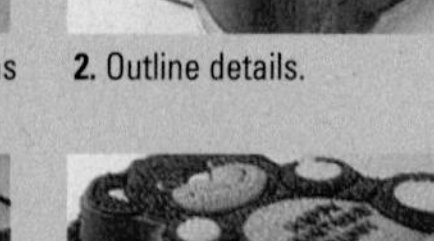

2. Outline details.

3. Pipe in facial features, small details.

4. Cover areas with stars, stripes, zigzags or hair.

5. Add message. Edge top and base with borders. Attach flowers or trims.

Fondant/Gum Paste Techniques

Mickey Arms

See Wrapped Up in the Fun, p. 41.

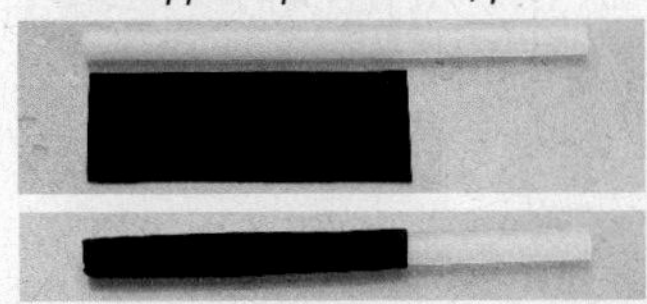

1. For arms, cover two plastic dowel rods with black fondant, leaving 4½ in. uncovered at bottom to insert into cake; let dry.
2. Roll out white fondant 3/16 in. thick. Using pattern and craft knife, cut hands. Using royal icing, outline hands with tip 3. Let dry on cornstarch-dusted surface.

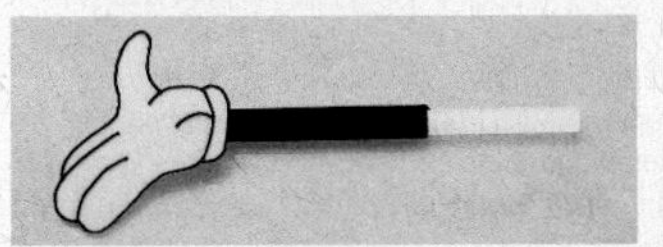

3. Attach hands to arms with melted candy; let set.

Scarf Ends, Hat and Skis

See He's A Ski Mogul, p. 54.

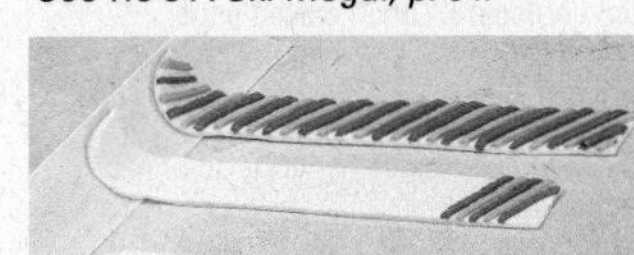

Use Extra Firm Fondant Recipe, p. 111.

For skis, tape one curved edge of a 2 in. flower former to a waxed paper-covered board, so that former sits upright, with curve facing toward the board. Roll white fondant ⅛ in. thick and, using pattern, cut 2 skis. Curve end up inside flower formers and let dry. Cut ⅛ in. wide strips of red and green fondant and attach diagonally to skis with damp brush. Continue attaching until entire ski is covered.

For ski pole baskets (not shown). Cut 1½ in. diameter circles in red fondant. Make center hole with wooden dowel rod, let dry.

For scarf ends, roll green fondant ⅛ in. thick on cornstarch-dusted surface and cut two 1½ x 3½ in. strips. Attach scarf ends to lollipop sticks using water; leave 3 in. of stick exposed.

For scarf fringe, cut ¾ in. wide strips of green fondant; use pizza cutter to cut ⅛ in. wide fringe pieces; attach to scarf with damp brush. Shape scarf ends into waves and let dry over cotton balls.

For hat, crush aluminum foil into a cone shape, 4 x 6 in. high; bend tip to one side. Roll out red fondant and wrap around foil, cut to fit and blend ends together with brush dipped in water.

For pompom, roll a 1¾ in. diameter ball of white fondant; attach to hat with thinned fondant, let dry.

Fondant Sash and Headpieces

See Miracle of the Manger, p. 56.

For Joseph's sash, tint a 2 in. fondant ball brown, roll out and cut a 7 x 2 in. rectangle; gather into 3 folds and wrap around body.

For Mary's veil, tint a 2 in. fondant ball blue; roll out and cut a 6 in. circle. Drape over head and shoulders.

For white headpieces on shepherds, roll 1½ in. fondant balls and cut into 4 ½ in. circles. Position on head.

Fondant Elves

See Santa's Helpers, p. 58.

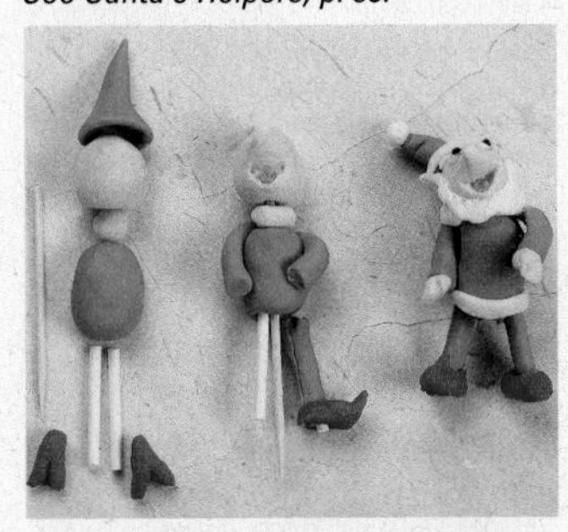

1. Divide 12 oz. white fondant and tint 9 oz. light copper, a very small amount black, a very small amount rose, reserve some white. Also use red and green from the Primary Color Variety Pack. **For Small Elf** (holding stamp): Roll ⅞ in. copper ball head, ⅜ in. copper ball neck and ⅞ in. green ball body. Shape body into 1 in. long log. Roll two ½ in. red ball shoes, form into "V" shapes. Roll ½ in. green cone hat. Cut two lollipop sticks to 1½ in. long for legs. Cut wooden skewer to 3 in. long for center support.
2. Assemble as follows, brushing pieces with water where needed to attach: Shape head into egg shape. Pull up a peak in center of head for nose. Poke hole under nose and pull down for mouth. Roll a tiny piece of rose fondant, shape into tongue and attach. Push head onto skewer. From bottom of skewer, push on neck and body. Insert lollipop sticks under body, on each side of skewer for legs. Wrap each leg in green fondant. Insert shoes over bottom of legs. Roll out 2 green logs 1½ in. long, attach to body for arms.
3. Roll two ⅜ in. copper ball hands; attach to ends of arms. Imprint fingers with edge of knife. Shape arms to hold stamp. Using tiny pieces of white, trim outfit, make eyes and beard. Add tiny pieces of black for eyes. Attach hat, add fur trim and pompom. Push skewer into craft block and set aside to dry.

For Medium Elf (pulling ribbon): Assemble following the Small Elf directions, with these changes. Use 1¼ in. copper ball for head, ⅜ in. copper ball for neck, 1¼ in. green ball for body—shape into 1 in. long log. Cut lollipop sticks to 2 in. and 2½ in. long for legs (the longer leg will be inserted into the cake top). Cut skewer 4 in. long. Shoes, hat, hands and facial features are the same as the Small Elf. Arms are 2 in. logs of fondant with a 1¾ in. lollipop stick in each. Arms are straight; join at hands to hold ribbon. Cut 3 in. long x ⅞ in. wide strip of red fondant for streamer. Pinch end and attach to elf's hands.

For Large Elf (holding FoodWriter): Assemble following the Medium Elf directions, with these changes. Legs are 2⅛ in. long. Shape arms to hold marker.

Fondant Graduates

See Tomorrow's Stars, p. 77.

1. Roll out fondant ⅛ in. thick and use small girl cutter from 101 Cutter Set (p. 142) to cut 14 graduates in copper or light brown. Repeat, cutting 14 blue gowns; trim off head portions to create round neckline, trim ¼ in. off arms to allow hands to show through gown. Roll twenty-eight ¼ in. black fondant balls and shape into ovals for shoes. Using pattern, cut 14 blue caps. Let all pieces dry several days on cornstarch-dusted surface. Make tassels following instructions on p. 77.
2. Attach gowns and shoes (not shown) to body with dots of icing. Let dry.
3. Decorate graduates with royal icing: Pipe tip 2 string and swirl hair. Add 2 tip 3 circles on head for cap base; attach cap. Using tip 1, pipe a dot button and string on top of cap; attach tassel.

Carriage, Bow and Handle

See Bless the Child, p. 74.

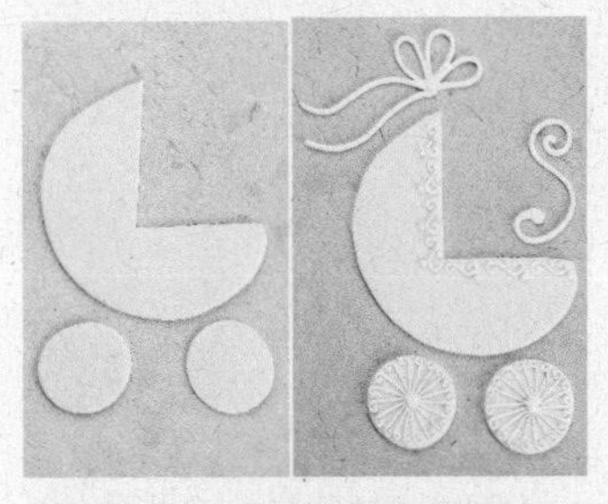

1. Knead 1 teaspoon Gum-Tex™ into 12 oz. fondant. Roll out ⅛ in. thick; cut out carriage using pattern. Cut 2 fondant wheels using largest round Cut-Out™. Let all pieces dry on cornstarch-dusted surface.
2. Using royal icing, decorate carriage with tip 2 scrolls and dots; add tip 2 wheel spokes. Let dry.

3. Cover bow and handle patterns with waxed paper; outline with tip 6 and royal icing. Let dry. Attach wheels, handle and bow to carriage with royal icing. Attach 2 lollipop sticks to back with royal icing, trimming as needed; let dry.

Gum Paste Flowers and Leaves

See Promised Forever, p. 85.

Divide gum paste recipe into 4ths. Tint ¼ Kelly Green/Moss Green combination and cut 40 leaves using cutter from Stepsaving Rose Bouquet Flower Cutter Set (p. 124) (make extra to allow for breakage). Place leaves on thin foam and imprint veins using veining tool. Let dry in various positions on crumpled foil or bubble wrap dusted with cornstarch. Divide remaining gum paste in half; tint half light rose, half light violet. Cut 25 flowers in each color using small rose cutter from Stepsaving set (make extras to allow for breakage). Using sharp knife, cut a ¼ in. slit toward center on each petal division. Place flowers on thin foam; ruffle petal edges with ball tool. Let flowers dry in cornstarch-dusted cavities of Candy Melting Plate (p. 147). Using dry brush, dust flowers and leaves with chalk grated through tea strainer. Pipe tip 2 dot centers in flowers. Set aside.

Fondant Bow

See Bold And Blue, p. 5.*

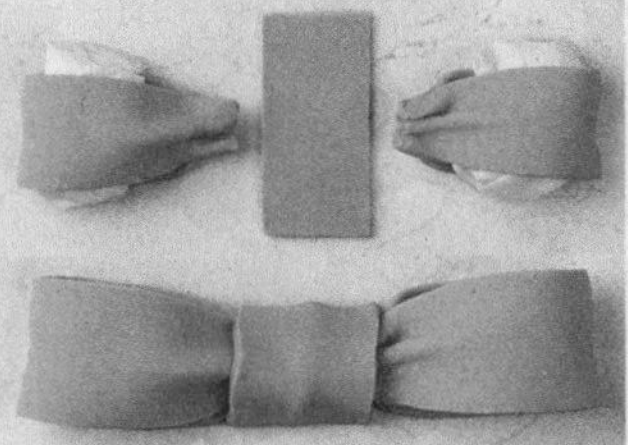

1. Roll out fondant ⅛ in. thick. Cut two 2 x 9 in. strips for loops. Cut 1½ x 4 in. strip for knot.
2. Pleat each end of bow loop strips. Fold strips over to form a loop. Brush ends lightly with water, align ends. Position cotton balls inside loops to keep shape.
3. Shape the knot by pleating each end of fondant strip and wrapping it around middle of the joined bow loops. For streamers, cut 1½ in. wide strips, 5 and 6 in. long; cut V-shapes at one end and pinch together other end to fit under loops. Let dry; remove cotton balls.

***NOTE:** Bow on cake uses white fondant.

Figure Piping Techniques

Figure piping is a way to really add personality to your cake. Your figures can be as lifelike or cartoonish as you want them to be. Begin with a base, then add familiar shapes such as dots, balls and strings that give the figure personality.

Once you have mastered pressure control, figure piping will be easy. Stiff consistency icing is the key to successful figure piping. For softer figures that are more to eat, use medium consistency buttercream icing. With buttercream, you can pipe figures directly on your cake, shortly ahead of the party. Royal icing shapes dry very hard, so they can be difficult to eat, but you can make them well in advance of the party. Pipe them ahead of time on waxed paper, let dry, then position figures on cake. Remember to store pre-made royal icing decorations in a cool, dry and dark place. Exposure to constant fluorescent lighting or bright sunlight can cause color to fade.

Camping Kids

(see Park Paradise, p. 15)

Tips: 1, 2A, 3, 5, 8, 12
Bags: Featherweight or Disposable decorating bags
Icing Consistency: Stiff royal icing
Hold Tip: Slightly above surface when piping body, inserted into body when piping arms and legs. Hold close to cake so icing attaches without scraping cake with tip and without flattening icing strings

1. **Make the body:** Figure pipe boy on waxed paper-covered craft block. Use tip 12 in an upright position and the basic icing build-up technique to pipe base with swimming trunks. Squeeze hard to build up a generous base, then slowly fill out the trunks by drawing up to desired height. Repeat same process for body torso.
2. **Make arms, legs and head:** Insert tip 8 into front of body and pipe legs; insert tip 8 into shoulders of body and pipe 8 arms. Pipe tip 12 ball head.
3. **Make hands, feet, facial features and hair:** Pipe tip 3 hands and feet with tip 3 fingers and toes. Pipe tip 1 hair and facial features.

NOTE: For boy at campfire, pipe body with tip 2A. Insert string licorice for stick and pipe tip 5 hot dog.

Lambs

(see Miracle of the Manger, page 56)

1. On waxed paper, using Royal Icing, pipe tip 7 log body, 2 in. long. Roll ½ in. Fondant ball head; position on body.
2. Cover body and head with tip 3 swirl fur.
3. Add tip 1 dot and string facial features and hooves. Let dry.

Grapes, Strawberries, Bananas

(see A Picnic with Pooh, p. 40)

For grapes: Using tip 4, pipe balls of icing, beginning with a single ball at the bottom of the bunch and increasing the number up to the stem end. Overpipe the bunch in the middle. Add tip 352 leaves and tip 2 curly vines.

For strawberries: Using tip 8, pipe teardrop shape; add tip 352 leaves and tip 2 dot seeds.
For bananas: Using tip 8, pipe crescent shape and add tip 3 stem and bottom accents.
For cherries: Using tip 8, pipe ball and add tip 2 stem.

Color Flow Techniques

WORKING WITH COLOR FLOW

1. Trace your design pattern onto parchment paper, then tape tracing paper onto a cake circle or the back of a cookie pan. Cover with waxed paper; smooth and tape. Using tip 2 and parchment bag half-filled with full strength Color Flow, squeeze, pull and drop icing string following pattern outline. Stop, touch tip to surface and pull away. If you will be using the same color to fill in, let outline dry a few minutes until it "crusts." To prevent bleeding of colors, let outline dry 1-2 hours before filling in.
2. Thin down Color Flow mixture with water. Cut opening in parchment bag to the size of tip 2. Fill in design with thinned Color Flow.
3. Let decorations air dry thoroughly, at least 48 hours. To remove, cut away waxed paper from board, then turn over and peel waxed paper off the Color Flow piece.

Hint: For curved decorations, dry pieces on flower formers. Since buttercream icing will break down Color Flow, either position Color Flow decoration on cake shortly before serving or place a piece of plastic wrap cut to fit on area first and Color Flow on sugar cubes.

To easily remove dried Color Flow, pull waxed paper backing over the edge of a table with one hand, while holding decoration with other hand. Waxed paper will pull off naturally. Or, with dried Color Flow resting on cookie sheet, place cardboard sheet over Color Flow, lift and turn over so that top of decoration rests on cardboard. Lift off waxed paper.

COVERING CAKES AND COOKIES WITH CANDY MELTS®* AND POURED ICINGS

A quick and easy way to give a professional-looking finish to all your baked goods! For Candy Melts®*, melt following package directions. For icings, follow recipe directions to reach pouring consistency. Place cooled cakes or cookies on cooling rack positioned over cookie sheet or pan. Pour candy or icing on center of item, spreading to edges with a spatula so that candy or icing drips down and covers sides. Let dry.

Sugar Molding Technique

Sugar Mold Recipe

2 cups granulated sugar
4 teaspoons water

Place sugar in a large mixing bowl. Mix sugar, making sure there are no lumps. Make a well in sugar and add water (if you are tinting sugar, blend icing color into water at this point). Rub mixture in hands and knead for about 1 minute or until well-blended and mixture packs like wet sand. Be sure there are no lumps in mixture.

NOTE: Keep sugar mixture covered with a damp cloth when not in use.

Hollowed Sugar Mold

Mix a double batch of the sugar mold recipe. Dust half Sports Ball Pan (p. 164) with cornstarch to prevent sticking. Pack sugar mixture into pan, pressing firmly with heel of hand. Scrape a metal spatula at a 45° angle over pan to remove excess sugar. Unmold at once by placing cardboard circle over pan and turning upside down. To loosen, tap top of pan with spatula and carefully lift pan off. Allow to dry 3 to 4 hours. When dry, turn sugar mold over and carefully hold in palm of hand. Do not squeeze or move molded sugar while holding or it will crack. Use a spoon to mark ¼ in. thick shell on the inside rim.

Gently scoop out soft sugar up to mark. Smooth inside and edge with your fingers. Place molded sugar, round side down, on cardboard circle to finish drying for about 24 hours, or place on cookie sheet in 200°F oven for 20 minutes. Allow to cool to room temperature before touching.

Candy Making Techniques

USING CANDY MELTS®*

Fast-melting confectionery coating wafers are the key to easy candy making. Smooth texture and great taste make Candy Melts your most convenient option for molding. Check out all the great colors on p. 146.

To Color

Add Candy Colors (p. 147) to melted Candy Melts®* a little at a time. Mix thoroughly before adding more color. Colors tend to deepen as they're mixed. Pastel colored candies are most appetizing, so keep this in mind. For some popular custom colors, see the chart below.

To Flavor

The creamy, rich taste of Candy Melts®* can be enhanced by adding approx. ¼ teaspoon oil-based Candy Flavor (p. 147) to 14 oz. (one pack) of melted Candy Melts®*. Never use alcohol based flavorings; they will cause coatings to harden.

Multicolored Candy

Painting Method

It's easy to mold with different areas of color—just use a decorator brush to "paint" the mold with melted Candy Melts®*. Refrigerate a few seconds until coating hardens, then fill mold to top with melted candy. Remember, only fill in one section of the mold at a time and let harden before adding more colors. Look for other ways to color and flavor your candy in our *Candy Making Beginner's Guide* (p. 222).

Layering Method

Pour melted coating into dry molds to desired height. Refrigerate until partially set. Pour melted contrasting color to desired height. Refrigerate until partially set. Repeat until desired number of layers are formed; refrigerate until firm and unmold.

Marbleizing Method

1. Separately melt two different colors of Candy Melts®*.
2. Stir colors together, using a lollipop stick to draw lines in mixture. Do not overmix.
3. Quickly spoon or place into molds, while mixture is still soft. Tap. Refrigerate until firm; unmold.

Candy Shells

Fill pan or mold to the top edge with melted candy. Tap on counter to remove air bubbles. Let chill in refrigerator for 10-15 minutes or until a ¼ in. shell has formed. Pour out excess candy, smooth top edges with spatula and chill for 15-20 minutes longer. Carefully unmold shells (if you have difficulty removing shells, place in freezer for 2-3 minutes, then unmold). Excess candy can be reheated and used again.

Candy Shells in Baking Cups

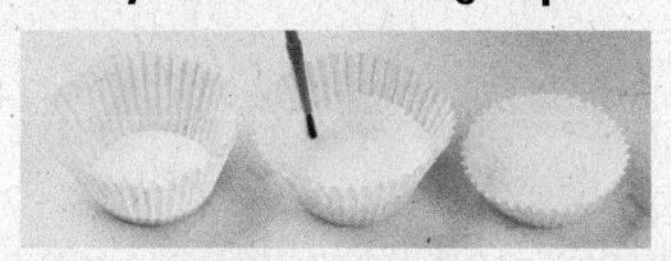

1. Add 1 to 2 Tablespoons of melted candy in the bottom of a standard muffin cup.
2. Brush candy slightly up sides, about halfway to top, forming an even edge.
3. Refrigerate 5 to 8 minutes. Repeat process if desired, for a thicker shell. Refrigerate until firm. Carefully peel baking cup off candy shell.

Umbrella

See Fun's A Shore Thing, p. 26

1. Make candy shell using Sports Ball pan half and yellow Candy Melts®* (see Candy Shells technique on this page).

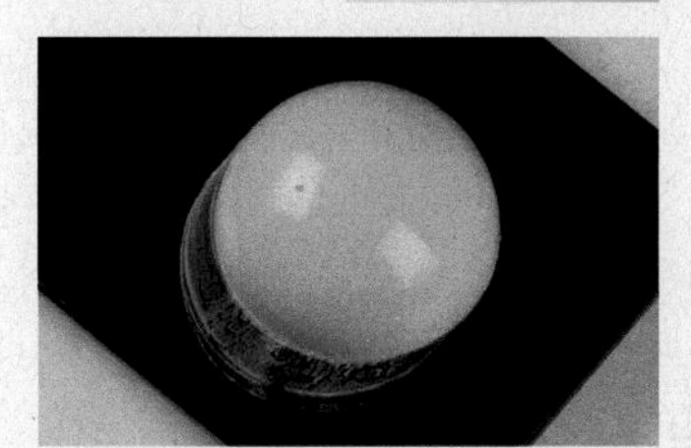

2. Unmold and quickly slide ball half over warming tray or warm cookie sheet to level edges.

Candy Plaques from Pans

Simply pour melted candy into the center of the area to be molded. Fill to ⅛ - ¼ in. thick. Tap pan gently to break up air bubbles and spread candy evenly. Refrigerate until firm, unmold onto hand or soft towel. Want to add more color? Use a disposable decorating bag to pipe one color at a time into pan. Refrigerate until firm, then repeat for each additional color.

To Remove Candy Plaques from Pans

Cut cake board to fit plaque inside pan. Place hand on board, invert pan and remove candy plaque on board.

Mickey Candy Plaque

See Wrapped Up in the Fun!, p. 41.

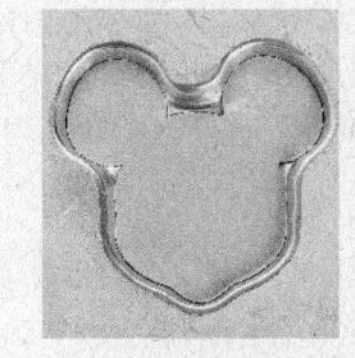

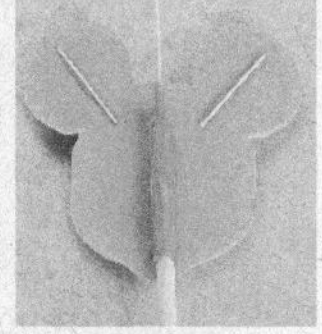

1. Tint melted white Candy Melts®* with a little orange Candy Color to achieve flesh tone used. Fill face portion of pan first, being careful not to fill above round area at top of face; next fill ear portions 1¼ in. thick. Refrigerate until firm.
2. To unmold, cut cardboard to fit inside pan. Let plaque come to room temperature. Place cardboard in pan and turn over to unmold. With melted candy, attach lollipop sticks diagonally to support each ear, attach plastic dowel rod vertically to center back allowing 6 in. to extend beyond neck to be inserted into cake later. Let set.
3. Turn plaque right side up. Using royal icing and tip 3, outline and pipe in eyes, nose, mouth and tongue (smooth with finger dipped in cornstarch). Cover ears and head with tip 16 stars.

*Brand confectionery coating.

Candy Plaque Graduate,

See Unlocking His Potential, p. 76.

1. Melt white, brown, red, yellow Candy Melts®*. (For skintone, add melted red and yellow to white). Make candy plaque in graduate pan, molding areas in this order: brown hair, yellow tassel, white diploma, skin tone face and hands, red cap and gown. **NOTE:** Make plaque to just below diploma; there is no need to mold entire body as it will be covered with locker door. Refrigerate to firm each area before starting the next.
2. Unmold, then pipe white eyes, brown pupils and brown message using melted candy in cut parchment bag. Let set.

Modeling a Candy Clay Rose

Start with the base and mold a cone approx. 1½ in. high from a ¾ in. diameter ball of candy clay. Next, flatten a ⅜ in. ball of candy clay into a circular petal about ¼ in. thick on one side and about the diameter of a dime. Make several petals this size. Wrap first petal around the point of the cone to form a bud. Now press 3 more petals around the base of the bud. Gently pinch edges of petals. Make 5 more petals using slightly larger balls of candy clay. Flatten, then thin edge with finger and cup petals. Press petals under first row of petals. Continue adding petals, placing them in between and slightly lower than previous row. For a fuller flower, continue adding petals in this manner.

Candy Clay Blossoms

See Heart's Treasure, p. 85.

Prepare a candy clay recipe, let cool, then knead together with 12 oz. fondant. Tint a 1 in. ball of mixture peach. Cut 25 each white and peach blossoms using forget-me-not cutter from Floral Collection Set (reserve remaining mixture). Place blossoms on thick foam and cup centers using small end of ball tool. Pipe tip 2 dot centers; let dry on small flower formers dusted with cornstarch.

Candy Clay Basket

See A Bear in the Air, p. 65.

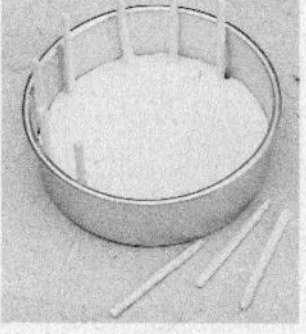

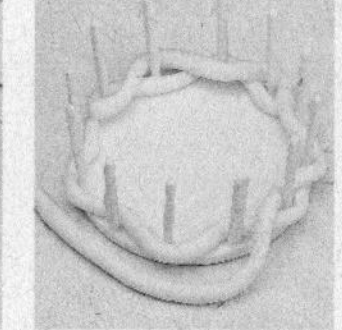

1. Cut 12 in. lollipop sticks to 3 in. long. Dip sticks into ½ pk. of melted Candy Melts®*, tap to remove excess and let dry approximately 30 minutes on waxed paper. Remelt remaining candy and pour ¼ in. deep in pan; insert 12 sticks evenly around edge. Refrigerate to set overnight.
2. Roll candy clay ropes, 24 x ½ in. diameter. Weave rope pieces around sticks, blending ends and trimming off excess in each row and adding new rows to reach basket top.
3. For top, twist 2 ropes together and insert on sticks.

CUSTOM CANDY COLORS MIXING CHART

You can mold candy in virtually any color using Candy Melts® and our Primary and Garden Candy Color Sets. Below are some popular colors and how to achieve them.*

START WITH...		THEN ADD...		TO GET...
WHITE (Candy Melts®*)	+	BLACK (Candy Color)	=	SHADES OF GRAY
BLUE (Candy Melts®*)	+	BLACK (Candy Color)	=	NAVY BLUE
WHITE (Candy Melts®*)	+	PINK (Candy Melts®* or Color)	=	FLESH TONES
WHITE (Candy Melts®*)	+	LIGHT COCOA (Candy Melts®*)	=	ETHNIC FLESH TONES
YELLOW (Candy Melts®*)	+	BLUE (Candy Melts®* or Color)	=	LEAF GREEN
WHITE (Candy Melts®*)	+	½ RED ½ BLUE (Candy Colors)	=	BLACK

2005 PRODUCT SHOPS

FIND IT FAST… ORDER WITH EASE!

Welcome to the most complete selection of cake decorating products anywhere! Here you'll find all the great Wilton tools, ingredients, accents and more you need to create every design in this Yearbook.

Go ahead and browse! Our shops are conveniently organized to help you find what you need fast. Whether you're decorating a batch of holiday cookies or creating a 3-tiered wedding cake, it's easy to find everything on your list.

When you're ready to buy, we make it a breeze! Charge your order 4 easy ways at your convenience:

PHONE TOLL-FREE
800-794-5866
8:00 am-4:30 pm, Monday-Friday CST
(RETAIL CUSTOMERS ONLY)

FAX TOLL-FREE
888-824-9520
24 HOURS A DAY/7 DAYS A WEEK

ORDER ON-LINE
www.wilton.com
24 HOURS A DAY/7 DAYS A WEEK

MAIL YOUR ORDER
Use the convenient retail order form in this book.

Se Habla Español!
Para mas informacion, marque 800-436-5778

Cake Decorating

Create your greatest cakes with the essentials decorators count on. Time-saving tools. Precise tips. Quality icings. Plus, the most exciting new products for fondant decorating!

fondant fun!™

Wilton presents the easy system for fondant decorating! Colorful, Ready-To-Use Rolled Fondant. Cut-Outs™ and Cake Stamps™ that create fun shapes. Brush-On Color™ and Icing Writer™ to add vivid designs. Easy-to-use tools that help you roll, cut and color to achieve exciting new decorations!

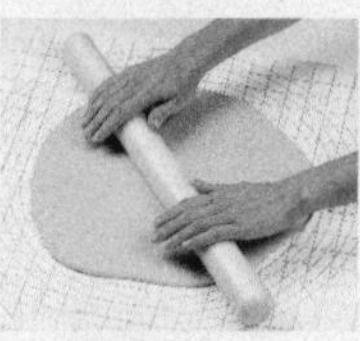
1. Roll out.

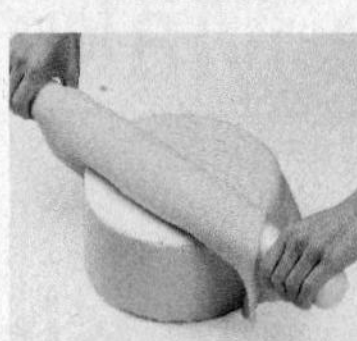
2. Layer over cake.

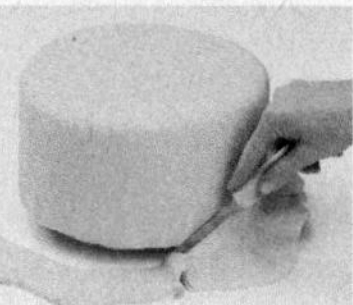
3. Trim and decorate.

READY-TO-USE ROLLED FONDANT

Fondant has never been more convenient and fun for decorating! With Wilton Ready-To-Use Rolled Fondant, the color is already mixed in for no kneading, no mess, no guesswork. The 24 oz. (1½ lb.) package, available in white and pastel colors, covers an 8 in. 2-layer cake plus decorations; the 80 oz. package (5 lbs.), available in white only, covers a 2-layer 6 in., 8 in. and 10 in. round tiered cake plus decorations. Certified Kosher.

White
24 oz. (1½ lb.) Pk.
710-P-2076 $5.99

White
80 oz. (5 lb.) Pk.
710-P-2180 $18.99

Pastel Pink
24 oz. (1½ lb.) Pk. 710-P-2181 $7.99

Pastel Blue
24 oz. (1½ lb.) Pk. 710-P-2182 $7.99

Pastel Yellow
24 oz. (1½ lb.) Pk. 710-P-2183 $7.99

Pastel Green
24 oz. (1½ lb.) Pk. 710-P-2184 $7.99

FONDANT MULTI PACKS

Convenient four-pouch assortments of primary, neon, pastel or natural colors are perfect for making multi-colored decorations. The color is already mixed in. . . no kneading, no mess, no guesswork. Great for flowers, borders and fun shapes. The 17.6 oz. package contains four 4.4 oz. packs. Certified Kosher. **$8.99**

Primary Colors
Green, Red, Yellow, Blue
710-P-445

Neon Colors
Purple, Orange, Yellow, Pink
710-P-446

Pastel Colors
Blue, Yellow, Pink, Green
710-P-447

Natural Colors
Light Brown, Dark Brown, Pink, Black
710-P-448

CAKE STAMPS™

Stamp colorful designs onto your fondant-covered cakes, cupcakes or cookies—it's easy and fun!

Shapes range from 1 to 1½ in.

- Four exciting stamp sets, each with six lively designs!
- Food-safe, with convenient handles for even imprinting.
- Use with Brush-On Color and Color Tray to create brilliant shapes!

Stamping is easy! NEW!

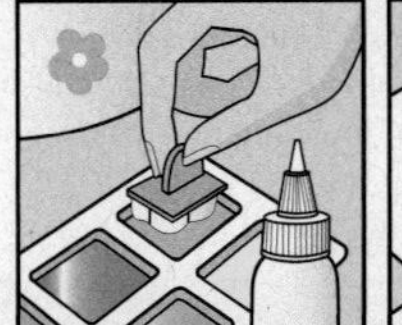

1. Fill Color Tray with Brush-On Color. Dip a Stamp into color.

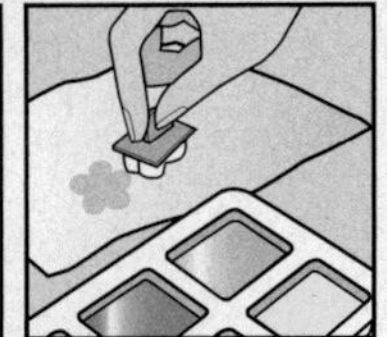

2. Press Stamp on parchment paper or paper towel to get the look just right.

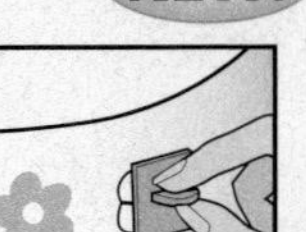

3. Press the fun design onto your fondant-covered cake. Rinse stamp in warm water and pat dry whenever changing colors.

Geometric
Star, Square, Square Border, Triangle, Round, Heart
417-P-181 Set/6 $4.49

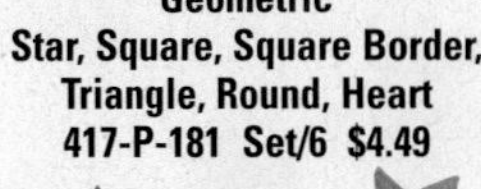

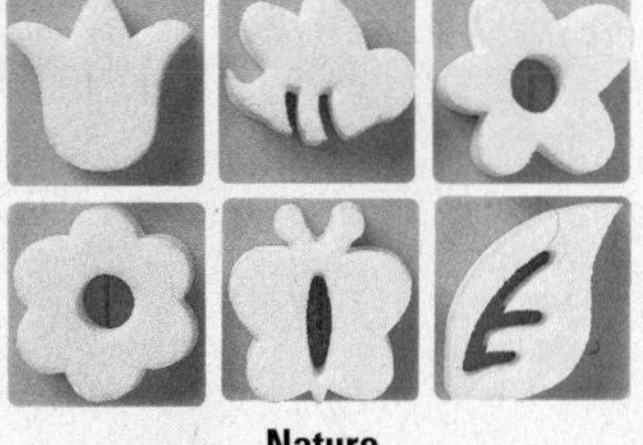

Nature
Tulip, Bee, 5-Petal Flower, 6-Petal Flower, Butterfly, Leaf
417-P-182 Set/6 $4.49

Romantic
Champagne Glass, Spiral, Dove Left, Dove Right, Bow, Bell
417-P-183 Set/6 $4.49

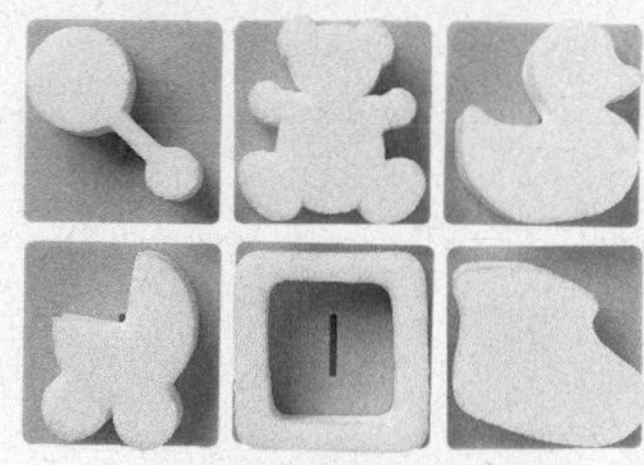

Baby
Rattle, Bear, Duck, Carriage, Frame, Shoe
417-P-184 Set/6 $4.49

CUT-OUTS™

With Cut-Outs, it's easy to make fun 3-D shapes for your fondant cakes and cupcakes. Just roll out fondant, press down with cut-out and lift away. Remove shapes with a small spatula.

Stainless steel shapes range from ⅝ in. to 2½ in.

- Fast, fun way to brighten any fondant cake!
- Great assortments of shapes for any occasion.
- Perfect for highlighting with Brush-On Color™ or Icing Writer™.

Look what you can do! NEW!

1. Layered decorations! Stack cut-out fondant pieces in different sizes and colors.

2. Fondant fill-ins! Use a smaller cut-out to remove the center of your fondant decoration. Fill in with a different color!

3. Cake insets! Cut out shapes from your fondant-covered cake, then replace the pieces with your favorite colors.

Square
417-P-431 Set/3 $2.49

Round
417-P-432 Set/3 $2.49

Star
417-P-433 Set/3 $2.49

Heart
417-P-434 Set/3 $2.49

Flower
417-P-435 Set/3 $2.49

Funny Flower
417-P-436 Set/3 $2.49

Leaf
417-P-437 Set/3 $2.49

People
417-P-441 Set/6 $3.99

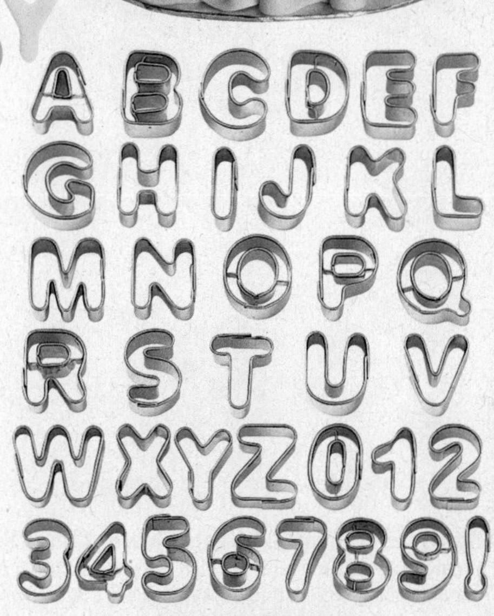

Alphabet/Number
417-P-442 Set/37 $14.99

fondant fun!™

BRUSH-ON COLOR™ NEW!

Ready-to-use edible decorating paint adds a vivid finish to fondant shapes! Just pour into the Color Tray (p. 125), then brush on or stamp on your fondant-covered cake. In seconds, you can add brilliant designs in a rainbow of bright colors. 3 oz. bottles. Certified Kosher.
$2.49

Blue		
610-P-922		
Red 610-P-920	**Yellow** 610-P-921	**Orange** 610-P-923
Green 610-P-924	**Pink** 610-P-925	**Violet** 610-P-926

ICING WRITER™ NEW!

Squeeze on colorful accents—flowers, swirls, messages and more—with this ready-to-use icing! It's easy to control for precise decorating: Just squeeze the bottle and icing flows easily from the built-in round tip. Trace imprinted shapes made with Cut-Outs or draw dazzling freehand designs. Dries to a smooth, satin finish. 3 oz. bottles. Certified Kosher.
$2.49

Blue		
710-P-2227		
Red 710-P-2225	**Yellow** 710-P-2226	**White** 710-P-2228
Green 710-P-2229	**Pink** 710-P-2230	**Violet** 710-P-2231

FOODWRITER™ EDIBLE COLOR MARKERS

Use like ink markers to add fun and dazzling color to countless foods. Kids love 'em! Decorate on fondant, Color Flow, royal icing, even directly on cookies. Brighten everyday foods like toaster pastries, cheese, fruit slices, bread and more. Each set includes five .35 oz. FoodWriter pens. Certified Kosher.

Primary Colors

Yellow, Green, Red, Blue, Black

Fine Tip
609-P-100
Set/5 $7.99

Bold Tip NEW!
609-P-115
Set/5 $7.99

FINE TIP
BOLD TIP

Neon Colors

Purple, Orange, Pink, Light Green, Black

Fine Tip NEW!
609-P-116
Set/5 $7.99

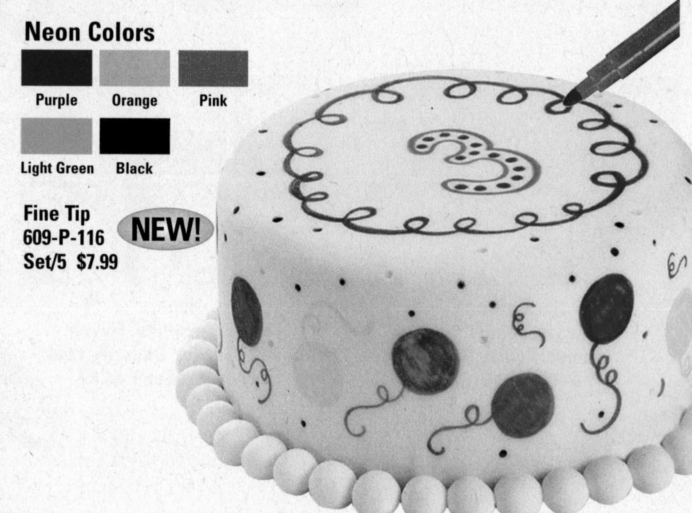

FONDANT AND GUM PASTE DECORATION SETS

Floral Collection Flower Making Set

Make incredibly lifelike gum paste flowers. Full-color how-to book includes many arranging ideas and step-by-step instructions. Kit includes 24 plastic cutters, 1 leaf mold, 3 wood modeling tools, protector flap, 40-page instruction book and 2 foam squares for modeling.
1907-P-117 Set/32 $19.99
Book only 907-P-117 $8.99

IDEAS & INSTRUCTIONS
Stepsaving Rose Bouquets
with FORGET-ME-NOTS
IDÉES ET INSTRUCTIONS
Bouquets de Roses Pratiques
AVEC LES MYOSOTIS

Stepsaving Rose Bouquets Flower Cutter Set

Create gorgeous fondant and gum paste roses and forget-me-nots using cutters and book in this set. Cutters include large and small rose, rose leaf, calyx and forget-me-not.
1907-P-1003 Set/6 $7.99

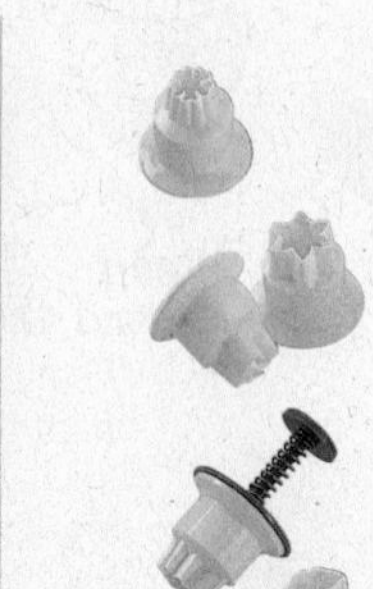

Floral Garland Cutter/Ejector Set

Quickly and easily cuts and positions fondant or gum paste flowers on cakes. Includes ejector, 5 cutters and instructions.
1907-P-1001 Set/7 $9.99

Romance Accents Fondant Mold Set

Just press fondant into molds, then release pretty designs to attach to your cake. Great for weddings, molded candy and more! Set includes mold for cherubs, flowers and beautiful borders (8 designs), knife/point tool for trimming and releasing and instruction book.
1907-P-1006 Set/3 $7.99

FONDANT TOOLS AND ACCESSORIES

Rolling Pin

NEW!

Roll out fondant evenly for easy cutting and shaping with this non-stick roller. It's easy to handle—just the right size for preparing small amounts of fondant to place on your cake. Perfect for use with Fondant Multi Packs and Cut-Outs™. 9 x 1 in. diameter.
1907-P-1205 $5.99

Color Tray

NEW!

Become a true fondant artist with this convenient tray! Pour in Brush-On Color (at left) and use Cake Stamps (p. 123) or the Brush Set below to add vivid designs to fondant cakes.
1907-P-1208 $2.99

Easy-Glide Fondant Smoother

Essential tool for shaping and smoothing rolled fondant on your cake. Works great on top, edges and sides! Shapes fondant to sides of cake so that no puffed areas appear. Trim any excess with a sharp knife. 6¼ in. long x 3¼ in. wide.
1907-P-1200 $4.99

Roll out and cut fun shapes!

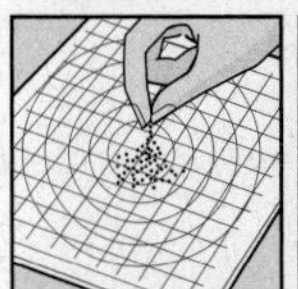

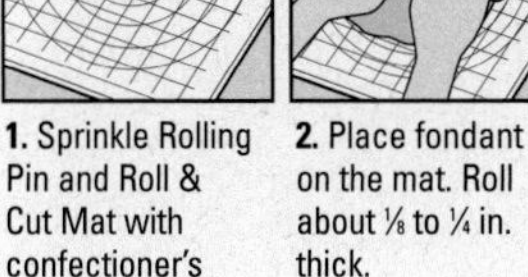

1. Sprinkle Rolling Pin and Roll & Cut Mat with confectioner's sugar.

2. Place fondant on the mat. Roll about ⅛ to ¼ in. thick.

3. Cut pieces with Cutter/Embosser or Cut-Outs™ (p. 123).

Brush Set

NEW!

Add a special touch of color to your fondant-covered cake! It's easy and fun with these fine-bristle brushes and Brush-On Color or Icing Writer. Three tip designs—round, square and bevel—help you achieve different painted effects.
1907-P-1207 Set/3 $2.99

Great painting ideas!

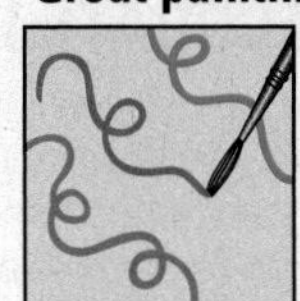

1. Use the round tip brush for lively streamers and dots.

2. Use the square tip brush for lace-look brush embroidery. Draw design with Icing Writer, then pull design outlines toward center with brush.

3. Use the bevel tip brush to paint pretty free-hand designs.

Cutter/Embosser

NEW!

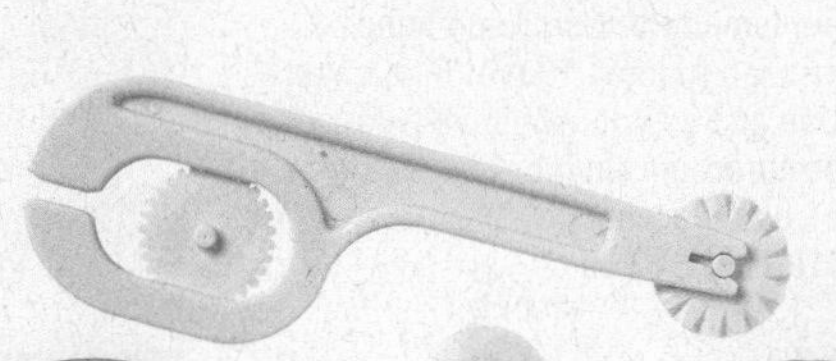

Three detachable wheels—straight, wavy and ridged—for cutting and for embossing of patterns on fondant. Light, easy-rolling design cuts at the perfect angle. Comfortable handle also stores wheels.
1907-P-1206 $3.99

Emboss designs in fondant!

1. To cut strips, attach the straight-edge cutting wheel of the Cutter/Embosser—just snap the axle into the handle slot. Roll out fondant on the Roll & Cut Mat (at left) using grid marks to determine width. Roll the wheel along a ruler to cut perfect strips.

2. For embossing, attach one of the two pattern wheels—wavy or ridged. Roll wheel along strip in any direction.

3. Wheels create great-looking dots or waves to give your fondant cake terrific texture! Remove strips from mat with an angled spatula.

Roll & Cut Mat

NEW!

For precise measuring, rolling and cutting of fondant or dough. Pre-marked circles for exact sizing. Square grid helps you cut precise strips. Non-stick surface for easy release.
409-P-412 $8.99

Quick Ease Roller

Makes it easy to prepare small pieces of fondant and gum paste for cutting flowers and designs. Wooden roller fits comfortably in palm of hand.
1907-P-1202 $4.99

Confectionery Tool Set

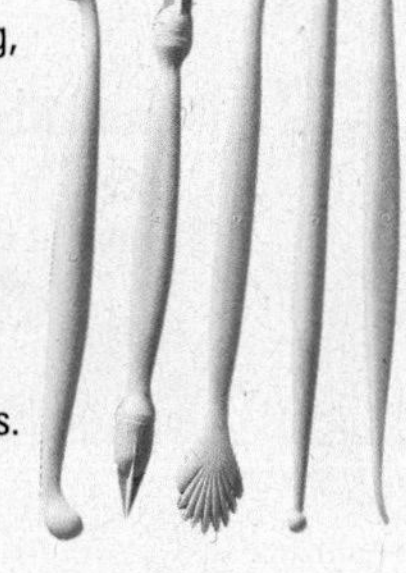

Invaluable tools for shaping, imprinting and stenciling—helping you achieve lifelike confectionery flowers. Ideal for marking patterns in fondant cakes, shaping marzipan fruits. Includes plastic Dogbone, Umbrella, Shell, Ball and Veining tools.
1907-P-1000 Set/5 $9.99

FONDANT AND GUM PASTE INGREDIENTS

Glycerin

Stir into dried out fondant, gum paste and icing color to restore consistency. 2 oz. Certified Kosher.
708-P-14 $1.99

Glucose

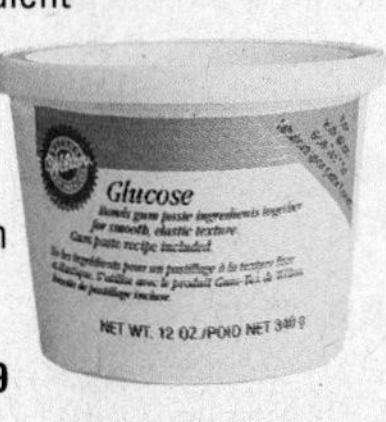

Essential ingredient for making fondant and gum paste from scratch. Use with Wilton Gum-Tex™. 12 oz.
707-P-107 $3.49

Gum-Tex™

Makes fondant and gum paste pliable, elastic, easy to shape. Flip-top can has a plastic resealable lid. 6 oz.
707-P-117 $7.49

Gum Paste Mix

Just add water and knead. Workable, pliable dough-like mixture molds into beautiful flowers and figures. 1 lb.
707-P-124 $5.99

Icings

All Wilton icings are formulated for decorating as well as taste. That's because Wilton insists on providing you with the perfect consistency icing for decorating. Our quality ingredients mean better results for you.

Ready-To-Use Decorator Icings

Wilton makes the only ready-to-use icing that is the perfect consistency for decorating. Delicious taste, too. One can covers two 8 or 9 in. layers or one 9 x 13 in. cake. 16 oz. **$2.49**

White 710-P-118

Chocolate 710-P-119

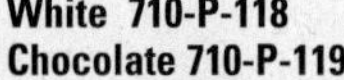

Creamy White Buttercream Icing Mix

Our convenient mix has the delicious taste and creamy texture of homemade buttercream icing—enough to ice a 1-layer 8 in. cake. Use just as you would your favorite buttercream recipe. Makes 1½ to 2 cups. Certified Kosher.

710-P-112 $2.99

Vanilla Whipped Icing Mix

Our light, whipped icing is the ideal texture for decorating in an easy-to-make, delicious mix. Just add ice water and it whips up velvety-smooth for icing or decorating. Light and delicate flavor. Makes 4 cups. Certified Kosher Dairy.

710-P-1241 $4.49

Meringue Powder

Primary ingredient for royal icing. Stabilizes buttercream, adds body to boiled icing and meringue. Replaces egg white in many recipes. Resealable top opens for easy measuring. 4 oz. can makes 5 recipes of royal icing; 8 oz. can makes 10 recipes. Certified Kosher.

4 oz. can 702-P-6007 $4.99

8 oz. can 702-P-6015 $7.99

Color Flow Mix

Create dimensional flow-in designs for your cake. Just add water and confectioner's sugar. 4 oz. can makes ten 1½ cup batches. Certified Kosher.

701-P-47 $7.49

Piping Gel

Pipe messages and designs or glaze cakes before icing. Use clear or tint with icing color. 10 oz. Certified Kosher.

704-P-105 $3.49

VANILLA ICE CREAM MIX NEW!

At last, an ice cream mix that's great for decorating, spreading or scooping. Wilton Vanilla Ice Cream Mix helps decorators create ice cream cakes and pies with beautiful piped effects no regular ice cream can achieve. The exclusive formula holds its shape to make beautiful borders and designs—including shells, stars and rosettes. Yet Vanilla Ice Cream Mix is easy to spread for filled cakes. Goes on easy, right after mixing, no softening time needed. Just add whipping cream and milk. Also great for delicious ice cream treats like sandwiches, sundaes and milk shakes. 11.2 oz. box makes 7 cups of ice cream. Instructions and recipes included. Certified Kosher Dairy.

704-P-671 $5.99

READY-TO-DECORATE ICING

Anyone can decorate with Wilton Ready-to-Decorate Icing! Our brilliant colors and easy-to-use tips make it a breeze to add an exciting finishing touch to treats—without mixing or mess. Just slip one of the four free tips over the nozzle and start the fun. Decorating couldn't be easier!

Colors match Wilton Icing Colors (p. 127). 6.4 oz. Certified Kosher. **$3.49**

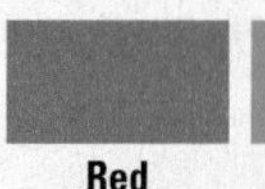

Red	Green	White	Black	Pink
710-P-4400	710-P-4401	710-P-4402	710-P-4404	710-P-4406

Blue	Violet	Yellow	Orange
710-P-4407	710-P-4408	710-P-4409	710-P-4410

Four FREE decorating tips included:

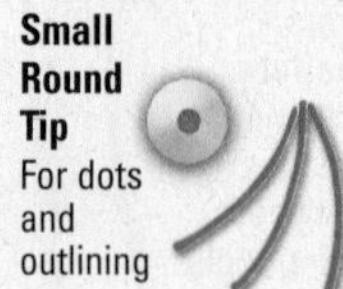

Small Round Tip For dots and outlining

Leaf Tip For basic and ruffled leaves

Large Round Tip For writing and printing

Star Tip For stars, swirls and pretty borders

Flavorings

Decorators trust Wilton flavorings for great taste that won't change icing consistency. Wilton flavors are concentrated—only a drop or two adds delicious taste to icings, cakes, beverages and other recipes.

NO-COLOR FLAVORINGS

Recommended by and used in Wilton Method Classes, these delicious flavors won't change your icing color. Essential for making pure white icings for wedding cakes and maintaining vibrant colors in all your decorating. Certified Kosher.

Clear Vanilla Extract

2 oz.
604-P-2237 $1.79
8 oz.
604-P-2269 $4.79

No-Color Butter Flavor

2 oz.
604-P-2040 $1.79
8 oz.
604-P-2067 $4.79

No-Color Almond Extract

2 oz.
604-P-2126 $1.79

Pure Vanilla Extract

The world's finest vanilla is from Madagascar. Unmatched flavor and aroma to enhance cakes, puddings, pie fillings, custards, salad dressings and more. 4 oz.

604-P-2270 $7.99

Tube Icings, Gels

Tube Decorating Icings

The same high quality as our Ready-To-Use Icing, in a convenient tube. Create flowers, borders and more. Ideal for those small areas of color on character cakes. Use with our Tip and Nail Set or Coupler Ring Set and any standard-size Wilton metal tip (not included). Colors match Wilton Icing Colors shown at right. 4.25 oz. Certified Kosher. **$1.79**

Lemon Yellow 704-P-236
Orange 704-P-212
Red 704-P-218
Pink 704-P-230
Violet 704-P-242
Royal Blue 704-P-248
Leaf Green 704-P-224
Kelly Green 704-P-227
Chocolate 704-P-254
White 704-P-200
Black 704-P-206

Coupler Ring Set

Attach Wilton standard size metal decorating tips onto Wilton tube icings to create any technique.
418-P-47306 Set/4 $1.49

Tip and Nail Set

Tips easily twist onto Wilton tube icings to create many decorating techniques. Includes Star, Round, Leaf and Petal Tips, Flower Nail.
418-P-47300 Set/5 $1.79

Tube Decorating Gels

Add shimmering accents, colorful highlights and sparkle to your decorating with these transparent gels. Create a beautiful stained-glass effect and add distinctive writing and printing. Great for cakes and cookies. Colors match Wilton Icing Colors shown at right. .75 oz. Certified Kosher. **$1.29**

Red 704-P-318
Pink 704-P-330
Violet 704-P-342
Lemon Yellow 704-P-336
Orange 704-P-312
Royal Blue 704-P-348
Leaf Green 704-P-324
Brown 704-P-354
White 704-P-302
Black 704-P-306

Tube Icing and Gel Color Chart

Lemon Yellow	Orange	Red	Pink
Violet	Royal Blue	Leaf Green	†Kelly Green
†Chocolate	Brown	White	Black

†Not available in gel.

Icing Colors

Wilton color is made to produce deeper, richer color by adding just a small amount. Our concentrated gel formula helps you achieve the exact shade you want without thinning your icing. You'll find a rainbow of colors, ready to blend together for creating your own custom shades.

*Note: Large amounts of these colors may affect icing taste.

Use No-Taste Red for large areas of red on a cake. When using Black, start with chocolate icing to limit the amount of color needed.

‡Daffodil Yellow is an all-natural color. It does not contain Yellow #5. The color remains very pale.

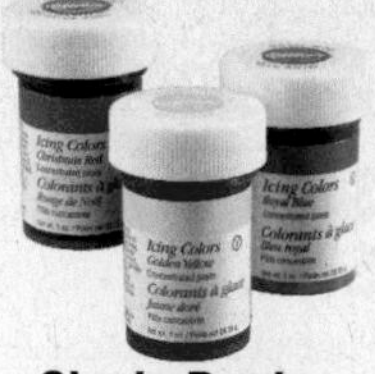

Single Bottles

1 oz. Certified Kosher.
$1.89
(except where otherwise noted)

Ivory 610-P-208	Daffodil Yellow‡ 610-P-175 $1.99	Buttercup Yellow 610-P-216	Golden Yellow 610-P-159	Lemon Yellow 610-P-108	Copper (skin tone) 610-P-450	Creamy Peach 610-P-210	Rose Petal Pink 610-P-410	Terra Cotta 610-P-206	Orange 610-P-205
Red-Red* 610-P-906 $1.99	Christmas Red* 610-P-302	Red (no-taste) 610-P-998 $1.99	Rose 610-P-401	Burgundy 610-P-698 $1.99	Pink 610-P-256	Violet 610-P-604	Delphinium Blue 610-P-228	Cornflower Blue 610-P-710	Royal Blue 610-P-655
Sky Blue 610-P-700	Teal 610-P-207	Kelly Green 610-P-752	Leaf Green 610-P-809	Moss Green 610-P-851	Juniper Green 610-P-234	Brown 610-P-507	Black* 610-P-981		

Primary 4-Icing Colors Set

Lemon Yellow, Sky Blue, Christmas Red, Brown in .5 oz. jars. Certified Kosher.
601-P-5127 Set/4 $4.29

8-Icing Colors Set

Lemon Yellow, Sky Blue, Christmas Red, Brown, Orange, Violet, Pink and Leaf Green in .5 oz. jars. Certified Kosher.
601-P-5577 Set/8 $9.99

12-Icing Colors Set

Our most popular collection creates the spectrum of primary colors plus skin tones, teal and burgundy. Lemon Yellow, Teal, No-Taste Red, Brown, Copper (Lt. Skin tone), Violet, Pink, Burgundy, Golden Yellow, Royal Blue, Black, Kelly Green in .5 oz. jars. Certified Kosher.
601-P-5580 Set/12 $12.99

White-White Icing Color

Stir in to whiten icing made with butter or margarine. Perfect for wedding cakes. 2 oz. Certified Kosher.
603-P-1236 $2.99

Glycerin

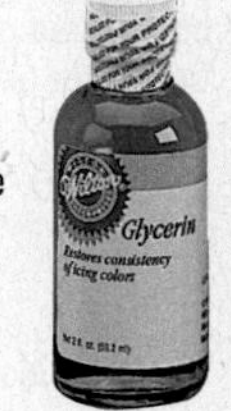

Stir into dried out icing color to restore consistency. 2 oz. Certified Kosher.
708-P-14 $1.99

Pastel 4-Icing Colors Set

Willow Green, Cornflower Blue, Creamy Peach, Rose Petal Pink in .5 oz. jars. Certified Kosher.
601-P-25588 Set/4 $4.29

Garden Tone 4-Icing Colors Set

Buttercup Yellow, Delphinium Blue, Aster Mauve, Juniper Green, in .5 oz. jars. Certified Kosher.
601-P-4240 Set/4 $4.29

Color Mist™ Food Color Spray

This easy-to-use spray gives decorators the versatility and dazzling effects of an airbrush in a convenient can! Creates a rainbow of excitement on so many desserts. Use it to transform a plain iced cake with sensational color, add splashes of holiday color to iced cookies and cupcakes. Great for party desserts—highlighting whipped topping or ice cream with color. No mess, taste-free formula; add a little color or a lot.

Colors match Wilton Icing Colors above. 1.5 oz. Certified Kosher. **$2.99**

Red 710-P-5500	Blue 710-P-5501	Yellow 710-P-5502	Green 710-P-5503
Violet 710-P-5504	Pink 710-P-5505	Black 710-P-5506	Orange 710-P-5507

Sprinkles

SPARKLING SUGARS

NEW!

Put that extra dazzle in your decorating! These easy-pour sugars have a coarse texture and a brilliant sparkle that makes cupcakes, cookies and cakes really shine. 8.25 oz. bottles. Certified Kosher.
$3.99

White
710-P-992

Lavender/White
710-P-993

Rainbow
710-P-994

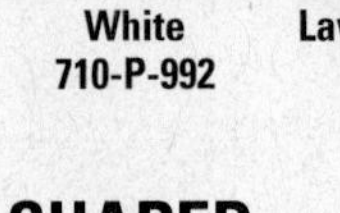

SHAPED SPRINKLES

Pour on the fun! Great shapes and colors add a dash of excitement to cakes, cupcakes, ice cream and more.

Plastic shaker bottles for convenient pouring and storing. Certified Kosher.

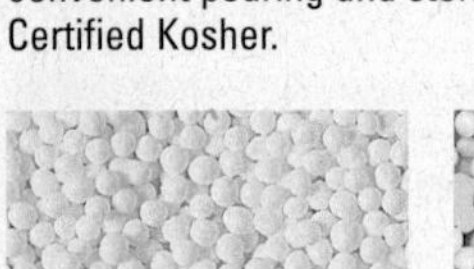

White Nonpareils
3 oz. bottle
710-P-773 $1.99

Rubber Ducky Mix
2.5 oz. bottle
710-P-798 $1.99

Cinnamon Drops
3 oz. bottle
710-P-769 $1.99

Rainbow Nonpareils
3 oz. bottle
710-P-772 $1.99

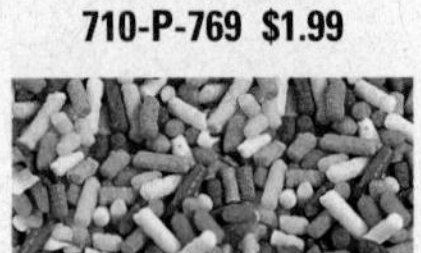

Rainbow Jimmies
2.5 oz. bottle
710-P-776 $1.99
6.25 oz. bottle
710-P-994 $3.99

Chocolate Jimmies
2.5 oz. bottle
710-P-774 $1.99

COLORED SUGARS

Extra-fine sugar is excellent for filling in brightly colored designs on cakes, cupcakes and cookies. Controlling the flow is easy with the flip-top shaker bottles. 3.25 oz. bottles. Certified Kosher.
$1.99

Yellow
710-P-754

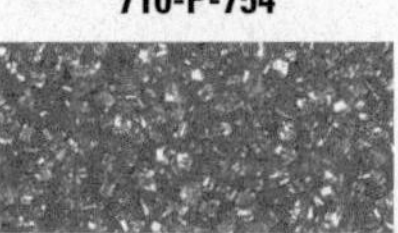

Pink
710-P-756

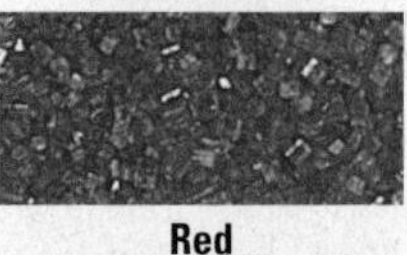

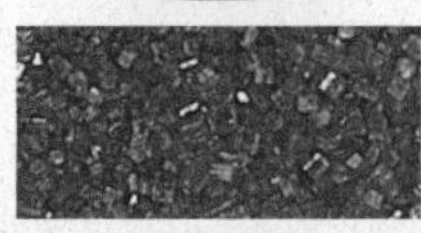

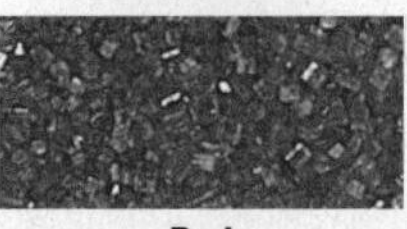

Red
710-P-766

Light Green
710-P-752

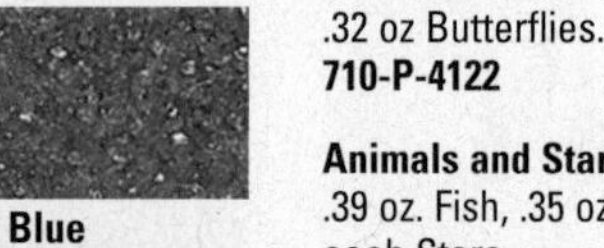

Blue
710-P-750

Orange
710-P-759

Lavender
710-P-758

Dark Green
710-P-764

Black
710-P-762

ASSORTMENTS

They're so convenient! Assorted fun shapes in an easy-pour flip-top bottle. Top cupcakes, ice cream and other goodies. Certified Kosher. **$4.99**

6-Mix

Flowerful Medley
.39 oz. each Confetti, Colorful Leaves, Daisies, Pastel Hearts, .35 oz. Wild Flowers, .32 oz Butterflies.
710-P-4122

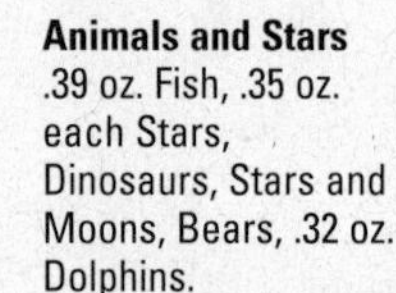

Animals and Stars
.39 oz. Fish, .35 oz. each Stars, Dinosaurs, Stars and Moons, Bears, .32 oz. Dolphins.
710-P-4123

Nonpareils
.5 oz. each Pink, Orange, Green, Red, Yellow, Purple.
710-P-4125

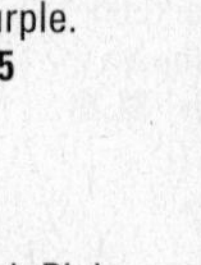

Jimmies
.42 oz. each Pink, Orange, Green, Red, Yellow, Blue.
710-P-4127

4-Mix

Brights Sugars
1.1 oz. each Yellow, Light Green, Lavender, Pink.
710-P-651

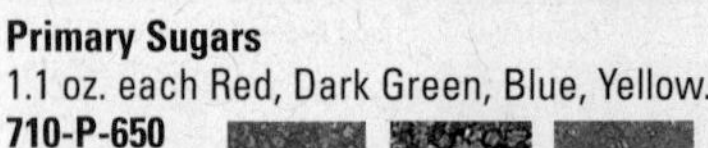

Primary Sugars
1.1 oz. each Red, Dark Green, Blue, Yellow.
710-P-650

Cake Sparkles™

NEW!

Add shimmering color to cakes, cupcakes, cookies and ice cream! Brilliant edible glitter in a great variety of colors is great for stencilling, highlighting messages, snow scenes. .25 oz. Certified Kosher.
$2.89

Silver
703-P-1285

White
703-P-1290

Yellow
703-P-1272

Purple
703-P-1266

Blue
703-P-1314

Red
703-P-1284

Green
703-P-1278

Pink
703-P-1260

Orange
703-P-1308

Black
703-P-1302

Baking Accessories

Bake Easy!™ Non-Stick Spray

For cakes that turn out beautifully every time, start by spraying pans with Bake Easy. This convenient non-stick spray helps your cakes release perfectly with fewer crumbs for easier icing and a flawless decorated cake. Just a light, even coating does the job. Use Bake Easy for all mixes and recipes—cupcakes, brownies, breads and more. Versatile for all types of baking and cooking. 6 oz.
702-P-6018 $2.99

Cake Release

No need to grease and flour your baking pan—Cake Release coats in one step. Simply spread Cake Release lightly on pan bottom and sides with a pastry brush and add batter. Cakes release perfectly without crumbs every time, giving you the ideal surface for decorating. In convenient dispensing bottle. 8 oz. Certified Kosher.
702-P-6016 $3.49

Pastry Brush

Flexible, absorbent bristles for efficient brushing; seamless nylon shaft holds bristles securely. Great for applying Cake Release. 1½ in. wide.
417-P-449 $2.99

Non-Stick Parchment Paper

Use Wilton silicone-treated non-stick parchment to line baking pans and cookie sheets—a non-fat alternative that saves cleanup time. Roll out cookie dough between 2 sheets, dough won't stick and will easily transfer to your cookie sheet. You can even reuse it for the next batch. Oven-safe to 400°F, parchment is great for conventional ovens, microwaves and the freezer. Double roll is 41 square feet, 15 in. wide. Certified Kosher.
415-P-680 $4.99

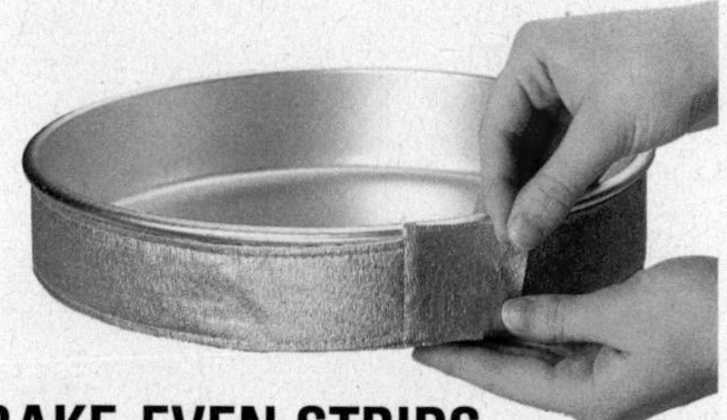

BAKE-EVEN STRIPS

Cakes bake perfectly level and moist, without cracking, when you wrap these strips around the pan before baking. Oven-safe, instructions and clips included.

Small Set

Two 30 x 1½ in. wide strips, enough for two 8 or 9 in. round pans.
415-P-260 Set/2 $7.49

Large Set

Four strips, 36, 43, 49 and 56 in. long x 1½ in. wide. Enough for one each: 10, 12, 14, 16 in. round pans.
415-P-262 Set/4 $15.99

CAKE STENCILS VARIETY PACK

Our collection of 4 stencil designs gives you several ways to make birthday and everyday cakes more festive. Decorating with stencils is so easy—just place on your iced cake, then sprinkle away with Wilton Cake Sparkles™, add exciting Wilton Sugars in a rainbow of colors or use Color Mist™ food color spray. Also works beautifully with Wilton Rolled Fondant—fill in designs with sugars or decorate with FoodWriter™ markers. Includes Happy Birthday, Flower, Swirl and Heart designs.
417-P-148
Pk./4 $6.99

6-PIECE COVERED MIXING BOWL SET

Perfect for preparing decorating icings—clear lids snap on tight to keep icing the right texture. Includes one each 1, 2 and 3 quart nesting bowls with easy-grip handles and easy-pour spouts for better control. Rubberized base keeps bowls from sliding on countertops. Measurements clearly marked for precise mixing. Dishwasher safe.
417-P-469 Set/6 $12.99

CAKE LEVELERS

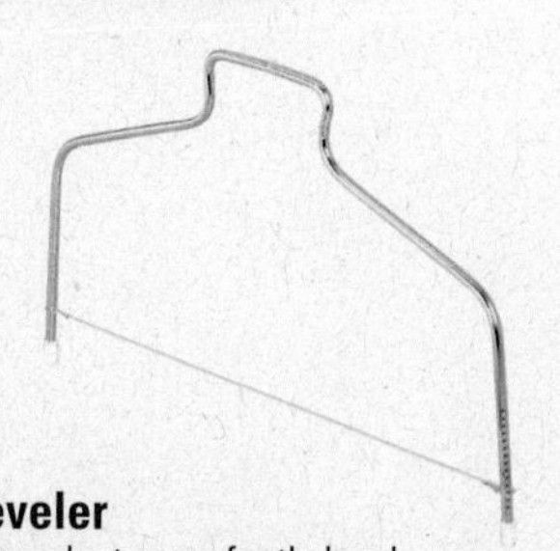

Cake Leveler

Make your cake top perfectly level for precise decorating—just place adjustable wire in notches to desired height up to 2 in. and glide through the cake. Makes torting easy, too! For cakes up to 10 in. wide.
415-P-815 $2.99

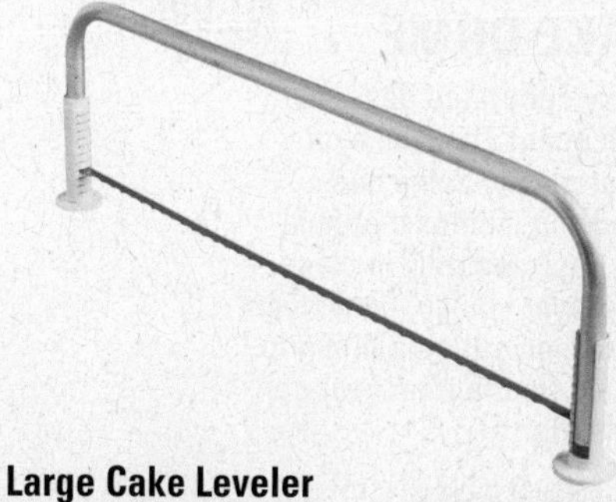

Large Cake Leveler

Blade easily levels and tortes cakes up to 18 in. diameter. Adjusts up to 3 in. high—just twist feet to lock into notch at desired height then glide the stainless steel blade through your cake.
417-P-1198 $19.99

Servers and Savers

CUPCAKES 'N MORE™ DESSERT STAND

NEW!

Easy to assemble!
Just stack each layer of cupcakes onto the locking center rod.

Keeps looking great!
Non-toxic, silver-finished metal has a durable non-chip finish.

Holds 23 cupcakes!
Perfect batch size for most standard cake mixes.

Collapsible design
Stores easily and safely.

Angled holders
Give the best view of cupcake tops!

Individually decorated cupcakes are the perfect way to add a personal touch to celebrations. Now, with Cupcakes 'N More, you have the perfect way to serve them! The look is fresh and fun, featuring bold silver-finished wire spirals to securely hold each cupcake. The twisting, towering design is perfect for any setting—showers, kids' birthdays, weddings, holidays and more. 12 in. high x 13 wide.
307-P-826 $29.99

Cake Dome
An elegant way to display and protect your cake—looks great in any setting. The unbreakable polycarbonate dome gives a clear view of the cake as it rests on the graceful pedestal. The 7½ in. high crystal clear dome is the ideal height for multi-layer cakes, angel food, cupcakes and muffins. Pedestal is approximately 12½ in. diameter and can be stored inside dome. Holds up to a 10 in. round cake. Instructions and recipes included.
307-P-702 $29.99

Cake Saver
The convenient way to carry decorated cakes! Its generous size accommodates borders and cake top decorations easily. Great for carrying or storing angel food, cheese cakes, pies and layer cakes. Fits a 10 in. round cake with borders or a 12 in. cake without borders. 14 in. round base and 6 in. high cover.
415-P-905 $12.99

PORTABLE CAKE DOME

NEW!

Carry decorated desserts with ease! The 6 in. high clear plastic dome has 3 locking latches that hold the base securely in place wherever you go. Convenient handle gives you a firm grip for a safe trip from your car to the party.

The elegant base is approximately 13 in. diameter and holds and stores up to 10 in. round cake or pie, cupcakes, cookies and more.
2105-P-9952 $14.99

Lazy Daisy Server
Stationary sturdy white plastic stand with doily design and scalloped edges. 5 in. high with 12 in. diameter plate. Can hold cakes up to 10 in. diameter.
307-P-700 $8.99

Decorating Stands

A quality cake stand is a must for easy decorating. Stands lift your cake off the work surface so you can create borders conveniently. And they rotate as well, allowing you to decorate all the way around the cake without straining.

Tilting Cake Turntable

It tilts! Decorate any part of your cake conveniently!

The Tilting Cake Turntable moves to 3 preset angles—12°, 24°, and level—and locks in place, making every decorating technique easier! 6 in. high turntable smoothly rotates in any of the angled positions for effortless decorating of top borders, stringwork, lettering on top and sides of cake, more. Includes lock to prevent rotation. Non-slip base, 12 in. diameter.
307-P-894 $59.99

Professional Turntable

Extra strength and effortless turning for decorating tiered wedding cakes. Heavy-duty aluminum stand is 4⅝ in. high with 12 in. diameter plate. Holds cakes up to 16 in. diameter.
307-P-2501 $59.99

Revolving Cake Stand

Turns in either direction with easy-rotating ball bearings. 3 in. high, 11 in. diameter plate is white molded plastic. Holds cakes up to 10 in. diameter.
415-P-900 $10.99

Trim 'N Turn Cake Stand

Turns smoothly on hidden ball bearings for easy decorating and serving. Flute-edged 12 in. plate is white molded plastic. Holds cakes up to 10 in. diameter.
2103-P-2518 $7.99

Decorating Tools

ICING SCULPTOR™

Now your cakes can have an elegant sculpted finish that will give them a beautiful professional look. It's easy with the Icing Sculptor. Just insert any combination of the 64 design blades—mix and match between the 14 sculpting edges to create your favorite customized effects. Then glide the comb over the iced cake sides to create attractive ridges that will beautifully frame your design. Create hundreds of pattern combinations—wide or narrow ridges, dramatic swirls and vertical designs too.

Includes sculptor handle, 64 design blades and complete instructions. This versatile tool has a patent pending.
2104-P-12 Set/66 $12.99

So Easy!
Select the sculpting blades you want and slide into handle. Press sculptor into iced cake as you rotate cake on turntable.

So Versatile!
Mix and match between the 14 edge designs on 64 blades to achieve the perfect look for your cake.

Get 8 of each 2-Sided Design Blade

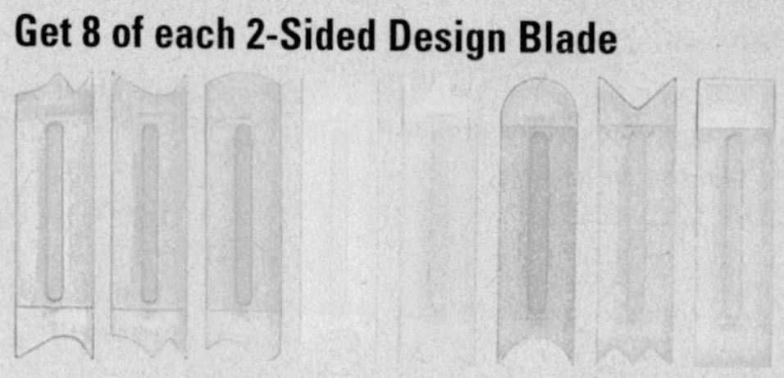

Decorating Comb

Run edge across your iced cake to form beautiful ridges. 12 x 1½ in.; plastic.
417-P-156 $1.29

Decorating Triangle

Each side adds a different contoured effect to iced cakes. Easy to hold; 5 x 5 in.; plastic.
417-P-162 $0.99

Garland Marker

Adjusts to 7 preset widths and varying depths to easily mark perfectly uniform garlands on cake sides. Instructions included.
409-P-812 $3.99

Hand & Wrist Support Gloves

Makes decorating and other creative tasks more comfortable! Use whenever you work with your hands. Their exclusive spandex and nylon construction supports vital areas of the hand and wrist to help you work more comfortably, while the breathable fabric reduces perspiration. Hand & Wrist Support Gloves promote circulation and massage muscles to reduce fatigue. Lightweight, fingerless design gives you the freedom of motion you need for all kinds of tasks including computer work, painting, sewing, knitting, quilting, crocheting and more. Machine or hand wash.
417-P-488 Pk./2 $19.99

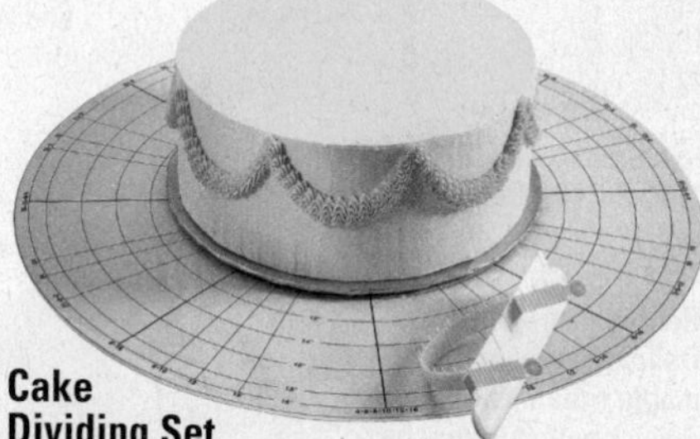

Cake Dividing Set

Measures equal sections of your cake for precise placement of garlands, stringwork and other designs. Cake Dividing Wheel marks up to 16 divisions on cakes up to 20 in. diameter. Garland Marker adjusts to 7 widths. Instructions included.
409-P-806 Set/2 $8.99

Practice Board with Patterns Set

Includes stand and 20 full-size patterns. 9 x 6 in.
406-P-9464 $6.99

All-Purpose Decorating Gloves

Food-safe disposable gloves keep your hands clean, odor-free and protected in and out of the kitchen. Prevent color stains when tinting fondant, keep fingerprints off homemade candy, eliminate burning of skin when cutting hot, spicy foods. Great when working with craft paint and glue, too. Easy to slip-on, gloves fit either hand.
417-P-1642 Pk./20 $2.99

Prepare delicious desserts, toppings, fillings and whipped cream quickly and easily!

DESSERT Whipper PRO™

The Dessert Whipper Pro makes it easy to add a luxurious look and rich taste to your favorite desserts and drinks! Create the Classic Strawberry Pie with pretty rosettes of fresh whipped cream. Top off sundaes with dollops of chocolate and caramel-flavored cream. Fill cream puffs or cannoli with a rich, creamy center. Or serve cups of hot cocoa crowned with chocolate mint cream.

With the Dessert Whipper Pro, it's a breeze to whip up all these luscious toppings and fillings. Just pour ingredients in the canister, twist on a charger, shake and dispense using the filling or decorating tips. No mess or guessing: everything is perfectly blended in the canister. The easy-press lever and one-hand operation give you great portion control—anyone can make desserts look great.

Uses iSi charger cartridges, which twist on safely and easily. Complete set includes Dessert Whipper Pro, 10 charger cartridges, 2 decorating tips and recipe booklet.
2104-P-1290 $59.99

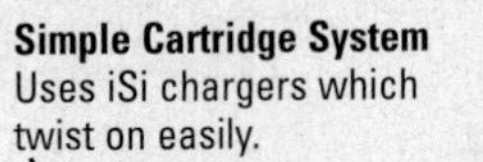

Simple Cartridge System
Uses iSi chargers which twist on easily.

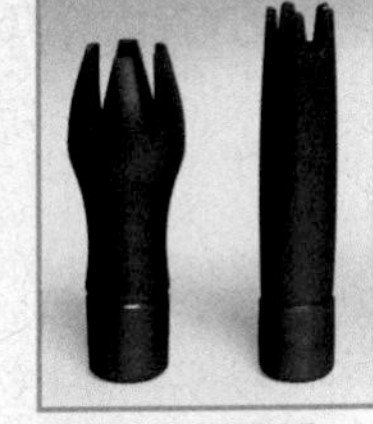

TWO VERSATILE TIPS
Use straight tip for filling, tulip tip for decorating.

Easy-Press Lever
Provides portion control.

High Yield Design
Produces 5 times the amount of liquid whipping cream poured in!

Brushed Aluminum
Easy to handle and resists smudges.

iSi Charger Cartridges
2104-P-1447 Set/5 $5.99

Recipe Book Included!
Delicious recipes for maple cream, strawberry whip, chocolate/mocha mousse, peach mousse, cranberry whip and more.

SO EASY TO USE!

1. Fill canister with cream.

2. Twist on a charger.

3. Remove charger, replace cap & shake.

4. Press handle to dispense.

Press Sets

Block Letter Press Set

Includes Best, Happy, Wishes, Anniversary, Birthday, and Congratulations and letter holder. Word height ⅞ in.
2104-P-2077
Set/6 $3.69

Make-Any-Message Letter Press Set

Imprint the perfect sentiment! Press words up to 10 ½ in. wide, letters ¾ in. high.
2104-P-10
Set/56 $7.99

Designer Pattern Press Set

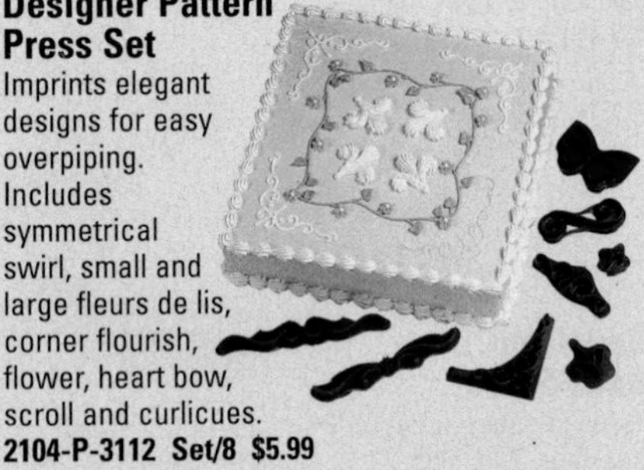

Imprints elegant designs for easy overpiping. Includes symmetrical swirl, small and large fleurs de lis, corner flourish, flower, heart bow, scroll and curlicues.
2104-P-3112 Set/8 $5.99

Italic Make-Any-Message Press Set

Pretty and sophisticated letters for a custom message. Press words up to 10 ½ in. wide, letters ¾ in. high.
2104-P-2277
Set/58 $7.99

Decorator Favorites Pattern Press Set

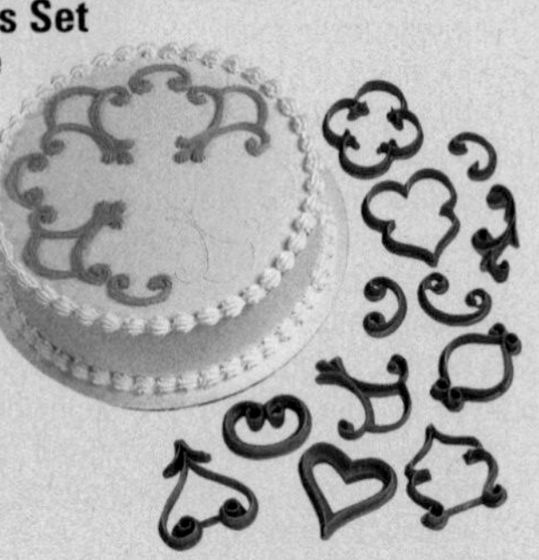

Includes double heart; fleur de lis; medallion; open heart; closed scroll; heart; large, medium and small c-scrolls; crest; double scroll and vine.
2104-P-3160
Set/12 $5.99

Script Message Press Set

Combine the words Best, Happy, Wishes, Birthday, Anniversary, and Congratulations. Word height ⅞ in.
2104-P-2061
Set/6 $3.69

Dessert decorator Pro™

It's easy to add beautiful decorations to any dessert or appetizer in minutes! Designed for comfortable one-handed decorating and effortless tip positioning, this is the most convenient dessert tool you'll ever use.

Create beautiful decorations—shells, stars, rosettes, leaves. The great recipe book included is filled with fabulous ideas to serve your family and friends: Decorate desserts with elegant whipped cream or icing designs. Dress up pastry shells with dramatic swirls of mousse. Add sophistication to savories with pretty piped cream cheese or seafood spread decorations. With Dessert Decorator Pro, you can do it all!

415-P-850 $29.99

Rotating Cylinder
Just turn to place the tip in the correct position for any decoration.

Pull-Out Plunger
Inner ring pushes filling smoothly through cylinder.

Ergonomic Design
Easy, comfortable grip for right or left hand. Outer sleeve fits your fingers like a glove.

Stainless Steel Cylinder
Preferred by pastry chefs because stainless won't transfer flavors and it maintains temperature of fillings.

Convenient Thumb Lever
The ideal distance from cylinder for comfortable one-handed decorating.

Fits Virtually Any Tip/Coupler
Use with the tips included or with most other Wilton tips.

Durable Construction
Cylinder and plunger are housed in an impact-resistant sleeve for years of great decorating performance.

Easy To Fill and Clean
Most parts detach with ease; wash in warm, soapy water.

DESSERT DECORATOR PRO INCLUDES ALL THIS:

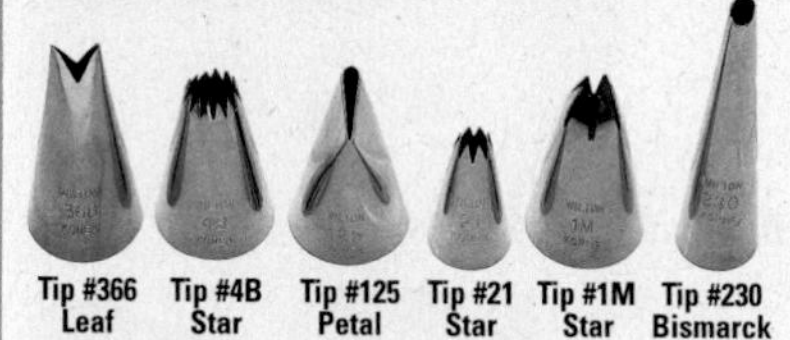

Six Durable Nickel-Plated Tips
Quality metal tips produce perfectly-shaped decorations every time.

Two Tip Couplers
Two sizes to hold standard (small) and large tips.

Tips in bag for size reference only. Tips included are shown at left.

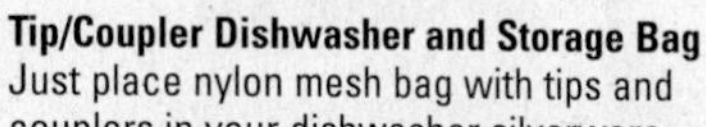

Tip/Coupler Dishwasher and Storage Bag
Just place nylon mesh bag with tips and couplers in your dishwasher silverware rack for easy tip and coupler cleaning.

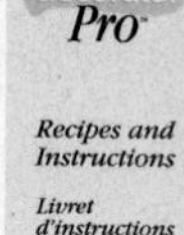

Recipes and Instructions
Includes delicious recipes and easy decorating instructions for elegant desserts and appetizers.

Create sensational decorations for desserts and appetizers in minutes! One easy-to-use tool does it all—tops pies with fancy whipped cream lattice designs, accents deviled eggs with a pretty rosette, decorates party crackers with savory spreads, fills cupcakes with buttercream for the perfect kids' party treat. The complete set includes 6 tips and 2 couplers for making pretty designs like stars, shells, flowers, petals, lattice/basketweave, leaves and more. The Dessert Decorator Max also works with virtually any Wilton tip, giving you complete versatility. Instruction/recipe booklet is filled with easy step-by-step decorating instructions and delicious ideas for sweet and savory foods.

415-P-854 $24.99

Pull-Out Plunger
Inner ring pushes icing through cylinder; cleans easily with soap and water.

Ergonomic Design
Finger-grip barrel is easy to handle in right or left hand.

Convenient Thumb Lever
Lets you hold tool and decorate with one hand.

Easy To Fill and Clean
Parts detach easily; top rack dishwasher safe.

Rotating Cylinder
Places tip in the perfect decorating position with an easy turn.

Great Recipe Booklet!

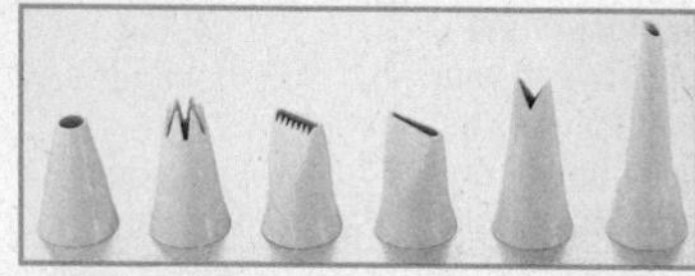

Six Tips Included!

Basic Dessert Decorator

Give your cakes and pastries a beautiful finishing touch in seconds. The easy-to-control lever helps you fill and decorate all kinds of desserts. Decorating nozzles can pipe stars, rosettes, shells and many other accents. Works great with Wilton Buttercream Icing Mix and Whipped Icing Mix, p. 126.

415-P-825 $10.99

Decorating Bags

Featherweight® Decorating Bags
Use these easy-handling bags over and over. Lightweight, strong and flexible polyester will never get stiff. Coated to prevent grease from seeping through. May be boiled; dishwasher safe. Instructions included. Sold singly.

8 in. 404-P-5087 $2.49
10 in. 404-P-5109 $3.89
12 in. 404-P-5125 $4.89
14 in. 404-P-5140 $6.29
16 in. 404-P-5168 $7.59
18 in. 404-P-5184 $8.29

Disposable Decorating Bags
Just use, then toss. Strong, flexible plastic. 12 in. size fits standard tips and couplers. Also perfect for melting Candy Melts® in the microwave.

2104-P-358 Pk./12 $3.99

2104-P-1358 Pk./24 $6.29

Disposable Decorating Bag Dispenser Box
Now in convenient Value Packs! These dispenser boxes make it easy to pull out one bag at a time, so you can keep your decorating space uncluttered.

2104-P-1273 Pk./50 $11.99
2104-P-1249 Pk./100 $19.99

50 Pack

Parchment Triangles
Make your own disposable decorating bags with our grease-resistant vegetable parchment paper. The professional's choice for convenience and quick bag preparation.

12 in. 2104-P-1206 Pk./100 $4.99

15 in. 2104-P-1508 Pk./100 $5.99

Spatulas

ROSEWOOD
Quality rosewood handle spatulas have been favorites for years. They have strong, flexible stainless steel blades and sturdy handles.

Straight Blade
11 in.; 6 in. blade.
409-P-7695 $4.99
8 in.; 4¼ in. blade.
409-P-6044 $2.99

Angled Blade
12 in.; 6¼ in. blade.
409-P-135 $5.99
8 in.; 4½ in. blade.
409-P-739 $2.99

Tapered Blade
8 in.; 4 in. blade.
409-P-518 $2.99

COMFORT GRIP™
Decorate with greater comfort, more control and less fatigue, thanks to contoured handle with finger pad. Flexible stainless steel blade is perfect thickness for gliding over icing.

Straight Blade
15 in.; 10⅛ in. blade.
409-P-6030 $9.99
11 in.; 6 in. blade.
409-P-6018 $5.99
8 in.; 4½ in. blade.
409-P-6006 $3.99

Angled Blade
15 in.; 9⅞ in. blade.
409-P-6036 $9.99
13 in.; 7¾ in. blade.
409-P-6024 $6.49
8 in.; 4½ in. blade.
409-P-6012 $4.49

Tapered Blade
8 in.; 4 in. blade.
409-P-6003 $3.99

Tip Accessories
Maintain the quality of your Wilton metal decorating tips with these tools.

Tip/Coupler Dishwasher and Storage Bag
Place nylon mesh bag in dishwasher silverware rack for easy tip and coupler cleaning. Tips not included. 5¾ x 6 in.
417-P-1640 Pk./2 $2.99

DECORATING COUPLERS
Couplers make it easy to change decorating tips on the same icing bag.

Standard Coupler
Fits all decorating bags and standard tips.
411-P-1987 $0.59

Large Coupler
Use with large decorating tips and 14 to 18 in. Featherweight Bags.
411-P-1006 $1.19

Tip Saver
Restores bent tips to their proper shape; opens clogged tips. Place tip over pointed or cone-shaped end, put on cover and twist back and forth to reshape. Heavy-duty plastic.
414-P-909 $2.79

Tip Covers

Take filled bags along for touch ups—just slip over tip and go. Plastic.
414-P-915 Pk./4 $0.99

Tip Brush
Great for cleaning small tip openings. Plastic bristles. ¼ x 4 in. long.
418-P-1123 $1.19

Tipsaver Cases

Small case holds 26 tips; large case holds 52 tips Tips not included.
Small 405-P-8773 $4.99
Large 405-P-7777 $6.99

Flower-Making Accessories

Flower Lifter
Easily transfers buttercream flowers from nail to cake without damage. Angled design keeps your hands from touching the cake. Detachable blades for easy cleaning. Plastic. 5¼ in. long.
417-P-1199 $2.99

Flower Nail No. 7
For basic flower making. Provides the control you need when piping icing flowers. Just rotate the nail between your thumb and fingers as you pipe a flower on the head. Stainless steel. 1½ in.
402-P-3007 $0.99

Lily Nail Set
Essential for making cup flowers. Includes ½, 1¼, 1⅝ and 2½ in. diameter cups.
403-P-9444 Set/8 $1.99

Flower Former Set
Dry icing leaves and flowers in a convex or concave shape. Three each of 1½, 2 and 2½ in. wide holders, all 11 in. long.
417-P-9500 Set/9 $5.99

Decorating Sets

The Supreme Set

"The Works". Decorate many advanced wedding, floral and basketweave cakes as well as basic cakes. This 53 pc. set includes: metal decorating tips #2, 3, 5, 7, 12, 16, 18, 21, 32, 47, 65, 67, 101, 103, 104, 129, 225 and 352; 24 disposable 12 in. decorating bags, two tip couplers, 5 icing colors (.5 oz. each), one 1¼ in. flower nail No. 9; 8 in. angled spatula; storage tray and a 40-page book: *Cake Decorating Beginner's Guide*.
2104-P-2546 Set/53 $27.99

The Deluxe Set

Create many advanced floral cakes and basic wedding cakes. This 37 pc. set includes: metal decorating tips #3, 5, 7, 12, 16, 21, 32, 67, 104 and 225; 18 disposable 12 in. decorating bags, two tip couplers, 4 icing colors (.5 oz. each), one 1¼ in. flower nail No. 9, storage tray and a 40-page book: *Cake Decorating Beginner's Guide*.
2104-P-2540 Set/37 $18.99

101 Piece Tool Caddy Collection

This convenient caddy contains our most complete collection of tools, colors and flavors for the cake decorator. It's a great way to organize, carry and store the essentials—tips, couplers, colors, spatulas and more. Lift-out tray holds tips, couplers, brushes and colors securely. Upright storage prevents spills and makes it easy to find what you need. Generous storage area keeps books, spatulas, bags and other large supplies neatly organized.
2109-P-861
Set/101 $120.00

Save over $30 Compared to individual prices

Includes These Tools:
- 8 Icing Colors: Golden Yellow, No-Taste Red, Brown, Violet, Pink, Royal Blue, Black, Kelly Green in .5 oz. jars
- 3 Couplers (2 standard, 1 large)
- 2 Tip/Coupler Dishwasher and Storage Bags
- Tip Cleaning Brush
- 24 Disposable 12 in. Decorating Bags
- 3 Professional Reusable Decorating Bags (8, 10 and 16 in.)
- 4 Tip Covers
- Tip Saver
- Flower Nail #7
- 3 Spatulas (8 and 13 in. Angled, 8 in. Tapered)
- Flower Lifter
- Garland Marker
- *Decorating Cakes* Book
- 20 All-Purpose Disposable Decorating Gloves
- Practice Board with Patterns
- 2 Bake-Even Strips
- 8 oz. Clear Vanilla and No-Color Butter Flavors
- Cake Leveler
- Quick Ease Roller
- Easy-Glide Fondant Smoother
- Decorating Brush

Plus 18 Tips:
- Round #1, 2, 2A, 3, 12
- Star #16, 18, 21, 32
- Basketweave #48
- Leaf #67, 352
- Petal #102, 103, 104, 125
- Drop Flower #2D
- Cake Icer #789

The Basic Set

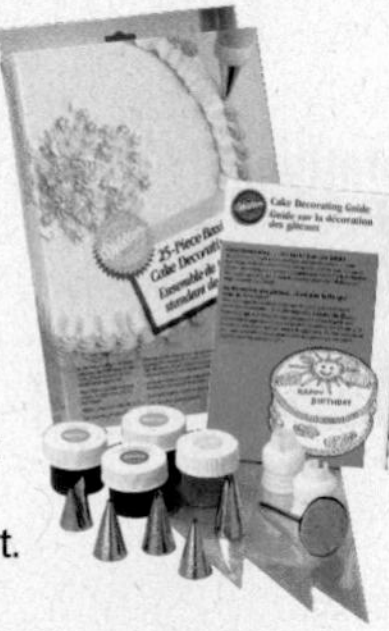

A solid foundation set for decorating. This 25 pc. set includes: metal decorating tips #3, 16, 21, 67 and 104; 12 12 in. disposable decorating bags; two tip couplers; 4 icing colors (.5 oz. each); 1¼ in. flower nail No. 9; 12-page instruction booklet.
2104-P-2536 Set/25 $9.99

The Starter Set

Perfect for Wilton character cakes! This 18 pc. set includes: metal decorating tips #3, 16, 21 and 67; 6 disposable 12 in. decorating bags; 2 tip couplers; 5 liquid color packets (.067 fl. oz. each); 10-page instruction booklet.
2104-P-2530 Set/18 $6.99

50 Piece Tool Caddy Decorating Set

Great Value!

Save $17 Compared to individual prices

We've put together the perfect set for beginning and advanced decorators. The generous selection of tips, colors and tools gives you the flexibility to decorate virtually any kind of cake. There's also plenty of room to add new items and keep everything organized to save you time. Set includes all tools specified as needed in our Course I class.
2109-P-859 Set/50 $49.99

Includes These 19 Tips:
- Round #2, 3, 5, 7, 12
- Open Star #16, 18, 21, 32
- Basketweave #47
- Leaf #67, 352
- Petal #101, 103, 104
- Multi-Opening #233
- Drop Flower #225
- Closed Star #133
- Large Drop Flower #2004 (2D)

Plus Tools:
- Tip Brush
- Decorating Brush
- Flower Nail No. 7
- 2 Standard Couplers
- 18 Disposable Bags
- One 10 in. Professional Bag
- 8 in. Angled Spatula
- Four .5 oz. Icing Colors: Lemon Yellow, Christmas Red, Royal Blue, Leaf Green
- Practice Board with stand
- *Cake Decorating Beginner's Guide*

Tip Sets

Deluxe Tip Set

Includes: 26 metal decorating tips: #2, 4, 7, 13, 16, 17, 18, 30, 42, 46, 47, 61, 65, 66, 67, 74, 78, 97, 98, 101, 102, 103, 104, 106, 107 and 199; 1¼ in. flower nail (No. 9); tip coupler; plastic tipsaver case.
2104-P-6666
Set/29 $24.99

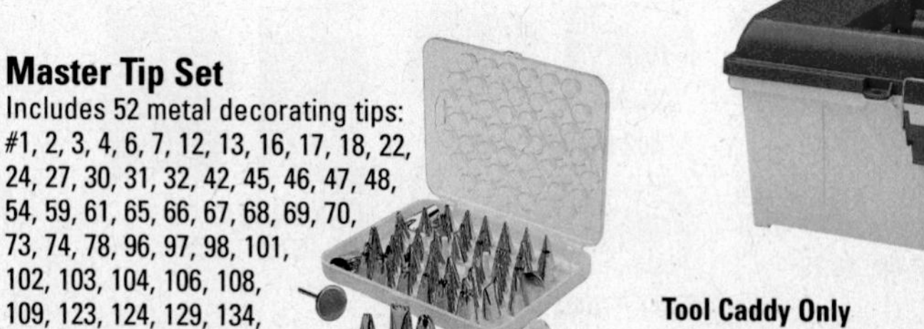

Master Tip Set

Includes 52 metal decorating tips: #1, 2, 3, 4, 6, 7, 12, 13, 16, 17, 18, 22, 24, 27, 30, 31, 32, 42, 45, 46, 47, 48, 54, 59, 61, 65, 66, 67, 68, 69, 70, 73, 74, 78, 96, 97, 98, 101, 102, 103, 104, 106, 108, 109, 123, 124, 129, 134, 136, 195, 199 and 2C; two standard tip couplers; two 1¼ in. flower nails (No. 9); plastic tipsaver case.
2104-P-7778 Set/57 $39.99

Tool Caddy Only

Lift out tray keeps 48 tips and 12 color jars in easy reach (tips and colors not included). Stores colors upright to prevent spilling.
409-P-860 $19.99

Decorating Tips

All tips work with standard bags and couplers, unless otherwise indicated. Nickel-plated brass. Dishwasher safe.

ROUND TIPS

Outline, lettering, dots, balls, beads, stringwork, lattice, lacework.

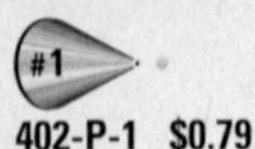
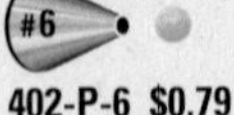

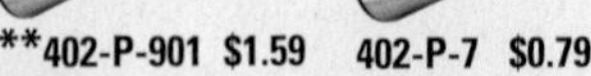

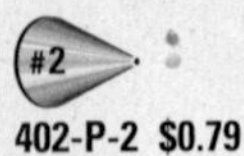
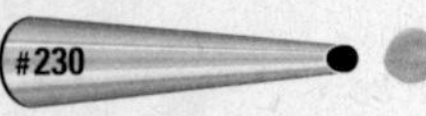

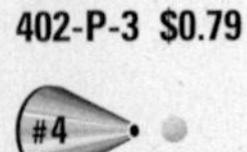
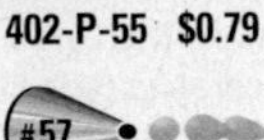

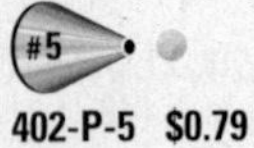

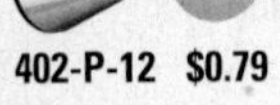
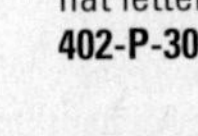

#1 402-P-1 $0.79

#1L **402-P-901 $1.59

#1s 402-P-1009 $1.29

#2 402-P-2 $0.79

#3 402-P-3 $0.79

#4 402-P-4 $0.79

#5 402-P-5 $0.79

#6 402-P-6 $0.79

#7 402-P-7 $0.79

#8 402-P-8 $0.79

#9 402-P-9 $0.79

#10 402-P-10 $0.79

#11 402-P-11 $0.79

#12 402-P-12 $0.79

#2A *Smaller version of 1A. 402-P-2001 $1.39

#1A Bold borders, figure piping. *402-P-1001 $1.59

#230 Fill eclairs and bismarcks. 402-P-230 $1.99

#55 402-P-55 $0.79

#57 402-P-57 $0.79

#301 flat lettering. 402-P-301 $0.79

DROP FLOWER TIPS

Small (106-225); medium (131-194); large (2C-1G) great for cookie dough.

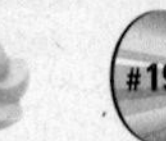

#106 402-P-106 $1.39

#107 402-P-107 $1.39

#108 **402-P-108 $1.39

#109 **402-P-109 $1.59

#129 402-P-129 $1.39

#224 402-P-224 $1.39

#225 402-P-225 $1.39

#131 402-P-131 $1.39

#190 **402-P-190 $1.59

#191 402-P-191 $1.39

#193 402-P-193 $1.39

#194 **402-P-194 $1.59

#140 402-P-140 $1.59

#195 **402-P-195 $1.39

#2C *402-P-2003 $1.39

#2D *402-P-2004 $1.39

#2E *402-P-2005 $1.39

#2F *402-P-2006 $1.39

#1B *402-P-1002 $1.59

#1C *402-P-1003 $1.59

#1E *402-P-1005 $1.59

#1F *402-P-1006 $1.59

#1G *402-P-1007 $1.59

PETAL TIPS

Realistic flower petals, dramatic ruffles, drapes, swags and bows.

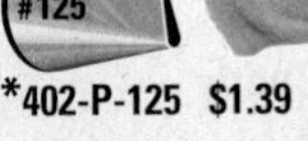

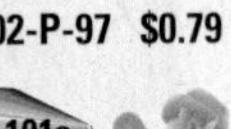

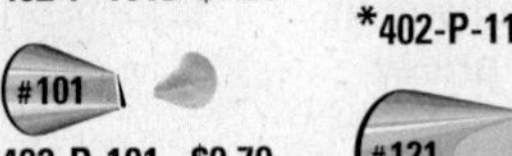
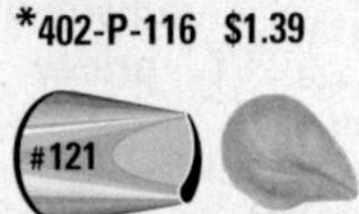
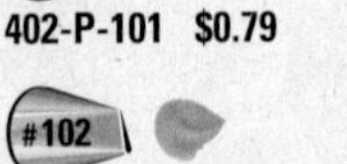
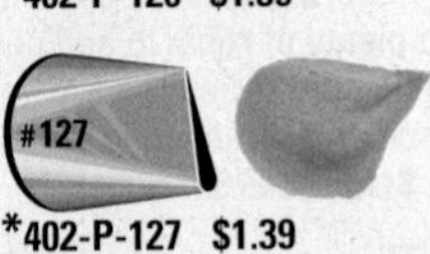

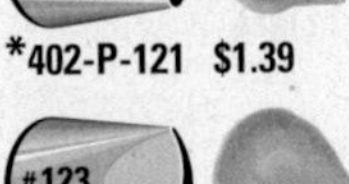
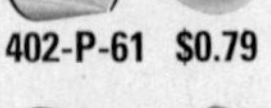
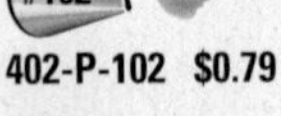
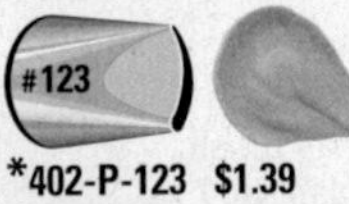

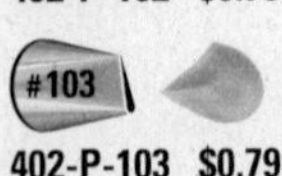

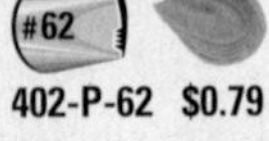
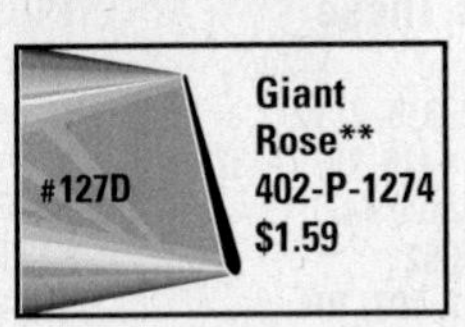
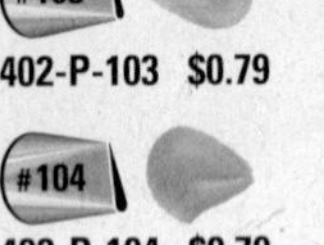
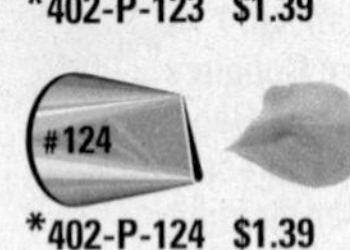
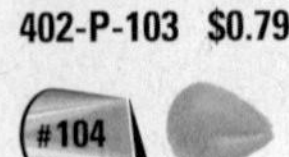

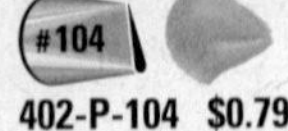

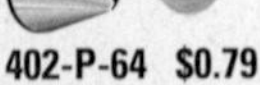

#59s/59° 402-P-594 $0.79

#59 402-P-59 $0.79

#60 402-P-60 $0.79

#61 402-P-61 $0.79

#62 402-P-62 $0.79

#64 402-P-64 $0.79

#97 402-P-97 $0.79

#101s 402-P-1019 $1.29

#101 402-P-101 $0.79

#102 402-P-102 $0.79

#103 402-P-103 $0.79

#104 402-P-104 $0.79

#150 402-P-150 $1.39

#116 *402-P-116 $1.39

#121 *402-P-121 $1.39

#123 *402-P-123 $1.39

#124 *402-P-124 $1.39

#125 *402-P-125 $1.39

#126 *402-P-126 $1.39

#127 *402-P-127 $1.39

#127D Giant Rose** 402-P-1274 $1.59

Decorating Tips Poster
Lists all Wilton tips and their uses; grouped in families, for quick reference when decorating. 28 x 22 in.
909-P-190
$2.99

BASKETWEAVE TIPS

44, 45 make only smooth stripes; rest of basketweave tips make both smooth and ribbed stripes.

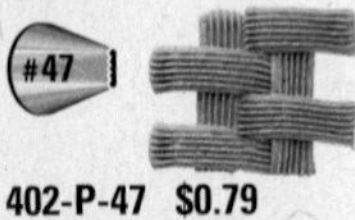

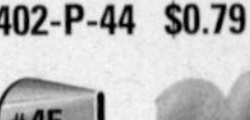

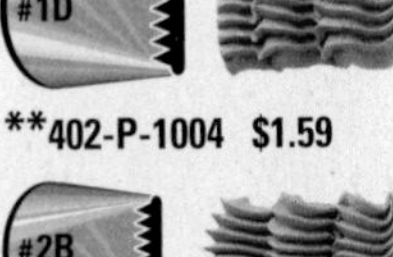

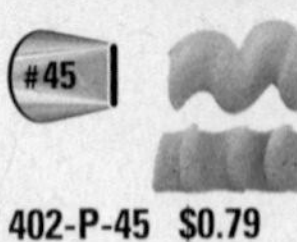

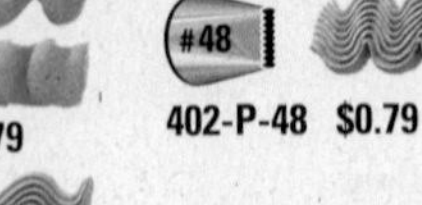

#44 402-P-44 $0.79

#45 402-P-45 $0.79

#46 402-P-46 $0.79

#47 402-P-47 $0.79

#48 402-P-48 $0.79

#1D **402-P-1004 $1.59

#2B *402-P-2002 $1.39

#789 Cake Icer.** 409-P-789 $2.59

MULTI-OPENING TIPS

Rows and clusters of strings, beads, stars, scallops.

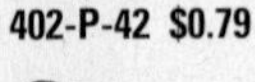
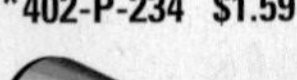
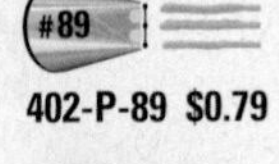

#42 402-P-42 $0.79

#89 402-P-89 $0.79

#134 **402-P-134 $1.59

#233 402-P-233 $1.39

#234 *402-P-234 $1.59

#235 *402-P-235 $1.39

Triple Star. *402-P-2010 $2.49

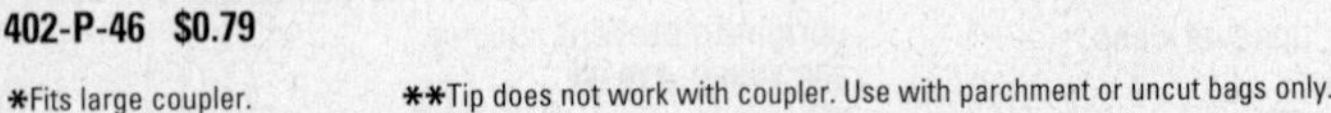

*Fits large coupler. **Tip does not work with coupler. Use with parchment or uncut bags only.

OPEN STAR TIPS

Star techniques, drop flowers; the finely cut teeth of 199 thru 364 create decorations with many ridges; use 6B and 8B with pastry dough too.

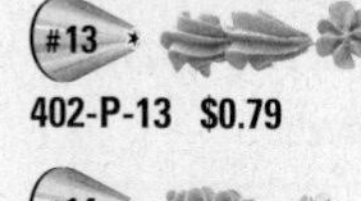

- #13 — 402-P-13 $0.79
- #14 — 402-P-14 $0.79
- #15 — 402-P-15 $0.79
- #16 — 402-P-16 $0.79
- #17 — 402-P-17 $0.79
- #18 — 402-P-18 $0.79
- #19 — 402-P-19 $0.79

- #20 — 402-P-20 $0.79

- #21 — 402-P-21 $0.79

- #22 — 402-P-22 $0.79

- #32 — 402-P-32 $0.79

- #199 — 402-P-199 $1.39

- #362 — 402-P-362 $1.39

- #363 — 402-P-363 $1.39
- #364 — 402-P-364 $1.39
- #172 — **402-P-172 $1.39

- #1M — (2110) *402-P-2110 $1.39

- #4B — **402-P-4400 $1.39
- #6B — **402-P-6600 $1.39
- #8B — **402-P-8800 $1.59

LEFT HANDED TIP SETS

NEW!

LEFT-HAND

Now left-handers can achieve the same beautiful flowers as right-handed decorators! Nickel-plated brass tips fit standard bags and couplers.

#106L #107L #59°L #97L #116L

Drop Flower Set
Includes Left tips #106 and #107 for making small swirled flowers.
†418-P-613 Set/2 $2.99

Petal Set
Includes Left tip #59° for violets, Left tip #97 for Victorian roses and Left tip #116 for large Wilton roses.
†418-P-612 Set/3 $2.99

SPECIALTY TIPS

Shells, ropes, hearts, Christmas trees, ring candle holders!

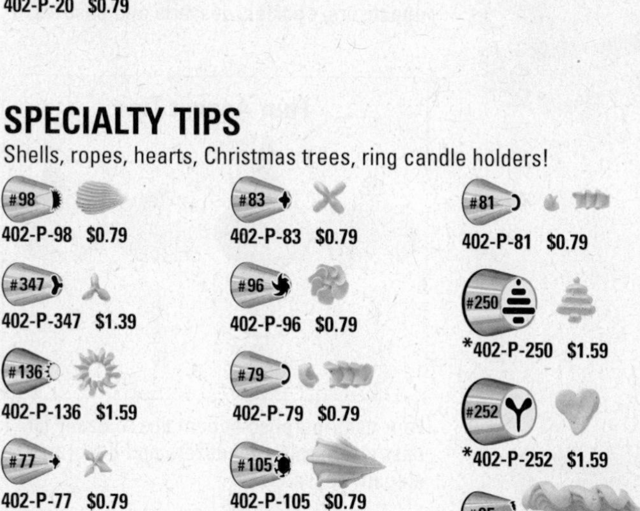

- #98 — 402-P-98 $0.79
- #347 — 402-P-347 $1.39
- #136 — 402-P-136 $1.59
- #77 — 402-P-77 $0.79
- #78 — 402-P-78 $0.79
- #83 — 402-P-83 $0.79
- #96 — 402-P-96 $0.79
- #79 — 402-P-79 $0.79
- #105 — 402-P-105 $0.79
- #80 — 402-P-80 $0.79
- #81 — 402-P-81 $0.79
- #250 — *402-P-250 $1.59

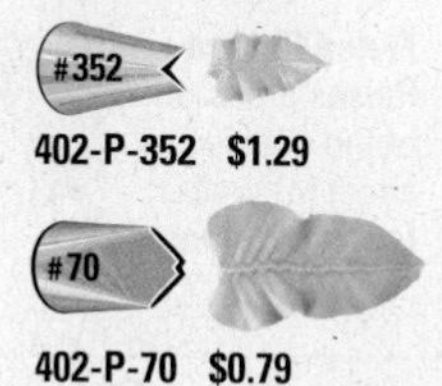

- #252 — *402-P-252 $1.59
- #95 — 402-P-95 $0.79

LEAF TIPS

So realistic! Ideal for shell-motion borders too.

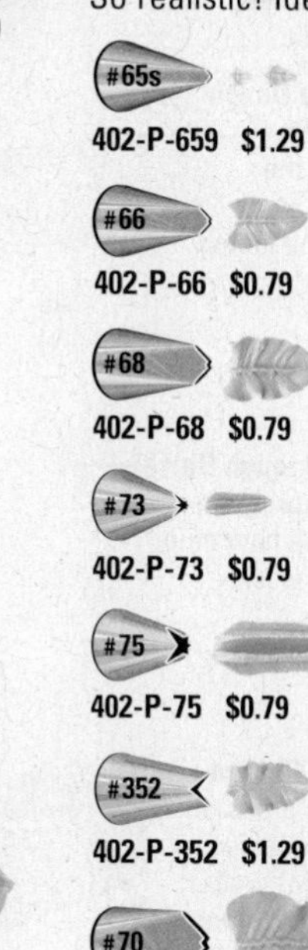

- #65s — 402-P-659 $1.29
- #66 — 402-P-66 $0.79
- #68 — 402-P-68 $0.79
- #73 — 402-P-73 $0.79
- #75 — 402-P-75 $0.79
- #352 — 402-P-352 $1.29
- #70 — 402-P-70 $0.79
- #65 — 402-P-65 $0.79
- #67 — 402-P-67 $0.79
- #69 — 402-P-69 $0.79
- #74 — 402-P-74 $0.79

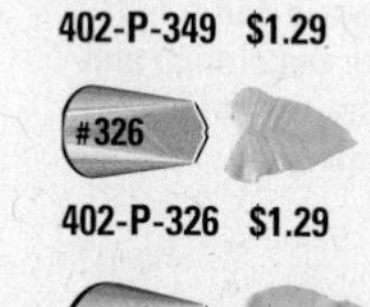

- 349/352s — 402-P-349 $1.29
- #326 — 402-P-326 $1.29
- #112 — **402-P-112 $1.39
- #113 — *402-P-113 $1.39
- #115 — *402-P-115 $1.39

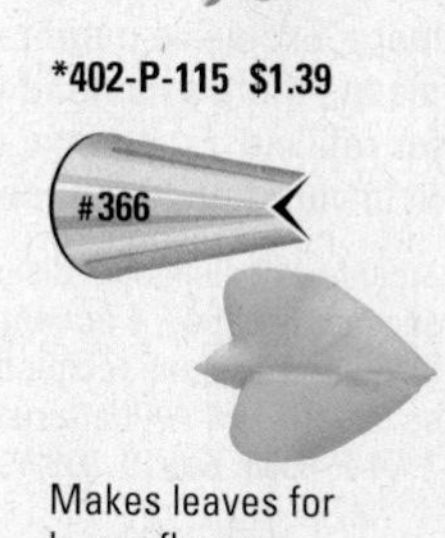

- #366 — Makes leaves for larger flowers. *402-P-366 $1.59

CLOSED STAR TIPS

Create deeply grooved shells, stars and fleurs-de-lis.

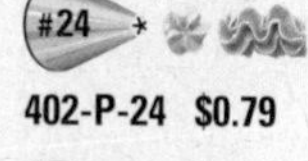

- #24 — 402-P-24 $0.79
- #26 — 402-P-26 $0.79
- #27 — 402-P-27 $0.79

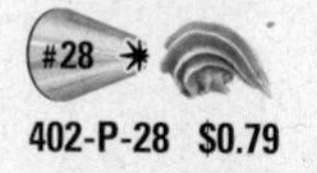

- #28 — 402-P-28 $0.79

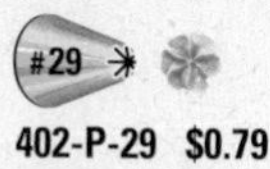

- #29 — 402-P-29 $0.79

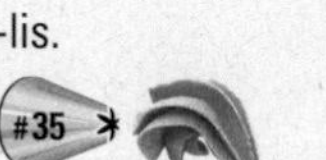

- #30 — 402-P-30 $0.79
- #31 — 402-P-31 $0.79
- #33 — 402-P-33 $0.79

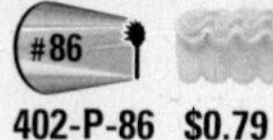

- #35 — 402-P-35 $0.79

- #133 — 402-P-133 $0.79

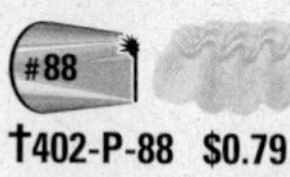

- #54 — 402-P-54 $0.79

RUFFLE TIPS

Plain, fluted, shell-border, special effects.

- #86 — 402-P-86 $0.79
- #87 — †402-P-87 $0.79
- #88 — †402-P-88 $0.79
- #100 — 402-P-100 $0.79
- #353 — 402-P-353 $1.29
- #340 — 402-P-340 $1.29
- #401 — 402-P-401 $0.99

- #402 — *402-P-402 $1.39

- #406 — *402-P-406 $1.59

- #403 — **402-P-403 $1.59

† For left-handers

Cookie Making

Wilton has just what you need to make cookies fun! Easy-to-use presses, colossal cutter sets, fun stencils, colorful icings and unique toppings sure to create unforgettable cookies!

Cookie Presses

Wilton has four great ways to press cookies—the best selection of feature-packed presses anywhere! From our new Comfort Grip™ Press, designed for easy handling and filling, to our powerful cordless Cookie Master™ Plus, cookie-making has never been more convenient.

COOKIE MASTER™ *Plus*

Cordless Cookie Press

Distinctive Cookies

Snacks & Appetizers

Desserts & More!

Our cordless cookie press is so powerful and easy to operate, you'll use it all year to create cookies, appetizers, desserts and more. Exclusive patented reverse action means there's no need to take press apart for refilling. Ergonomic design is shaped to fit in your hand for excellent comfort.

Includes 12 aluminum disks in classic and seasonal shapes, 4 accent tips for decorating and filling and 2 bonus recipe booklets—sweet and savory. Uses 4 AA batteries, not included.
2104-P-4008 Set/19 $39.99

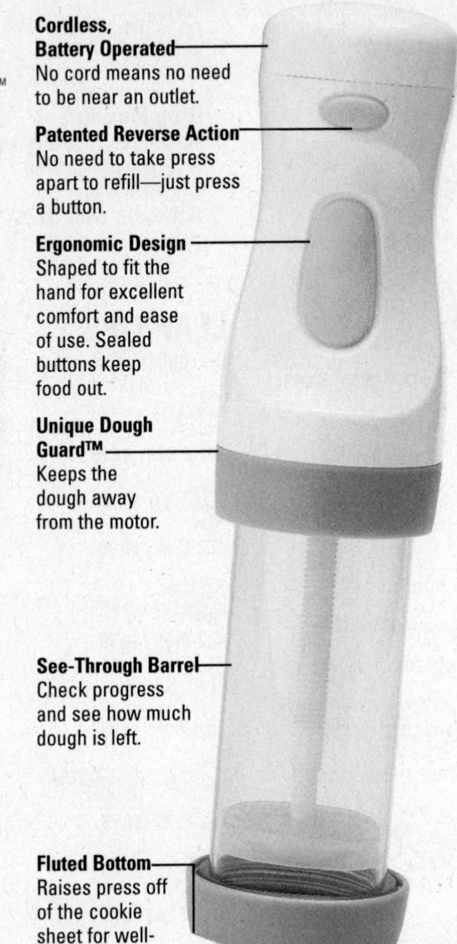

Cordless, Battery Operated No cord means no need to be near an outlet.

Patented Reverse Action No need to take press apart to refill—just press a button.

Ergonomic Design Shaped to fit the hand for excellent comfort and ease of use. Sealed buttons keep food out.

Unique Dough Guard™ Keeps the dough away from the motor.

See-Through Barrel Check progress and see how much dough is left.

Fluted Bottom Raises press off of the cookie sheet for well-formed designs

Twelve Disk Designs

Twelve aluminum disks in classic & seasonal shapes to create distinctive snacks, appetizers, cookies, desserts and pastries.

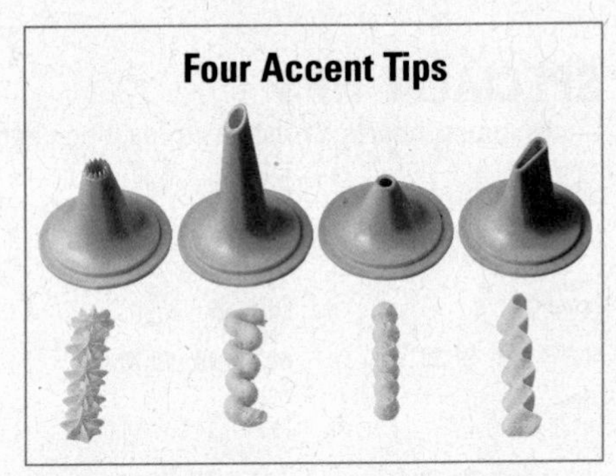

Four Accent Tips

Four multi-purpose accent tips to easily fill pastries, garnish appetizers and decorate elegant desserts.

COMFORT GRIP™ Cookie Press

NEW!

Comfort Grip™ Cookie Press
Experience a classic press that is truly comfortable. Its ergonomic handle feels great in any hand—the easy-squeeze action releases perfectly shaped dough. The clear barrel takes the guesswork out of refilling. Fluted bottom raises the press off the cookie sheet to help you create better shapes.

Includes 12 plastic disks in a wide variety of shapes and our classic spritz recipe.
2104-P-4011 Set/13 $12.99

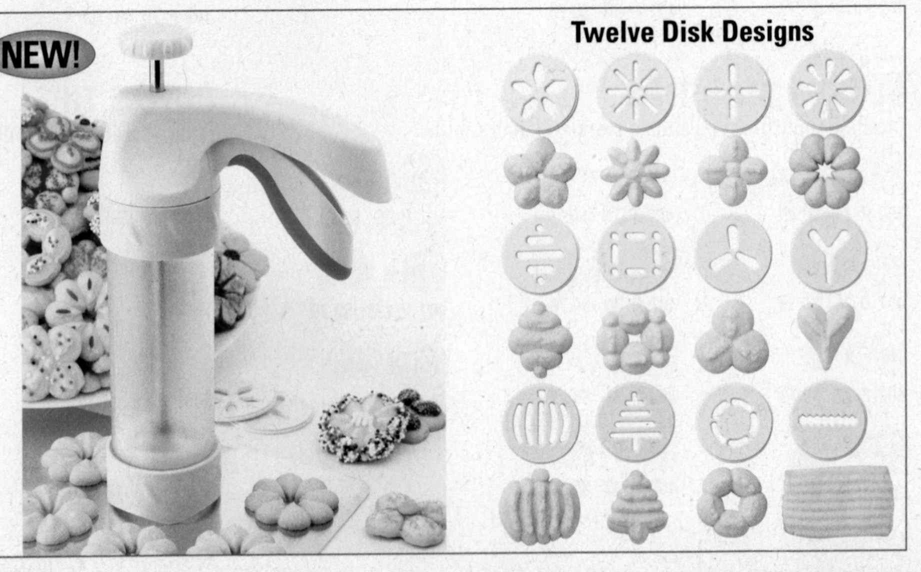

Twelve Disk Designs

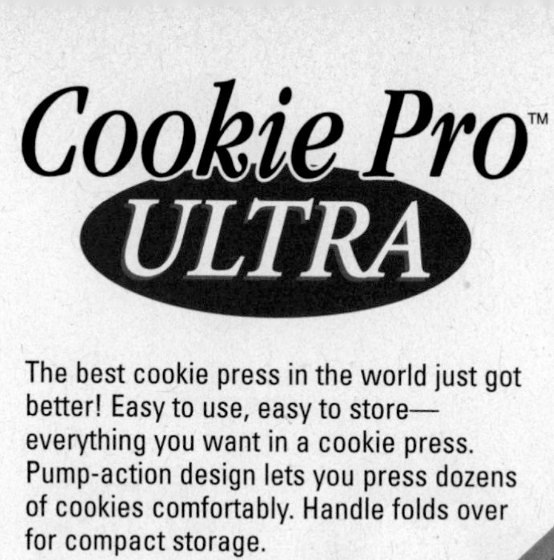

The best cookie press in the world just got better! Easy to use, easy to store—everything you want in a cookie press. Pump-action design lets you press dozens of cookies comfortably. Handle folds over for compact storage.

Includes 10 aluminum disks in an attachable storage case. Recipes included.
2104-P-4010 Set/12 $24.99

Pump Action
For greater efficiency and ease of use.

Space Saving Design
Unique flip-over handle for easy and convenient storage.

Internal Spring-Loaded Piston
For exceptional reliability and efficient pressing.

Side Grips
Prevent hands from slipping.

Ergonomically-Designed Comfort Grip™ Handle
Helps you press comfortably even when making large batches of cookies.

Heavy-Duty Construction
Cast aluminum and stainless steel.

Finger-Grip Disk Ring
Makes changing disks easy.

No More Missing Disks!
Storage case attaches to cookie press when not in use.

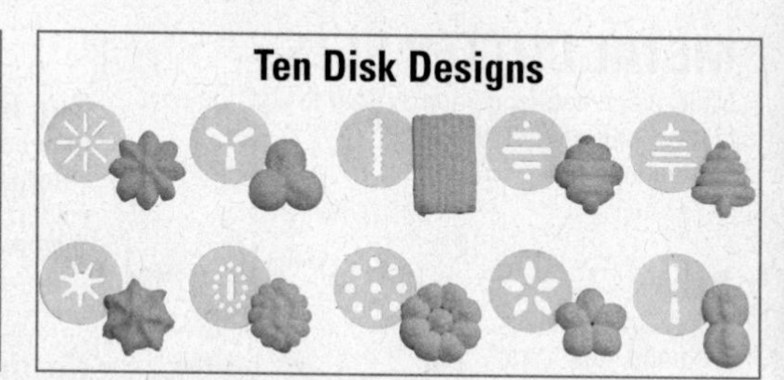

Ten Disk Designs Included!
Long-lasting aluminum disks are dishwasher safe.

Discover the cookie press that takes convenience and comfort to the max! With the Cookie Max™, you'll see the difference from the first batch. An easy pump action gives you more control—one click of the plunger equals one perfect cookie, every time. The handle is cushioned, for a sure, comfortable grip. The see-through barrel and raised bottom let you see the cookie and your remaining dough as you press. No clogging, easy cleaning.

Includes 12 plastic disks in favorite shapes, easy instructions and 3 delicious recipes.
2104-P-4003 Set/13 $17.99

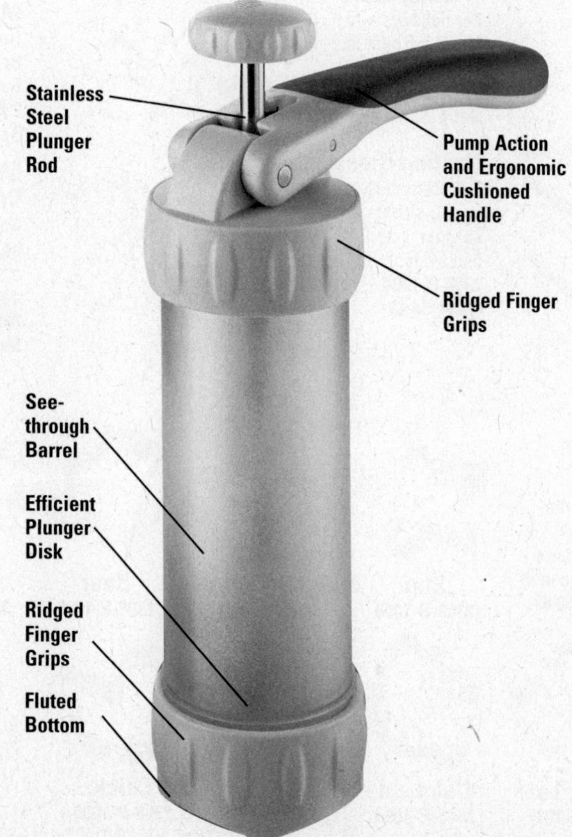

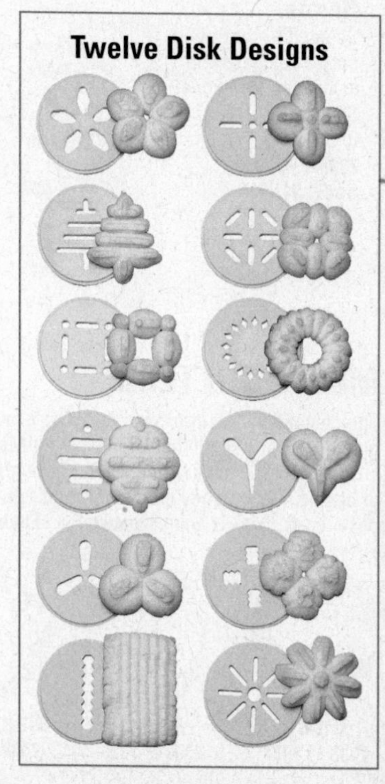

Cookie Cutters

These versatile designs are sure to spark your creativity!

COMFORT GRIP™ CUTTERS

Easy-grip stainless steel cutters with extra-deep sides are perfect for cutting so many favorite foods into spectacular shapes. Ideal for brownies, biscuits, sandwiches, sheet cakes, cheese, crispy rice treats, fudge and much more. The cushion grip gives you comfortable control even when cutting into thick desserts. Recipe included. Each approximately 4 x 4 x 1¾ in. deep. **Each $2.99**

Star
2310-P-605

Teddy Bear
2310-P-609

Round
2310-P-608

Square Crinkle
2310-P-611

Heart
2310-P-616

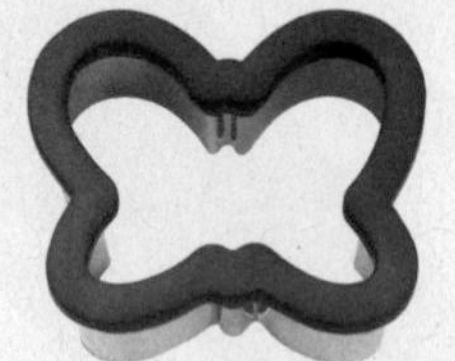

Butterfly
2310-P-614

Flower
2310-P-613

Daisy
2310-P-619

METAL CUTTER SETS

Multi-piece sets add variety. Built to last, they cut cleanly and release easily. Recipe included.

Basic
Geometric, crinkle diamond, heart, half moon, star and flower. Each approx. 3 in.
2308-P-1235
Set/6 $4.99

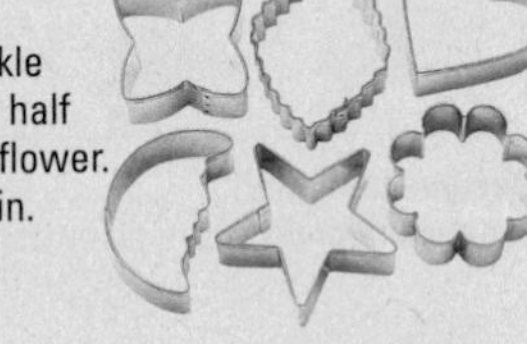

Animals
Horse, dove, lion, duck, pig and cat. Each approx. 3 in.
2308-P-1236
Set/6 $4.99

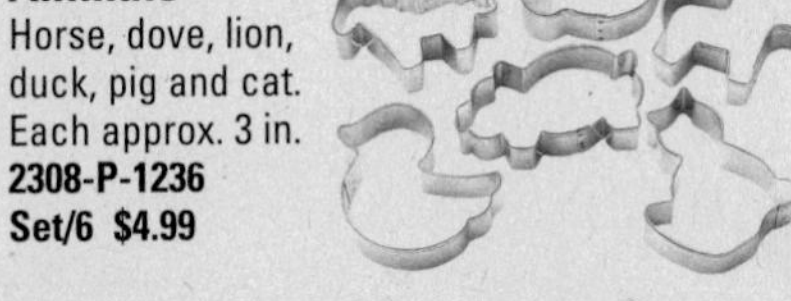

Hearts
Seven different heart cutter designs from stylized to traditional. Sizes range from 1½ to 3 in.
2308-P-1237
Set/7 $4.99

Bug Buddies NEW!
Cute cookie crawlers! Includes butterfly, caterpillar, bee, ladybug, dragonfly and spider. Each approx. 3 in.
2308-P-1245 Set/6 $4.99

Nesting From The Heart
Two crinkled and two smooth. Largest is approx. 5 in.
2308-P-1203
Set/4 $4.49

Nesting Stars
For holidays and more! Largest is approx. 5 in.
2308-P-1215
Set/4 $4.49

Nesting Blossoms
Cut pretty flowers in four sizes. Largest is approx. 5 in. wide.
2308-P-1204
Set/4 $4.49

Mini Romantic NEW!
Butterfly, heart, bell, crinkled heart, tulip, and blossom. Each approx. 1½ in.
2308-P-1225
Set/6 $2.99

Mini Noah's Ark
Horse, ark, elephant, bear, giraffe and lion. Each approx. 1½ in.
2308-P-1206
Set/6 $2.99

Mini Geometric Crinkle
Square, circle, heart, diamond, oval and triangle. Each approx. 1½ in.
2308-P-1205
Set/6 $2.99

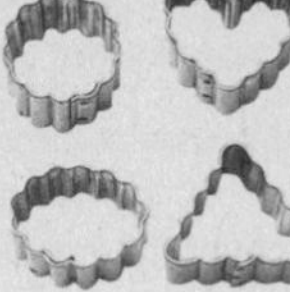

METAL CUTTERS

The classic metal cutter was Grandma's favorite but she never had all these fun shapes! Metal cutters from Wilton are built to last through years of cookie making; they cut cleanly and release with ease. Each shape is approximately 3 in. **Each $0.69**

Star
2308-P-1008

Gingerbread Boy
2308-P-1002

Bear
2308-P-1009

Heart
2308-P-1003

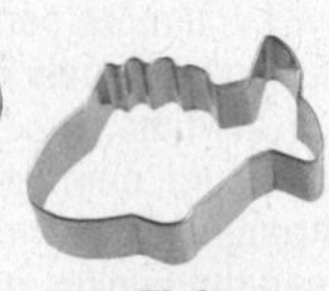

Fish
2308-P-1017

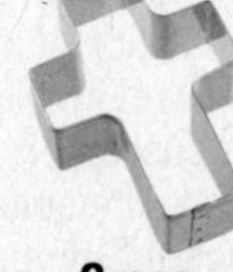

Cross
2308-P-1018

Daisy
2308-P-1007

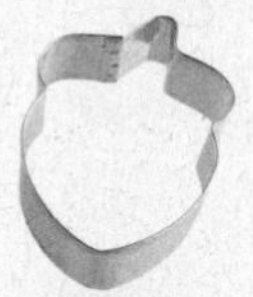

Acorn
2308-P-1020

Maple Leaf
2308-P-1021

Oak Leaf
2308-P-1013

Butterfly
2308-P-1015

Chick
2308-P-1000

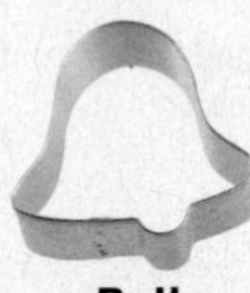

Bell
2308-P-1006

Circle
2308-P-1010

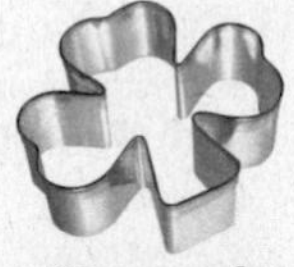

Shamrock
2308-P-1011

SOLID COPPER CUTTERS

The warmth and beauty of copper make these cutters ideal for displaying and adding that decorative touch to your kitchen. These beautiful, heirloom-quality copper cutters have smoothly rolled edges for that finishing touch. Each approximately 5½ in. diameter. **Each $6.99**

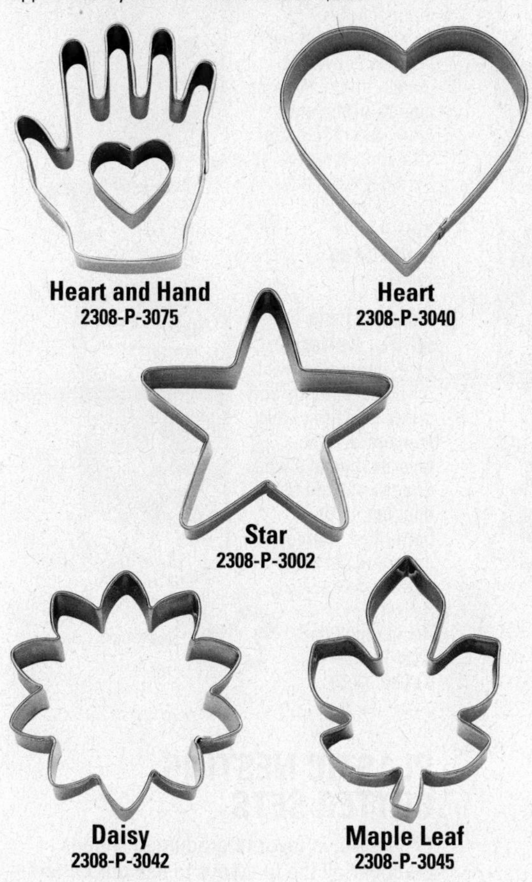

Heart and Hand 2308-P-3075

Heart 2308-P-3040

Star 2308-P-3002

Daisy 2308-P-3042

Maple Leaf 2308-P-3045

Ice-A-Cookie™

Instant fun for all your cookies! The soft, squeezable pouch is easy to handle and the patented snip tip and screw-on decorating cap help you control the flow—use the snip tip for icing cookies and the cap for decorating lines and designs. Delicious vanilla-flavored icing dries to a smooth, satin finish. Draw fun shapes, messages, decorate with Cake Sparkles™ (not included) and more! Each 10.59 oz. pouch decorates approximately two dozen 3 in. round cookies. Certified Kosher.
White 710-P-416 $3.99

FoodWriter™ Edible Color Markers

Use like ink markers to add fun and dazzling color to countless foods. Kids love 'em! Decorate on fondant, color flow, royal icing designs and cookies. Brighten everyday foods like toaster pastries, cheese, fruit slices, bread and more. Each set includes five .35 oz. FoodWriter pens. Certified Kosher.

PRIMARY COLORS

Yellow | Green | Red | Blue | Black

Fine Tip
609-P-100
Set/5 $7.99

Bold Tip
609-P-115
Set/5 $7.99

NEW!

FINE TIP

BOLD TIP

NEON COLORS

Purple | Orange | Pink | Light Green | Black

Fine Tip
609-P-116
Set/5 $7.99

NEW!

STENCIL-A-COOKIE™ CUTTER & STENCIL SETS

Using the fun-shaped cutter and stencil, it's easy to serve cookies with exciting colorful designs. Just cut cookies, then use the stencil and Wilton FoodWriter™, Cake Sparkles™, Colored Sugars or Color Mist™ Food Color Spray to create dazzling shapes on top after baking. Cookies look great iced with Wilton Ice-A-Cookie™ sold above. Set includes one metal cutter and two stencils (same design). **Set/3 $1.99**

Heart 2308-P-1401

Butterfly 2308-P-1402

Flower 2308-P-1403

House 2308-P-1404

Star 2308-P-1405

Bear 2308-P-1400

Cookie Cutters

PLASTIC COOKIE CUTTER SETS

101 Cookie Cutters!
With this set, you're covered—for any occasion, any season, any age! Make cookies featuring favorite holiday and theme shapes like sports, flowers, animals and more. Or use the complete alphabet and numeral collections included to create the perfect cookie message. Great for cutting all kinds of food into fun shapes—perfect for crafting, too. Average cutter size approx. 3½ x 3½ in. Recipe included.
2304-P-1000 Set/101 $14.99

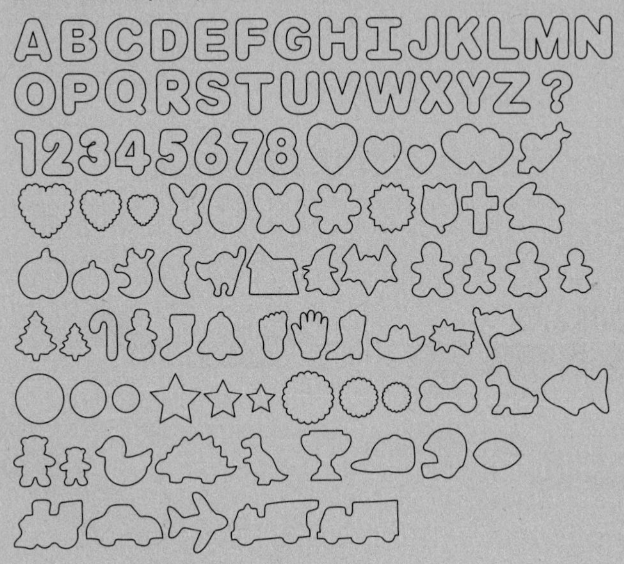

A-B-C and 1-2-3 50-Pc. Cutter Set
Complete alphabet and numeral collection, great for cookies, brownies, gelatin treats, learning games, crafts and more. Average cutter size approx. 3½ x 3½ in. Recipe included.
2304-P-1054
Set/50 $8.99

Animal Pals 50-Pc. Cutter Set
Everyone will go wild for cookies, foods and crafts made with this menagerie of 50 favorite animal shapes. Shapes include fish, dog, cat, birds, butterflies, reptiles and more. Average cutter size approx. 3½ x 3½ in. Recipe included.
2304-P-1055
Set/50 $8.99

PLASTIC COOKIE CUTTERS

With our large variety of brightly-colored cutter shapes, the making is as much fun as the eating! Child-safe design means kids can help.

Each approx. 3 in. x 4 in. **Each $0.69**

Fish 2303-P-128
Dinosaur 2303-P-112
Teddy Bear 2303-P-133
Butterfly 2303-P-116
Puppy 2303-P-137
Star 2303-P-135
Hand 2303-P-147
Foot 2303-P-113
Girl 2303-P-120
Boy 2303-P-124
Dog Bone 2303-P-123
Locomotive Engine 2303-P-139
6 Pt. Star 2303-P-122
Heart 2303-P-100
Cat 2303-P-118
Duck 2303-P-148
Cross 2303-P-141
Ice Cream Cone 2303-P-111
Sailboat 2303-P-129
Airplane 2303-P-101
Flower 2303-P-117
Four-Leaf Clover 2303-P-134

PLASTIC NESTING CUTTER SETS

Child-safe, in favorite graduated shapes. Discover all the fun ways to use our cutters—for bread shapes, stencils, sun catchers and so much more.

Teddy Bears
From cub to grizzly size! 1¾ to 6⅜ in. tall.
2304-P-1520
Set/4 $2.99

Blossom
Create pretty blooms with plastic cutters in sizes from 1⅛ to 4½ in.
2304-P-116
Set/6 $2.99

Heart
Great for tracing valentines! 1½ to 4⅛ in.
2304-P-115
Set/6 $2.99

Star
For crafts, cookies or patterns in your iced cake. 1⅝ to 4⅝ in.
2304-P-111
Set/6 $2.99

Cookie Bakeware and Accessories

COOKIE TREAT PANS

Cookie treats on a stick are so easy! Just press cookie dough into pan, insert a cookie stick, then bake, cool and decorate. Create your own cookie blossoms for that special someone; also great for rice cereal treats and candy.

Recipe included. Each pan makes 6 individual treats, 3½ in. x ¼ in. deep. Aluminum. **Each $7.99**

Star
2105-P-8102

Round
2105-P-8105

Blossom
2105-P-8109

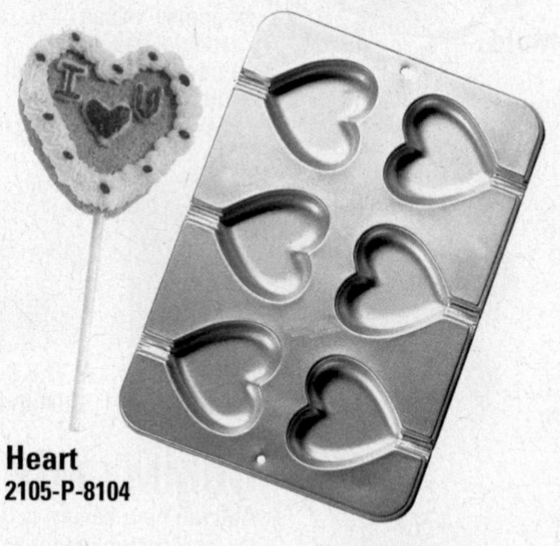

Heart
2105-P-8104

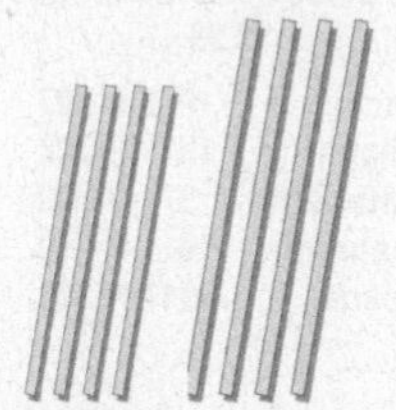

Cookie Treat Sticks
For fun cookie pops.
6 in. 1912-P-9319
Pk./20 $1.99
8 in. 1912-P-9318
Pk./20 $2.99

Clear Party Bags
4 x 9½ in. Each pack contains 25 bags and 25 ties.
1912-P-1240
Pk./25 $1.99

GIANT COOKIE PANS

Our Giant Cookie Pans help you create a jumbo pan cookie in a shape that will be a big hit for any occasion. Specially designed for one package of refrigerated dough, they are also great for brownies and pizza!

Each shape is approximately ¾ in. deep and can be used with recipes that call for a standard 13 x 9 in. pan. Aluminum. **Each $5.99**

Round
2105-P-6201

Heart
2105-P-6203

COOKIE SHEETS

Wilton Cookie Sheets are extra thick aluminum and heat evenly for perfect, evenly-browned bottoms.

Aluminum
Extra-thick construction.
Jumbo 14 x 20 in.
2105-P-6213 $15.99
12½ x 16½ in.
2105-P-2975 $11.99

Insulated Aluminum
Two quality aluminum layers sandwich an insulating layer of air for perfect browning without burning.
16 x 14 in.
2105-P-2644 $15.99

COOLING GRIDS

Chrome-Plated
Sturdy design will never rust.
13 in. Round
2305-P-130 $6.99
10 x 16 in.
2305-P-128 $4.99
14½ x 20 in.
2305-P-129 $7.99

Non-Stick
Cookies and cakes won't crack with our slick non-stick coating.
13 in. Round
2305-P-230 $8.49
10 x 16 in.
2305-P-228 $7.99
14½ x 20 in.
2305-P-229 $11.99

3-Pc. Stackable Chrome-Plated
Use singly or stack to save space while cooling three batches of cookies at the same time.
Individual grids, 13½ x 9¾ x 3 in. high; stacked grids are 9¾ in. high.
2305-P-151 $11.99

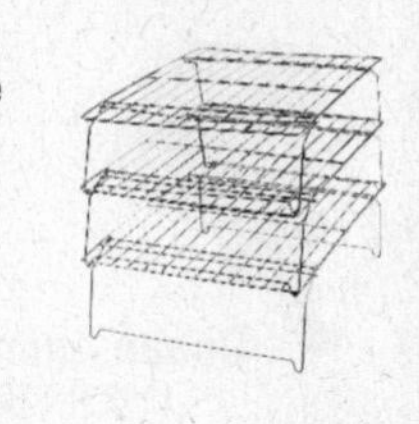

COOKIE SPATULA

Stainless steel spatula with riveted rosewood handle.
417-P-470 $3.99

SUGAR CRYSTALS

Brighten up plain cookies fast with our colorful decorating sugars. Just sprinkle these extra-fine sugars on cookies before baking. Controlling the flow is easy with the flip-top shaker bottle. Certified Kosher. 4.4 oz.
Each $4.99

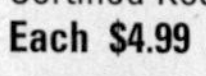

Brights 4-Mix
Contains 1.1 oz. each Pink, Yellow, Light Green, Lavender.
710-P-651

Primary 4-Mix
Contains 1.1 oz. each Red, Dark Green, Blue, Yellow.
710-P-650

Wilton for Kids™

Candy's even more fun when kids make it themselves! Wilton Gummy and Kandy Clay kits and accessories make it easy for kids to make the coolest candies in amazing shapes and flavors!

GUMMY! ALL NEW!

Kids will have a wild time making gummy dinosaurs, flowers, funny faces and more with Wilton for Kids kits, molds, tools and gummy mixes. Just follow the easy steps to make great-tasting gummys in 10 minutes! Recommended for ages 4 and above.

Easy as 1•2•3...

Mix

Shake

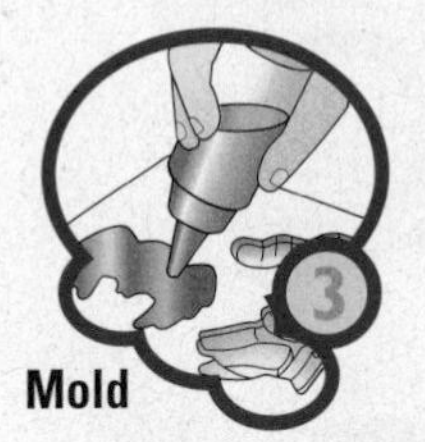

Mold

GUMMY MOLDS

Each includes 4 molds, 16 different shapes kids love!
$3.99

Zoo Animals
1902-P-616

Ocean Animals
1902-P-615

Transportation
1902-P-617

Make Over
1902-P-626

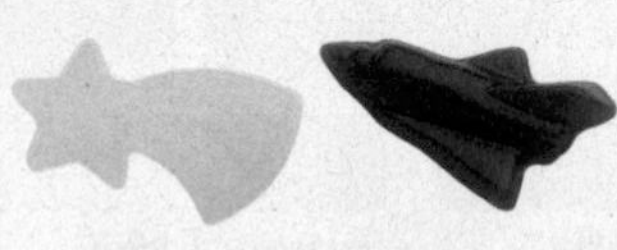

Space Exploration
1902-P-628

Ready to Eat in under 10 Minutes!

GUMMY-MAKING KITS

Everything's included for kids to make 16 yummy gummys. Check out the fun shapes! Easy to mix and mold—just pop in the fridge and pop out your candies in 10 minutes. **$4.99**

Each kit includes:
- Mold with 4 fun shapes, mixing bottle and funnel.
- 4 gummy mixes (.7 oz. each) in assorted artificial flavors.
- 1 packet of Sour Sugar (.7 oz.) for covering your gummys.
- Easy-to-follow instructions.

Creepy Critters
2104-P-1617

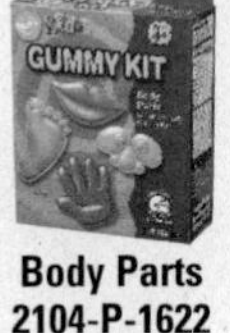

Body Parts
2104-P-1622

Food Fun
2104-P-1623

Glam Girl **2104-P-1616** | **At The Beach** **2104-P-1618** | **Funny Faces** **2104-P-1619** | **Dinosaurs** **2104-P-1620** | **Bloomin' Buds** **2104-P-1621**

GUMMY MIX FLAVORS

Add fun new flavors to your Gummy Making Kit and keep the gummy fun going! Each package includes five pouches (.7 oz. each)—enough to make 20 pieces of gummy candy, complete instructions. Artificial flavors. **$3.99**

Cherry	**1911-P-301**	**Peach**	**1911-P-307**
Watermelon	**1911-P-302**	**Lemon**	**1911-P-308**
Grape	**1911-P-303**	**Strawberry**	**1911-P-309**
Orange	**1911-P-304**	**Blueberry**	**1911-P-310**
Green Apple	**1911-P-305**	**Banana**	**1911-P-321**
Bubble Gum	**1911-P-306**		

Blue Raspberry
1911-P-320

GUMMY SOUR SUGAR

Add a sour kick to your favorite gummy flavors! Includes five pouches (.7 oz. each)—enough to cover 80 pieces.
1911-P-1930 $3.99

GUMMY-MAKING ACCESSORIES

Making gummys is more fun with the right tools! Kid-safe tools help kids mold gummys and pick up candy with ease.

Tool Kit
Includes bottle and funnel for easy mixing and filling, and scrubber brush for cleaning bottle and molds in a flash. Instructions included.
1904-P-1702
$3.99

Accessory Kit
Kids can give their gummys a dip in Sour Sugar using the tweezers and dipping tray in this kit. Sour Sugar is included in Gummy Candy-Making Kits and also sold separately.
1904-P-1703 $3.99

Look for more fun Gummy Kits featuring kids' favorite characters on pages 188-199.

WILTON FOR KIDS™

Kandy Clay™

The Modeling Clay You Can Eat!

It's the krazy, kolorful kandy kids can make into any shape! Roll it, shape it and stretch it into anything they can imagine —adorable animals, silly space aliens and more. When they're done, they'll have a sweet treat to eat! Here are the kits and kandy kids need to play with Kandy Clay.

KANDY CLAY ACTIVITY KITS

A fun way for kids to spend the day—each theme kit includes all the colorful, yummy candy needed to create great shapes to play with and eat!

Kits contain 12 Kandy pouches (.5 oz. each) in assorted artificial flavors, plus sculpting tool, cardboard window gift box and complete instructions unless otherwise noted. **$5.99**

Farm Friends
Includes cardboard Play Barn.
2104-P-3651

Kandy Kingdom
2104-P-3652

Chomp-A-Saurus
2104-P-3653

Kandy Kreatures
2104-P-5015

Kandy Kruisers
Contains thirteen .5 oz. Kandy pouches.
2104-P-5018

Glam Gear
Includes Mini Purse.
2104-P-5019

Monster Madness
2104-P-5021

Kandy Kritters
Includes cardboard Play Bug House.
2104-P-5023

Kandy Games
Includes Reversible Game Board for checkers, tic-tac-toe.
2104-P-5029

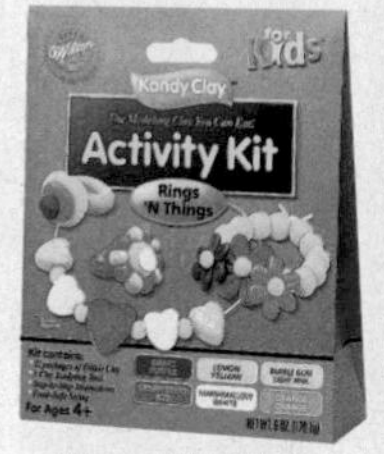

Rings 'N Things
Includes Food-Safe String.
2104-P-5030

KANDY CLAY COLOR PACKS

Get creative—grab the flavors and colors you love to add to your Kandy Clay shapes! Each pack includes twelve .5 oz. packages. Artificial flavors. **$3.99**

Single-Color Packs

Strawberry Red **1911-P-436**
Chocolate Brown **1911-P-437**
Lemon Yellow **1911-P-438**
Green Apple Green **1911-P-439**
Watermelon Hot Pink **1911-P-435**

Bubble Gum Light Pink **1911-P-440**
Grape Purple **1911-P-441**
Crystal Punch Light Blue **1911-P-442**
Blue Raspberry **1911-P-443**
Orange Orange **1911-P-445**

Multi-Color Packs

Pastel Colors
Includes: Peanut Butter Light Brown, Crystal Punch Light Blue, Peach Light Peach, Marshmallow White, Banana Light Yellow, Bubble Gum Light Pink.
1911-P-336

Primary Colors
Includes: Blueberry Blue, Green Apple Green, Lemon Yellow, Marshmallow White, Cherry Red, Chocolate Brown.
1911-P-335

Bright Colors
Includes: Blue Raspberry Blue, Lime Green, Orange Orange, Marshmallow White, Watermelon Hot Pink, Grape Purple.
1911-P-333

KANDY CLAY TOOL SETS

Made for little hands! Kids will have more fun playing with Kandy Clay when they use kid-sized tools for cutting, carving and rolling.

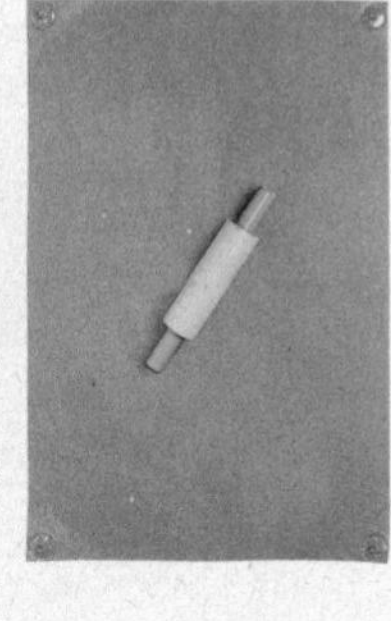

Play Mat/ Rolling Pin Set
The rolling pin rolls out Kandy Clay in no time flat! The mat keeps it from sticking to the counter.
1904-P-1551
$3.99

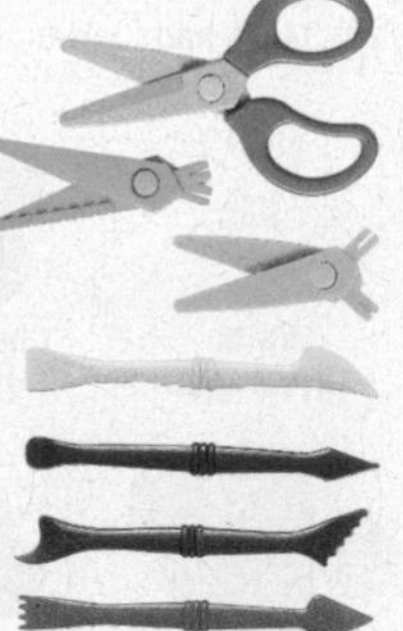

Scissors/ Sculpting Tool Set
Kid-safe scissors have 3 snap-on blades that fit on the same handle. Four sculpting tools help carve fun shapes.
1904-P-1121
$3.99

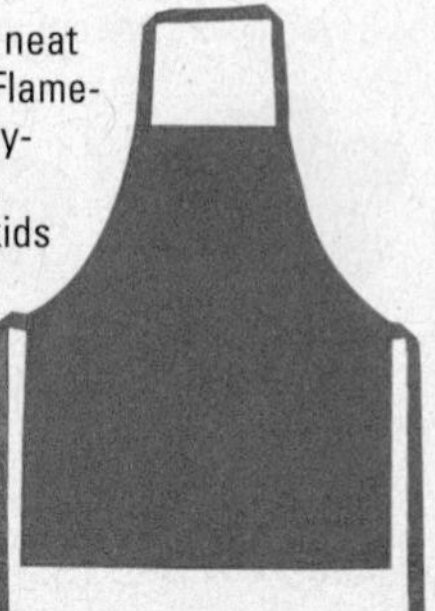

Apron
Keep clothes neat as you play! Flame-resistant, easy-clean plastic; one size fits kids ages 4 and above.
1904-P-1025
$3.99

Mini Clay Cutter Set
12 fun shapes: star, girl, fish, sailboat, puppy, heart, bear, hand, elephant, apple, dinosaur, ice cream cone. Kid-safe plastic; 1¼ in. each.
509-P-256
$1.99

Look for more fun Kandy Clay Kits featuring kids' favorite characters on pages 188-199.

Candy Making

Let Wilton show you how great candy can be! Start with our Candy Melts® and molds for beautiful candy in 3 easy steps—just melt, mold and serve.*

Kids' Candy-Making Kits

It's a whole new way for kids to have fun with candy! Imagine a burger with the works, a treat-filled treasure chest or a tiered birthday cake, all made of delicious candy. Now imagine your favorite kids having a blast making them come to life. These Wilton kits make it fun for every kid to melt, mold and assemble a great looking candy project.

Kits include easy-to-follow instructions that stress safe candy making with help from an adult. All kits include 2 molds, Candy Melts®* in assorted colors, melting bags and instructions; other contents noted below. Recommended for ages 8 and above. **$9.99**

Treasure Chest
Swashbuckling Fun! Create a bounty of fun jewels in a cool candy chest. Includes decorating brush and 19.5 oz. Candy Melts®.
2104-P-1196

Cruisin' Candy
Your pit crew will love putting this candy racecar together! Includes decorating brush and 22.5 oz. Candy Melts®.
2104-P-1197

Party Cakes
Little decorators will have a great time creating a 3-tiered masterpiece! Includes decorating brush and 19.5 oz. Candy Melts®.
2104-P-1198

Flower Fancy
Mold flowers on "stem" sticks. Includes 10 green lollipop sticks, decorating brush, cardboard wrap-around fence and 15 oz. Candy Melts®.
2104-P-1069

Burger Blast
Fun in a bun! Kids build the perfect burger, from patty to pickles. Includes 25 oz. Candy Melts®.
2104-P-1064

Pizza Chef
Toppings look great—there are even two delivery boxes for fun gifting. Includes 20 oz. Candy Melts®.
2104-P-1065

Greeting Cards
They're really "eating" cards. Includes 10 gift bags/ties and 20 oz. Candy Melts®.
2104-P-1066

Funny Faces
Create loony lolli-people! Includes 6 lollipop sticks and decorating brush and 20 oz. Candy Melts®.
2104-P-1067

Candy Melts®*

Versatile, creamy, easy-to-melt wafers are ideal for all your candy making—molding, dipping or coating. Their delicious taste can be varied with our Candy Flavors.

Light and Dark Cocoa are all natural, cocoa flavor; colors are artificially vanilla flavored. 14 oz. bag. Certified Kosher. **$2.50**

Peanut Butter
1911-P-481

Light Cocoa
1911-P-544

Dark Cocoa
1911-P-358

Red
1911-P-499

White
1911-P-498

Chocolate Mint
1911-P-1920

Lavender
1911-P-403

Pink
1911-P-447

Yellow
1911-P-463

Orange
1911-P-1631

Blue
1911-P-448

Green
1911-P-405

*Brand confectionery coating.

Candy-Making Tools

Squeeze Bottles

Melt candy with ease, then fill your mold without mess! Our convenient bottles now are available in three sizes so you can melt just the amount of Candy Melts®* you need. Melt candy right in the bottle, then squeeze out into molds. Great way to store and reheat leftover candy.

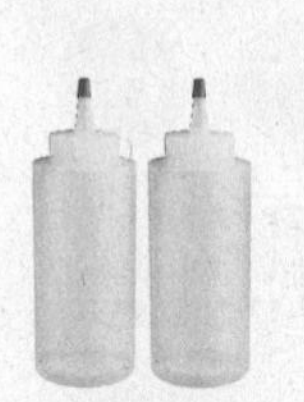

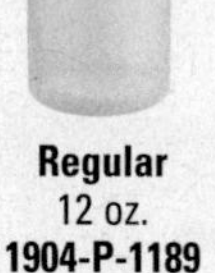

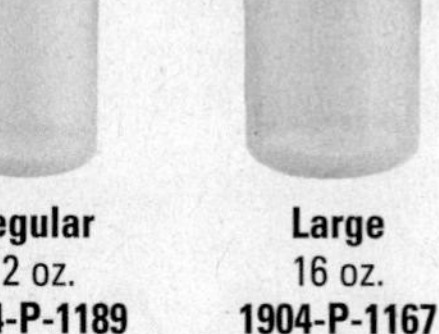

Mini	Regular	Large
6 oz.	12 oz.	16 oz.
1904-P-1166	**1904-P-1189**	**1904-P-1167**
Pk./2 $1.99	**$1.69**	**$1.99**

Candy Melting Plate

Microwave-melt up to 11 Candy Melts® colors at one time for less mess! Plastic with non-slip grip edge. Includes decorating brush.
1904-P-8016 $2.99

Metal Dipping Set

Professional-quality stainless steel with wooden handles. 8¾ in. long.
1904-P-925
Set/2 $9.99

Candy Dipping Set

Easy-handling spoon and fork, each 7¾ in. long.
1904-P-800
Set/2 $2.99

Decorator Brush Set

Plastic, durable bristles, easy-to-hold handle.
2104-P-9355
Set/3 $1.49

Easy-Pour Funnel

Push-button controls flow of candy. 5 x 4 in., nylon.
1904-P-552 $3.99

Candy Thermometer

Precise measurement essential for preparing hard candy, nougat, more.
1904-P-1200 $14.99

Wedding Candy Favor Kits

NEW!

Everything you need to make 10 beautiful favors for your wedding or shower celebration.

Includes 12 oz. white Candy Melts®*, candy mold (1 design, 8 cavities), 2 disposable decorating bags and 10 white truffle boxes. Need more favors? Simply buy more Candy Melts®* (p. 146) and truffle boxes (p. 149); each additional 14 oz. bag of Candy Melts®* makes 28 candies to fill 14 boxes. **$7.99**

Wedding Cakes
2104-P-1073

Wedding Bells
2104-P-1072

Candy Creme Centers

Now delectable creme-filled candies are easy as can be. Only Wilton has smooth, luscious creme centers in an easy-to-use tube. Just squeeze your favorite flavor into a candy shell, then seal. Made from premium ingredients for unsurpassed taste. Each tube fills 16-20 candies.

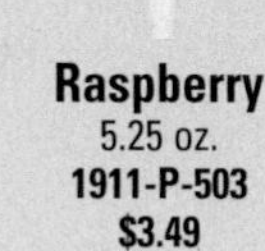

Raspberry	Vanilla
5.25 oz.	6.25 oz.
1911-P-503	**1911-P-502**
$3.49	**$3.49**

Candy Color and Flavoring Sets

Primary Candy Color Set

Concentrated oil-based colors blend easily with Wilton Candy Melts®. Includes Yellow, Orange, Red and Blue; .25 oz. jars. Certified Kosher.
1913-P-1299 Set/4 $3.99

Garden Candy Color Set

Create pretty pastel colors! Concentrated oil-based colors blend easily with Wilton Candy Melts®. Includes Pink, Green, Violet and Black; .25 oz. jars. Certified Kosher.
1913-P-1298 Set/4 $3.99

Candy Flavoring Set

Add your favorite. Includes Peppermint, Cherry, Cinnamon and Creme de Menthe; .25 oz . bottles.
1913-P-1029 Set/4 $5.49

Novelty Candy Molds

More fun shapes and greater detail make Wilton Candy Molds the world's favorite way to create candy. Look at the variety! You can do it all, from exciting kids' party treats to elegant wedding and shower favors. Molding and coloring couldn't be easier, when you use Wilton Candy Melts®. Look for terrific design ideas and molding instructions on every mold package.*

Alphabet
26 designs, 26 cavities.
2115-P-1563 $1.99

Numerals
10 designs, 10 cavities.
2115-P-1564 $1.99

Stars
1 design, 12 cavities,
2115-P-1554 $1.99

Party Time
6 designs, 8 cavities.
2115-P-1516 $1.99

Rubber Ducky
1 design, 6 cavities.
2115-P-1565 $1.99

Smiley Face
1 design, 9 cavities.
2115-P-1715 $1.99

Seashells
5 designs, 11 cavities.
2115-P-1561 $1.99

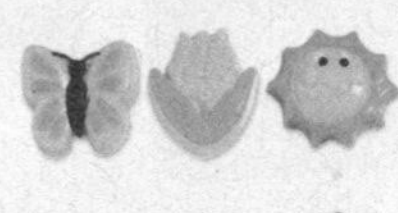
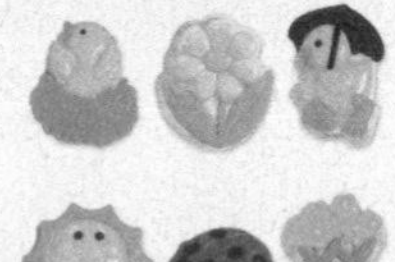

Springtime Treats
8 designs, 8 cavities.
2115-P-1716 $1.99

Roses in Bloom
1 design, 10 cavities.
2115-P-1738 $1.99

Roses and Buds
3 designs, 9 cavities.
2115-P-1708 $1.99

Wedding Shower
5 designs, 10 cavities.
2115-P-1711 $1.99

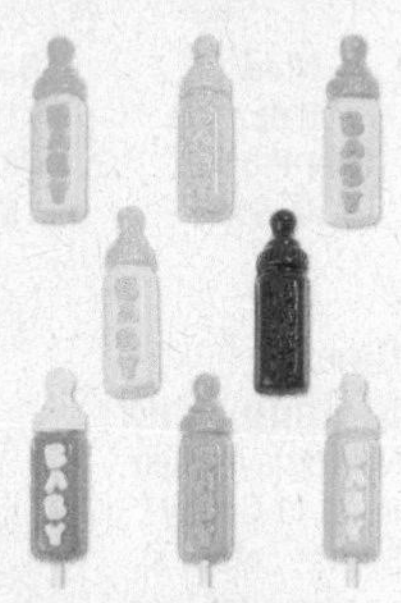

Baby Bottles
1 design, 6 cavities.
2115-P-1560 $1.99

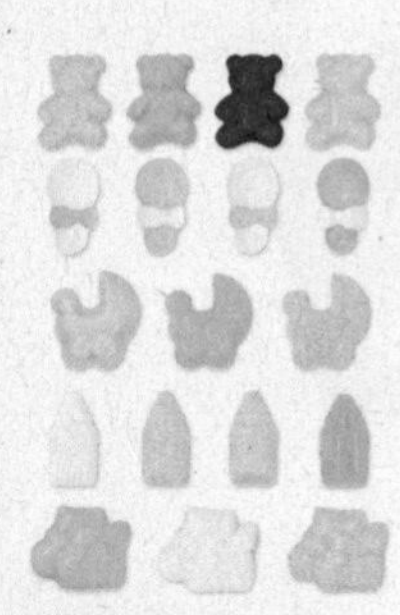

Mini Baby Icons
5 designs, 20 cavities.
2115-P-1537 $1.99

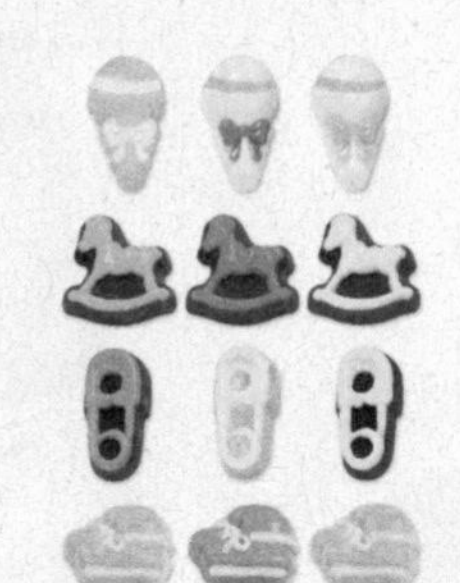

Baby Shower
4 designs, 11 cavities.
2115-P-1710 $1.99

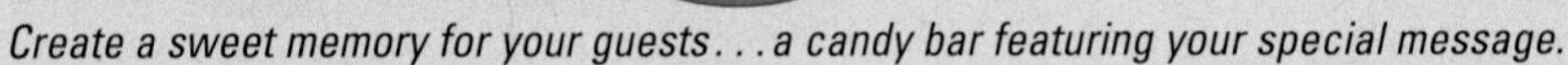

CANDY BAR MOLDS NEW!

Create a sweet memory for your guests. . . a candy bar featuring your special message.

Molding is easy using Wilton Candy Melts®* (p. 146). Present them beautifully in Candy Bar Boxes (p. 149). Each candy bar measures 3¼ in. wide x 1¾ in. tall x ¼ in. deep. 1 design, 4 cavities. **$1.99**

Add-A-Message
2115-P-1356

Our Wedding
2115-P-1409

Thank You
2115-P-1410

Classic Candy Molds

Wilton has a great selection of traditional shapes for creating elegant candy gift boxes and party trays. For luscious filled candies or popular mint patties, our well-defined molds help you turn out perfect candy every time.

Classic Mini Bars
1 design,
14 cavities.
2115-P-1723
$1.99

Peanut Butter Cups
1 design,
10 cavities.
2115-P-1522
$1.99

Deep Heart Truffle
1 design,
7 cavities.
2117-P-100
$1.99

Truffles
1 design,
12 cavities.
2115-P-1521
$1.99

Roses
3 designs,
12 cavities.
2115-P-1713
$1.99

Gift Truffles
1 design,
13 cavities.
2115-P-1728
$1.99

Mint Discs
1 design,
16 cavities.
2115-P-1739
$1.99

Cordial Cups
Mold a candy "glass" to serve dessert liqueurs! Or, fill with whipped cream and add to cocoa or coffee.
1 design,
6 cavities.
2115-P-1535
$1.99

*Brand confectionery coating.

Lollipop Accessories

Create the perfect pop with sticks in every size, cool colors too, and clear wrappers for easy giving.

Rainbow Lollipop Sticks

Add pizzazz to your pops! Food-safe plastic sticks; 5 each red, yellow, blue and green. Not for oven or microwave use. 4 in.
1912-P-9316
Pk./20 $1.99

Lollipop Sticks

Sturdy paper sticks in 4 sizes. Not for oven use.

4 in.
1912-P-1006
Pk./50 $1.99

6 in.
1912-P-1007
Pk./35 $1.99

8 in.
1912-P-9320
Pk./25 $1.99

11¾ in.
1912-P-1212
Pk./20 $3.99

Lollipop Wrapping Kit

Cover your candy lollipops and special treats for gift-giving! Contains 18 sticks, 18 bags, 18 twist ties.
1904-P-1193 $1.99

Clear Treat Bags

Let your fun candy and cookie treats show through! 3 x 4 in.
1912-P-2347
Pk./50 $2.69

Candy Wraps and Boxes

Your homemade candy deserves a beautiful presentation. Wilton has everything you need to wrap and package your candy like a pro. Designed to keep candies fresh, protected and attractive for gift-giving.

Candy Gift Boxes

For attractive gift-giving and stay-fresh storage.

1 lb. White Candy Boxes Pk./3 $2.49
1904-P-1172

½ lb. Candy Boxes Pk./3 $1.99

White 1904-P-1150	**Red** 1904-P-1152
Gold 1904-P-1151	**Silver** 1904-P-1153

Gold Elastic Ties

Pre-tied with a bow. Use with Candy Gift Boxes.
1904-P-1186 Pk./5 $1.49

Candy Box Liners

Padded paper liners cushion candy and prevent breakage. Use with Candy Gift Boxes.
1904-P-1191 Pk./4 $1.49

Candy Cups

Crisply-pleated, just like professionals use. White glassine-coated paper.

1 in. diameter.
1912-P-1243 Pk./100 $1.49

1¼ in. diameter.
1912-P-1245 Pk./75 $1.49

Foil Wrappers

Bright, shiny coverings for candy and lollipops! 4 x 4 in. squares.
Pk./50 $1.99

Gold
1904-P-1197

Silver
1904-P-1196

Red
1904-P-1198

Candy Bar Boxes

NEW!

Designed to hold candies made in our Candy Bar Molds (p. 148), the window displays your special message.
Pk./10 $3.99

White
1904-P-1157

Silver
1904-P-1159

Truffle Boxes

An elegant look, with a lock-close top that forms a perfect "bow". Holds 2-3 pieces of candy.
Pk./4 $1.99

White
1904-P-1154

Silver
1904-P-1155

Gold
1904-P-1156

Candy-Coated Spoons

*Turn an ordinary cup of coffee into a mocha delight! These candy-coated spoons are a delight to make, use or give as gifts. Choose the mold or the kit, then add Wilton Candy Melts®*and Candy Flavors to create your own taste sensations.*

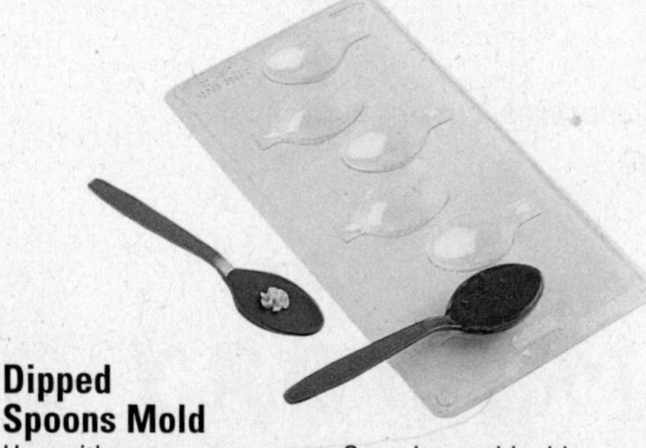

Dipped Spoons Mold

Use with your own spoons. Contains mold with 1 design and 6 cavities, and instructions.
2115-P-1722 $1.99

Dipped Spoons Kit

Includes 6 plastic spoons, 6 bags, 6 twist ties and instructions.
1904-P-1192 $1.99

Party

You've written the guest list—now start your decorating list here! From baking cups to candles, cake toppers to treat bags, Wilton has the great-looking designs you want.

Baking Cups

The easiest way to dress up a cupcake! Just put 'em together using Wilton Baking Cups and Icing Decorations in your favorite themes. Ideal for holding candy and nuts, too.

Made of microwave-safe paper unless otherwise noted. Jumbo cups are 2¼ in. diameter, standard cups are 2 in. diameter, mini cups are 1¼ in. diameter, bon bon cups are 1 in. diameter.

NEW!

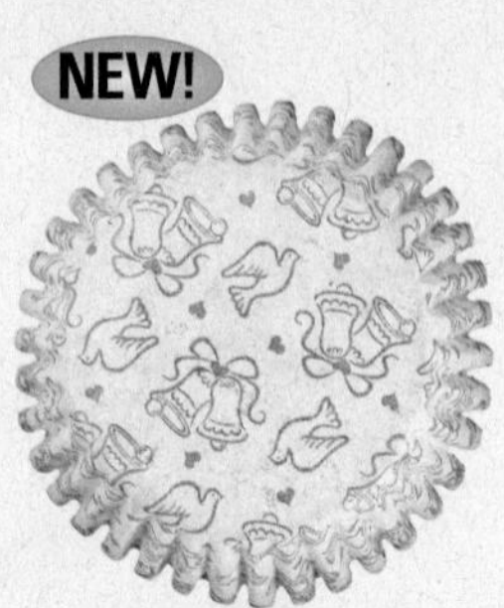

Wedding
Standard 415-P-119 Pk./50 $1.49
Mini 415-P-120 Pk./75 $1.49

NEW!

Smiley Face
Standard 415-P-261
Pk./50 $1.49

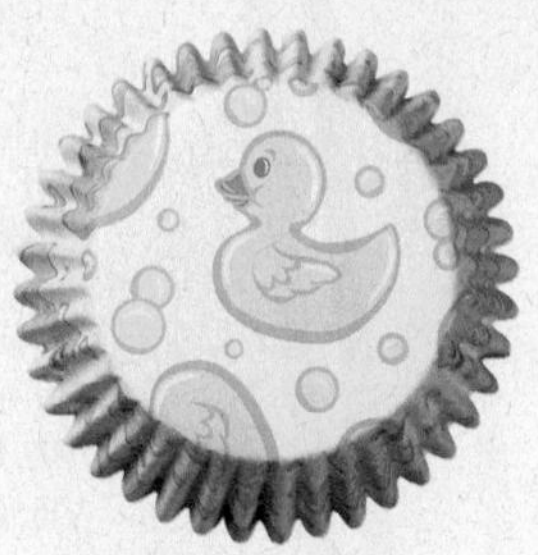

Rubber Ducky
Standard 415-P-378
Pk./50 $1.49

Party Time
Standard 415-P-258
Pk./50 $1.49

Baseball
Standard 415-P-298
Pk./50 $1.49

Football
Standard 415-P-297
Pk./50 $1.49

Soccer
Standard 415-P-296
Pk./50 $1.49

White $1.49
Jumbo 415-P-2503 Pk/50
Standard 415-P-2505 Pk./75
Mini 415-P-2507 Pk./100

Assorted Pastel
25 pink, 25 yellow, 25 blue.
Standard 415-P-394
Pk./75 $1.49

Gold Foil
Wax-laminated paper on foil.
Standard
415-P-206 Pk./24 $1.49
Bon Bon
415-P-306 Pk./75 $1.49

Silver Foil
Standard 415-P-207 $1.49
(24 pure aluminum/24 paper)
Bon Bon 415-P-307 $1.49
(36 pure aluminum/36 paper)

Gold Foil Petite Loaf*
Wax-laminated paper on foil.
415-P-452 Pk./24 $1.49

White Petite Loaf*
Microwave-safe paper.
415-P-450 Pk./50
$1.49

*Petite Loaf Cups are 3¼ x 2 in. and fit Petite Loaf Pan p. 160.

Nut and Party Cups
Mini 1¼ oz.
415-P-500 Pk./36 $1.69
Standard 3 ¼ oz.
415-P-400 Pk./24 $1.69

Icing Decorations

Wilton Icing Decorations are perfect for topping cupcakes, cookies and ice cream. Mint-flavored edible shapes are Certified Kosher.

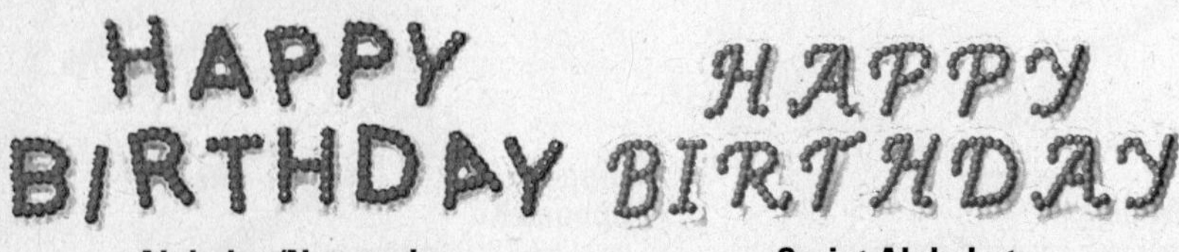

Alphabet/Numerals
710-P-494 Pk./70 $2.09

Script Alphabet
710-P-546 Pk./62 $2.09

Rubber Ducky
710-P-293
Pk./12 $2.09

Baseball Mitt
710-P-475
Pk./9 $2.09

Soccer Ball
710-P-477
Pk./9 $2.09

Football
710-P-478
Pk./9 $2.09

Party Bags

Wrap up cookies, candies, favors and more with color and fun! Your gift will be a sensation in our Pizazz designs—they really catch the light with a dazzling reflective pattern in 4 bright colors.

Contains 20, 4 x 9½ in. bags and 20 twist ties, unless otherwise noted.
Pk./20 $1.99

Clear
(not shown)
1912-P-1240 Pk./25 $1.99

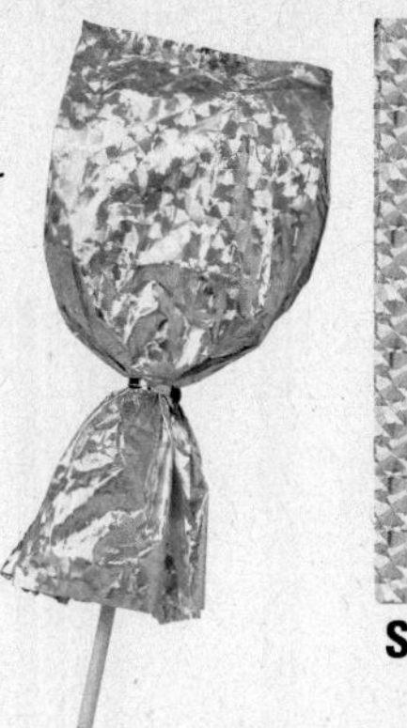

Silver Pizazz
1912-P-1020
Pk./8

Gold Pizazz
1912-P-1022
Pk./8

Red Pizazz
1912-P-1019
Pk./8

Blue Pizazz
1912-P-1021
Pk./8

Wedding
1912-P-2364

Rubber Ducky
1912-P-1275

Baby
1912-P-2365

Colorful Stars
1912-P-2362

Smiley Face
1912-P-2361

Red
1912-P-2357

Yellow
1912-P-2359

Pink
1912-P-2363

Blue
1912-P-2356

Candles

Wilton gives you more choices! Top your cake with candles in the perfect colors—and check out our exciting new lattice, twist, shimmer and pearlized designs on pages 152-153.

PICK SETS

Put your celebration message in lights! These bright candle picks are a unique and easy way to spell out the party theme on your cake top. Fun colors are just right for the occasion.

Happy Birthday
2811-P-785 Set/15 $1.99

Over The Hill
2811-P-786 Set/13 $1.99

Congratulations
2811-P-787 Set/15 $1.99

3 in. high. Shown below with picks.

NUMERALS

Festive way to mark age or year on cakes. Each 3 in. high. **$0.79**

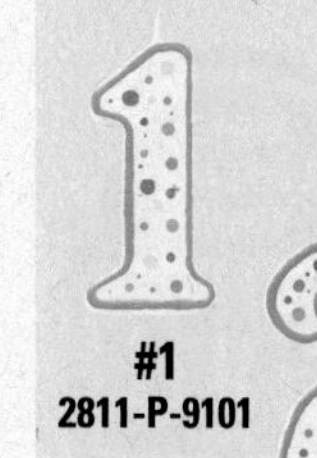

#1
2811-P-9101

#2
2811-P-9102

#3
2811-P-9103

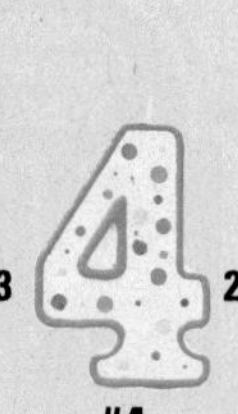

#4
2811-P-9104

#5
2811-P-9105

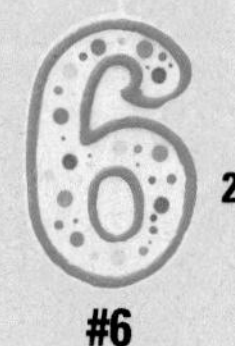

#6
2811-P-9106

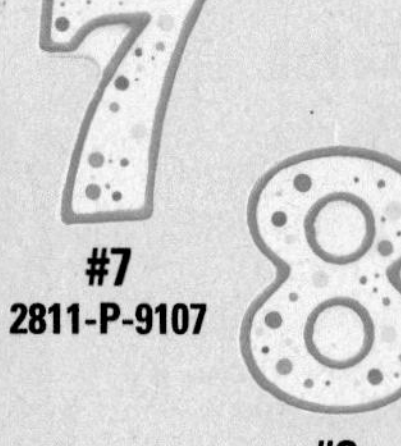

#7
2811-P-9107

#8
2811-P-9108

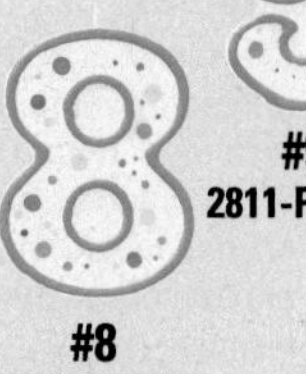

#9
2811-P-9109

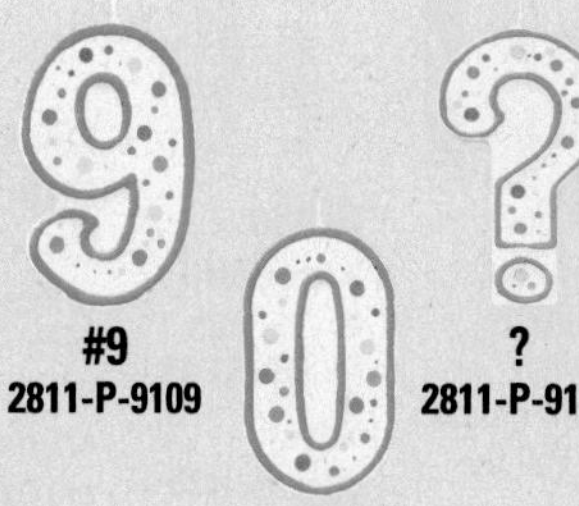

#0
2811-P-9100

?
2811-P-9110

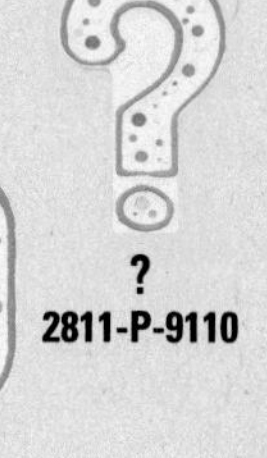

Pink #1
2811-P-240

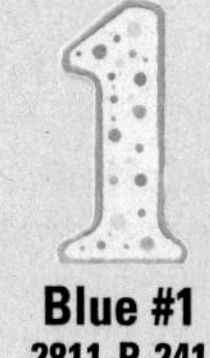

Blue #1
2811-P-241

Candles

CLASSIC

NEW! NEW!

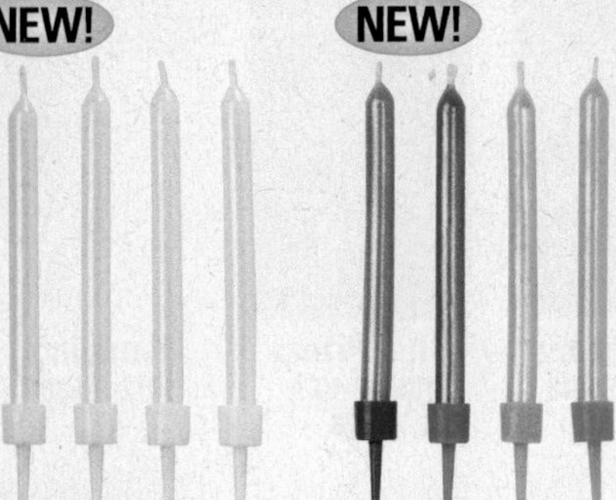

Pearlized

Watch them shimmer from the moment you light them! The radiant colors will look great on any cake. 2½ in. high.
Pk./10 $1.99

White
2811-P-3658

Multicolor
2811-P-3665

Celebration

2½ in. high.
Pk./24 $0.69

White
2811-P-207

Pink
2811-P-213

Red
2811-P-209

Blue
2811-P-210

Black
2811-P-224

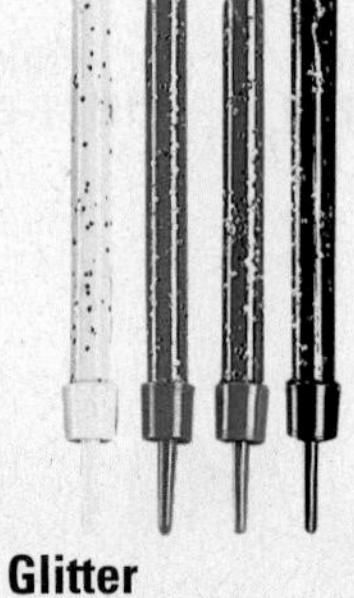

Glitter

Candleholders included. 2½ in. high.
Pk./10 $0.99

White
2811-P-248

Pink
2811-P-244

Blue
2811-P-246

Black
2811-P-247

Assorted Celebration

Classic spirals in attractive two-tones.
2½ in. high.
2811-P-215
Pk./24 $0.69

"Trick"

Blow 'em out—they relight!
2½ in. high.
Assorted colors: White, Yellow, Pink, Blue.
2811-P-220
Pk./10 $0.99

Silver and Gold

2¼ in. high.
Pk./10 $1.49

Silver
2811-P-9123

Gold
2811-P-9122

NOVELTY

NEW! NEW!

Long Candles

Sized right for larger cakes or for making a bold statement on any cake. 5⅞ in. high.
Pk./12 $1.99

White
2811-P-773

Multicolor
2811-P-777

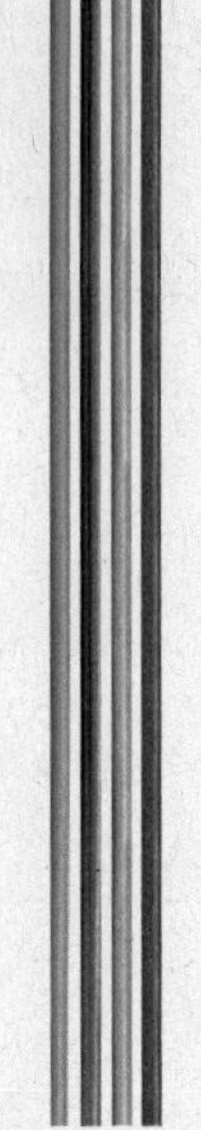

Slenders

6½ in. high.
2811-P-1188
Pk./24 $0.79

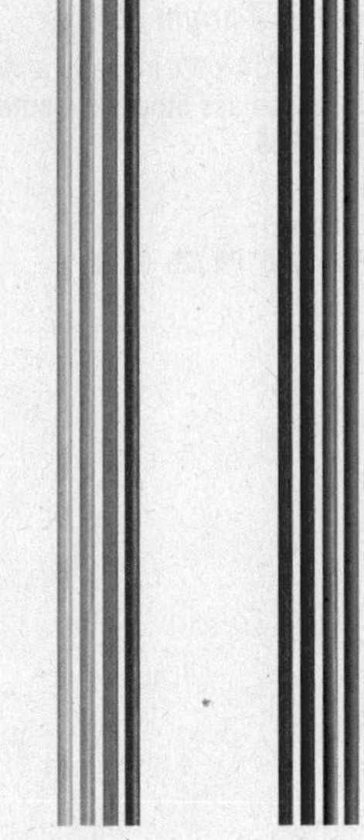

"Trick" Sparklers

Blow 'em out—they relight!
6½ in. high.
Pk./18 $0.99

Assorted
2811-P-1230

Red and Blue
2811-P-704

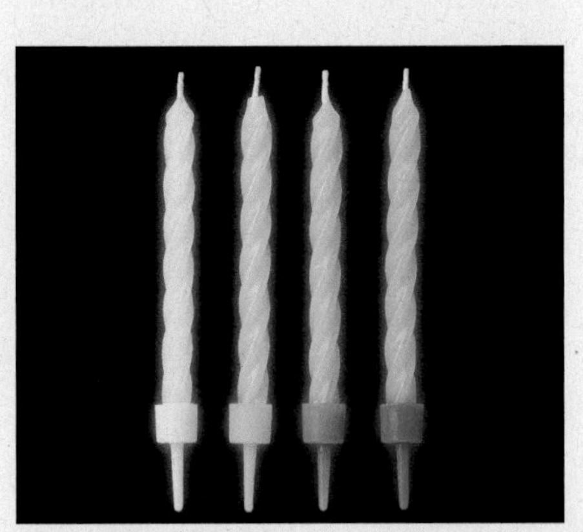

Glow-in-the-Dark Candles

They light up the room even before you light them! These luminous candles will lend an extra touch of fun to any celebration. Assorted colors: white, yellow, green, blue. 2½ in. high.
2811-P-165 Pk./10 $1.99

Musical Candle

Plays "Happy Birthday To You".
4¾ in. high.
2811-P-1231
$3.69

Over The Hill Candles

The secret of aging is keeping your sense of humor! These Wilton candles help anyone face those big birthdays with a smile!
2¾ in. high. **$1.99**

2811-P-9111

2811-P-9112

2811-P-9314

SOFT COLORS

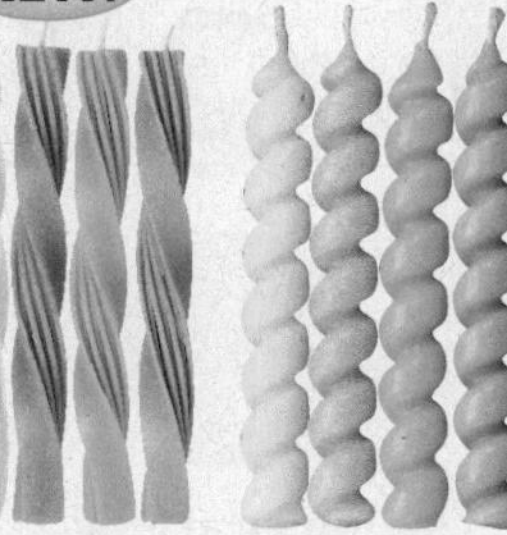

NEW! **Shimmer** 2½ in. high. **2811-P-3664 Pk./8 $1.99**

NEW! **Lattice** 2½ in. high. **2811-P-3657 Pk./8 $1.99**

NEW! **Twist** 2½ in. high. **2811-P-3661 Pk./8 $2.49**

Corkscrew 2½ in. high. **2811-P-775 Pk./8 $2.49**

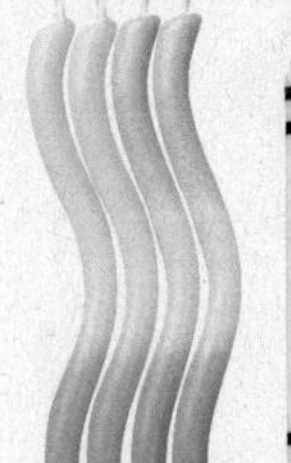
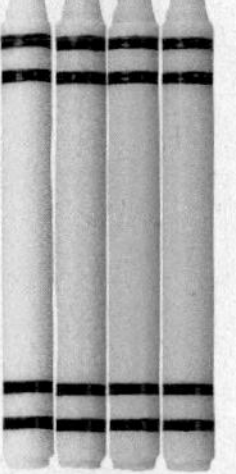
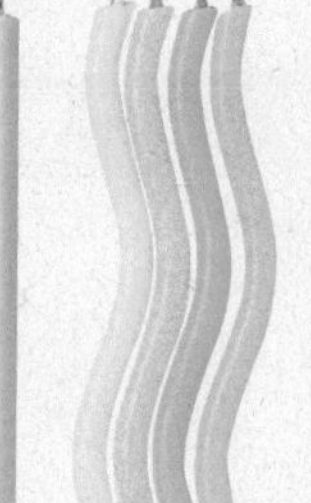

Tricolor 2½ in. high. **2811-P-782 Pk./10 $1.99**

Jumbo Crayons 3¼ in. high. **2811-P-292 Pk./8 $1.49**

Triangle "Trick" Sparklers 2½ in. high. **2811-P-288 Pk./9 $0.99**

Wavy "Trick" Sparklers 2½ in. high. **2811-P-289 Pk./10 $1.99**

Rounds 2½ in. high. **2811-P-291 Pk./24 $0.69**

Party Thins 8 in. high. **2811-P-255 Pk./20 $0.99**

RAINBOW COLORS

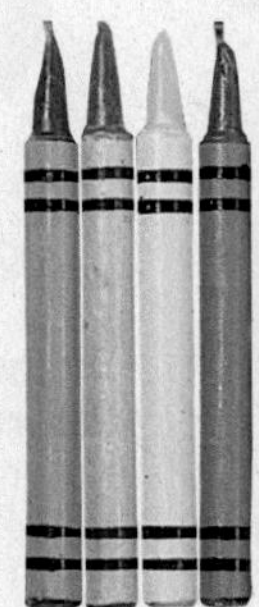

NEW! **Shimmer** 2½ in. high. **2811-P-3663 Pk./8 $1.99**

NEW! **Lattice** 2½ in. high. **2811-P-3656 Pk./8 $1.99**

NEW! **Twist** 2½ in. high. **2811-P-3660 Pk./8 $2.49**

Corkscrew 2½ in. high. **2811-P-778 Pk./8 $2.49**

Tricolor 2½ in. high. **2811-P-779 Pk./10 $1.99**

Crayons
Jumbo 3¼ in. high. **2811-P-226 Pk./8 $1.49**
Regular 2½ in. high. **2811-P-227 Pk./10 $1.49**

Triangle "Trick" Sparklers 2½ in. high. **2811-P-278 Pk./9 $0.99**

Wavy "Trick" Sparklers 2½ in. high. **2811-P-272 Pk./10 $1.99**

Rounds 2½ in. high. **2811-P-284 Pk./24 $0.69**

Party Thins 8 in. high. **2811-P-239 Pk./20 $0.99**

HOT COLORS

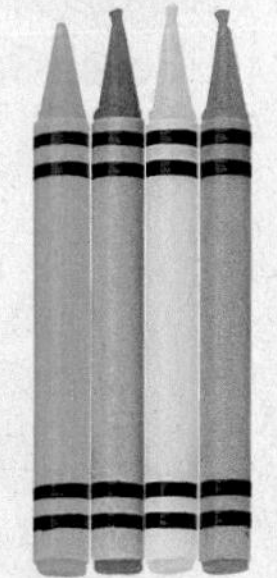

NEW! **Shimmer** 2½ in. high. **2811-P-3662 Pk./8 $1.99**

NEW! **Lattice** 2½ in. high. **2811-P-3655 Pk./8 $1.99**

NEW! **Twist** 2½ in. high. **2811-P-3659 Pk./8 $2.49**

Corkscrew 2½ in. high. **2811-P-776 Pk./8 $2.49**

Tricolor 2½ in. high. **2811-P-781 Pk./10 $1.99**

Jumbo Crayons 3¼ in. high. **2811-P-282 Pk./8 $1.49**

Triangle "Trick" Sparklers 2½ in. high. **2811-P-276 Pk./9 $0.99**

Wavy "Trick" Sparklers 2½ in. high. **2811-P-270 Pk./10 $1.99**

Rounds 2½ in. high. **2811-P-225 Pk./24 $0.69**

Party Thins 8 in. high. **2811-P-237 Pk./20 $0.99**

Candles

4-PIECE SETS

When all eyes are on your cake, you'll appreciate the amazing color and detail of Wilton candles. Fun theme designs will give you a great look for any occasion.

Handpainted, clean burning quality.

NEW!

Ice Cream
Approx. 2¼ in. high.
2811-P-9349 Set/4 $3.29

NEW!

Tropical Fish
Approx. 1½ in. high.
2811-P-9333 Set/4 $3.29

NEW!

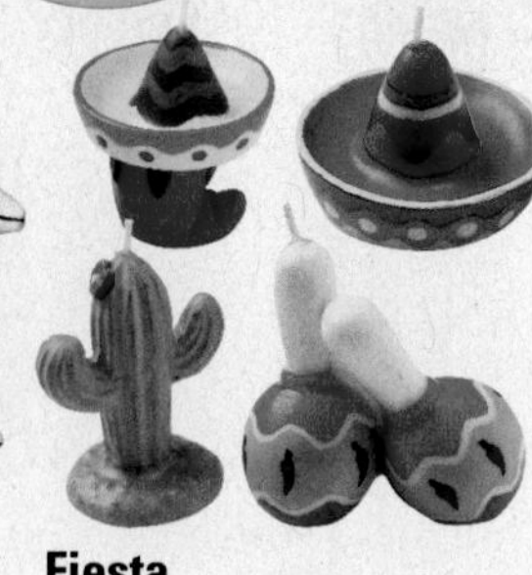

Fiesta
Approx. 1¾ in. high.
2811-P-9345 Set/4 $3.29

NEW!

Farm
Approx. 1⅝ in. high.
2811-P-9347 Set/4 $3.29

Baby Things
Approx. 2 in. high.
2811-P-855 Set/4 $3.29

Party Time
Approx. 1½ in. high.
2811-P-860 Set/4 $3.29

Take Me Out To The Ballgame
Approx. 2 in. high.
2811-P-9341 Set/4 $3.29

Firefighting
Approx. 1½ in. high.
2811-P-9339 Set/4 $3.29

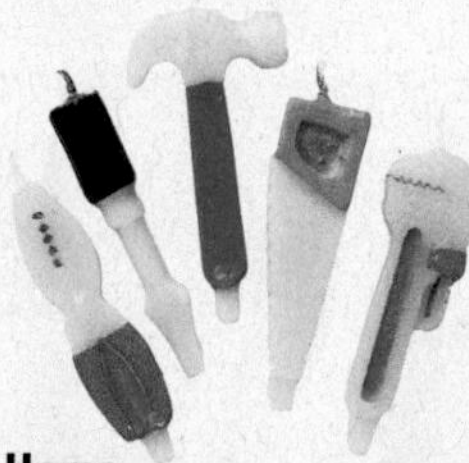

Home Improvement Tools
Approx. 2¼ in. high.
2811-P-9136 Set/5 $3.29

Construction Vehicles
Approx. 1¾ in. long.
2811-P-858 Set/4 $3.29

Race Cars
Approx. 1¾ in. high.
2811-P-9135 Set/4 $3.29

6-PIECE SETS

Popular subjects for any party—including fun shapes for all the major sports.

NEW!

Smiley Faces
1½ in. high.
2811-P-9351 Set/6 $3.29

NEW!

Beach Sandals
⅜ in. high, ⅞ in. long.
2811-P-9352 Set/6 $3.29

Rubber Duckies
1½ in. high.
2811-P-9337
Set/6 $3.29

Margaritas
1¼ in. high.
2811-P-9343
Set/6 $3.29

Champagne Bottles
2 in. high.
2811-P-163
Set/6 $3.29

Beer Cans
1¾ in. high.
2811-P-9326
Set/6 $3.29

Soccer Balls
1 in. high.
2811-P-9322
Set/6 $3.29

Basketballs
1¾ in. high.
2811-P-9323
Set/6 $3.29

Footballs
2 in. high.
2811-P-757
Set/6 $3.29

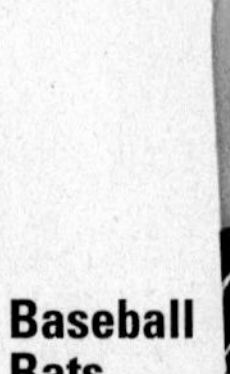

Baseball Bats
2¾ in. high.
2811-P-750
Set/6 $3.29

Golf Balls
2 in. high.
2811-P-9324
Set/6 $3.29

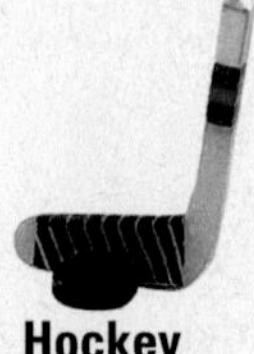

Hockey Sticks and Pucks
2¼ in. high.
2811-P-725
Set/6 $3.29

Bowling Pins and Ball
Six 2 in. high pins, one 1 in. ball.
2811-P-760
Set/7 $3.29

Cake Toppers

With Wilton Toppers, a decorated cake is just minutes away! The excellent detail you expect from Wilton is evident in every design.

Small Derby Clowns Set
2 in. high with pick.
2113-P-2759 Set/6 $1.99

Circus Balloons Set
12 in a bunch, 3 bunches per set, 6½ in. high.
2113-P-2366 Set/36 $2.69

Dinosaur Party Set
Reptile revelry!
1¾ to 2½ in. high.
2113-P-9420 Set/4 $3.99

Carousel Separator Set
Snaps together fast—sturdy pony pillars and separator plates provide strong support. Set includes four 9 in. high pony pillars and two 10 in. diameter separator plates.
2103-P-1139 Set/6 $11.99

Tumbling Bears Set
Adorable acrobats,
2 to 2½ in. high.
2113-P-9421 Set/4 $3.99

Circus Animals Set
Handpainted performers,
2½ to 3 in. high.
2113-P-9422 Set/4 $3.99

Jungle Animals Set
Spectacular safari,
1¾ to 3 in. high.
2113-P-2095 Set/4 $3.99

DOLL PICKS

Teen Doll Pick
Her hair and face are prettier than ever—she'll give your Wonder Mold cakes a realism and sophistication unlike anything you've seen. 7¾ in. high with pick. **$2.99**
Brunette 2815-P-101
Blond 2815-P-102
Ethnic 2815-P-103

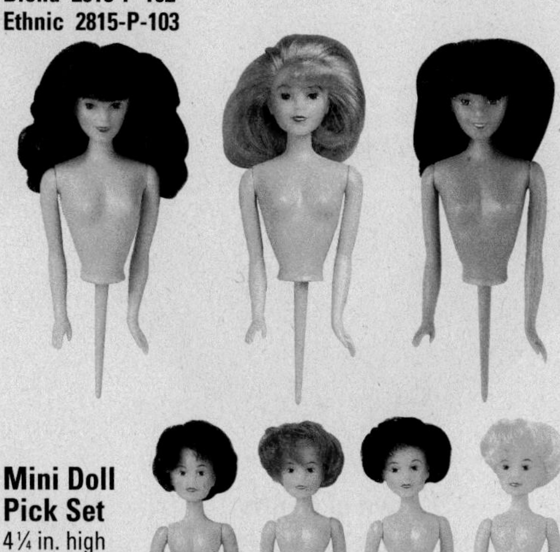

Mini Doll Pick Set
4¼ in. high with pick.
1511-P-1019
Set/4 $5.99

SPORTS THEME

Baseball Set*
Batter, catcher, three fielders and pitcher,
2⅛ to 2¾ in. high.
2113-P-2155 Set/6 $2.99

Basketball Set*
Includes 1 forward, 2 centers, 3 guards and 1 hoop, 2¼ to 4 in. high.
2113-P-2237 Set/7 $2.99

Football Set*
Eight players and two goal posts, 1½ to 4½ in. high.
2113-P-2236 Set/10 $2.99

Soccer Set*
Seven players and two nets,
1¾ to 2 in. high.
2113-P-9002 Set/9 $2.69

Golf Set*
Includes 4½ in. high golfer plus three each: 2½ in. wide greens, 4 in. high flags, 5 in. clubs and golf balls.
1306-P-7274 Set/13 $2.69

Frustrated Fisherman*
4½ in. high.
2113-P-2384
$3.49

RELIGIOUS

Inspiring decorations that add a beautiful touch to spiritual events.

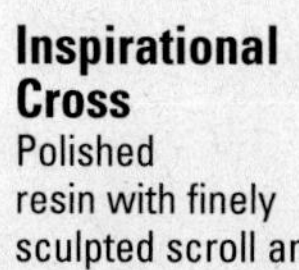

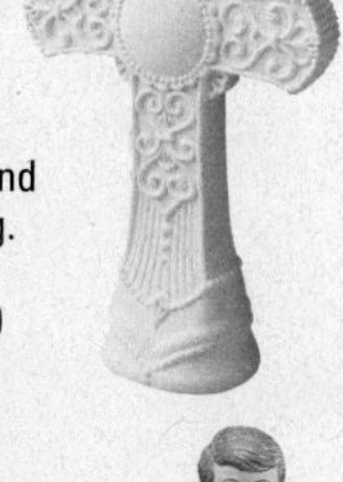

Inspirational Cross
Polished resin with finely sculpted scroll and bead highlighting.
5½ in. high.
202-P-206 $11.99

Communion Girl†
3½ in. high.
2113-P-7878
$3.49

Communion Boy†
3½ in. high.
2113-P-7886
$3.49

†Designed by Ellen Williams

*CAUTION: Contains small parts. Not recommended for use by children 3 years and under.

Bakeware

Wilton is the favorite bakeware brand of decorators. From fun novelty shapes for birthday cakes to dramatic cast aluminum styles for elegant desserts, count on Wilton for the best results.

Dimensions®

DECORATIVE BAKEWARE

With our non-stick cast aluminum bakeware, anyone can create desserts with elegant shapes and spectacular detail. Heavyweight cast aluminum conducts heat extremely evenly, and allows for uniquely sculpted shapes you will be proud to serve. Bake in non-stick cast aluminum as you would in any aluminum pan. Cakes and breads rise high and bake evenly. The premium non-stick surface means foods release perfectly and cleanup is a breeze. Lifetime Warranty.

6 Cavity Mini Hearts
Each cavity 4 in. x 2 in. deep.
6 cup capacity;
takes 3 to 3½ cups of cake batter.*
2105-P-5012 $24.99

Crown of Hearts
11 in. wide x 2½ in. deep.
10 cup capacity;
takes 6½ to 7 cups of cake batter.*
2105-P-5011 $24.99

Queen of Hearts
9 in. diameter x 3¼ in. deep.
10 cup capacity;
takes 6½ to 7 cups of cake batter.*
2105-P-5001 $24.99

Belle
9 in. diameter x 3¾ in. deep.
10 cup capacity;
takes 6½ to 7 cups of cake batter.*
2105-P-1186 $24.99

Cascade
9½ in. diameter x 4¾ in. deep.
10 cup capacity;
takes 6½ to 7 cups of cake batter.*
2105-P-1199 $24.99

Jewel
8¾ in. diameter x 4 in. deep.
10 cup capacity;
takes 6½ to 7 cups of cake batter.*
2105-P-1187 $24.99

*For cakes, fill pans ½ to ⅔ full.

Non-Stick Bakeware

Our premium non-stick bakeware combines superior non-stick performance, serving convenience and elegant design, to provide the highest level of baking satisfaction.

- *Oversized handles for safe lifting of the pan*
- *Pan dimensions permanently stamped into handles*
- *Heavy-duty steel construction prevents warping*
- *Durable, reinforced non-stick coating offers superior release and easy cleanup*
- *10-Year Warranty*

CAKE AND PIE PANS

9 x 1½ in. Round Cake
2105-P-408 $6.99

2105-P-408

9 x 9 x 2 in. Square Cake
2105-P-407 $7.99

11 x 7 x 1½ in. Biscuit/Brownie
2105-P-443 $8.49

13 x 9 x 2 in. Oblong Cake
2105-P-411 $10.99

2105-P-411

13 x 9 x 2 in. Oblong Cake w/Plastic Cover
2105-P-423 $13.99

9 x 1½ in. Deep Pie w/Fluted Edges
2105-P-438 $6.99

COOKIE PANS AND SHEETS

Small Cookie
13¼ x 9¼ x ⅝ in.
2105-P-436 $9.99

Medium Cookie
15¼ x 10¼ x ¾ in.
2105-P-412 $10.99

2105-P-412

Large Cookie/Jelly Roll
17¼ x 11½ x 1 in.
2105-P-413 $11.99

Jumbo Air Insulated Sheet
18 x 14 in.
2105-P-422 $17.99

2105-P-422

SPECIALTY PANS

Fluted Tube
9¾ x 3⅜ in.
2105-P-416 $11.99

6 Cavity Mini Fluted Tube
4⅛ x 2 in.
2105-P-445 $14.99

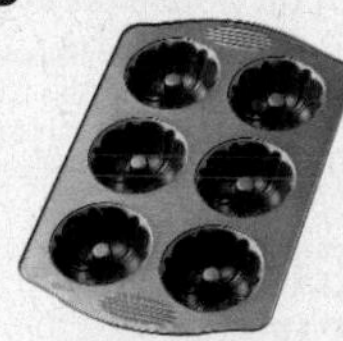
2105-P-445

Angel Food
9⅜ x 4¼ in.
2105-P-415 $13.99

14 in. Pizza Crisper
14 x ⅝ in.
2105-P-420 $11.99

2105-P-420

MUFFIN AND LOAF PANS

6 Cup Regular Muffin
2105-P-405 $8.49

2105-P-405

12 Cup Mini Muffin
2105-P-403 $5.99

12 Cup Regular Muffin
2105-P-406 $11.99

Large Loaf
9¼ x 5¼ x 2¾ in.
2105-P-402 $6.99

2105-P-402

4 Cavity Mini Loaf
5¾ x 3 x 2⅛ in.
2105-P-444 $14.99

SPRINGFORM PANS

4 x 1¾ in. Round
2105-P-453 $4.99

6 x 2¾ in. Round
2105-P-447 $8.99

2105-P-435

9 x 2¾ in. Round
2105-P-414 $11.99

10 x 2¾ in. Round
2105-P-435 $12.99

4 x 1¾ in. Heart
2105-P-457 $6.99

9 x 2¾ in. Heart
2105-P-419 $14.99

2105-P-419

COOLING GRIDS

10 x 16 in.
2305-P-228
$7.99

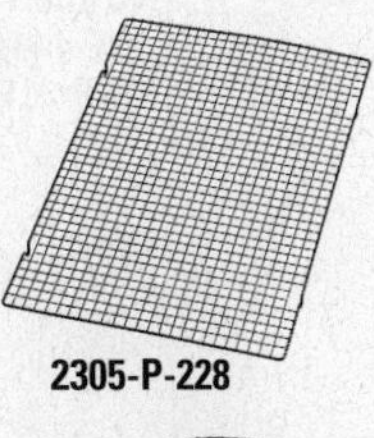
2305-P-228

14½ x 20 in.
2305-P-229
$11.99

13 in. Round
2305-P-230
$8.49

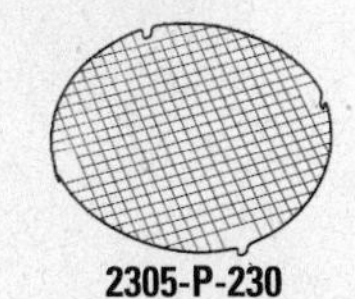
2305-P-230

3-Tier Stackable NEW!
15⅞ x 9⅞ in. stackable 3-tier grid.
2105-P-459
$9.99

2105-P-459

TART/QUICHE PANS

9 x 1⅛ in. Round
2105-P-442 $8.99

11 x 1⅛ in. Round
2105-P-450 $9.99

2105-P-450

10 x 1⅛ in. Heart
2105-P-452 $8.99

2105-P-452

Round 3-Pc. Set
8 x 1⅛ in., 9 x 1⅛ in., and 10 x 1⅛ in.
2105-P-451 Set/3 $19.99

Brioche 6-Pc. Set
3¼ x 1¼ in.
2105-P-6762 Set/6 $5.99

2105-P-6762

Tartlet 6-Pc. Set
4¾ x 1⅞ x ½ in.
2105-P-6761 Set/6 $5.99

4 in. Tart 4-Pc. Set
4 x ¾ in. with removable bottom.
2105-P-466 $8.99

4 in. Tart/Quiche 6-Pc. Set
4 x ¾ in. with removable bottom.
2105-P-441 $12.99

RATED #1 BY GOOD HOUSEKEEPING!

Decorator Preferred®

Professional Aluminum Bakeware

*Our most popular bakeware—built with the most features to help decorators bake their best. Compare these benefits to any brand and discover why Decorator Preferred was rated #1 by Good Housekeeping.**

*The May 1999 Good Housekeeping Institute Report rates this Wilton Professional Pan #1 out of 31 different 9 in. round pans.

STRAIGHT SIDES

Bake perfect 90° corners for the precise look wedding cakes require. Ordinary bakeware has rounded corners, giving cakes rounded edges.

GRIP LIP EDGES

Extra-wide rims make heavy filled pans easy to handle.

PURE ALUMINUM

The best material for baking cakes—creates a light, golden brown cake surface, beautiful for decorating.

SUPERIOR THICKNESS

Thicker than ordinary bakeware, built to distribute heat evenly for more consistent baking.

HANDCRAFTED CONSTRUCTION

Sheets and squares are handwelded for excellent detail and durability.

LIFETIME WARRANTY

Superior construction and performance designed and guaranteed to last a lifetime.

ROUNDS

What a selection of sizes—including the hard-to-find 18 in. Half Round, which lets you bake and ice two halves to create one 18 in. round cake.

6 x 2 in. deep
2105-P-6122 $5.99

8 x 2 in. deep
2105-P-6136 $6.99

9 x 2 in. deep
2105-P-6137 $7.99

10 x 2 in. deep
2105-P-6138 $8.99

12 x 2 in. deep
2105-P-6139 $10.99

14 x 2 in. deep
2105-P-6140 $15.99

16 x 2 in. deep
2105-P-6141 $17.99

6 x 3 in. deep
2105-P-6106 $6.99

8 x 3 in. deep
2105-P-6105 $7.99

10 x 3 in. deep
2105-P-6104 $9.99

12 x 3 in. deep
2105-P-6103 $12.99

14 x 3 in. deep
2105-P-6102 $15.99

16 x 3 in. deep
2105-P-6101 $18.99

18 x 3 in. deep Half Round
2105-P-6100 $19.99

3-Pc. Round Set
6, 10 and 14 in. diameter x 3 in. deep.
2105-P-6114 Set/3 $31.99

SHEETS

Extra-thick aluminum distributes heat efficiently on these large pans.

9 x 13 x 2 in. deep
2105-P-6146 $14.99

11 x 15 x 2 in. deep
2105-P-6147 $16.99

12 x 18 x 2 in. deep
2105-P-6148 $19.99

SQUARES

Perfect 90° corners give you the flawless look necessary for wedding tiers.

8 x 2 in. deep
2105-P-6142 $8.99

10 x 2 in. deep
2105-P-6143 $12.99

12 x 2 in. deep
2105-P-6144 $15.99

HEARTS

Ultimate heart cake is beautiful for showers, weddings, more!

6 x 2 in. deep
2105-P-600 $4.99

8 x 2 in. deep
2105-P-601 $5.99

10 x 2 in. deep
2105-P-602 $7.99

12 x 2 in. deep
2105-P-607 $9.99

14 x 2 in. deep
2105-P-604 $11.99

16 x 2 in. deep
2105-P-605 $13.99

Contour

Create cakes with an elegant, rounded top edge. This is the perfect shape for positioning rolled fondant. 9 x 3 in. deep.
2105-P-6121 $10.99

Heating Core

Distributes heat to bake large cakes evenly. Recommended for pans 10 in. diameter or larger. Releases easily from cake.
3½ x 3½ x 4 in. diameter.
417-P-6100 $5.99

Springform Pans

When shopping for a springform pan, you want strong construction and an easy-release design that will let you remove a perfect cheesecake every time. Wilton springform pans are built tough, with strong springlocks that hold up year after year. The removable waffle-textured bottom design keeps crusts from sticking while distributing heat evenly. Springlock releases sides. Aluminum.

6 x 3 in. deep
2105-P-4437 $9.99

8 x 3 in. deep
2105-P-8464 $10.99

9 x 3 in. deep
2105-P-5354 $11.99

10 x 3 in. deep
2105-P-8465 $12.99

Performance Pans™

The classic aluminum pans—durable, even-heating and built to hold their shape through years of use. We named them Performance Pans because they perform beautifully. These are great all-purpose pans. You'll use them for casseroles, entrees, baked desserts and more. Wilton has sold millions of Performance Pans because decorators and bakers know they can depend on them.

NEW ON OUR COVER!

SweetHeart Pan
A gently curving shape gives the classic heart a more romantic flair. Whether you accent it with pretty icing flowers or pair it with bold fondant decorations, this cake will charm guests for birthdays, Mother's Day, Valentine's Day, showers and more. Takes 1 standard mix. 10¼ x 11 x 2 in. deep. Aluminum.
2105-P-1197 $9.99

SQUARES

6 x 2 in. deep
507-P-2180 $5.99

8 x 2 in. deep
2105-P-8191 $7.99

10 x 2 in. deep
2105-P-8205 $9.99

12 x 2 in. deep
2105-P-8213 $12.99

14 x 2 in. deep
2105-P-8220 $16.99

16 x 2 in. deep
2105-P-8231 $18.99

ROUNDS

6 x 2 in. deep
2105-P-2185 $5.99

8 x 2 in. deep
2105-P-2193 $6.99

10 x 2 in. deep
2105-P-2207 $7.99

12 x 2 in. deep
2105-P-2215 $10.99

14 x 2 in. deep
2105-P-3947 $13.99

16 x 2 in. deep
2105-P-3963 $16.99

2-Pan Round Set
9 x 2 in. deep
2105-P-7908 $11.99

SHEETS

9 x 13 x 2 in. deep
2105-P-1308 $9.99

11 x 15 x 2 in. deep
2105-P-158 $13.99

12 x 18 x 2 in. deep
2105-P-182 $15.99

Covered Baking Pan
Clear, durable cover makes it easy to transport desserts and keep them fresh at home. 11 x 15 x 2 in. deep.
2105-P-3849 $18.99

PERFORMANCE PANS™ SETS

These are the classic shapes every baker needs. Wilton has them in convenient graduated-size sets, to help you create fabulous tiered cakes or individual cakes in exactly the size you want. Quality aluminum holds its shape for years. Each pan is 2 in. deep, except where noted.

Heart Pan Set
Create the ultimate tiered heart cake—a beautiful way to celebrate showers, weddings and more. Now redesigned for a perfect fit when used with our Decorator Preferred® Heart Separator Plates shown on page 214. Includes 6, 10, 12 and 14 in. pans. Aluminum.
2105-P-606 Set/4 $29.99

Round Pan Set
Includes 6, 8, 10, 12 in. pans.
2105-P-2101 Set/4 $26.99

Round Pan Set, 3 in. Deep
Includes 8, 10, 12, 14 in. pans.
2105-P-2932 Set/4 $37.99

Oval Pan Set
Includes 7¾ x 5⅝ in.; 10¾ x 7⅝ in.; 13 x 9⅞ in. and 16½ x 12⅜ in. pans.
2105-P-2130 Set/4 $29.99

Square Pan Set
Includes 8, 12, 16 in. pans.
2105-P-2132 Set/3 $37.99

Hexagon Pan Set
Includes 6, 9, 12, 15 in. pans.
2105-P-3572 Set/4 $30.99

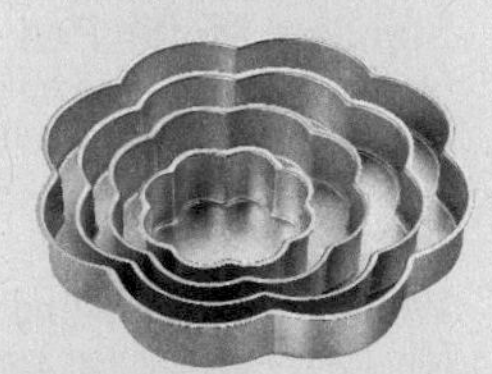

Petal Pan Set
Includes 6, 9, 12, 15 in. pans.
2105-P-2134 Set/4 $29.99

Specialty Pans

CLASSIC ANGEL FOOD

If you're looking for a healthy dessert, you can't do better than angel food! It's delicious with a simple fresh fruit topping. Removable inner core sleeve, cooling legs. Aluminum.

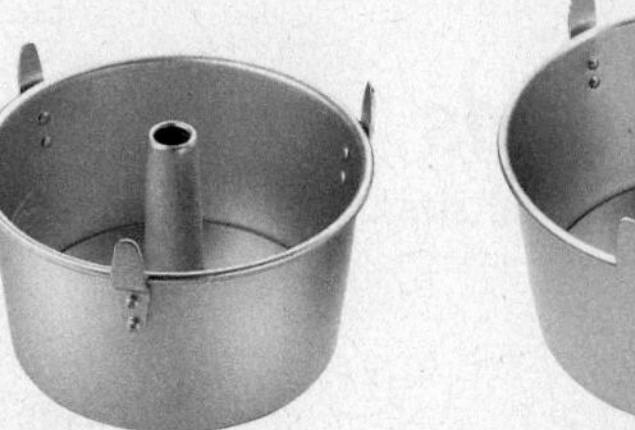

7 x 4½ in. deep
Takes ½ standard mix.
2105-P-9311 $11.99

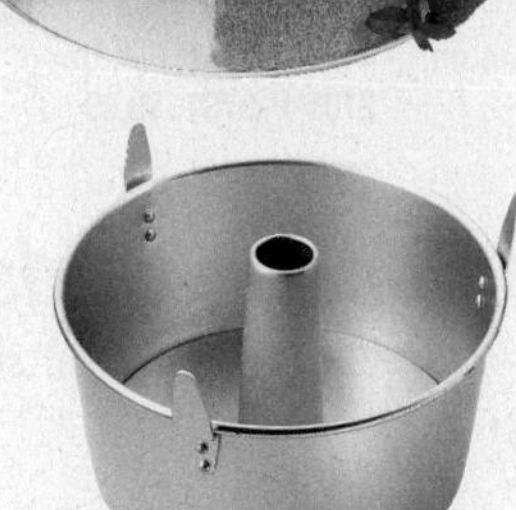

10 x 4 in. deep
Takes 1 standard mix.
2105-P-2525 $14.99

Ring Mold
Turn out spectacular cakes, gelatin molds and more. Takes approx. 1½ standard cake mixes. 10½ x 3 in. deep. Aluminum.
2105-P-4013 $9.99

Fancy Ring Mold
Beautiful sculpted pan, ideal for pound cakes, mousse and more! Takes 1 standard mix. 10 in. diameter x 3 in. deep. Aluminum.
2105-P-5008 $9.99

Cookie Sheets and Pans

A warped sheet can ruin a batch of cookies. With Wilton Cookie Sheets, you won't worry about warping. The extra-thick aluminum heats evenly for perfectly browned bottoms. Versatile sheets are great for baking appetizers, turnovers and more.

Aluminum
Extra-thick construction heats evenly for perfectly browned bottoms.

Jumbo 14 x 20 in.
2105-P-6213 $15.99

12½ x 16½ in.
2105-P-2975
$11.99

Insulated Aluminum
Two quality aluminum layers sandwich an insulating layer of air for perfect browning without burning.

14 x 16 in.
2105-P-2644
$15.99

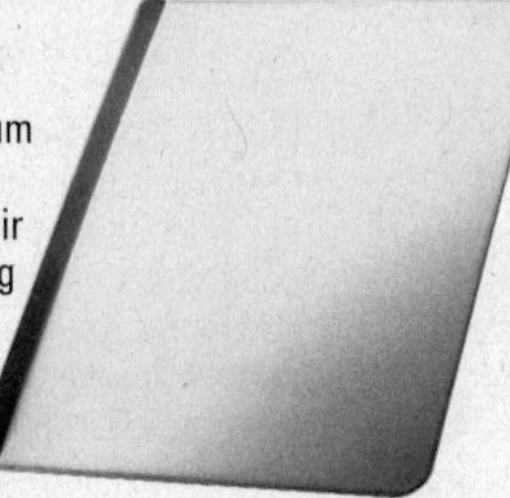

Jelly Roll and Cookie Pans
Wilton pans are 1 in. deep for fuller-looking desserts.

10½ x 15½ x 1 in. deep.
2105-P-1269 $10.99

12 x 18 x 1 in. deep.
2105-P-4854 $12.99

Muffin Pans

With so many great Wilton muffin pans to choose from, you'll be making muffins—and cupcakes—more often. You'll love our mini pans for the perfect brunch muffins and the jumbo size pan for bakery-style muffins and cupcakes.

Standard Muffin Pan
Most popular size for morning muffins, after-school cupcakes and desserts. Twelve cups, each 3 in. diameter x 1 in. deep. Aluminum.
2105-P-9310 $14.99

White Standard Baking Cups **(shown on p. 150)**
Microwave-safe paper. 2 in. diameter.
415-P-2505 Pk./75 $1.49

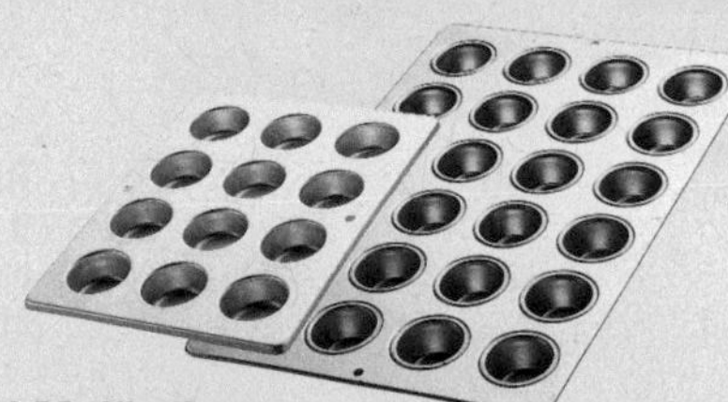

Mini Muffin Pans
Great for mini cheesecakes, brunches, large gatherings. Cups are 2 in. x ¾ in. deep. Aluminum.
12 Cup 2105-P-2125 $9.99
24 Cup 2105-P-9313 $15.99

White Mini Baking Cups **(shown on p. 150)**
Microwave-safe paper. 1¼ in. diameter.
415-P-2507 Pk./100 $1.49

Jumbo Muffin Pan
Make super-size cupcakes and muffins. Six cups, each 4 x 2 in. deep. Aluminum.
2105-P-1820 $15.99

White Jumbo Baking Cups **(shown on p. 150)**
Microwave-safe paper. 2¼ in. diameter.
415-P-2503 Pk./50 $1.49

Loaf Pans

It's all in the crust. Wilton Loaf Pans bake bread with hearty, crisp crusts and soft, springy centers. Our superior anodized aluminum promotes better browning, resulting in the perfect texture for all your breads.

Petite Loaf Pan
Great for single-size dessert cakes, frozen bread dough. Nine cavities, each 2½ x 3⅜ x 1½ in. deep. Aluminum.
2105-P-8466 $9.99

Mini Loaf Pan
Everyone loves personal-sized nut breads or cakes. Six cavities are 4½ x 2½ x 1½ in. deep. Aluminum.
2105-P-9791 $9.99

9 x 5 in. Loaf Pan
Favorite size for homemade breads and cakes. 2¾ in. deep. Aluminum.
2105-P-3688 $6.99

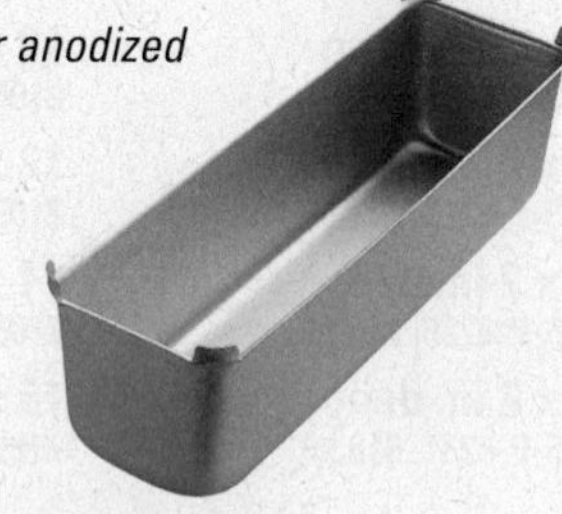

Long Loaf Pan
Legs provide support for cooling angel food cakes, breads or classic cakes. 16 x 4 x 4½ in. deep. Aluminum.
2105-P-1588 $12.99

Chrome-Plated Cooling Grids

Sturdy design will never rust. Great selection of popular sizes.

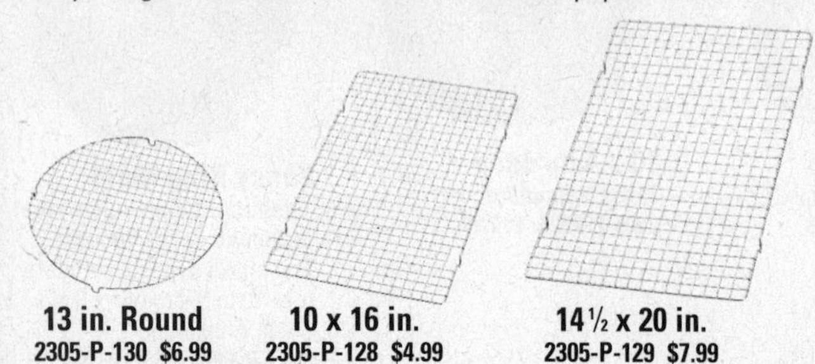

13 in. Round
2305-P-130 $6.99

10 x 16 in.
2305-P-128 $4.99

14½ x 20 in.
2305-P-129 $7.99

3-Tier Stackable
Use singly or stack to save space while cooling three cake layers or batches of cookies at the same time. Individual grids 13½ x 9¾ x 3 in. high; stacked grids are 9¾ in. high.
2305-P-151 $11.99

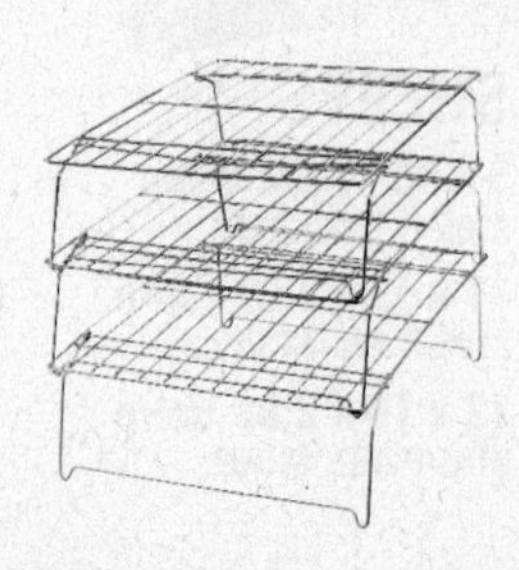

Mini Shaped Pans

Mini Tiered Cakes
One cake mix makes 10-15 mini tiered cakes, perfect for individual wedding, shower and birthday desserts. Six cavity pan is 14 x 10¾ in.; individual cavities are 4 x 4¾ x 1¼ in. deep. Aluminum.
2105-P-3209 $10.99

Mini Embossed Hearts
One cake mix makes 12-18 mini hearts, beautifully scalloped for weddings, showers and brunches. Six cavity pan is 14 x 10¾ in.; individual cavities are 3½ x 3¼ x 1¼ in. deep. Aluminum.
2105-P-3210 $10.99

Mini Fluted Mold Pan
One cake mix makes 12-14 mini fluted molds. Six cavity pan is 14¾ x 9¾ in.; individual cavities are 4 x 1¼ in. deep. Aluminum.
2105-P-2097 $17.99

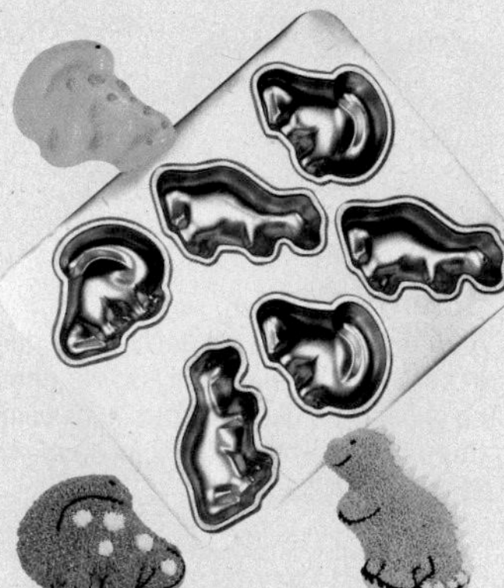

Mini Train Pan
One cake mix makes 14-16 mini train. Six cavity pan is 13¾ x 10½ x 1 in. deep; individual cavities are 4¼ x 3¾ x 1 in. deep. Aluminum.
2105-P-4499 $10.99

Mini Dinosaur Pan
One cake mix makes 12-15 prehistoric treats. Six cavity pan is 13¾ x 10½ x 1 in. deep; individual cavities are 4 x 3 x 1 in. deep. Aluminum.
2105-P-4498 $10.99

Mini Bear Pan
One cake mix makes 12-14 mini bears. Six cavity pan is 14½ x 11½ in.; individual cavities are 4⅜ x 4¾ x 1¼ in. deep. Aluminum.
2105-P-4497 $10.99

Mini Star Pan
One cake mix makes 12-14 mini stars. Six cavity pan is 14½ x 11 in.; individual cavities are 4¾ x 1¼ in. deep. Aluminum.
2105-P-1235 $10.99

Wonder Mold Pans

Mini Wonder Mold
Use with Mini Doll Picks for a quartet of party treats. Great with Wilton's Classic Wonder Mold (at right) for a color-coordinated bridal party centerpiece. One cake mix makes 4 to 6 cakes. Pan is 10 x 10 x 3 in. deep. Individual cakes are 3½ x 3 in. Aluminum.
2105-P-3020 $9.99

Mini Doll Picks
4¼ in. high with pick.
1511-P-1019
Pk./4
$5.99

Classic Wonder Mold
Creates an elegant 3-D shape for decorating fabulous dress designs. Use with our Teen Doll Pick to make the doll of your dreams. Pan is 8 in. diameter and 5 in. deep; takes 5–6 cups of firm-textured batter. Heat-conducting rod assures even baking. Kit contains pan, rod, stand, 7 in. brunette doll pick and instructions. Aluminum/plastic.
2105-P-565 $16.99

Teen Doll Pick
Her hair and face are prettier than ever to give your Wonder Mold cakes a realism and sophistication unlike anything you've seen.
7¾ in. high with pick.
$2.99
Brunette
2815-P-101
Blond
2815-P-102

Ethnic Doll Pick
Beautiful face for realistic doll cakes.
7¾ in. high with pick.
2815-P-103
$2.99

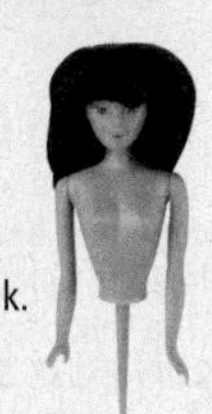

Novelty Shaped Pans

Animal Crackers Pan
Make a zoo full of fun animals with this versatile pan! Pick your favorite from the menagerie of critters on the box—pig, cat, giraffe or panda bear—or create a furry face of your own. One-mix pan is 10¾ x 9¼ x 2 in. deep. Aluminum.
2105-P-4945 $9.99

Ice Cream Cone Pan
You'll find room for this cone at any celebration, from birthdays to backyard barbecues, from picnics in the park to school socials. Like a real ice cream cone, create endless flavor and color combinations. One-mix pan is 13¾ x 9¼ x 2 in. deep. Aluminum.
2105-P-2087 $9.99

Topsy Turvy Pan
Give your cake decorating a fun new slant. Our topsy turvy "tiered" cake is just the right look for wacky birthdays, wild parties and special occasions that call for something different. One-mix pan is 10¼ x 12 x 2 in. deep. Aluminum.
2105-P-4946 $9.99

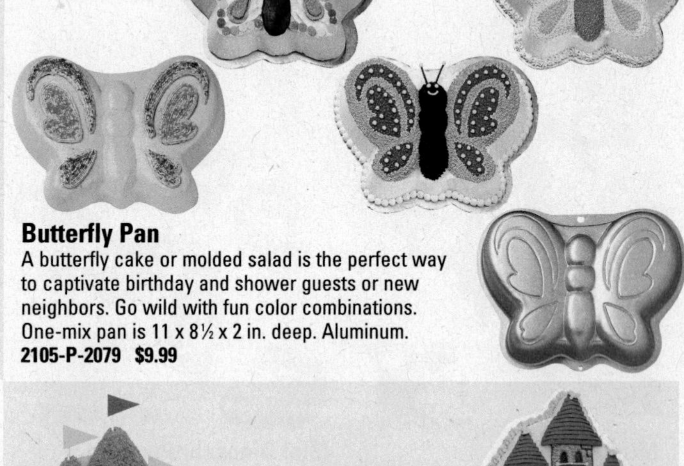

Butterfly Pan
A butterfly cake or molded salad is the perfect way to captivate birthday and shower guests or new neighbors. Go wild with fun color combinations. One-mix pan is 11 x 8½ x 2 in. deep. Aluminum.
2105-P-2079 $9.99

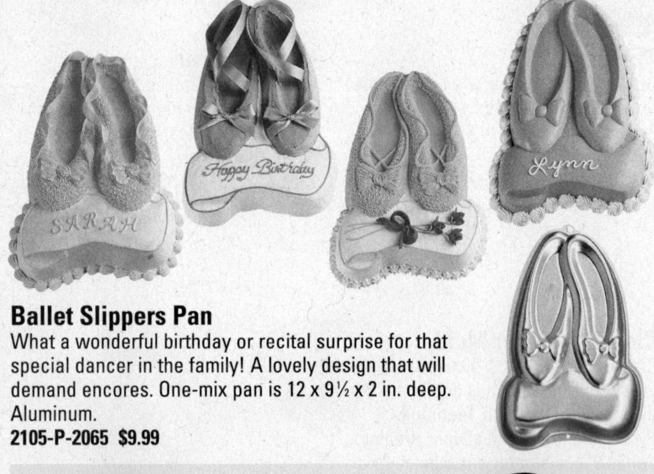

Ballet Slippers Pan
What a wonderful birthday or recital surprise for that special dancer in the family! A lovely design that will demand encores. One-mix pan is 12 x 9½ x 2 in. deep. Aluminum.
2105-P-2065 $9.99

Enchanted Castle Pan
A royal treat for little girls' birthdays or any important event. Wonderful for molded sugar or ice cream. One-mix pan is 11½ x 11¾ x 2 in. deep. Aluminum.
2105-P-2031 $9.99

Juggling Clown Pan
Ladies and gentlemen, boys and girls, let the greatest clown on earth entertain at your birthday, school and holiday celebrations! Fun for kids and adults alike. One-mix pan is 13 x 10¾ x 2 in. deep. Aluminum.
2105-P-572 $9.99

Partysaurus Pan
Our prehistoric party animal is a must-have at all sorts of fun fests—a kid's birthday favorite. One-mix pan is 16 x 10 x 1⅞ in. deep. Aluminum.
2105-P-1280 $9.99

3-D Rubber Ducky Pan

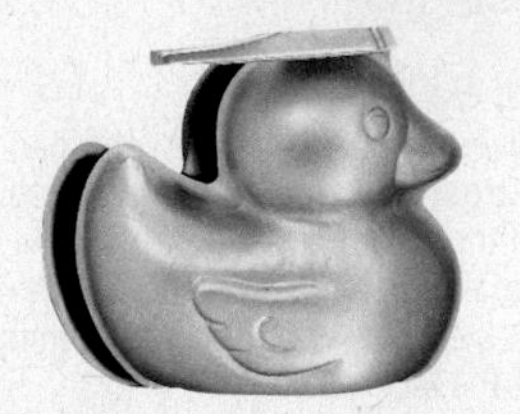

This bath-time favorite will make the biggest splash for birthdays, baby showers and school celebrations. Five adorable designs included. Two-piece pan takes 5½ cups batter, 9 x 5 x 7 in. high. Aluminum.
2105-P-2094 $12.99

Cuddly Lamb Pan

You'll find a flock of useful ideas for this fleecy friend. His sweet smile is the perfect welcome for baby showers, Easter brunches, birthday parties. See the label for 4 great ideas, including a luscious vanilla mousse and a coconut and candy decorated cake. One-mix pan is 11¾ x 8¾ x 2 in. deep. Aluminum.
2105-P-4947 $9.99

Mini Stand-Up Bear Pan Set

Convenient size for baking cakes and molding candy, ice cream and sugar. Includes baking stand, four clips and instructions. Two-piece pan takes 1 cup of batter; standard pound cake mix makes about 4 cakes. Assembled cakes are 4 x 3¼ x 4¾ in. high. Aluminum.
2105-P-489 Set/8 $10.99

Huggable Teddy Bear Pan

This classic toy shape never hibernates! From birthdays and baby showers to school parties, he's being used all year. One-mix pan is 13½ x 12¼ x 2 in. deep. Aluminum.
2105-P-4943 $9.99

Stand-Up Cuddly Bear Set

Five innovative decorating ideas on the box! Two-piece pan takes 6⅔ cups of firm textured batter. Includes 6 clips, heat-conducting core and instructions. Pan is 9 x 6¾ x 8⅝ in. high. Aluminum.
2105-P-603 Set/10 $19.99

Playful Pup Pan

This frisky little guy just begs to be a part of all kinds of celebrations! He does the trick for birthdays, obedience school parties, get-well wishes and even welcome celebrations for a new puppy. One-mix pan is 12 x 9 x 2 in. deep. Aluminum.
2105-P-2064 $9.99

Book Pans

This open book details life's important chapters —birthdays, baby showers, graduations and more. Five ways to decorate included. Aluminum.

One-Mix Pan
13 x 9½ x 2 in. deep.
2105-P-972 $9.99

Two-Mix Pan
Serves up to 30.
15 x 11½ x 2¾ in. deep.
2105-P-2521 $13.99

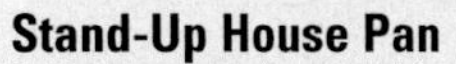

Stand-Up House Pan

Address your guests with a delightful "welcome home". Halloween haunted houses, Easter hutches, Christmas cottages, school houses and even dog houses are just a few ideas in store for this pan. Cakes can stand up or lay flat. One-mix pan is 9 x 3 x 8¾ in. high. Aluminum.
2105-P-2070 $12.99

Novelty Shaped Pans

Sports Ball Pan Set

Choose your own sporting passion, then use this four-piece set to create the perfect cake centerpiece. Includes two 6 in. diameter half-ball pans and two metal baking stands. Each pan half takes 2½ cups batter. Aluminum.
2105-P-6506 Set/4 $10.99

Mini Ball Pan

Individually-sized, so everyone can catch a little treat of their own. Ice two mini balls and push together for a 3-D effect. One cake mix makes 10–12 mini balls. Six cavities, each 3½ x 3½ x 1½ in. deep. Aluminum.
2105-P-1760 $10.99

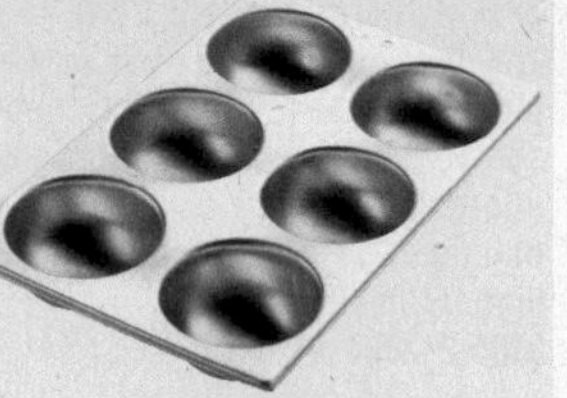

First and Ten Football Pan

Touching down at Super Bowl parties, homecomings, award dinners and much more. One-mix pan is 12 x 7¾ x 3 in. deep. Aluminum.
2105-P-6504 $9.99

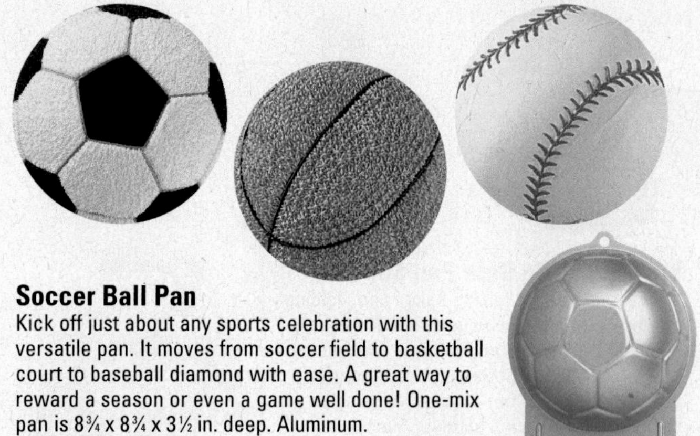

Soccer Ball Pan

Kick off just about any sports celebration with this versatile pan. It moves from soccer field to basketball court to baseball diamond with ease. A great way to reward a season or even a game well done! One-mix pan is 8¾ x 8¾ x 3½ in. deep. Aluminum.
2105-P-2044 $9.99

Star Pan

What better way to honor the celebrity in your life? Brighten birthdays, opening nights, even law enforcement occasions. One-mix pan is 12¾ x 12¾ x 1⅞ in. deep. Aluminum.
2105-P-2512 $9.99

Guitar Pan

Whether your musical choice is classical or pure rock 'n' roll, a guitar cake sets the tone for fun at your next party! Celebrate school band concerts, kid and adult birthdays! One-mix pan is 16½ x 8½ x 2 in. deep. Aluminum.
2105-P-570 $9.99

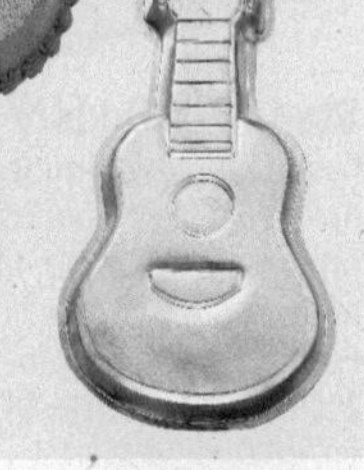

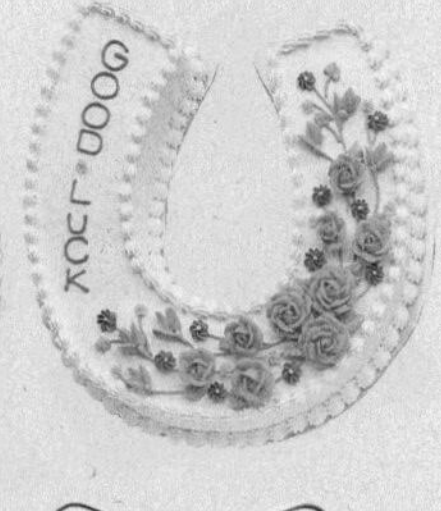

Horseshoe Pan

Say "good luck" at graduations, birthdays, bon voyage parties! One-mix pan is 11½ x 12 x 1¾ in. deep. Aluminum.
2105-P-3254 $9.99

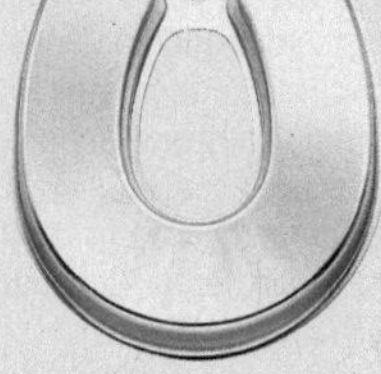

Over The Hill Tombstone Pan

Optimistically mark the passing of one more year. One-mix pan is 13 x 9¼ x 2 in. deep. Aluminum.
2105-P-1237 $9.99

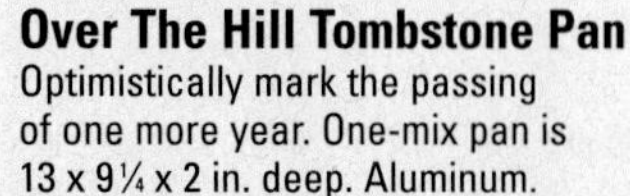

Little Hero Pan

Capture the imagination of your special little heroes by bringing their favorite figures to life—fireman, policeman, soldier, astronaut...the list goes on! Create a birthday party that will win everyone's heart. One-mix pan is 13¼ x 6½ x 2 in. deep. Aluminum.
2105-P-2077 $9.99

Little Pirate Pan

Unlock the many decorating treasures to be found in this one fun pan. The cute pirate-in-training design is easy to transform into a sailor, scientist and just about any character that suits the guest of honor. One-mix pan is 9 in. x 14¼ in. x 2 in. deep. Aluminum.
2105-P-2078 $9.99

Choo-Choo Train Pan Set

Here's the little 3-D engine with a trainload of uses. Two-piece pan snaps together to create a cake 10 x 4 x 6 in. high. Takes 6 cups batter. Aluminum.
2105-P-2861 Set/2 $11.99

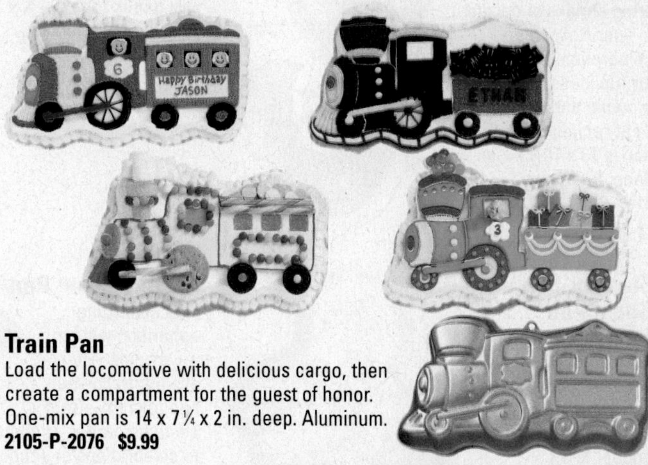

Train Pan

Load the locomotive with delicious cargo, then create a compartment for the guest of honor. One-mix pan is 14 x 7¼ x 2 in. deep. Aluminum.
2105-P-2076 $9.99

Tractor Pan

Down on the farm has never been so much fun. This tractor is great for cultivating good times, children's birthday parties, school events and theme get-togethers. One-mix pan is 13½ x 9½ x 2 in. deep. Aluminum.
2105-P-2063 $9.99

Firetruck Pan

For the family firefighter or a little hero-in-the-making, the occasion calls for a five-alarm celebration. One-mix pan is 15½ x 8½ x 2 in. deep. Aluminum.
2105-P-2061 $9.99

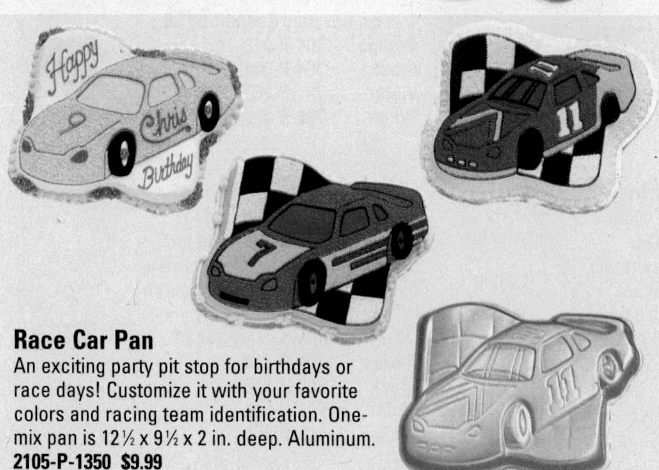

Race Car Pan

An exciting party pit stop for birthdays or race days! Customize it with your favorite colors and racing team identification. One-mix pan is 12½ x 9½ x 2 in. deep. Aluminum.
2105-P-1350 $9.99

3-D Cruiser Pan

What a fun way to celebrate a new driver in the family, welcome travelers home or create the car of your dreams. Bake exciting 3-D cakes, ready to customize for all occasions. One-mix pan is 11 x 6¾ x 4 in. high. Aluminum.
2105-P-2043 $10.99

Seasonal

Wilton makes every time of year worth celebrating! With so many fun ways to serve cakes, cookies and other treats, it's easy to let everyone taste the excitement of each season.

HALLOWEEN

Bakeware

NEW!

Just Batty Pan
A little silly, a little scary—this pan will bring shrieks of delight to your Halloween celebration. See label for fun ideas using brownie and gelatin treat recipes! One-mix pan is 13 x 10½ x 2 in. deep. Aluminum.
2105-P-6411 $7.99

Jack-O-Lantern Pan
Carve out his happy features for your next Halloween party. One-mix pan is 12¼ x 11⅝ x 2 in. deep. Aluminum.
2105-P-3068 $7.99

Stand-Up Jack-O-Lantern Pan
They won't say boo to your 3-D dessert! Ideas and instructions for all skill levels. Two-piece pan is 7 x 5¼ x 6½ in. deep and takes 5 cups of pound cake batter. Aluminum.
2105-P-3150 Set/2 $10.99

Petite Jack-O-Lantern Pan
Make personal petite smiling pumpkins. One mix makes 9-13 dozen jack-o-lanterns. 12 cavities, each 2 x 2 x 1⅛ in. deep. Aluminum.
2105-P-8462 $8.99

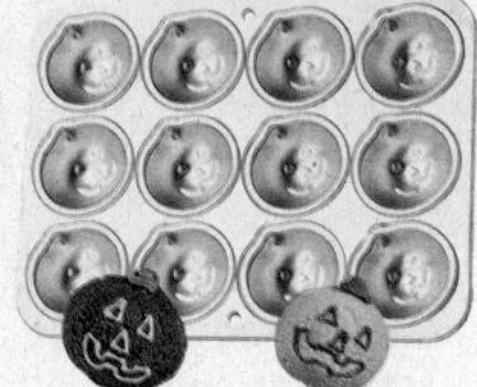

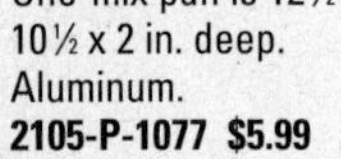

Step-By-Step Ghost Pan **NEW!**
This happy haunter adds spirit to any witching hour! With only three easy decorating steps he'll appear in an instant—just bake, ice and decorate. One-mix pan is 12½ x 10½ x 2 in. deep. Aluminum.
2105-P-1077 $5.99

Spooky Ghost Pan
This appetizing apparition will be a welcome vision at all your Halloween happenings—from costume parties at home to celebrations at school. Great for easy-to-decorate cakes and gelatin desserts. One-mix pan is 11½ x 11½ x 2 in. deep. Aluminum.
2105-P-2090 $7.99

Mini Ghost Pan
Create gobs of goblins at one time! One mix makes 9-15 ghosts ready for decorating. 6 cavities, each 4 x 4⅞ x 1⅜ in. deep. Aluminum.
2105-P-3845 $9.99

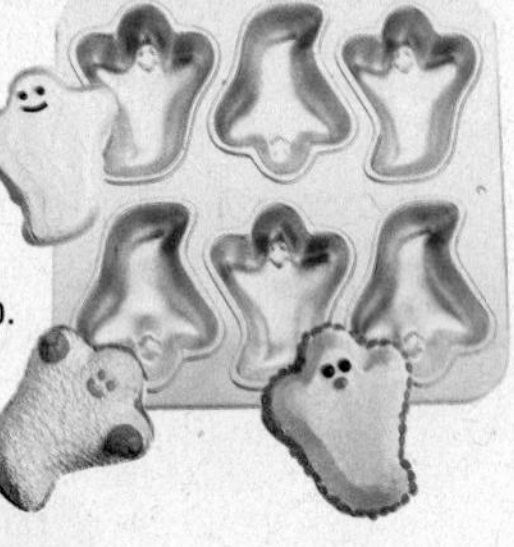

Colors & Icings

HALLOWEEN COLOR GUIDE

Orange | Black | Violet | White

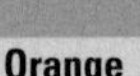

Halloween Icing Colors Set
.5 oz. jars of Black and Orange. Certified Kosher.
601-P-3010 Set/2 $2.99

FoodWriter™ Edible Color Markers

Use like ink markers to add fun, dazzling color to countless foods. Kids love 'em! Decorate on fondant, Ice-A-Cookie™ icing, Color Flow, royal icing designs and cookies. Includes Black and Orange markers. .35 oz. Certified Kosher.
609-P-101 Set/2 $3.99

Tube Decorating Icing
Tubes can be used with our Tip and Nail Set or Coupler Ring Set (p. 127) and any standard size Wilton metal tip. Colors match Wilton Icing Colors (p. 127). 4.25 oz. Certified Kosher. **$1.79**

Orange	**704-P-212**
Black	**704-P-206**
Violet	**704-P-242**
White	**704-P-200**

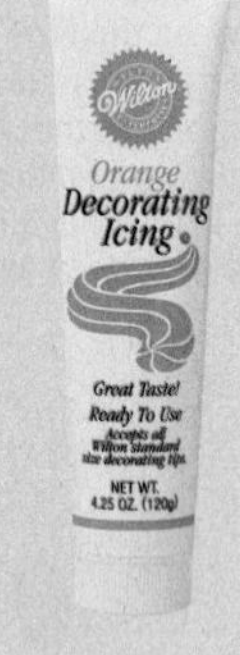

Color Mist™ Food Color Spray
Gives decorators the versatility and dazzling effects of an airbrush in a convenient can! Use it to transform a plain iced cake with sensational color, add splashes of holiday color to iced cookies and cupcakes. No mess, taste-free formula. 1.5 oz. Certified Kosher. **$2.99**

Orange	**710-P-5507**
Black	**710-P-5506**
Violet	**710-P-5504**

Ready-To-Decorate Icing
Anyone can decorate with Wilton Ready-to-Decorate Icing! Our brilliant colors and four decorating tips make it a breeze to add an exciting finishing touch to treats—without mixing or mess. 6.4 oz. Certified Kosher. **$3.49**

Orange	**710-P-4410**
Black	**710-P-4404**
Violet	**710-P-4408**
White	**710-P-4402**

Tube Decorating Gel
Transparent gels are great for writing messages and decorating cakes and cookies. Colors match Wilton Icing Colors (p. 127). .75 oz. Certified Kosher. **$1.29**

Orange	**704-P-312**
Black	**704-P-306**
Violet	**704-P-342**
White	**704-P-302**

Party

Baking Cups
Microwave-safe paper.
Standard size, 2 in. diameter.
Pk./50 $1.49

NEW!

Just Batty
415-P-250

Spooky Ghost
415-P-371

Glowing Pumpkins
415-P-223

Party Bags
Colorful Halloween designs for candy and cookie treats.
20 plastic bags, 20 ties included. 4 x 9½ in.
Pk./20 $1.99

NEW!

Just Batty
1912-P-2058

Spooky Ghost
1912-P-1040

Glowing Pumpkins
1912-P-2352

FOIL FUN PIX®
NEW!
Add a shimmering, spooky touch to cakes, cupcakes, ice cream and more. Approx. 3½ in. tall.
Pk./12 $1.99

Just Batty
2113-P-1346

Jack-O-Lantern
2113-P-713

Icing Decorations
Wilton Icing Decorations are perfect for topping cupcakes, cookies and ice cream. Mint-flavored. Certified Kosher.
$2.09

NEW!

Just Batty
710-P-273 Pk./9

Petite Ghosts
710-P-3030 Pk./12

Pumpkin Face
710-P-3012 Pk./12

Petite Spiders and Bats
710-P-3036 Pk./11

Candy

NEW!
Just Batty Lollipop Mold
3 designs, 8 cavities.
2115-P-1411 $1.99

Spooky Ghost Candy Mold
1 design, 8 cavities.
2115-P-1407 $1.99

Mini Ghost and Pumpkin Candy Mold
2 designs, 19 cavities.
2115-P-1735 $1.99

Halloween Lollipop Sticks
4 in. plastic sticks; 10 black and 10 orange.
1912-P-9313
Pk./20 $1.99

Halloween Candy Colors Set
Add concentrated oil-based color to Wilton Candy Melts®*. Contains Orange and Black; .25 oz. jars. Certified Kosher.
1913-P-1295 Set/2 $2.99

Candy Melts®*
Ideal for all your candy making—molding, dipping or coating. Artificially vanilla flavored unless otherwise indicated. 14 oz. bag.
Certified Kosher. **$2.50**

Light Cocoa	1911-P-544
Dark Cocoa	1911-P-358
Chocolate Mint	1911-P-1920
Orange	1911-P-1631
Yellow	1911-P-463
Dark Green	1911-P-405
White	1911-P-498
Lavender	1911-P-403

Gummy Making Kit
NEW!
Kids will have a great time making 16 yummy gummy candies in just minutes! Everything they need is included: mold with 4 fun Halloween designs, four .7 oz. pouches of gummy mix (Grape, Lemon, Orange and Blue Raspberry), one .7 oz. packet of Sour Sugars for covering gummys, squeeze bottle and funnel. Just add water to the mix, shake, fill molds and pop in your refrigerator. Ages 4 and up.
2104-P-3064 $4.99

Pumpkin Popcorn Ball Kit
NEW!
Have a ball making and decorating the spookiest popcorn treats ever! With this kit, it's easy to make 8 colorful, crunchy popcorn balls to give and serve. Includes 4 oz. popcorn kernels, orange color pouch, 8 sets of pumpkin face icing decorations, 8 fun party bags and complete instructions.
2104-P-1103 $7.99

Halloween Lollipop Kit
Everything you need to make easy, fun Halloween treats! Includes one lollipop mold (3 designs, 8 cavities), 10 oz. Candy Melts®* (5 oz. White, 2.5 oz. each Orange and Light Cocoa), 10 lollipop sticks (8 in.), 10 lollipop bags with ties, 3 disposable decorating bags and one decorator brush.
2104-P-1236 $6.99

See pages 144-149 for more Wilton candy items.

*Brand confectionery coating.

HALLOWEEN

ICE-A-COOKIE™

Instant fun for all your Halloween cookies! Transform cookies with fun colors and dazzling designs. The soft, squeezable pouch is easy to handle; the patented snip tip and screw-on decorating cap help you control the flow. Use the snip tip for icing cookies and the cap for decorating lines and designs. Delicious artificially vanilla-flavored icing dries to a smooth, satin finish. Draw fun shapes, messages, decorate with Cake Sparkles™ (not included) and more! Each pouch decorates approximately twenty-four 3 in. round cookies. 10.59 oz. pouch. Certified Kosher. **$3.99**

Orange **710-P-332**
Black **710-P-331**
White **710-P-330**

Sprinkles

INDIVIDUAL BOTTLES

Shake up your Halloween treats with fun colors and designs. Plastic bottles for convenient pouring and storing. Certified Kosher. **$1.99**

Halloween Sprinkle Sparks
2.5 oz. bottle
710-P-612

Ghost Mix
2.5 oz. bottle
710-P-767

Halloween Mix
2.5 oz. bottle
710-P-788

Orange Sugar
3.5 oz. bottle
710-P-759

Black Sugar
3.5 oz. bottle
710-P-762

Purple Sugar
3.5 oz. bottle
710-P-758

Sparkling Sugars

NEW!

A coarse texture and a brilliant sparkle. 8.25 oz. Certified Kosher. **$3.99**

Orange/White
710-P-572

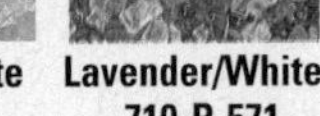

Lavender/White
710-P-571

Cake Sparkles™

Edible glitter, .25 oz. bottle. Certified Kosher. **$2.89**

Orange
703-P-1308

Black
703-P-1302

Purple
703-P-1266

ASSORTMENTS

4-Mix

.8 oz. Halloween Mix, 1 oz. Halloween Nonpareils, 1.2 oz. each of Black and Orange Sugars. Certified Kosher.
710-P-728 **$4.99**

6-Mix

1 oz. Halloween Mix, 1 oz. Bat Mix, 1.3 oz. Halloween Nonpareils, 1.3 oz. each of Black, Orange and Purple Sugars. Certified Kosher.
710-P-727 **$5.99**

Stencil Sets

STENCIL-A-COOKIE™ CUTTER & STENCIL SETS

Using the fun-shaped stencils and cutter, it's easy to serve cookies with exciting colorful designs for the season. Just cut cookies, then use the stencils and Wilton FoodWriter™, Cake Sparkles™, Colored Sugars or Color Mist™ Food Color Spray (not included) to create dazzling shapes on top after baking. Cookies look great iced with Wilton Ice-A-Cookie™ sold above. Set includes one metal cutter and two stencils (same design). **Set/3** **$1.99**

NEW!

Just Batty
2308-P-1413

Jack-O-Lantern
2308-P-1406

Ghost
2308-P-1407

Halloween Cupcake and Cookie Stencils

Turn plain treats into ghoulish goodies with a stenciled Halloween design. Just place one of the fun designs over your baked treat, then sprinkle with Wilton Cake Sparkles™ or Colored Sugars or spray with Color Mist™ Food Color Spray (p. 166). 5 designs.
417-P-1203 **$2.49**

Gingerbread Kits NEW!

No baking, just fun! Everything you need is included to make one of 3 great haunted designs.

Pre-Baked/Pre-Assembled Haunted Castle

Ready to decorate–just attach tower pieces and go! Includes gingerbread castle, 3 tower pieces and 1 easel piece, orange and black decorating icing mixes, assorted candies, 4 ghost icing decorations, decorating bags and tips, cardboard base and instructions. Castle measures 8½ x 4 x 9 in. high.
2104-P-1449 **$12.99**

Pre-Baked Haunted Castle

Kit includes pre-baked gingerbread castle pieces, orange and black decorating icing mixes, 2 bat and 2 ghost icing decorations, assorted candies, decorating bags and tips, cardboard base and instructions. Castle measures 8½ x 4 x 9 in. high.
2104-P-5507 **$12.99**

Cookie Cutters, Pans

COMFORT GRIP™ CUTTERS

These easy-grip cutters with extra-deep sides are perfect for cutting so many favorite foods into spectacular shapes. The cushion grip gives you comfortable control even when cutting thick desserts. Recipe included. Stainless steel sides, 4½ x 4½ x 1½ in. deep. **$2.99**

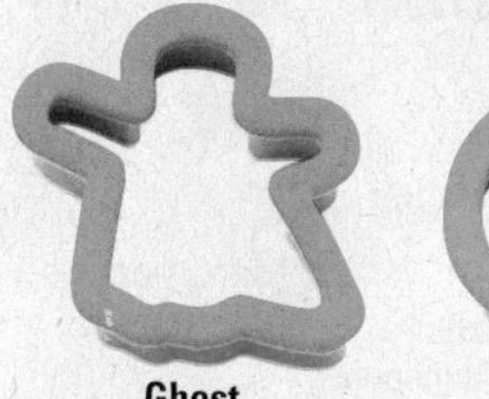

Ghost
2310-P-607

Pumpkin
2310-P-600

GRIPPY™ CUTTERS

4 Pc. Grippy™ Bag Set NEW!

Safe, easy cutting, with a comfortable grip and deep plastic sides. Mesh bag for convenient storing and giving. Four shapes include ghost, cat, pumpkin and bat, approx. 3½ in.
2311-P-255 Set/4 $3.99

METAL CUTTERS

Put variety in your cookie-making with fun Halloween multi-shape sets. There are styles to please everyone. Recipe included.

Nesting Cutter Sets

Create boo-tiful Halloween treats in four sizes. Quality metal cuts neatly and is easy to handle. Sizes from 2¼ to 4½ in.
Set/4 $4.49

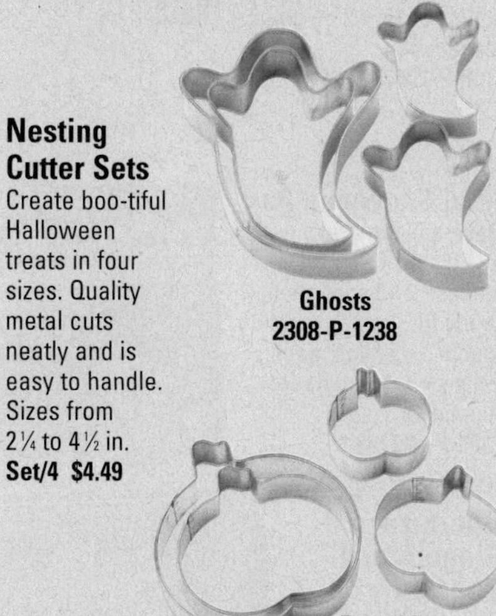

Ghosts
2308-P-1238

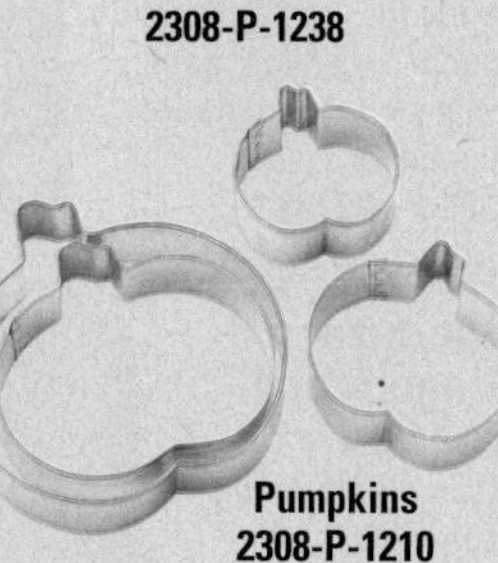

Pumpkins
2308-P-1210

Halloween Mini Cutter Set

Set of 6 includes cat, bat, pumpkin, ghost, moon and skull, each approx. 1½ in.
2308-P-1211
Set/6 $2.99

Colorful Cutter Sets

Our metal cutters look great with their bright colors and fun shapes. Perfect for hanging until your next cookie-baking bash.

Halloween Cutter Set
Set of 9 includes bat, ghost, cat, witch, moon, witch's broom, tombstone, house and pumpkin, each approx. 3 to 3¾ in. Colored aluminum.
2308-P-2501 Set/9 $9.99

Spooky Shapes Cutter Set
Set of 4 includes moon, pumpkin, witch and ghost, each approx. 3 in. Coated metal.
2308-P-1200 Set/4 $4.49

PLASTIC CUTTERS

Child-safe designs mean kids can have a great time helping. And remember all the fun ways to use our cutters—for bread shapes, stencils, sun catchers and so much more. Recipe included.

Jack-O-Lantern Canister Cutter Set

A smiling jack-o-lantern stores 10 cutter shapes. Canister is 5¼ x 5¼ in.; cutters are 2¼ to 3½ in.
2304-P-1035 Set/11 $5.99

Spooky Cookie Cutter Set

Favorite frightening shapes, measuring from 3 to 4¼ in.
2304-P-9210
Set/10 $3.99

Jack-O-Lantern Nesting Cutter Set

Graduated sizes from 2⅜ to 5 in. wide.
2303-P-191
Set/4 $2.99

COOKIE PANS

Jack-O-Lantern Giant Cookie Pan

Ideal for refrigerated dough and brownie mix. Pan is 11½ x 10½ in. Recipe included. Aluminum.
2105-P-6207 $5.99

Jack-O-Lantern Cookie Treat Pan

Create your own cookie blossoms for that special someone; also great for adding fun shapes to other goodies like rice cereal treats and candy pops. Recipe included. Six-cavity pan, each cavity measures 3¼ x 3¼ x ¼ in. deep. Aluminum.
2105-P-8100 $7.99

Cookie Treat Sticks

6 in. 1912-P-9319 Pk./20 $1.99
8 in. 1912-P-9318 Pk./20 $2.99

CHRISTMAS

Bakeware

Jolly Santa Pan

He's the ideal season's greeter for your holiday festivities. Instructions for four different decorating ideas included. One-mix pan is 13¾ x 10 x 2 in. deep. Aluminum.
2105-P-2091 $7.99

Step-By-Step Snowman Pan

Just bake, ice and decorate. He's also perfect for molding gelatin and ice cream, salads, baking bread and more. One-mix pan is 12 x 9¼ x 2 in. deep. Aluminum.
2105-P-2083 $5.99

Step-By-Step Tree Pan

Quick, easy and so right for the season. Just bake, ice and decorate. One-mix pan is 10¼ x 14 x 2 in. deep. Aluminum.
2105-P-2058 $5.99

Snowflake Pan

Capture the beauty and wonder of a single snowflake. Perfect for gelatin and mousse recipes, too! One-mix pan is 12¼ x 11½ x 2 in. deep. Aluminum.
2105-P-2067 $7.99

Mini Snowman Pan

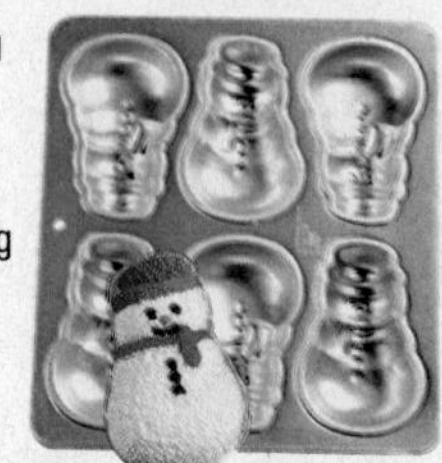

Bake a blizzard of snowmen! One mix makes 12-18 snowmen, ready for your decorating touch. 6 cavities, each 2⅞ x 4⅝ x 1⅛ in. deep. Aluminum.
2105-P-472 $9.99

Bite-Size Gingerbread Boy Pan

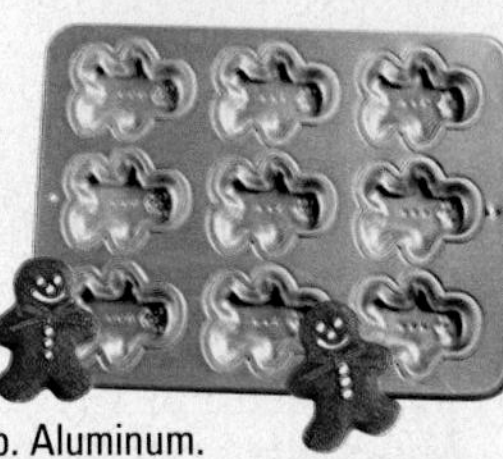

Bake plenty of fun little guys for everyone. One mix makes 24-36 boys. 9 cavities, each 2¾ x 3⅜ x ¾ in. deep. Aluminum.
2105-P-926 $9.99

Petite Christmas Tree Pan

Ideal for bite-size muffins, brownies, tarts or gelatins. One mix makes 7-11 dozen trees. 12 cavities, each 2 x 2½ x ¾ in. deep. Aluminum.
2105-P-8463 $8.99

Stand-Up Snowman Pan

Makes a delightful 3-D holiday centerpiece. Instructions for five different decorating ideas included. Each pan half is 9¼ x 6¾ x 2½ in. deep. Pan takes six cups of pound cake batter. No heating core needed. Aluminum.
2105-P-2047 Set/2 $10.99

Cookie Pans

Christmas Tree Giant Cookie Pan

Ideal for refrigerated cookie dough or brownie mix. Recipe and instructions included. 13 x 12 x ¾ in. deep. Aluminum.
2105-P-6206 $5.99

Cookie Treat Pans

Treats on a stick are so easy; just press dough or rice cereal treat mixture into the pan, insert a cookie stick, then bake, cool and decorate. Each pan makes six individual treats, approx. 4 in high x ½ in. deep. Recipe included. Aluminum. **$7.99**

Christmas Tree
2105-P-8101

Snowman
2105-P-8107

Star
2105-P-8102

Cookie Treat Sticks

6 in. 1912-P-9319
Pk./20 $1.99

8 in. 1912-P-9318
Pk./20 $2.99

Colors & Icings

CHRISTMAS COLOR GUIDE

Red | Kelly Green | Leaf Green | White

Holiday Icing Colors Set

.5 oz. jars, Red-Red and Kelly Green. Certified Kosher.
601-P-3011 Pk./2 $2.99

Color Mist™ Food Color Spray

The dazzling effects of an airbrush in a convenient can! Use it to transform a plain iced cake with sensational color, add splashes of holiday color to iced cookies and cupcakes. No mess, taste-free formula. 1.5 oz. Certified Kosher. **$2.99**

Green	**710-P-5503**
Red	**710-P-5500**

FoodWriter™ Edible Color Markers

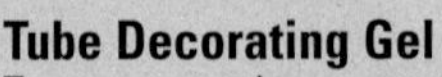

Use like ink markers to add fun, dazzling color to countless foods. Kids love 'em! Decorate on fondant, Ice-A-Cookie™ icing, Color Flow, royal icing designs and cookies. Includes Green and Red markers .35 oz. Certified Kosher.
609-P-102 Set/2 $3.99

Ready-to-Decorate Icing

Anyone can decorate with Wilton Ready-to-Decorate Icing! Our brilliant colors and four decorating tips make it a breeze to add an exciting finishing touch to treats—without mixing or mess. 6.4 oz. Certified Kosher. **$3.49**

Green	**710-P-4401**
Red	**710-P-4400**
White	**710-P-4402**

Tube Decorating Icing

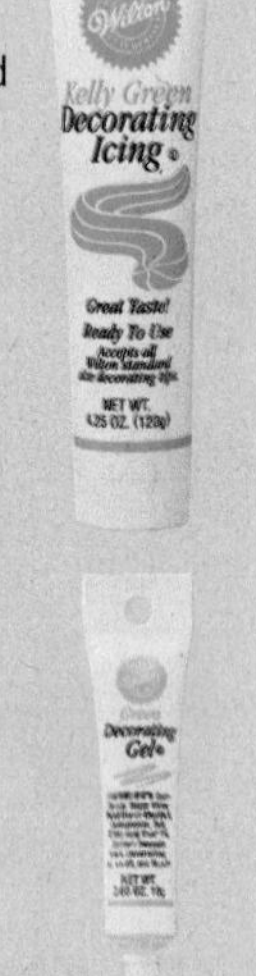

Can be used with our Tip and Nail Set or Coupler Ring Set (p. 127) and any standard size Wilton metal tip. Colors match Wilton Icing Colors (p. 127). 4.25 oz. Certified Kosher.
$1.79

Kelly Green	**704-P-227**
Red	**704-P-218**
White	**704-P-200**

Tube Decorating Gel

Transparent gels are great for writing messages and decorating cakes and cookies. Colors match Wilton Icing Colors (p. 127). .75 oz. Certified Kosher. **$1.29**

Leaf Green	**704-P-324**
Red	**704-P-318**
White	**704-P-302**

BON BON CUPS

Red Foil
415-P-314
Pk./75
$1.49

Silver Foil
415-P-307
Pk./72 $1.49
(36 pure aluminum 36 paper)

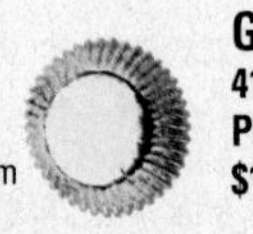

Gold Foil
415-P-306
Pk./75
$1.49

MINI CUPS

Red/Green Paper
Mixed, glassine paper.
1912-P-1247
Pk./75 $1.49

PETITE LOAF BAKING CUPS

Ideal for gift breads. Fits Petite Loaf Pan (p.160). Microwave-safe paper. White.
415-P-450 Pk./50 $1.49

Party

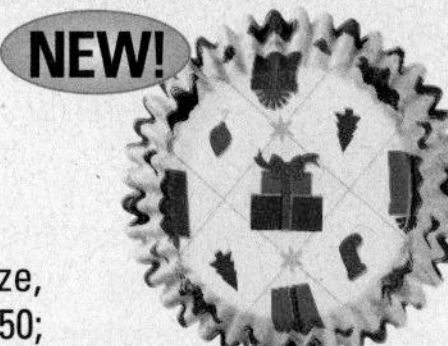

NEW!

Baking Cups
Microwave-safe paper. Standard size, 2 in. diameter, Pk./50; Mini size, 1¼ in. diameter, Pk./75.
$1.49

Gifts Galore
Standard 415-P-403
Mini 415-P-402

Jolly Santa
Standard 415-P-372
Mini 415-P-373

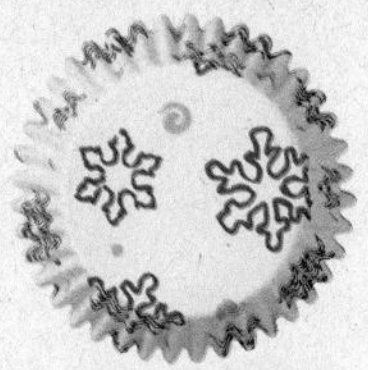

Snowflake
Standard 415-P-392
Mini 415-P-393

Gingerbread Boy
Standard 415-P-350
Mini 415-P-2009

NEW!

Foil Fun Pix®
Festive designs add a shimmering holiday touch to cakes, cupcakes, ice cream and more. Approx. 3½ in. tall.
Pk./12 $1.99

Gifts Galore
2113-P-715

Tree
2113-P-1345

NEW!

Party Bags
Colorful Christmas designs for candy and cookie treats. 20 plastic bags, 20 ties included. 4 x 9½ in.
Pk./20 $1.99

Gifts Galore
1912-P-1023

Jolly Santa
1912-P-1041

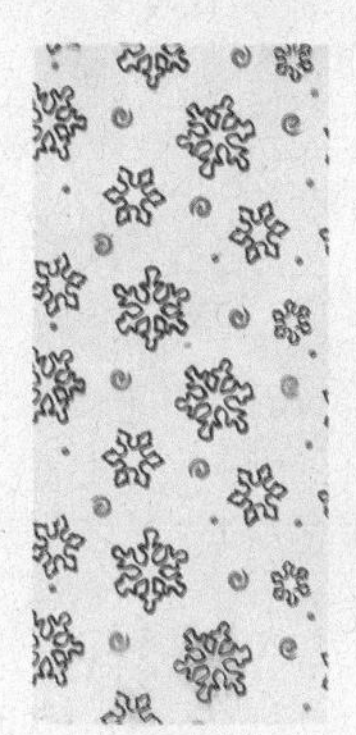

Snowflake
1912-P-1274

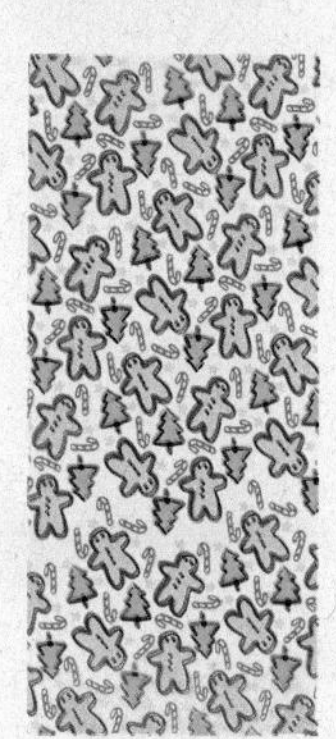

Gingerbread Boy
1912-P-2223

NEW!

Icing Decorations
Wilton Icing Decorations are perfect for topping cupcakes, cookies and ice cream. Mint-flavored. Certified Kosher.
$2.09

Gifts Galore
710-P-274 Pk./9

Jolly Santa
710-P-256
Pk./9

Petite Snowflake
710-P-543
Pk./12

Mini Gingerbread Boy
710-P-464 Pk./18

Candy

NEW!

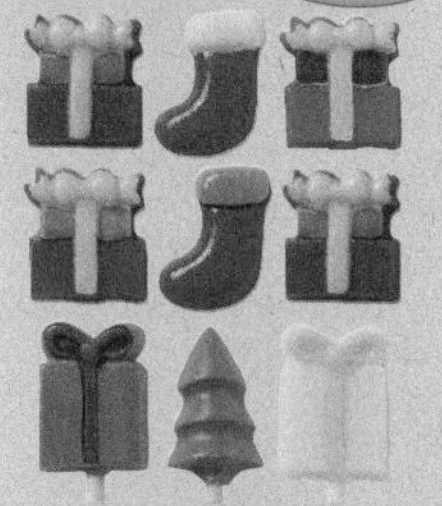

Gifts Galore Lollipop Mold
4 designs, 10 cavities.
2115-P-1566 $1.99

Santa Lollipop Mold
1 design, 9 cavities.
2115-P-1706 $1.99

Snowflake Lollipop Mold
1 design, 9 cavities.
2115-P-1705 $1.99

Mini Gingerbread Candy Mold
4 designs, 12 cavities.
2115-P-1539 $1.99

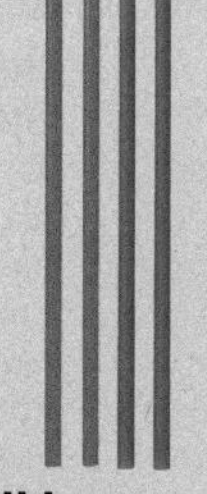

Holiday Lollipop Sticks
4 in. plastic sticks; 10 red, 10 green.
1912-P-9315
Pk./20 $1.99

Holiday Candy Colors Set
Add concentrated oil-based color to Wilton Candy Melts®*. Contains Red and Green; .25 oz. jars. Certified Kosher.
1913-P-1297 Set/2 $2.99

NEW!

Gummy Making Kit
Kids will have a great time making 16 yummy gummy candies in just minutes! Everything they need is included: mold with 4 fun holiday designs, four .7 oz. pouches of gummy mix (Cherry, Banana, Blueberry and Green Apple), one .7 oz. packet of Sour Sugars for covering gummys, squeeze bottle and funnel. Just add water to the mix, shake, fill molds and pop in your refrigerator. Ages 4 and up.
2104-P-3063 $4.99

NEW!

Christmas Lollipop Kit
Everything you need to make dazzling holiday treats! Includes 1 lollipop mold (3 designs, 9 cavities), 10 oz. Candy Melts®* (5 oz. Red, 2.5 oz. each White and Green), 10 lollipop sticks, (6 in.), 10 lollipop bags with ties, 3 disposable decorating bags, 1 decorator brush and complete instructions.
2104-P-1048 $6.99

Candy Melts®*
Ideal for all your candy making —molding, dipping or coating. Artificially vanilla flavored unless otherwise indicated. 14 oz. bag. Certified Kosher.
$2.50

Light Cocoa	**1911-P-544**
Red	**1911-P-499**
Dark Cocoa	**1911-P-358**
White	**1911-P-498**
Chocolate Mint	**1911-P-1920**
Dark Green	**1911-P-405**
Yellow	**1911-P-463**

*Brand confectionery coating.

See pages 144-149 for more Wilton candy items.

CHRISTMAS

ICE-A-COOKIE™

The soft, squeezable pouch is easy to handle; the patented snip tip and screw-on decorating cap help you control the flow. Use the snip tip for icing cookies and the cap for decorating lines and designs. Delicious artificially vanilla-flavored icing dries to a smooth, satin finish. Draw fun shapes, messages, decorate with Cake Sparkles™ (not included) and more! Each pouch decorates approximately twenty-four 3 in. round cookies. 10.59 oz. pouch. Certified Kosher. **$3.99**

Red **710-P-334**
Green **710-P-333**
White **710-P-335**

Sprinkles

INDIVIDUAL BOTTLES

Shake up your holiday treats with fun colors and designs. Plastic bottles for convenient pouring and storing. Certified Kosher. **$1.99**

Snowflake Mix
2.5 oz. bottle
710-P-797

Christmas Sprinkle Sparks
2.5 oz. bottle
710-P-613

Gingerbread Boy Mix
2.5 oz. bottle
710-P-795

Christmas Tree Mix
2.5 oz. bottle
710-P-792

Cinnamon Drops
3 oz. bottle
710-P-769

Chocolate Jimmies
2.5 oz. bottle
710-P-774

Red Sugar
3.25 oz. bottle
710-P-766

Dark Green Sugar
3.25 oz. bottle
710-P-764

Sparkling Sugars

NEW!

Easy-pour sugars have a coarse texture and brilliant sparkle. 8.25 oz. Certified Kosher. **$3.99**

Red/ White
710-P-998

Green/ White
710-P-997

White
710-P-995

Cake Sparkles™

Edible glitter, .25 oz. bottle. Certified Kosher. **$2.89**

Red
703-P-1284

Green
703-P-1278

White
703-P-1290

ASSORTMENTS

4-Mix
Includes .75 oz. Christmas Tree Mix, 1 oz. Christmas Nonpareils, 1.1 oz. Dark Green and Red Sugars. Certified Kosher.
710-P-729 **$4.99**

6-Mix
Includes 1 oz. Christmas Tree Mix, 1 oz. Christmas Jimmies, 1 oz. Gingerbread Boy Mix, 1.3 oz. Christmas Nonpareils, 1.3 oz. Dark Green and Red Sugars. Certified Kosher.
710-P-734 **$5.99**

Cookie and Stencil Sets

Holiday Cookie Cutter and Sprinkles Set

Fun-shaped cutters and colorful sprinkles for the sweetest Christmas cookies ever! Just follow the easy recipe included, cut cookies, top with sugars and bake. Includes four metal cutters and 2.5 oz. Christmas Tree Mix, 3.25 oz. each Dark Green and Red sugars. Certified Kosher.
2109-P-1807 **Set/7** **$12.99**

Holiday Cupcake and Cookie Stencils

Turn plain treats into holiday visions. Just place one of the fun designs over your baked treat, then sprinkle with Wilton Cake Sparkles™ or Colored Sugars or use FoodWriter™ Edible Color Markers or Color Mist™ Food Color Spray (p. 170). Five designs.
417-P-1246 **$2.49**

STENCIL-A-COOKIE™ CUTTER & STENCIL SETS

Using the fun-shaped stencils and cutter, it's easy to serve cookies with exciting colorful designs for the season. Just cut cookies, then use the stencils and Wilton FoodWriter™, Cake Sparkles™, Colored Sugars or Color Mist™ Food Color Spray (not included) to create dazzling shapes on top after baking. Cookies look great iced with Wilton Ice-A-Cookie™ sold above. Set includes one metal cutter and two stencils (same design). **Set/3** **$1.99**

NEW!

Gifts Galore
2308-P-1414

Tree
2308-P-1408

Snowman
2308-P-1409

Gingerbread Boy
2308-P-1410

Cookie Cutters

COPPER CUTTERS

The warmth and beauty of copper make these cutters ideal for adding that decorative touch to your kitchen. These heirloom-quality copper cutters have smoothly rolled edges for that finishing touch.

Holiday Cutters

Each approximately 5½ in. diameter.
$6.99

Snowflake
2308-P-3079

Snowman
2308-P-3081

Gingerbread Boy
2308-P-3001

Christmas Tree
2308-P-3000

Star
2308-P-3002

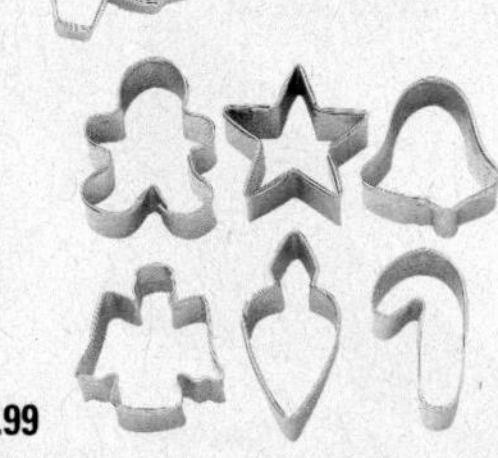

Holiday Mini Set

Gingerbread boy, star, bell, angel, Christmas light and candy cane. Each is approx. 1¾ in.
2308-P-3708 Set/6 $7.99

COMFORT GRIP™ CUTTERS

These easy-grip cutters with extra-deep sides are perfect for cutting so many favorite foods into spectacular shapes. The cushion grip gives you comfortable control even when cutting thick desserts. Recipe included. Stainless steel sides, 4½ x 4½ x 1½ in. deep.
$2.99

Christmas Tree
2310-P-604

Snowman
2310-634

Star
2310-P-605

Gingerbread Boy
2310-P-602

GRIPPY™ CUTTERS

4 Pc. Grippy™ Bag Set

NEW!

Safe, easy cutting, with a comfortable grip and deep plastic sides. Mesh bag for convenient storing and giving. Four shapes include stocking, tree, star and gingerbread boy, each approx. 3½ in.
2311-P-256
Set/4 $3.99

METAL CUTTERS & SCOOP

Put variety in your cookie-making with fun Christmas multi-shape sets. There are styles to please everyone. Recipe included.

Colorful Cutter Sets

Our metal cutters look great with their bright colors and fun shapes. Perfect for hanging on the tree until your next cookie-baking bash.

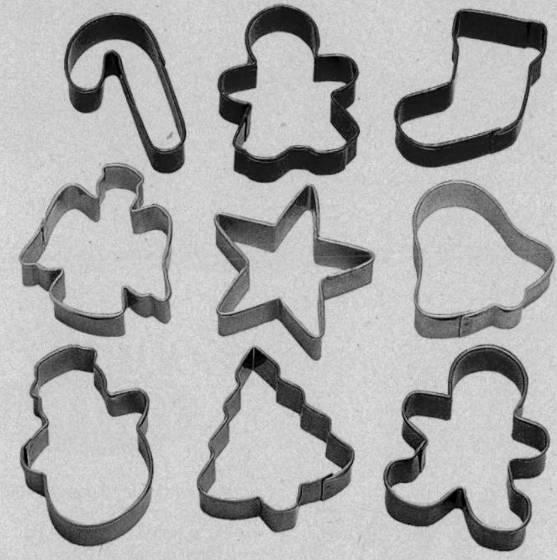

Holiday Cutter Set
Candy cane, gingerbread girl, stocking, angel, star, bell, snowman, tree and gingerbread boy, each approx. 3 to 3¾ in. Colored aluminum.
2308-P-2500 Set/9 $9.99

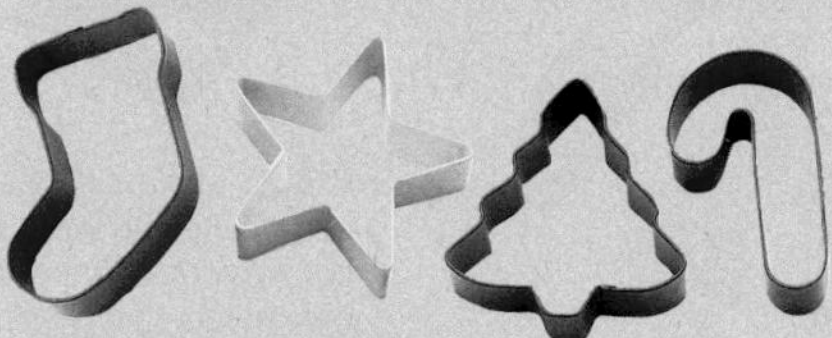

Jolly Shapes Cutter Set
Stocking, star, tree and candy cane, each approx. 3 in. Coated metal.
2308-P-1201 Set/4 $4.49

Nesting Cutter Sets

Bake your favorite holiday shapes in four fun sizes! Quality metal cuts neatly and is easy to handle. Sizes from 5 to 2½ in.
Set/4 $4.49

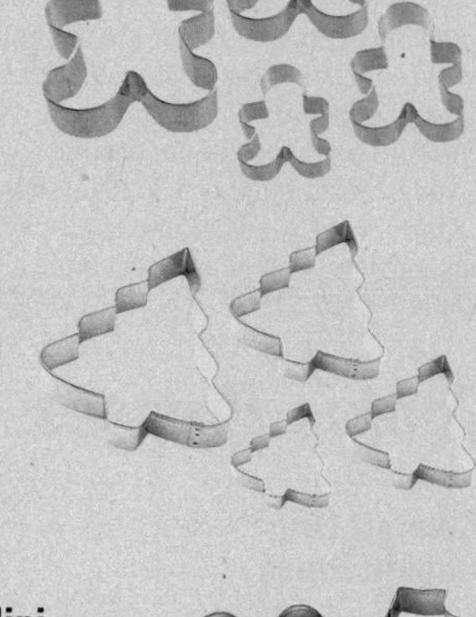

Snowflakes
2308-P-1244

Gingerbread Boys
2308-P-1239

Trees
2308-P-1212

Holiday Mini Cutter Set

Bell, gingerbread boy, holly leaf, tree, candy cane and angel, each approx. 1½ in.
2308-P-1214 Set/6 $2.99

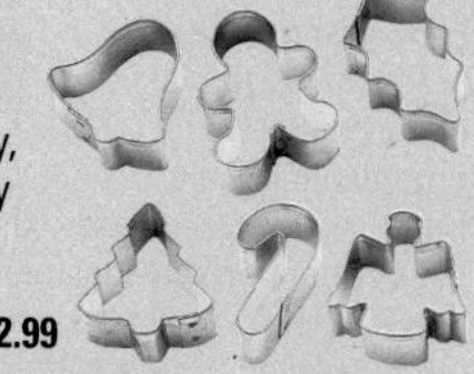

Holiday Red Cookie Scoop

NEW!

Festive color and convenient design come together to make holiday baking more fun! Scoops and releases approx. 1 Tbsp. of dough with ease. Dishwasher safe plastic.
417-P-320
$2.49

PLASTIC CUTTERS

Child-safe design means kids can have a great time helping. And remember all the fun ways to use our cutters—for bread shapes, stencils, sun catchers and so much more. Recipe included.

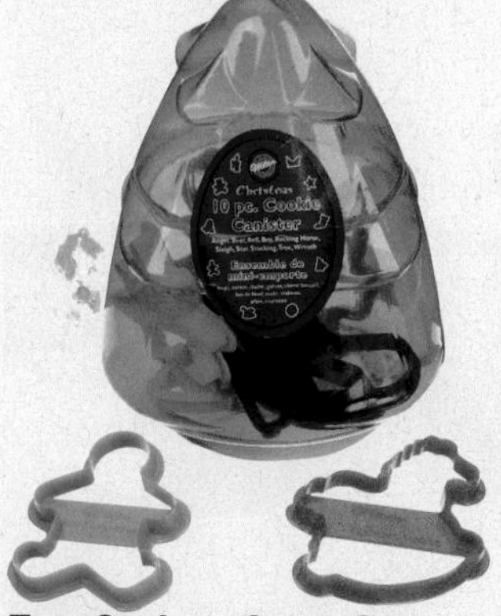

Tree Canister Cutter Set

A jolly holiday tree holds 10 merry perimeter shapes. Includes angel, bear, bell, boy, rocking horse, sleigh, star, stocking, tree and wreath shapes. Canister is 7½ x 5½ in.; cutters are 2¼ to 3½ in.
2304-P-97 Set/11 $5.99

Christmas Collection Cutter Set

Merry shapes that make holiday baking a breeze! Set includes tree, snowman, Santa, drum, stocking, nutcracker, star, bear, candy cane and rocking horse. Each approx. 3 x 4 in.
2304-P-802 Set/10 $3.99

Individual Cookie Cutters

Great shapes for end-of-year celebrations! 3 x 4 in. high. **$0.69**

5-Pt. Star
2303-P-135

Christmas Tree
2303-P-132

Gingerbread Kits

Pre-Baked Ultimate Gingerbread House Kit

NEW!

Get ready for the ultimate gingerbread experience! This house is so huge, with tons of icing and colorful candy, that everyone can have a great time building and decorating to celebrate the holiday season. Everything you need is inside—pre-baked house pieces, two pre-baked trees, 3 packages of decorating icing mix, 2 decorating bags and 2 nickel-plated tips, boy and girl icing decorations, loads of candy for decorating and complete instructions for assembling and decorating. House measures 10¾ x 9 x 11¾ in. high.

2104-P-1598 $39.99

Pre-Baked Gingerbread House Kit

No baking—get right to the fun of assembling and decorating your festive gingerbread house.

Kit includes pre-baked gingerbread house sections, decorating icing mix, assorted candies for decorating, decorating bag and tip, cardboard base and complete instructions with great decorating ideas. House measures 5¼ x 5½ x 4¾ in. high.

2104-P-1537 $9.99

Cookie Presses

Comfort Grip™ Cookie Press

COMFORT GRIP™
Cookie Press

Experience a classic press that is truly comfortable. Its ergonomic handle feels great in your hand—the easy-squeeze action releases perfectly shaped dough. Clear barrel takes the guesswork out of refilling. Fluted bottom raises press off the cookie sheet for better shapes.

Includes 12 plastic disks in a variety of shapes and our classic spritz recipe.

2104-P-4011 Set/13 $12.99

Twelve Disk Designs

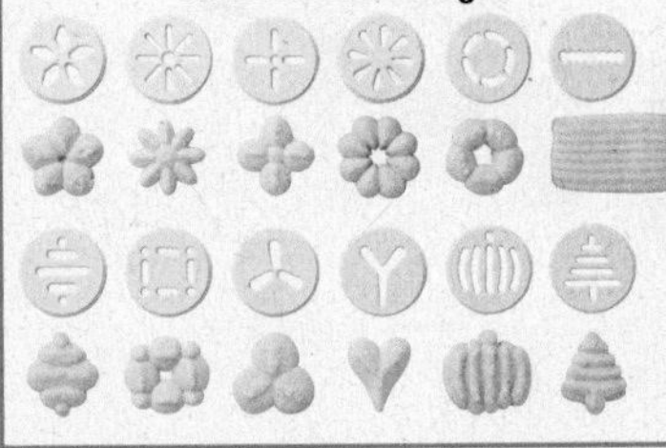

Cookie Pro™ ULTRA

IMPROVED!

Easy to use, easy to store—everything you want in a cookie press. Pump-action design lets you press dozens of cookies comfortably. Handle folds over for compact storage. Includes 10 aluminum disks and an attachable storage case. Recipes included.

2104-P-4010 Set/12 $24.99

No More Missing Disks! Storage case attaches to cookie press when not in use.

Space Saving Design Unique flip-over handle for easy and compact storage.

Ten Disk Designs

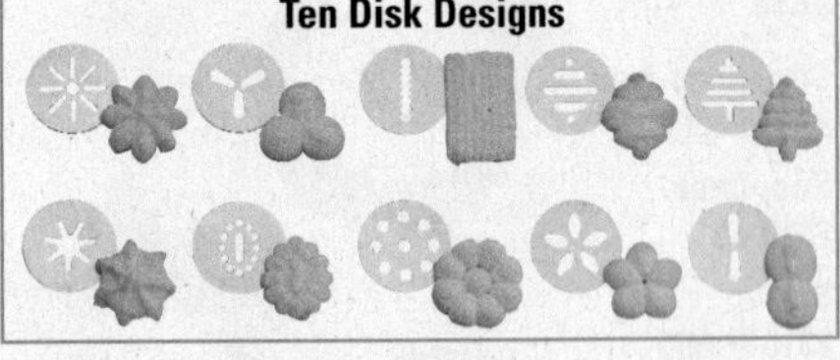

COOKIE MASTER™ Plus

Cordless Cookie Press

Our cordless cookie press is so powerful and easy to operate, you'll use it all year to create cookies, appetizers, desserts and more. Exclusive patented reverse action means there's no need to take press apart for refilling. Ergonomic design is shaped to fit in your hand for excellent comfort.

Includes 12 aluminum disks in classic and seasonal shapes, 4 accent tips for decorating and filling and 2 bonus recipe booklets—sweet and savory. Uses 4 AA batteries, not included.

2104-P-4008 Set/19 $39.99

Twelve Disk Designs

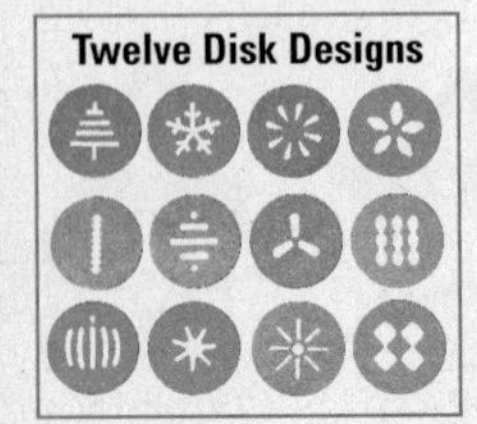

Four Accent Tips

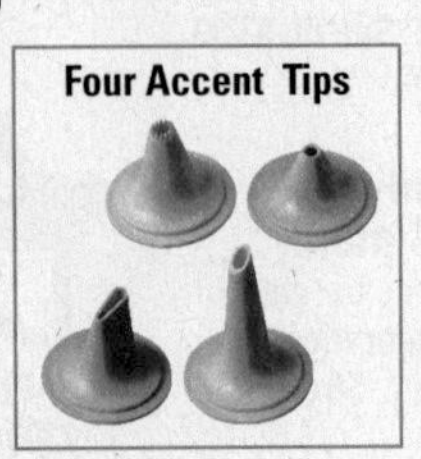

cookie max cookie press

MAXimum Control
Pump action dispenses a perfect cookie every time. 1 click of the plunger equals 1 cookie.

MAXimum Comfort
Soft cushioned pump handle reduces hand fatigue.

MAXimum Efficiency
Recessed plunger disk eliminates backflow—dough won't clog!

MAXimum Fun!
Makes 12 favorite shapes—easy instructions and 3 delicious recipes included.

2104-P-4003 Set/13 $17.99

Twelve Disk Designs

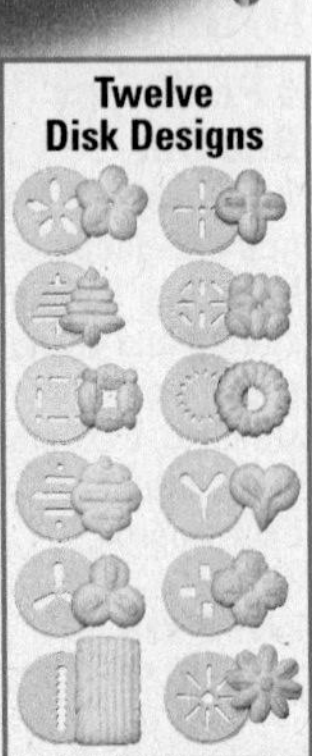

Gingerbread Kits

Pre-Baked and Pre-Assembled Gingerbread House Kit

The easiest-to-use gingerbread kit we've ever made! Pre-baked and pre-assembled so the family can get right to the fun of decorating. Kit includes assembled house with cardboard base, decorating icing, candies, decorating bag and tip and complete instructions with great decorating ideas. House measures 5½ x 5½ x 4½ in. high.
2104-P-1516 $12.99

Pre-Baked Gingerbread House Kit

No baking necessary! Real gingerbread pieces are ready to assemble and decorate (without the mess of baking). Kit includes pre-baked gingerbread pieces, decorating icing, assorted candies, decorating bag and tip, cardboard base and complete instructions with great decorating ideas. House measures 8 x 7 x 6½ in. high.
2104-P-1509 $12.99

Christmas Cookie Tree Kit

Create a beautiful Yule tree as a perfect holiday centerpiece—it's easy and fun! Just bake, stack and decorate. Kit includes 10 star cookie cutters in graduated sizes from small to large, 3 disposable decorating bags, round decorating tip, cookie and icing recipes, baking and decorating instructions for four great designs. Tree measures approx. 8 x 11 in. high.
2104-P-1555 $7.99

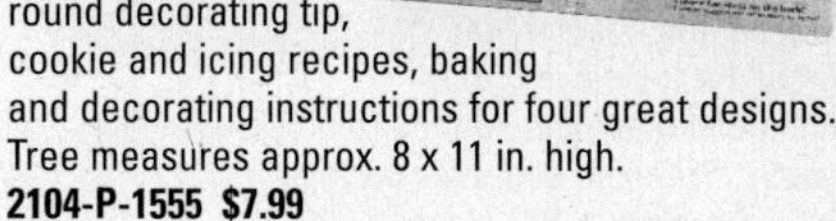

HANUKKAH

Cookie

Hanukkah Cutter Set NEW!

Includes Torah, menorah, star, and dreidel, each approx. 3 in. Colored metal.
2308-P-1262
Set/4 $4.49

6-Point Star Cookie Cutter

3 x 4 in. high.
2303-P-122 $0.69

Sprinkles

Plastic bottles for pouring and storing. 3.25 oz. Certified Kosher.
$1.99

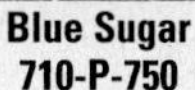

Blue Sugar	Yellow Sugar
710-P-750	710-P-754

Cake Sparkles™

Edible glitter, .25 oz. bottle. Certified Kosher.
$2.89

Blue	Yellow	White
703-P-1314	703-P-1272	703-P-1290

Ice-A-Cookie™

Transform cookies with fun colors and dazzling designs. The soft, squeezable pouch is easy to handle; the patented snip tip and screw-on decorating cap help you control the flow. Use the snip tip for icing cookies and the cap for decorating lines and designs. Delicious artificially vanilla-flavored icing dries to a smooth, satin finish. Draw fun shapes, messages, decorate with Cake Sparkles™ (not included) and more! Each pouch decorates approximately twenty-four 3 in. round cookies. 10.59 oz. pouch. Certified Kosher. **$3.99**
White 710-P-416

Candy

Hanukkah Candy Kit NEW!

Everything you need to make easy, fun Hanukkah treats! Includes 10 oz. Light Cocoa Candy Melts®*, Hanukkah candy mold (6 designs, 13 cavities), 25 gold foil squares (4 x 4 in.), 2 disposable decorating bags and 5 mesh coin bags. Complete instructions. Certified Kosher.
2104-P-1328 $6.99

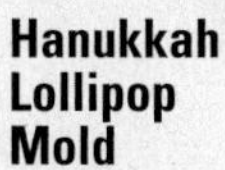

Hanukkah Lollipop Mold

5 designs, 10 cavities.
2115-P-1405
$1.99

Candy Melts®*

Ideal for all your candy making—molding, dipping or coating. Artificially vanilla flavored unless otherwise indicated. 14 oz. bag. Certified Kosher.
$2.50

Light Cocoa	1911-P-544	Yellow	1911-P-463
Dark Cocoa	1911-P-358	Blue	1911-P-448
Chocolate Mint	1911-P-1920	White	1911-P-498

*Brand confectionery coating.

See pages 144-149 for more Wilton candy items.

Colors & Icings

HANUKKAH COLOR GUIDE

Blue | Yellow | White

Color Mist™ Food Color Spray

The dazzling effects of an airbrush in a convenient can! Use it to transform a plain iced cake with sensational color, add splashes of holiday color to iced cookies and cupcakes. No mess, taste-free formula. 1.5 oz. Certified Kosher. **$2.99**
Blue 710-P-5501
Yellow 710-P-5502

Ready-to-Decorate Icing

Anyone can decorate with Wilton Ready-to-Decorate Icing! Our brilliant colors and four decorating tips make it a breeze to add an exciting finishing touch to treats—without mixing or mess. 6.4 oz. Certified Kosher. **$3.49**
Blue 710-P-4407
Yellow 710-P-4409
White 710-P-4402

Tube Decorating Icing

Tubes can be used with our Tip and Nail Set or Coupler Ring Set (p. 127) and any standard size Wilton metal tip. Colors match Wilton Icing Colors (p. 127). 4.25 oz. Certified Kosher. **$1.79**
Blue 704-P-248
Yellow 704-P-236
White 704-P-200

Tube Decorating Gel

Transparent gels are great for writing messages and decorating cakes and cookies. Colors match Wilton Icing Colors (p. 127). .75 oz. Certified Kosher. **$1.29**
Blue 704-P-348
Yellow 704-P-336
White 704-P-302

VALENTINE

Bakeware

DIMENSIONS® DECORATIVE BAKEWARE

With Dimensions, our non-stick cast aluminum bakeware, anyone can create Valentine desserts with elegant shapes and spectacular detail. Heavyweight cast aluminum conducts heat extremely evenly. Premium non-stick surface for easy release and cleanup. Aluminum.

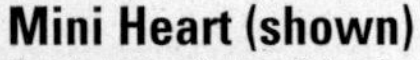

Mini Heart (shown)
Each heart is 4 x 2 in. deep. Six 1 cup cavities.
2105-P-5012 $24.99

Also available, shown on p. 156.

Queen Of Hearts
9 in. x $3\frac{1}{4}$ in. deep. 10 cup capacity.
2105-P-5001 $24.99

Crown Of Hearts
11 x $2\frac{1}{2}$ in. deep. 10 cup capacity.
2105-P-5011 $24.99

9 in. Non-Stick Heart Pan
Your classic heart cake will release perfectly from this non-stick pan. Cleanup is easy too. 9 x $2\frac{1}{4}$ in. deep. Non-stick steel.
2105-P-410 $9.99

Heart Springform Pans
Create elegant Valentine cheesecakes with these easy-releasing non-stick pans. Springlock sides, removable bottom for easy serving. Non-stick steel.

4 in. Mini
4 x $1\frac{3}{4}$ in. deep.
2105-P-457
$6.99

9 in.
9 x $2\frac{3}{4}$ in. deep.
2105-P-419
$14.99

Heart Tart Pan
Create luscious desserts and entrees with classic fluted edges. Non-stick; removable bottom. 10 x 1 in. deep. Non-stick steel.
2105-P-452 $8.99

Heart Pans
For graceful expressions of love on Valentine's Day or anytime, in just the size you need.
2 in. deep. Aluminum.

12 in.
2105-P-607
$9.99

9 in.
2105-P-5176
$7.49

6 in.
2105-P-600
$4.99

SweetHeart Pan
Its gently curving shape gives the classic heart a more romantic flair. Whether you accent it with pretty icing flowers or pair it with bold fondant decorations, this cake will charm guests for birthdays, Mother's Day, Valentine's Day, showers and more. One-mix pan is $10\frac{1}{4}$ x 11 x 2 in. deep. Aluminum.
2105-P-1197 $9.99

NEW! ON OUR COVER!

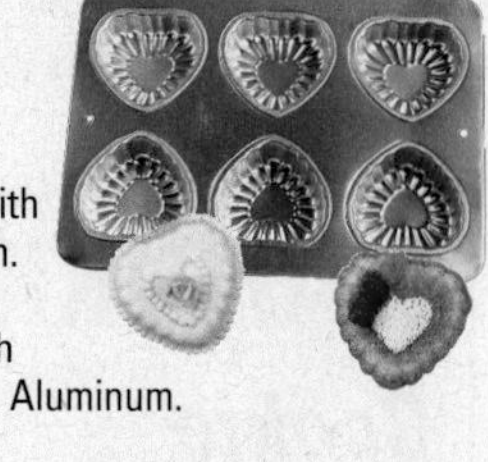

Mini Embossed Heart Pan
Beautiful scalloped shapes with raised centers to decorate with fruit or whipped cream. One mix makes 12-18 hearts. 6 cavities, each $3\frac{1}{2}$ x $3\frac{3}{8}$ x $1\frac{1}{4}$ in. deep. Aluminum.
2105-P-3210 $10.99

Mini Heart Pan
Great size for petit fours, individual brownies and more. One mix makes 12-18 hearts. 6 cavities, each $3\frac{5}{8}$ x $3\frac{1}{2}$ x 1 in. deep. Aluminum.
2105-P-11044 $9.99

Petite Heart Pan
Bite-size muffins, brownies and cookies will win hearts. One mix makes 10-15 dozen hearts. 12 cavities, each $1\frac{3}{4}$ x $1\frac{5}{8}$ x $\frac{1}{2}$ in. deep. Aluminum.
2105-P-2432 $8.99

Colors & Icings

VALENTINE COLOR GUIDE

Red	Pink	Violet	White

Valentine Icing Colors Set
Red-Red and Pink in .5 oz. jars. Certified Kosher.
601-P-5570 Set/2 $2.99

FoodWriter™ Edible Color Markers
Use like ink markers to add fun, dazzling color to countless foods. Kids love 'em! Decorate on fondant, Ice-A-Cookie™ icing, Color Flow, royal icing designs and cookies. Includes Pink and Red markers .35 oz. Certified Kosher.
609-P-103 Set/2 $3.99

Tube Decorating Icing
Tubes can be used with our Tip and Nail Set or Coupler Ring Set (p. 127) and any standard size Wilton metal tip. Colors match Wilton Icing Colors (p. 127). 4.25 oz. Certified Kosher.
$1.79

Red	**704-P-218**
Pink	**704-P-230**
Violet	**704-P-242**
White	**704-P-200**

Color Mist™ Food Color Spray
Gives decorators the versatility and dazzling effects of an airbrush in a convenient can! Use it to transform a plain iced cake with sensational color, add splashes of holiday color to iced cookies and cupcakes. No mess, taste-free formula. 1.5 oz. Certified Kosher. **$2.99**

Red	**710-P-5500**
Pink	**710-P-5505**
Violet	**710-P-5504**

Ready-to-Decorate Icing
Anyone can decorate with Wilton Ready-to-Decorate Icing! Our brilliant colors and four decorator tips make it a breeze to add an exciting finishing touch to treats—without mixing or mess. 6.4 oz. Certified Kosher. **$3.49**

Red	**710-P-4400**
Pink	**710-P-4406**
Violet	**710-P-4408**
White	**710-P-4402**

Tube Decorating Gel
Transparent gels are great for writing messages and decorating cakes and cookies. Colors match Wilton Icing Colors (p. 127). .75 oz. Certified Kosher.
$1.29

Red	**704-P-318**
Pink	**704-P-330**
Violet	**704-P-342**
White	**704-P-302**

Party

Baking Cups

Microwave-safe paper. Standard size, 2 in. diameter, Pk./50; Mini size, 1¼ in. diameter, Pk./75.
$1.49

NEW!

Hearts Remembered
Standard 415-P-274

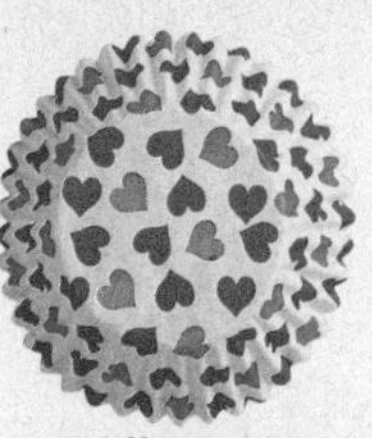

Hearts
Standard 415-P-210
Mini 415-P-310

Bon Bon Cups

Wax-laminated paper on red foil. 1¼ in. diameter
415-P-314 Pk./75 $1.49

Party Bags

Colorful Valentine designs for candy and cookie treats. 20 plastic bags, 20 ties included. 4 x 9½ in.
Pk./20 $1.99

NEW!

Hearts Remembered
1912-P-1292

Hearts
1912-P-1269

Red
1912-P-2357

Icing Decorations

Perfect for topping cupcakes, cookies and ice cream. Mint-flavored. Certified Kosher. **$2.09**

NEW!

Hearts Remembered
710-P-824 Pk./18

Petite
710-P-840 Pk./12

Candy

Heart Lollipop Mold

2 designs, 8 cavities.
2115-P-1709 $1.99

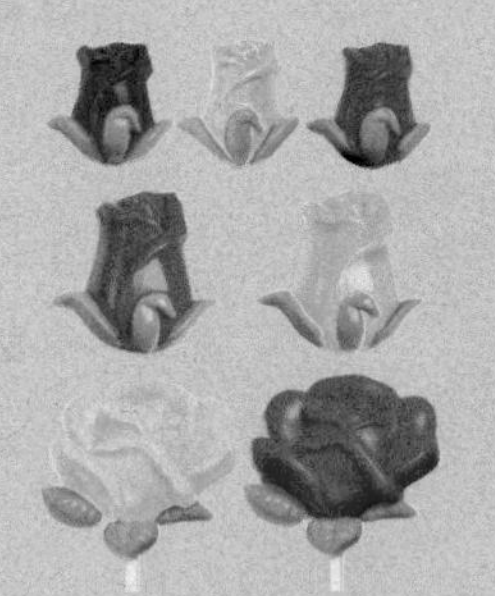

Roses and Buds Lollipop Mold

3 designs, 9 cavities.
2115-P-1708 $1.99

Hearts Candy Mold

1 design, 15 cavities.
2115-P-1712 $1.99

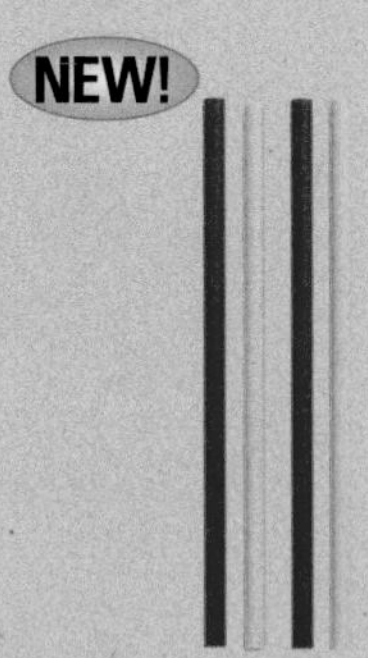

NEW!

Valentine Lollipop Sticks

4 in. plastic sticks; 10 red, 10 pink.
1912-P-9312 Pk./20 $1.99

Valentine Lollipop Kit

Everything you need to make easy, fun Valentine treats! Includes 1 Valentine lollipop mold (3 designs, 6 cavities), 10 oz. Candy Melts®* (5 oz. Red, 2.5 oz. each Pink and White), 10 lollipop bags with ties, 10 lollipop sticks (6 in.), 3 disposable decorating bags, decorator brush and complete instructions.
2104-P-1070 $6.99

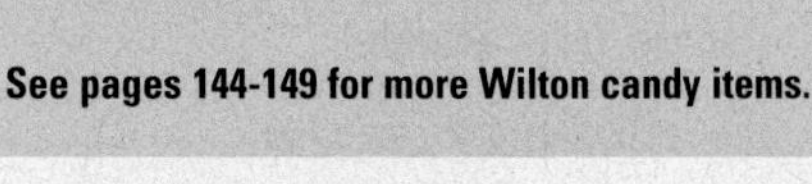

See pages 144-149 for more Wilton candy items.

CANDY MELTS®*

Ideal for all your candy making—molding, dipping or coating. Artificially vanilla flavored unless otherwise indicated. Certified Kosher.
14 oz. bag. **$2.50**

Red	**1911-P-499**
Pink	**1911-P-447**
White	**1911-P-498**
Light Cocoa	**1911-P-544**
Dark Cocoa	**1911-P-358**

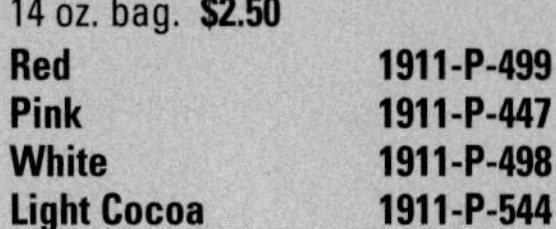

*Brand confectionery coating.

ICE-A-COOKIE™

Instant fun for all your Valentine cookies! Transform cookies with fun colors and dazzling designs. The soft, squeezable pouch is easy to handle; the patented snip tip and screw-on decorating cap help you control the flow. Use the snip tip for icing cookies and the cap for decorating lines and designs. Delicious artificially vanilla-flavored icing dries to a smooth, satin finish. Draw fun shapes, messages, decorate with Cake Sparkles™ (not included) and more! Each pouch decorates approximately twenty-four 3 in. round cookies. 10.59 oz. pouch. Certified Kosher. **$3.99**

Red **710-P-422**
Pink **710-P-417**
White **710-P-416**

Sprinkles

INDIVIDUAL BOTTLES

Shake up your Valentine treats with fun colors and designs. Plastic bottles for convenient pouring and storing. Certified Kosher. **$1.99**

Valentine Sprinkle Sparks
2.5 oz. bottle
710-P-825

Hearts Mix
2.5 oz. bottle
710-P-854

Kisses Mix
2.5 oz. bottle
710-P-855

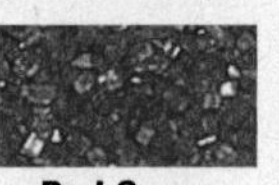

Red Sugar
3.25 oz. bottle
710-P-766

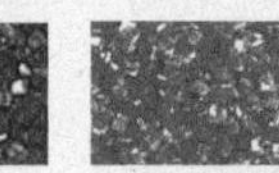

Pink Sugar
3.25 oz. bottle
710-P-756

Lavender Sugar
3.25 oz. bottle
710-P-758

Sparkling Sugars

Easy-pour sugars have a coarse texture and brilliant sparkle. 8.25 oz. Certified Kosher. **$3.99**

NEW!

Red/ White
710-P-367

Pink/ White
710-P-366

Cake Sparkles™

Edible glitter, .25 oz. bottle. Certified Kosher. **$2.89**

Red
703-P-1284

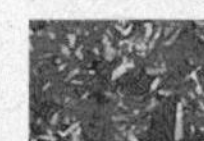

Pink
703-P-1260

Purple
703-P-1266

ASSORTMENTS

4-Mix

Contains .75 oz. Heart Mix, 1 oz. Sweetheart Nonpareils, 1 oz. each Pink and Red Sugars. Certified Kosher.
710-P-730 $4.99

6-Mix Assortment

Contains 1 oz. Kiss Mix, 1 oz. Heart Mix, 1.3 oz. Sweetheart Nonpareils, 1.3 oz. each Pink, Red and Lavender Sugars. Certified Kosher.
710-P-738 $5.99

Cookie Sets

HEART STENCIL-A-COOKIE™ CUTTER & STENCIL SET

Using the fun-shaped stencils and cutter, it's easy to serve cookies with exciting colorful designs for the season. Just cut cookies, then use the stencils and Wilton FoodWriter™, Cake Sparkles™, Colored Sugars or Color Mist™ Food Color Spray (not included) to create dazzling shapes on top after baking. Cookies look great iced with Wilton Ice-A-Cookie™ sold above. Set includes one metal cutter and two stencils (same design).
2308-P-1401 Set/3 $1.99

Sweetheart Cupcake and Cookie Stencils

Turn plain treats into visions of love. Just place one of the fun designs over your baked treat, then sprinkle with Wilton Cake Sparkles™ or Colored Sugars or spray with Color Mist™ Food Color Spray (p. 176). Five designs.
417-P-1208
$2.49

Cookie Pans

Heart Giant Cookie Pan

Create a giant-sized pan cookie or brownie in a heart shape that will be a big hit. Ideal for refrigerated dough and brownie mix. Recipe included. Pan is 11½ x 10½ x ½ in. deep. Aluminum.
2105-P-6203 $5.99

Heart Cookie Treat Pan

Just press cookie dough into pan, insert a cookie stick, then bake, cool and decorate. Create your own cookie blossoms for that special someone; also great for adding fun shapes to other goodies like rice cereal treats and candy pops. Each pan makes 6 individual treats, 3½ in. x ¼ in. deep. Aluminum.
2105-P-8104 $7.99

Cookie Treat Sticks

6 in. 1912-P-9319 Pk./20 $1.99
8 in. 1912-P-9318 Pk./20 $2.99

Cookie Cutters

COPPER CUTTERS

The warmth and beauty of copper make these cutters ideal for displaying and adding that decorative touch to your kitchen. These beautiful, heirloom-quality copper cutters have smooth rolled edges for that finishing touch. Recipe included.

Heart and Hand Cutter Set
A lovely way to display your devotion. Hand is 4¾ x 3¾ in., heart is 1⅝ x 1¾ in. Solid copper.
2308-P-3075
Set/2 $6.99

Heart Cutter
Beautiful solid copper cutter with deep sides. Great decorative piece, too. 5½ in. wide.
2308-P-3040 $6.99

METAL CUTTERS

Put variety in your cookie-making with fun Valentine multi-shape sets. There are styles to please everyone.

NEW!

Color Anodized Cutter Collection
Vivid Valentine colors bring a touch of romance to cookie-baking. Great variety of heart, hugs and kisses designs. Sizes range from 1 to 5 in. Colored Aluminum.
2308-P-2502 Set/9 $9.99

From The Heart Nesting Cutter Set
Nesting metal cutters give you a choice of sizes, with two crinkled shapes. Largest cutter is approximately 5 in.
2308-P-1203 Set/4 $4.49

Hearts Cutter Set
Love comes in all shapes and sizes. Includes seven different heart cutter designs from stylized to traditional. Sizes range from 1½ to 3 in.
2308-P-1237 Set/7 $4.99

Heart Cutter
Quality metal cuts neatly and is easy to handle. 3 in. wide.
2308-P-1003 $0.69

COMFORT GRIP™ CUTTER

This easy-grip stainless steel heart with extra-deep sides is perfect for cutting many favorite foods into heart shapes. The cushion grip gives you comfortable control even when cutting into thick desserts. Recipe included.
4½ x 4½ x 1½ in. deep.
2310-P-616 $2.99

PLASTIC CUTTERS

Nesting Hearts Cutter Set
Great for cookies, imprinting patterns in icing, cutting bread shapes and more. Sizes from 1¼ to 4⅛ in.
2304-P-115
Set/6 $2.99

Heart Cutter
3 x 4 in.
2303-P-100 $0.69

ST. PATRICK'S DAY

Shamrock Pan
Make it a lucky day for everyone! Celebrate St. Patrick's Day with this fun symbol of joy and celebration. Also great for school parties, birthdays, sports celebrations and much more. One-mix pan is 11¾ x 2 in. deep. Aluminum.
2105-P-185 $7.99

Shamrock Baking Cups
Microwave-safe paper. Standard size 2 in. diameter.
415-P-357
Pk./50 $1.49

Shamrock Party Bags
20 plastic bags, 20 twist ties included.
4 x 9½ in.
1912-P-2233
Pk./20 $1.99

Shamrock Icing Decorations
Sugar-flavored edible shamrocks.
Certified Kosher.
710-P-286
Pk./9 $2.09

Shamrock Metal Cookie Cutter
Quality metal cuts neatly and is easy to handle. Approx. 3 in.
2308-P-1011 $0.69

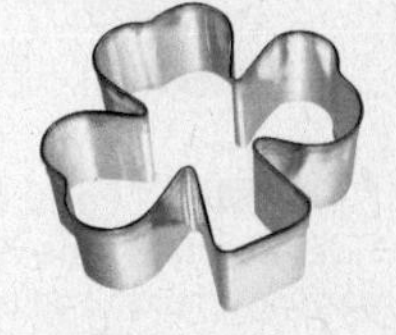

4-Leaf Clover Cutter
Cut cookies, sandwiches, use as party favors and in crafts. 3 in. wide.
2303-P-134 $0.69

EASTER

Bakeware

Cuddly Lamb Pan

NEW!

You'll find a flock of useful ideas for this fleecy friend. His sweet smile is the perfect welcome for baby showers, Easter brunches, birthday parties. See the label for four great ideas. One-mix pan is 11¾ x 8¾ x 2 in. deep. Aluminum.
2105-P-4947 $9.99

Stand-Up Lamb Pan

A gentle symbol of springtime. This 3-D lamb will charm everyone at your Easter table. Instructions included. Two-piece pan is 10 x 4½ x 7 in. high and takes 6 cups of pound cake batter. Aluminum.
2105-P-2010
Set/2 $10.99

Decorated Egg Pan

Great for molded desserts as well as cakes. Decorating instructions for five different designs included. One-mix pan is 9 x 11 x 3½ in. deep. Aluminum.
2105-P-174 $7.99

Step-By-Step Bunny Pan

NEW!

Just what you need to get springtime celebrations hopping—just bake, ice and decorate! He's also perfect for molded gelatin, ice cream, salads and more. One-mix pan is 9¾ x 14 x 2 in. deep. Aluminum.
2105-P-2074 $5.99

Cottontail Bunny Pan

He's handsomely dressed for your holiday table with a bright Easter bow. One-mix pan is 14 x 12 x 2 in. deep. Aluminum.
2105-P-175
$7.99

3-D Egg Pan

Hatch a great Easter centerpiece! Two-piece pan takes just one cake mix. Includes 2 ring bases for level baking of each half. Each half is 9 x 6 x 2¾ in. deep. Aluminum.
2105-P-4793
Set/4 $10.99

Mini Egg Pan

Make colorful place markers for the holiday table. One mix makes about 24-36 eggs. 8 cavities, each 3¼ x 2½ x 1 in. deep. Aluminum.
2105-P-2118 $9.99

3-D Bunny Pan

NEW!

Sure to get everyone's attention at your holiday brunch and beyond. Instructions for 5 different decorating ideas included. Two-piece pan is 7¼ x 7 x 4¾ in. deep. Pan takes 4½ cups of pound cake batter. No heating core needed. Aluminum.
2105-P-2042
Set/2 $10.99

Cross Pan

Truly inspiring for holidays, Christenings and other religious occasions. Bevel design is excellent for rolled fondant. Instructions included. One-mix pan is 14½ x 11⅛ x 2 in. deep. Aluminum.
2105-P-2509 $7.99

Mini Bunny Pan

Bake 6 treats quick as a bunny! One mix makes about 12-16 bunnies. 6 cavities, each 4⅜ x 3⅛ x ½ in. deep. Aluminum.
2105-P-4426 $9.99

Colors & Icings

EASTER COLOR GUIDE

Pink	Violet	Yellow	Green/ Leaf Green	White

Easter Icing Colors Set

Lemon Yellow and Violet in .5 oz. jars. Certified Kosher.
601-P-5571 Set/2 $2.99

FoodWriter™ Edible Color Markers

Use like ink markers to add fun and dazzling color to countless foods. Kids love 'em! Decorate on fondant, Ice-A-Cookie™ icing, Color Flow, royal icing designs and cookies. Includes Pink and Lavender markers. .35 oz. Certified Kosher.
609-P-104 Set/2 $3.99

Tube Decorating Icing

Tubes can be used with our Tip and Nail Set or Coupler Ring Set (p. 127) and any standard size Wilton metal tip. Colors match Wilton Icing Colors (p. 127). 4.25 oz. Certified Kosher.
$1.79

Pink	**704-P-230**
Violet	**704-P-242**
Yellow	**704-P-236**
Leaf Green	**704-P-224**
White	**704-P-200**

Color Mist™ Food Color Spray

Gives decorators the versatility and dazzling effects of an airbrush in a convenient can! Use it to transform a plain iced cake with sensational color, add splashes of holiday color to iced cookies and cupcakes. No mess, taste-free formula. 1.5 oz. Certified Kosher. **$2.99**

Pink	**710-P-5505**
Violet	**710-P-5504**
Yellow	**710-P-5502**
Green	**710-P-5503**

Ready-to-Decorate Icing

Anyone can decorate with Wilton Ready-to-Decorate Icing! Our brilliant colors and four decorating tips make it a breeze to add an exciting finishing touch to treats—without mixing or mess. 6.4 oz. Certified Kosher. **$3.49**

Pink	**710-P-4406**
Violet	**710-P-4408**
Yellow	**710-P-4409**
Green	**710-P-4401**
White	**710-P-4402**

Tube Decorating Gel

Great for writing messages and decorating cakes and cookies. Colors match Wilton Icing Colors (p. 127). .75 oz. Certified Kosher.
$1.29

Pink	**704-P-330**
Violet	**704-P-342**
Yellow	**704-P-336**
Green	**704-P-324**
White	**704-P-302**

Party

Baking Cups
Microwave-safe paper.
Standard size, 2 in. diameter.
Pk./50 $1.49

NEW!

Easter Patchwork
415-P-267

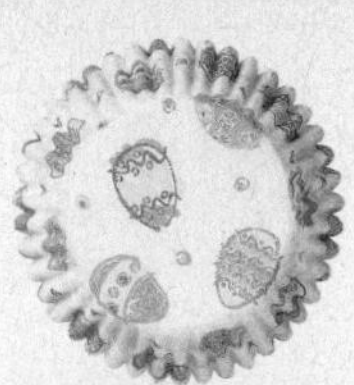

Decorated Eggs
415-P-354

Assorted Pastel
25 pink, 25 yellow, 25 blue.
415-P-394 Pk./75 $1.49

Party Bags
Colorful Easter designs for candy and cookie treats. 20 plastic bags, 20 ties included.
4 x 9½ in.
Pk./20 $1.99

NEW!

Easter Patchwork
1912-P-2383

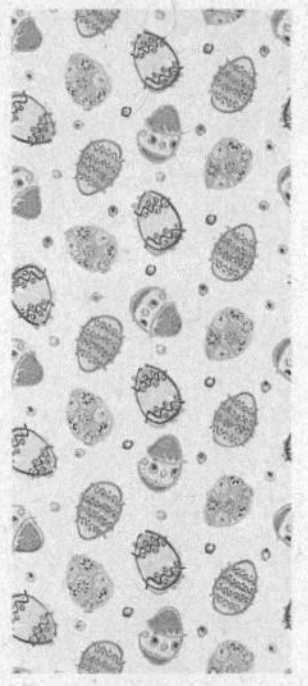

Decorated Eggs
1912-P-1258

Easter Pink
1912-P-2377

Icing Decorations
Wilton Icing Decorations are perfect for topping cupcakes, cookies and ice cream. Mint-flavored. Certified Kosher.
$2.09

NEW!

Springtime
710-P-885 Pk./12

Petite Eggs
710-P-528 Pk./12

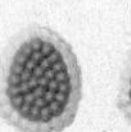

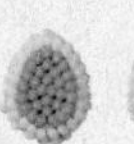

Mini Eggs
710-P-462 Pk./18

Candy

NEW!

Easter Treats Lollipop Mold
6 designs, 12 cavities.
2115-P-1408 $1.99

Lil' Bunnies Mini Candy Mold
4 designs, 12 cavities.
2115-P-1544 $1.99

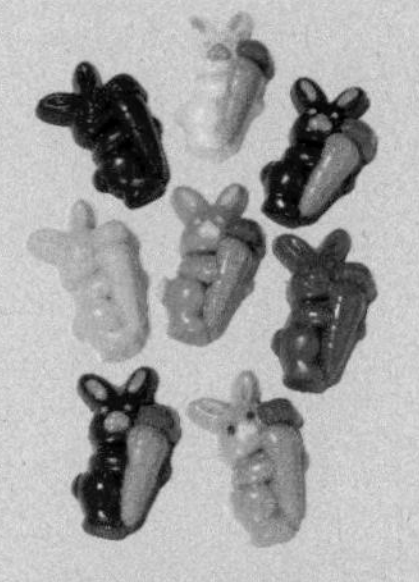

Bunnies 'n Carrots Candy Mold
1 design, 8 cavities.
2115-P-1556 $1.99

Hoppy Easter Lollipop Mold
8 designs, 9 cavities.
2115-P-1718 $1.99

NEW!

Easter Lollipop Sticks
4 in. plastic sticks; 10 yellow, 10 pink.
1912-P-9314 Pk./20 $1.99

NEW!

Easter Lollipop Kit
Everything you need to make easy Easter basket treats in fun egg, bunny and chick shapes! Includes 1 Easter lollipop mold (3 designs, 6 cavities), 10 oz. Candy Melts®* (5 oz. Pink, 2.5 oz. each Yellow and White), 10 lollipop bags with ties, 10 lollipop sticks (6 in.), 3 disposable decorating bags and decorator brush.
2104-P-1071 $6.99

Easter Eggs Candy Mold Set
Make festive candy or sugar eggs in 3 sizes. Includes 2-pc. egg molds: small (3 x 2¼ x 2½ in.), medium (4¼ x 3 x 3¼ in.) and large (5 x 4 x 3¾ in.), instructions.
2114-P-1215 $4.99

Candy Melts®*
Ideal for all your candy making—molding, dipping or coating. Artificially vanilla flavored unless otherwise indicated. 14 oz. bag. Certified Kosher. **$2.50**

Pink	**1911-P-447**
Lavender	**1911-P-403**
Yellow	**1911-P-463**
Blue	**1911-P-448**
White	**1911-P-498**
Chocolate Mint	**1911-P-1920**
Light Cocoa	**1911-P-544**
Dark Cocoa	**1911-P-358**

*Brand confectionery coating.

See pages 144-149 for more Wilton candy items.

EASTER

Stencil Sets

STENCIL-A-COOKIE™ CUTTER & STENCIL SETS

Using the fun-shaped stencils and cutter, it's easy to serve cookies with exciting, colorful designs for the season. Just cut cookies, then use the stencils and Wilton FoodWriter™, Cake Sparkles™, Colored Sugars or Color Mist™ Food Color Spray (not included) to create dazzling shapes on top after baking. Set includes one metal cutter and two stencils (same design). **Set/3 $1.99**

Egg
2308-P-1412

Bunny
2308-P-1411

Butterfly
2308-P-1402

Flower
2308-P-1403

Easter Cupcake and Cookie Stencils

Turn plain treats into spring sensations with a stenciled Easter design. Place one of the fun designs over your baked treat, then sprinkle with Wilton Cake Sparkles™ or Colored Sugars or spray with Color Mist™ Food Color Spray (p. 180). Five designs.
417-P-1219 $2.49

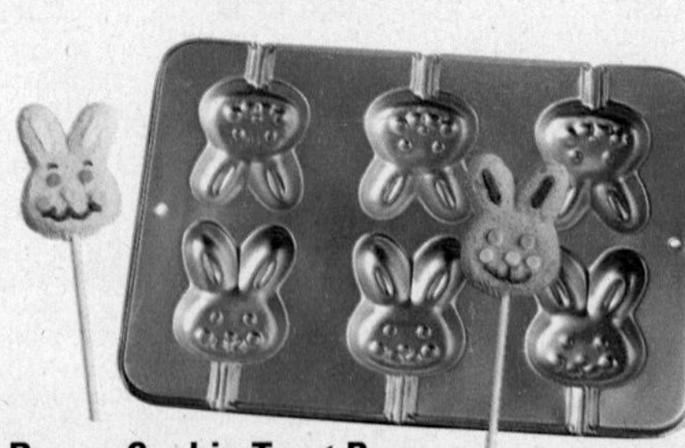

Bunny Cookie Treat Pan

Just press cookie dough into pan, insert a cookie stick, then bake, cool and decorate. Create your own cookie gifts for that special someone; great for adding fun shapes to other goodies like rice cereal treats and candy pops. Each pan makes 6 individual treats, 3½ x 2¾ x ¼ in. deep. Aluminum.
2105-P-8106 $7.99

Cookie Treat Sticks

6 in. 1912-P-9319 Pk./20 $1.99
8 in. 1912-P-9318 Pk./20 $2.99

Sprinkles

INDIVIDUAL BOTTLES

Shake up your Easter treats with fun colors and designs. Plastic bottles for convenient pouring and storing. Certified Kosher. **$1.99**

Pastel Sprinkle Sparks
2.5 oz. bottle
710-P-822

Pastel Easter Eggs
2.5 oz. bottle
710-P-900

Bunny/Ducks Mix
2.5 oz. bottle
710-P-870

Soft Pink Sugar
3.25 oz. Bottle
710-P-896

Soft Lavender Sugar
3.25 oz. Bottle
710-P-897

Soft Yellow Sugar
3.25 oz. Bottle
710-P-895

Soft Green Sugar
3.25 oz. Bottle
710-P-898

Sparkling Sugars

Easy-pour sugars have a coarse texture and brilliant sparkle. 8.25 oz. Certified Kosher. **$3.99**

Pink/White
710-P-369

Lavender/White
710-P-371

Yellow/ White
710-P-370

ASSORTMENTS

4-Mix
Includes 1 oz. Lt. Green Sugar, 1 oz. Yellow Sugar, 1 oz. Springtime Nonpareils and .75 oz. Bunnies and Ducks Mix. Certified Kosher.
710-P-736 $4.99

6-Mix
Includes 1 oz. Bunny and Ducks Sprinkle Mix, 1 oz. Egg Sprinkle Mix, 1 oz. Springtime Mix, 1.3 oz. Lavender, Pink and Green Sugars. Certified Kosher.
710-P-740 $5.99

Gingerbread

Pre-Baked and Pre-Assembled Bunny Hutch Cookie House Kit

Imagine how much fun the kids will have decorating this house! It's the perfect springtime project and a cute centerpiece for your Easter table. So hop to it—everything is included: a pre-baked, pre-built house, white and lavender decorating icing mixes, candies, pre-made icing decorations, two cookie bunny ears, two decorating bags and tips, cardboard base and complete instructions with great decorating ideas. House measures 5½ x 5¼ x 6 in. high.
2104-P-1592 $12.99

Cookie Cutters

COPPER CUTTER

The warmth and beauty of copper is ideal for displaying and adding that decorative touch to your kitchen. Our heirloom-quality bunny cutter has a smooth rolled edge for that finishing touch. Recipe included. 5½ in. wide.
2308-P-3046 $6.99

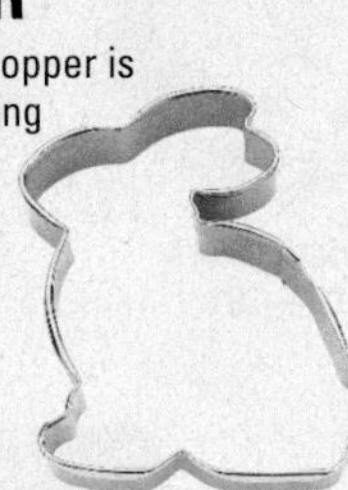

COMFORT GRIP™ CUTTERS

These easy-grip stainless steel cutters with extra-deep sides are perfect for cutting so many favorite foods into seasonal shapes. The cushion grip gives you comfortable control even when cutting thick desserts. Recipe included.
4½ x 4½ x 1½ in. deep. **$2.99**

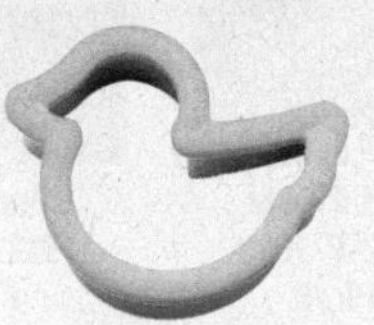

Chick
2310-P-625

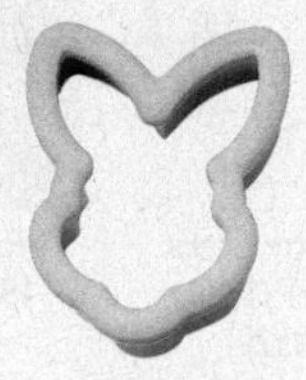

Bunny
2310-P-626

METAL CUTTERS

Put variety in your cookie-making with fun Easter multi-shape sets. There are styles to please everyone. Recipe included.

Easter Mini Cutter Set

Butterfly, daisy, tulip, bunny face, chick and bunny, each approx. 1½ in.
2308-P-1209
Set/6 $2.99

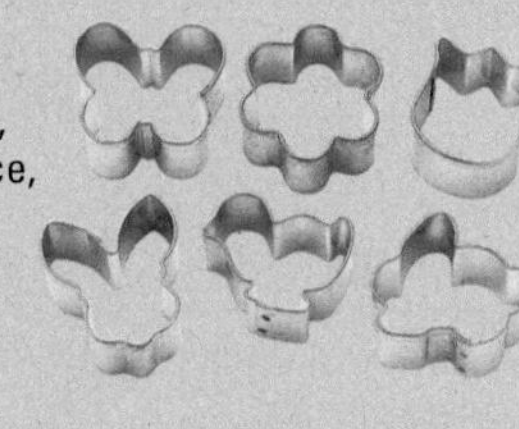

Bunnies Nesting Cutter Set

The whole bunny family in cutters from small to tall. Quality metal cuts neatly and is easy to handle. Sizes from 4¾ to 2¾ in.
2308-P-1208
Set/4 $4.49

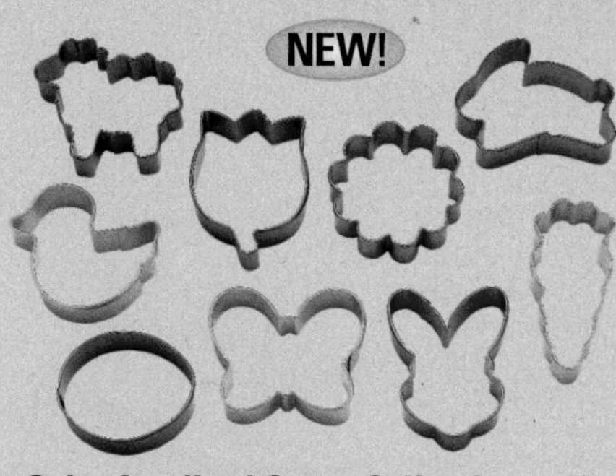

Color Anodized Cutter Collection

Springtime colors add a fresh look to your kitchen and fun to your baking. Lamb, chick, tulip, flower, bunny, egg, butterfly, bunny face, and carrot cutters are approx. 3 in. Colored Aluminum.
2308-P-2503 Set/9 $9.99

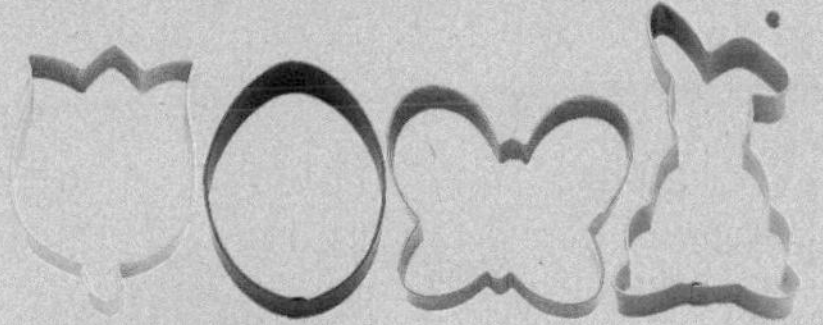

Hoppy Easter Colored Metal Cutter Set

Springtime favorites in pastels of the season. Tulip, egg, butterfly and bunny. Each approx. 3½ in.
2308-P-1207 Set/4 $4.49

PLASTIC CUTTERS

Child-safe design means kids can have a great time helping. And remember all the fun ways to use our cutters—for bread shapes, stencils, sun catchers and so much more.

Easter Egg Canister Cutter Set

A fun and convenient egg canister holds a collection of Easter cutters for holiday cookies. Ten cutters, each approx. 3½ in.
2304-P-95 Set/10 $5.99

Nesting Bunnies Cutter Set

Great for cookies, imprinting patterns in icing, cutting bread shapes and more. Sizes from 1¼ to 4⅛ in.
2303-P-9270 Set/4 $2.99

Easter Bite-Size Cutter Set

Bunny, chick, tulip, egg and bunny face shapes, each approx. 1½ in.
2303-P-9319 Set/5 $2.49

Individual Cutters

Child-safe plastic, approx. 3 x 4 in.
$0.69

Cross
2303-P-141

Duck
2303-P-148

Egg
2303-P-119

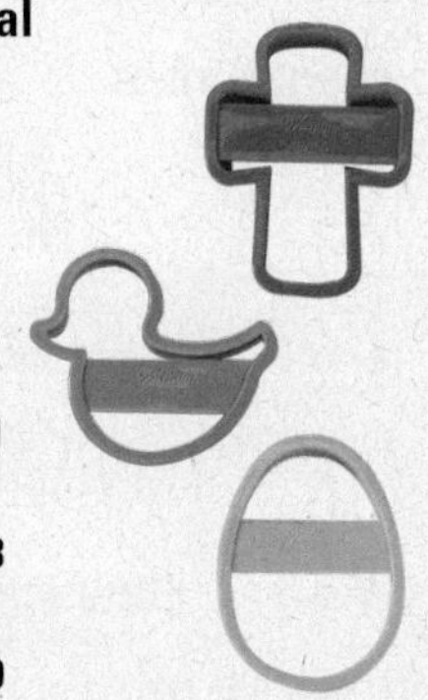

COMMUNION

Cross Pan

Beveled design is excellent for rolled fondant. Instructions included. One-mix pan is 14½ x 11⅛ x 2 in. deep. Aluminum.
2105-P-2509
$7.99

Inspirational Cross

Beautifully designed sculpted resin. 5½ in. high.
202-P-206 $24.99

Communion Girl*

3½ in. high.
2113-P-7878 $3.49

Communion Boy*

3½ in. high.
2113-P-7886 $3.49

*Designed by Ellen Williams.

PATRIOTIC

Bakeware

Stars and Stripes Pan
Decorate a grand old flag cake perfect for that July 4th cookout. Accent Old Glory with Piping Gel and fresh summer fruit. One-mix pan is 13 x 9 x 2 in. deep. Aluminum.
2105-P-183 $7.99

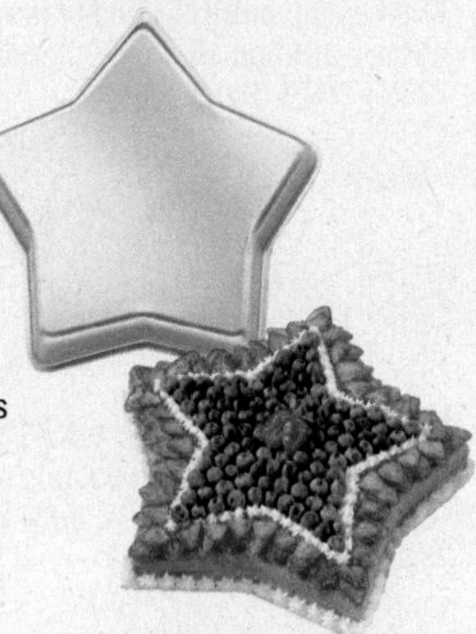

Star Pan
Your colorful star cake will set off sparks on the 4th and brighten parties all year long. One-mix pan is 12¾ x 1⅞ in. deep. Aluminum.
2105-P-2512 $9.99

Mini Star Pan
Personal-size desserts make everyone feel like a star. One mix makes 12-16 stars. 6 cavities, each 4¾ x 1 in. deep. Aluminum.
2105-P-1235 $10.99

Party

Baking Cups
Microwave-safe paper. Standard size, 2 in. diameter.
Pk./50 $1.49

USA
415-P-229

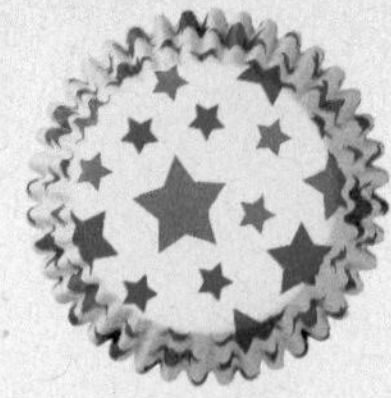

Patriotic Stars
415-P-381

Stars and Stripes
415-P-704

Party Bags
Colorful Patriotic designs for candy and cookie treats. Pizazz designs really catch the light with a dazzling reflective pattern. Pack contains 20 plastic 4 x 9½ in. bags and 20 twist ties, unless otherwise noted.
$1.99

USA
1912-P-1131
Pk./20

Patriotic Stars
1912-P-1254
Pk./20

Red Pizazz
1912-P-1019
Pk./8

Blue Pizazz
1912-P-1021
Pk./8

Icing Decorations
Perfect for topping cupcakes, cookies and ice cream. Mint-flavored. Certified Kosher. **$2.09**

USA Petite
710-P-500
Pk./12

Patriotic Stars
710-P-942 Pk./21

Patriotic Flags
710-P-726 Pk./9

PARTY PICKS

Many decorative uses.

Stars and Stripes
3 in. high.
2113-P-704
Pk./40 $1.29

Patriotic Foil Pix **NEW!**
Looks like a dazzling fireworks display on your holiday treats! Great for cakes, cupcakes. 4 in. high.
2113-P-712 Pk./12 $0.99

Colors & Icings

PATRIOTIC COLOR GUIDE

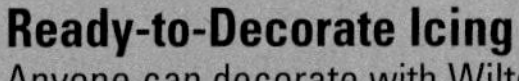

Red White Blue

Color Mist™ Food Color Spray
Gives decorators the versatility and dazzling effects of an airbrush in a convenient can! Use it to transform a plain iced cake with sensational color, add splashes of holiday color to iced cookies and cupcakes. No mess, taste-free formula.
1.5 oz. Certified Kosher. **$2.99**

Red	**710-P-5500**
Blue	**710-P-5501**

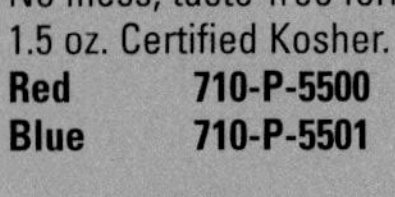

Tube Decorating Gel
Transparent gels are great for writing messages and decorating cakes and cookies. Colors match Wilton Icing Colors (p. 127). .75 oz
Certified Kosher. **$1.29**

Red	**704-P-318**
White	**704-P-302**
Royal Blue	**704-P-348**

Ready-to-Decorate Icing
Anyone can decorate with Wilton Ready-to-Decorate Icing! Our brilliant colors and four decorating tips make it a breeze to add an exciting finishing touch to treats—without mixing or mess.
6.4 oz. Certified Kosher. **$3.49**

Red	**710-P-4400**
White	**710-P-4402**
Blue	**710-P-4407**

Tube Decorating Icing
Tubes can be used with our Tip and Nail Set or Coupler Ring Set (p. 127) and any standard size Wilton metal tip. Colors match Wilton Icing Colors (p. 127).
4.25 oz. Certified Kosher. **$1.79**

Red	**704-P-218**
White	**704-P-200**
Royal Blue	**704-P-248**

Candles

Beer Cans
1¾ in. high.
2811-P-9326 Set/6 $3.29

Patriotic Star
1¾ in. high.
2811-P-763 Pk./4 $2.99

Red and Blue Sparklers
6½ in. high.
2811-P-704
Pk./18 $0.99

Cookie

COOKIE SETS

Stencil-A-Cookie™ Cutter & Stencil Set
Using the fun-shaped stencils and cutter, it's easy to serve cookies with colorful designs for the season. Just cut cookies, then use the stencils and Wilton Cake Sparkles™, Colored Sugars or Color Mist™ Food Color Spray (not included) to create dazzling shapes on top after baking. Cookies look great iced with Wilton Ice-A Cookie™ sold at right. Set includes one metal cutter and two stencils (same design).
2308-P-1405 $1.99

Patriotic Cupcake and Cookie Stencils
Turn plain treats into American classics with a stenciled patriotic design. Just place one of the fun designs over your baked treat, then sprinkle with Wilton Cake Sparkles™ or Colored Sugars color spray with Color Mist™ Food Color Spray (p. 184). Five designs.
417-P-131 $2.49

COOKIE CUTTERS

Red, White & Blue USA Colored Metal Cutter Set
Fun colored cutters for cookies everyone can take pride in. Cutters measure 3 in.
2308-P-1050 Set/3 $3.99

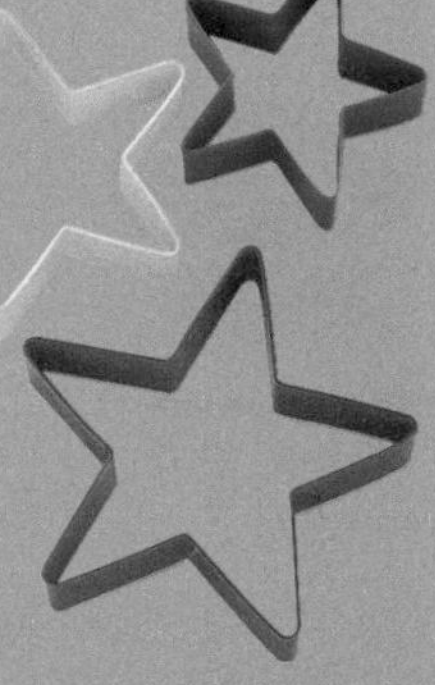

Red, White and Blue Stars Nesting Colored Metal Cutter Set
A colorful way to celebrate national holidays. Cutters measure 3¼ to 5 in.
2308-P-1240 Set/3 $3.99

Stars Nesting Metal Cutter Set
A parade of small to large stars to create fun cookies for the 4th or all year long. Sizes from 5 to 2½ in.
2308-P-1215 Set/4 $4.49

Star Comfort Grip™ Cutter
This easy-grip stainless steel cutter with extra-deep sides is perfect for cutting so many favorite foods into star shapes. The cushion grip gives you comfortable control even when cutting into thick desserts. Recipe included. 4½ x 1½ in. deep.
2310-P-605 $2.99

Star Metal Cookie Cutter
Quality metal is clean-cutting and easy to handle. 3 in.
2308-P-1008 $0.69

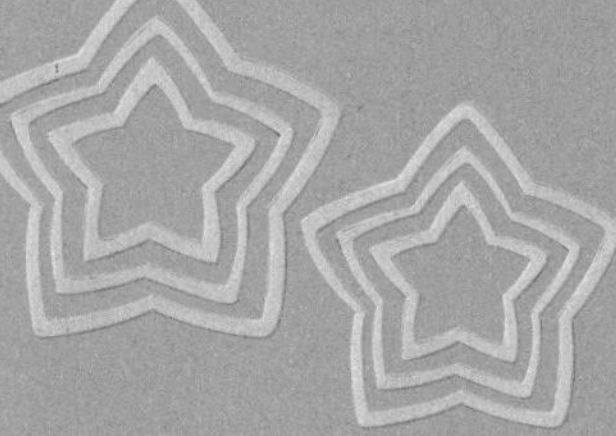

Nesting Stars Cutter Set
1⅝ to 4⅝ in.
2304-P-704
Set/6 $2.99

ICE-A-COOKIE™

The soft, squeezable pouch is easy to handle; the patented snip tip and screw-on decorating cap help you control the flow. Use the snip tip for icing cookies and the cap for decorating lines and designs. Delicious artificially vanilla-flavored icing dries to a smooth, satin finish. Each pouch decorates approximately twenty-four 3 in. round cookies. 10.59 oz. pouch. Certified Kosher. **$3.99**

Red 710-P-422
White 710-P-416

COOKIE PAN

Star Cookie Treat Pan
Just press cookie dough into pan, insert a cookie stick, then bake, cool and decorate. Create cookie stars, rice cereal treats and candy pops. Pan makes 6 individual treats, 3½ in. diameter x ¼ in. deep. Aluminum.
2105-P-8102 $7.99

Cookie Treat Sticks
6 in. 1912-P-9319 Pk./20 $1.99
8 in. 1912-P-9318 Pk./20 $2.99

Sprinkles

INDIVIDUAL BOTTLES

Plastic bottles for convenient pouring and storing. Certified Kosher. **$1.99**

Patriotic Sprinkle Sparks
2.5 oz. bottle **710-P-940**

Patriotic Mix
2.5 oz. bottle
710-P-786

Red Sugar
3.25 oz. bottle **710-P-766**

Blue Sugar
3.25 oz. bottle **710-P-750**

Cake Sparkles™
Edible glitter, .25 oz. bottle. Certified Kosher. **$2.89**

Red
703-P-1284

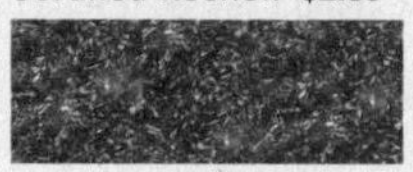

Blue
703-P-1314

ASSORTMENT

6-Mix
Includes 1 oz. each Red and Blue Jimmies and Patriotic Mix, 1.3 oz. each Red and Blue Sugar and .85 oz. Patriotic Sprinkle Sparks.
710-P-656 $5.99

GRADUATION

Bakeware

Smiley Grad Pan
Our grinning grad is a smart choice to honor any student who's made the grade—boy or girl, kindergartner to collegian. One-mix pan is 10¼ x 12 x 2 in. deep. Aluminum.
2105-P-2073 $7.99

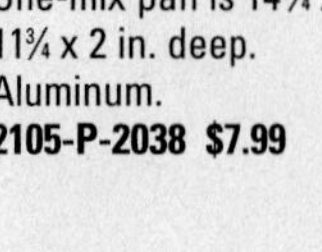

Graduate Pan
Honor male or female grads! One-mix pan is 14½ x 8¼ x 2 in. deep. Aluminum.
2105-P-1800 $7.99

Topping Off Success Pan
Decorate in your grad's school colors. One-mix pan is 14¾ x 11¾ x 2 in. deep. Aluminum.
2105-P-2038 $7.99

Book Pans
Books detail any of life's important chapters, including graduation. Aluminum.

Two-Mix Book Pan
11½ x 15 x 2¾ in. deep. Serves up to 30.
2105-P-2521 $13.99

One-Mix Book Pan
13 x 9½ x 2 in. deep.
2105-P-972 $9.99

Party

Baking Cups
Microwave-safe paper. Standard size, 2 in. diameter.
Pk./50 $1.49

Smiley Grad
415-P-294

Party Bags
Colorful grad designs for candy and cookie treats. 20 plastic bags, 20 ties included. 4 x 9½ in.
Pk./20 $1.99

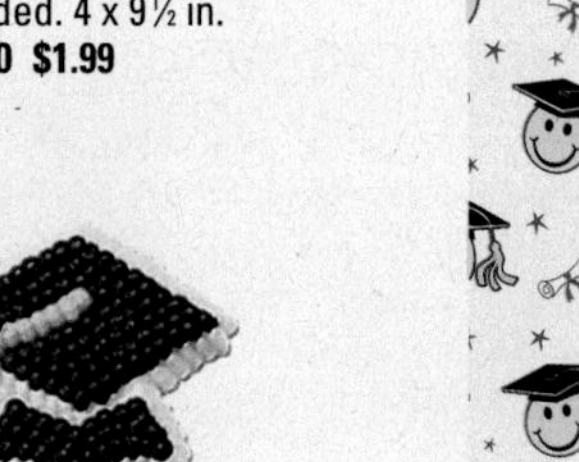

Smiley Grad
1912-P-1130

Icing Decorations
Wilton Icing Decorations are perfect for topping cupcakes, cookies and ice cream. Mint-flavored. Certified Kosher. **$2.09**

Petite Smiley Grad
710-P-503 Pk./12

Graduation Cap
710-P-473 Pk./9

Toppers

Graduation Toppers
Capture the day's excitement with our beautifully-detailed plastic toppers on a special cake. Approx. 4¼ in. high.

Female Graduate
2113-P-1821 $1.99

Male Graduate
2113-P-1823 $1.99

Glowing Graduate (girl)
2113-P-1833 $1.99

Successful Graduate (boy)
2113-P-4549 $1.99

Graduation Caps Set
Great party favors or cake toppers, 2 in. high.
Set/2 $1.99

White
2113-P-1800

Black
2113-P-1801

Candles

Candle Set
Caps and diplomas, 3 each, ½ to 2 in. high.
2811-P-1800 Set/6 $3.29

Champagne Bottles
2 in. high.
2811-P-163 Set/6 $3.29

Colors & Icings

GRADUATION AND AUTUMN COLOR GUIDE
Color Mist, Ready-to-Decorate Icing, Tube Decorating Icing and Tube Decorating Gel use the standard spectrum of Wilton colors.

Color Mist™ Food Color Spray
The dazzling effects of an airbrush in a convenient can! Use it to transform a plain iced cake with sensational color, add splashes of holiday color to iced cookies and cupcakes. No mess, taste-free formula. 1.5 oz. Certified Kosher. **$2.99**

Blue	**710-P-5501**
Red	**710-P-5500**
Yellow	**710-P-5502**
Green	**710-P-5503**
Violet	**710-P-5504**
Pink	**710-P-5505**
Black	**710-P-5506**
Orange	**710-P-5507**

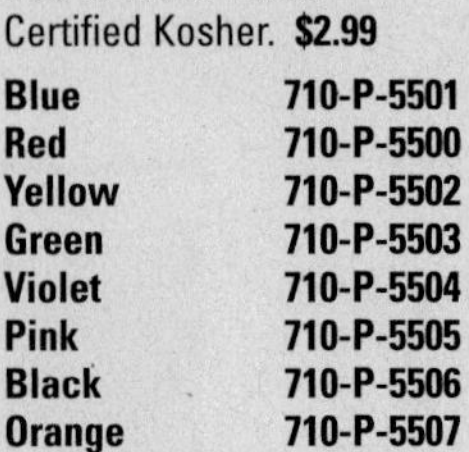

Ready-to-Decorate Icing
Anyone can decorate with Wilton Ready-to-Decorate Icing! Our brilliant colors and four decorating tips make it a breeze to add an exciting finishing touch to treats—without mixing or mess. 6.4 oz. Certified Kosher. **$3.49**

Blue	**710-P-4407**
Red	**710-P-4400**
Yellow	**710-P-4409**
Green	**710-P-4401**
Violet	**710-P-4408**
Pink	**710-P-4406**
Black	**710-P-4404**
Orange	**710-P-4410**
White	**710-P-4402**

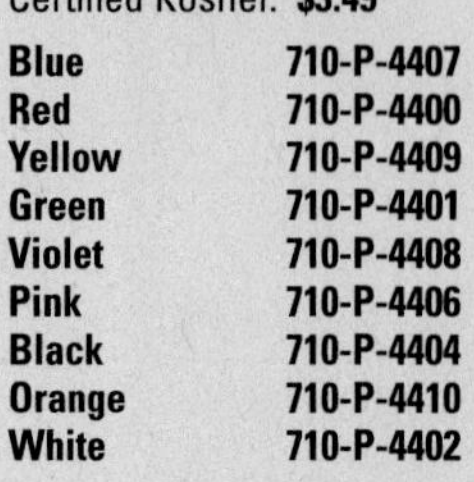

Tube Decorating Icing
Tubes can be used with our Coupler Ring Set or Tip and Nail Set (p. 127) and any standard size Wilton metal tip. Colors match Wilton Icing Colors (p. 127). 4.25 oz. Certified Kosher. **$1.79**

Royal Blue **704-P-248**
Red **704-P-218**
Lemon Yellow **704-P-236**
Leaf Green **704-P-224**
Kelly Green **704-P-227**
Violet **704-P-242**
Pink **704-P-230**
Black **704-P-206**
Orange **704-P-212**
White **704-P-200**
Chocolate **704-P-254**

Tube Decorating Gel
Transparent gels are great for writing messages and decorating cakes and cookies. Colors match Wilton Icing Colors (p. 127). .75 oz. Certified Kosher. **$1.29**

Royal Blue **704-P-348**
Red **704-P-318**
Lemon Yellow **704-P-336**
Leaf Green **704-P-324**
Violet **704-P-342**
Pink **704-P-330**
Black **704-P-306**
Orange **704-P-312**
White **704-P-302**
Brown **704-P-354**

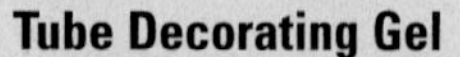

AUTUMN

Pumpkin Pie Pan
Holds one 15 oz. can of pumpkin pie filling. Use for apple, peach and cherry pies, too! Ideal for ready-to-bake pie crusts. 9 x 1½ in. deep. Aluminum.
2105-P-3970 $6.99

Sprinkles

INDIVIDUAL BOTTLES
Plastic bottles for convenient pouring and storing. Certified Kosher. **$1.99**

Leaves Mix	Red Sugar	Dark Green Sugar
2.5 oz. bottle	3.25 oz. bottle	3.25 oz.bottle
710-P-787	**710-P-766**	**710-P-764**

Cake Sparkles™
Edible glitter, .25 oz. bottle. Certified Kosher.
$2.89

Red
703-P-1284

Dark Green	Orange	Yellow
703-P-1278	**703-P-1308**	**703-P-1272**

ASSORTMENT
6-Mix
Includes 1.3 oz. each Yellow, Red, Orange and Light Green Sugar, 1 oz. Leaves Mix and Chocolate Jimmies. Certified Kosher.
710-P-751 $5.99

Party

Baking Cups
Microwave-safe paper. Standard size, 2 in. diameter. **Pk./50 $1.49**

NEW!

Harvest	Pumpkins	Colorful Leaves
415-P-512	**415-P-214**	**415-P-2000**

Party Bags
Colorful Autumn designs for candy and cookie treats. 20 plastic bags, 20 ties included. 4 x 9½ in.
Pk./20 $1.99

NEW!

Harvest	Pumpkins	Colorful Leaves
1912-P-1288	**1912-P-1267**	**1912-P-1252**

Icing Decorations
Wilton Icing Decorations are perfect for topping cupcakes, cookies and ice cream. Mint-flavored. Certified Kosher. **$2.09**

Petite Leaves	Leaves
710-P-230 Pk./12	**710-P-3003 Pk./12**

Candy

Caramel Apple Kit

A favorite fall tradition is now even more fun! Everything you need for dipping, topping and wrapping delicious gourmet apples is here—just bring your own apples and start the fun!* Includes 12 oz. rich caramels, 1 oz. Chocolate Flavored Bits, 1 oz. Toffee Crunch, 6 wooden sticks and 6 clear bags with ties. Makes 6 small or medium apples.
2104-P-1046 $7.99

NEW!

Harvest Lollipop Mold
4 designs, 8 cavities.
2115-P-3056 $1.99

Pumpkins Candy Mold
1 design, 11 cavities.
2115-P-1558 $1.99

Mini Leaves Candy Mold
2 designs, 12 cavities.
2115-P-1540 $1.99

Candy Melts®*
Ideal for all your candy making—molding, dipping or coating. Artificially vanilla flavored unless otherwise indicated. Certified Kosher. 14 oz. bags. **$2.50**

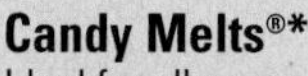
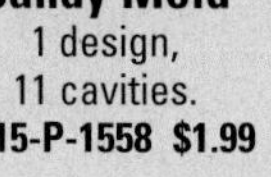

NEW!
Peanut Butter
1911-P-481

Red	1911-P-499	Dark Green	1911-P-405
Light Cocoa	1911-P-544	Dark Cocoa	1911-P-358
Orange	1911-P-1631	Chocolate Mint	1911-P-1920
Yellow	1911-P-463	White	1911-P-498
		Peanut Butter	1911-P-481

*Brand confectionery coating.

*To melt caramels, 3 Tablespoons of cream or evaporated milk are needed.

See pages 144-149 for more Wilton candy items.

Cookie

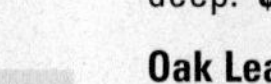

Autumn Cupcake and Cookie Stencils
Turn plain treats into visions of the season with a stenciled Autumn design. Just place one of the fun designs over your baked treat, then sprinkle with Wilton Cake Sparkles™ or Colored Sugars or spray with Color Mist™ Food Color Spray (p. 186).
Five designs.
417-P-1207 $2.49

COPPER CUTTERS
The warmth and beauty of copper make these cutters ideal for displaying. These beautiful, heirloom-quality solid copper cutters have smooth rolled edges for that finishing touch. Each approx. 5½ in. **$6.99**

Oak Leaf
2308-P-3077

Pumpkin
2308-P-3078

Maple Leaf
2308-P-3045

Apple
2308-P-3076

COMFORT GRIP™
Easy-grip stainless steel cutters with extra-deep sides. Great for cutting, cushioned plastic grip gives comfortable control. Recipe included. Approx. 4½ x 4½ x 1½ in. deep. **$2.99**

Oak Leaf
2310-P-633

Pumpkin
2310-P-600

Maple Leaf
2310-P-632

METAL CUTTERS

Leaves and Acorns Nesting Metal Cutter Set
Graduated acorns, oak and maple leaves, (3 each). 1¾ to 3¾ in. Recipe included.
2308-P-2000 Set/9 $5.99

Harvest Mini Metal Cutter Set
Six shapes: oak leaf, maple leaf, apple, pumpkin, elm leaf and acorn, each approx. 1½ in. Recipe included.
2308-P-1217 Set/6 $2.99

Character

Sharing birthday treats with the stars will make any kid's day! Wilton has today's favorite faces on fun party products for cakes, cookies and more.

Cake Pan
Cosmo and *Wanda's* wish-making ability may be lacking, but their power to make smiles appear is second to none! One-mix pan is 10¾ x 10¾ x 2 in. deep. Aluminum.
2105-P-6262 $10.99

Candle
Handpainted, clean-burning with magical details.
3⅜ in. high.
2811-P-6262
$3.99

Baking Cups
Standard size, microwave-safe paper. 2 in. diameter.
415-P-6262
Pk./50 $1.69

Icing Color Set
Includes four .5 oz. jars of Green, Skin Tone, Hot Pink and Lavender. Certified Kosher.
601-P-6262
Set/4 $4.99

Icing Decorations
Mint-flavored edible sugar shapes decorate cupcakes, cookies, ice cream and cake. Certified Kosher.
710-P-6262 Pk./9 $2.29

Treat Bags
Fill with candy, cookies and other goodies; great for gifts and surprises, too! Sixteen each 4 x 9½ in. bags and coordinating twist ties.
1912-P-6262
Pk./16 $1.99

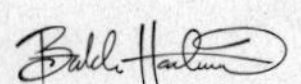

Fun Pix®
Shimmering fun for cupcakes, brownies, ice cream and more. 3 in. high.
2113-P-7040
Pk./24 $1.29

Cake Pan
Everyone loves her fun new look! From her bouncy hat to her sweet smile, she adds a "berry" happy touch to the party. One-mix pan is 11¼ x 10½ x 2 in. deep. Aluminum.
2105-P-7040 $10.99

Baking Cups
Standard size, microwave-safe paper. 2 in. diameter.
415-P-7040
Pk./50 $1.69

Candle
Handpainted, clean-burning with fun details. 3¼ in. high.
2811-P-7040 $3.99

Icing Decorations
Mint-flavored edible sugar shapes decorate cupcakes, cookies, ice cream and cake. Certified Kosher.
710-P-7041 Pk./9 $2.29

Treat Bags
Fill with candy, cookies and other goodies; great for gifts and surprises, too! Sixteen each 4 x 9½ in. bags and twist ties.
1912-P-7040 Pk./16 $1.99

Icing Color Set
Includes four .5 oz. jars: Red, Brown, Green and Skin Tone. Certified Kosher.
601-P-7040
Set/4 $4.99

Lollipop Making Kit
Everything you need to make a crop of berry fun pops with *Strawberry Shortcake* and friends! Includes lollipop mold (4 designs, 8 cavities), 10 oz. Candy Melts®* (Red, White and Blue), 3 disposable decorating bags, 1 decorating brush, 10 lollipop bags with ties and 10 lollipop sticks.
2104-P-7040 $7.99

*Brand confectionery coating.

Large Treat Bags
There's more room for fun goodies with this 8 x 8 in. size.
1912-P-7041
Pk./8 $1.99

SPIDER-MAN™

NEW!

Icing Decorations
Mint-flavored edible sugar shapes decorate cupcakes, cookies, ice cream and cake. Certified Kosher.
710-P-5052 Pk./9 $2.29

Cake Pan
The wizard of webs is back in action, on a pan that will grab every guest! Kids will love the great costume detail. One-mix pan is 9 x 12 x 2 in. deep. Aluminum.
2105-P-5052
$10.99

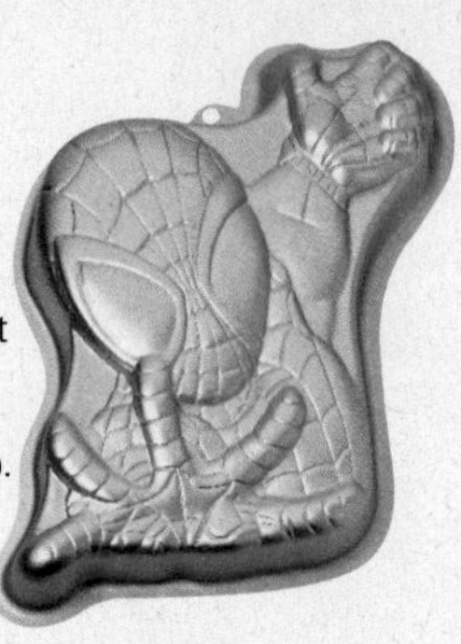

Baking Cups
Standard size, microwave-safe paper. 2 in. diameter.
415-P-5052
Pk./50 $1.69

Party Toppers
He's ready to sling his next web on these exciting handpainted toppers. Food-safe, great on cupcakes, brownies, cakes and other treats.
2¼ in. high.
2113-P-5052
Set/6 $3.99

Treat Bags
Fill with candy, cookies and other goodies; great for gifts and surprises, too! Sixteen each 4 x 9½ in. bags and twist ties.
1912-P-5052 Pk./16 $1.99

Make-a-Cookie Face Kit
Everything's here for you to decorate 12 fun, colorful cookies starring your favorite web-slinging hero. Includes cookie cutter, 12 sets of *Spider-Man* facial feature icing decorations, 4.25 oz. tube decorating icing, .75 oz. tube decorating gel, recipe and complete instructions.
2104-P-5052 $9.99

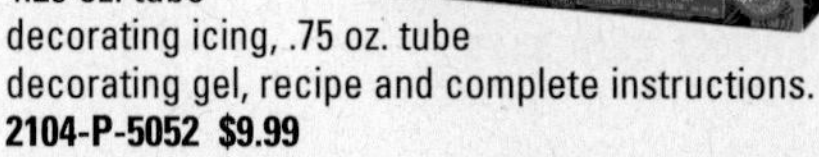

Candle
Handpainted, clean burning with exciting details.
3½ in. high.
2811-P-5052
$3.99

Kandy Clay™† Comic Book Page Activity Kit
Create the yummiest funnies ever—starring *Spider-Man* and made from the modeling clay you can eat! Includes twelve .5 oz. packs of Kandy Clay (Blue Raspberry Blue, Banana Yellow, Hot Fudge Black and Strawberry Red), two easy-to-fill Clay Molds for making 10 exciting *Spider-Man* shapes, Sculpting Tool for trimming shapes, complete instructions and Comic Book Board for displaying your *Spider-Man* adventure.
Ages 4 and up.
2104-P-5054 $6.99

Icing Color Set
Includes four .5 oz. jars: Light Blue, Dark Blue, Red and Black. Certified Kosher.
601-P-5052
Set/4 $4.99

Candy Bar Kit
Everything's included for you to make 8 of the coolest, yummiest candy bars anywhere, starring *Spidey*! Easy and fun—just melt, mold and enjoy. Includes 1 candy bar mold (4 designs, 4 cavities), 10 oz. Candy Melts®* (Red and Blue), 2 oz. candy toppings (Toffee and Chocolate) and 8 *Spider-Man* treat bags with matching stickers for fun gifts.
2104-P-5033 $7.99

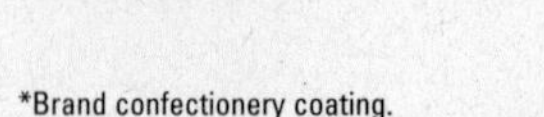

*Brand confectionery coating.

†Brand edible modeling clay.

SCOOBY-DOO!™

Cake Pan

As usual, *Scooby* gets right next to the food! This fun pan shows him about to put his canines into a big burger. One-mix pan is 10½ x 12 x 2 in. deep. Aluminum.
2105-P-3227 $10.99

NEW!

Mini Treats Cake Pan

NEW!

Get close-up with your favorite character and create all kinds of exciting single-size desserts. Great for cakes, candy, gelatin and brownies. The pan's intense color makes baking even more fun.
Four cavity pan is 11 x 9 in.; individual cavities are 3 x 5½ x ¾ in. deep. Aluminum.
2105-P-3228 $5.99

Edible Cake Decoration Set

Surround the fun-to-eat *Scooby-Doo* wafer with the cool icing decorations and add the Happy Birthday message to create instant excitement on any birthday cake.
711-P-3206 Set/20 $2.99

Party Toppers

NEW!

Scooby-Doo! is begging for attention on these fun handpainted toppers. Food-safe, great on cupcakes, brownies, cakes and other treats. 2½ in. high.
2113-P-3206 Set/6 $3.99

Candle

NEW!

Bright handpainted details. 3¾ in. high.
2811-P-3227 $3.99

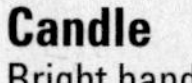

Icing Color Set

Includes four .5 oz. jars: Brown, Yellow, Black, Teal. Certified Kosher.
601-P-3206 Set/4 $4.99

Icing Decorations

Mint-flavored edible shapes. Certified Kosher.
710-P-3206 Pk./9 $2.29

Shaped Sprinkles

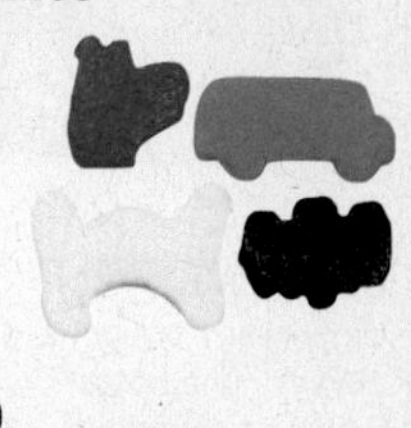

Shake up your *Scooby-Doo!* treats. 4-cell container is convenient for pouring and storing. 2.55 oz. Certified Kosher.
710-P-3207 $5.99

Baking Cups

Standard size, microwave-safe paper. 2 in. diameter.
415-P-3227
Pk./50 $1.69

Gummy Making Kit

NEW!

Kids will have a great time making 16 yummy gummy candies in just minutes! Everything they need is included: mold with 4 fun *Scooby-Doo!* designs, four .7 oz. pouches of gummy mix (Green Apple, Grape, Watermelon and Orange), .7 oz. packet of Sour Sugars for covering gummys, squeeze bottle and funnel. Just add water to the mix, shake, fill molds and pop in your refrigerator. Ages 4 and up.
2104-P-3211 $5.99

Treat Bags

Fill with candy, cookies and other goodies; great for gifts and surprises, too! Sixteen each 4 x 9½ in. bags and twist ties.
1912-P-3227 Pk./16 $1.99

Kandy Clay™† Mystery Machine Puzzle Activity Kit

NEW!

Kids will love making the only puzzle that's also a sweet treat to eat! Includes twelve .5 oz. packs of Kandy Clay (Grape Purple, Orange Orange, Green Apple Green and Blue Raspberry Blue), two easy-to-fill Clay Molds for making happy *Scooby-Doo!* shapes, Sculpting Tool for trimming shapes, complete instructions and Puzzle Board for putting clay puzzle pieces together. Ages 4 and up.
2104-P-3228 $6.99

Candy Bar Kit

NEW!

Everything's included for you to make 8 of the coolest, yummiest candy bars anywhere, starring *Scooby-Doo!* Easy and fun—just melt, mold and enjoy. Includes 1 candy bar mold (4 designs, 4 cavities), 10 oz. Candy Melts®* (Light Cocoa and Yellow), 2 oz. candy toppings (Chocolate and Graham Cracker Crunch), and 8 *Scooby-Doo!* treat bags with matching stickers for fun gifts.
2104-P-3209 $7.99

Make-a-Cookie-Face Kit

Everything's here for you to decorate 12 fun, colorful cookies that capture *Scooby's* snack-happy state of mind. Includes cookie cutter, 12 sets of *Scooby-Doo!* facial feature icing decorations, 4.25 oz. tube decorating icing, .75 oz. tube decorating gel, recipe and complete instructions. Certified Kosher.
2104-P-3207 $9.99

Lollipop Making Kit

Everything you need to make fun *Scooby-Doo!* lollipops! Includes 1 lollipop mold (4 designs, 8 cavities), 10 oz. Candy Melts®* (Light Cocoa, White and Yellow), 3 disposable decorating bags, 1 decorating brush, 10 lollipop bags with ties, and 10 lollipop sticks.
2104-P-3206 $7.99

Cake Pan

Wherever *Dora* goes, it's always "una fiesta!" Discover a world of party excitement with this great pan. One-mix pan is 13¾ x 10 x 2 in. deep. Aluminum.
2105-P-6300 $10.99

Mini Treats Cake Pan

NEW!

Get close-up with your favorite explorer and create all kinds of exciting single-size desserts. Great for cakes, candy, gelatin and brownies. The pan's intense color makes baking even more fun. One cake mix makes 15 mini cakes. Four cavity pan is 11 x 9 in.; individual cavities are 3¼ x 5 x ¾ in. deep. Aluminum.
2105-P-6301 $5.99

Party Toppers

NEW!

Dora has reached the top of your delightful party treats! Handpainted, food-safe; great on cupcakes, brownies, cakes and other treats. 2¼ in. high.
2113-P-6300 Set/6 $3.99

Candle

Handpainted, clean-burning with colorful details. 3¼ in. high.
2811-P-6300 $3.99

Icing Decorations

Mint-flavored edible sugar shapes decorate cupcakes, cookies, ice cream and cake. Certified Kosher.
710-P-6300
Pk./8 $2.29

Gummy Making Kit

Kids will have a great time making 16 yummy gummy candies in just minutes! Everything they need is included: mold with four exciting *Dora the Explorer* designs, four .7 oz. pouches of gummy mix (Grape, Blue Raspberry, Watermelon and Orange), .7 oz. packet of Sour Sugars for covering gummys, squeeze bottle and funnel. Just add water to the mix, shake, fill molds and pop in your refrigerator. Ages 4 and up.
2104-P-6303 $5.99

Icing Color Set

Includes four .5 oz. jars: Red, Pink, Brown and Skin Tone. Certified Kosher.
601-P-6300
Set/4 $4.99

Baking Cups

Standard size, microwave-safe paper. 2 in. diameter.
415-P-6300
Pk./50 $1.69

Make-a-Cookie-Face Kit

Everything's here for you to decorate 12 exciting, colorful cookies that capture *Dora the Explorer's* joyful personality. Includes cookie cutter, 12 sets of *Dora the Explorer* facial feature icing decorations, 4.25 oz. tube decorating icing, .75 oz. tube decorating gel, recipe and complete instructions. Certified Kosher.
2104-P-6302 $9.99

Treat Bags

Fill with candy, cookies and other goodies; great for gifts and surprises, too! Sixteen each 4 x 9½ in. bags and twist ties.
1912-P-6300
Pk./16 $1.99

Cake Pan

Everyone's favorite seafaring star will make a big splash at the party. One-mix pan is 13½ x 11¾ x 2 in. deep. Aluminum.
2105-P-5130 $10.99

Icing Decorations

Mint-flavored edible sugar shapes. Certified Kosher.
710-P-5130 Pk./9 $2.29

Shaped Sprinkles

4-cell container is convenient for pouring and storing *SpongeBob* (in 2 cells), Flower and Patrick shapes. 2.8 oz. Certified Kosher.
710-P-5131 $5.99

Treat Bags

Fill with candy, cookies and other goodies; great for gifts and surprises, too! Sixteen each 4 x 9½ in. bags and twist ties.
1912-P-5130 Pk./16 $1.99

Mini Treats Cake Pan

NEW!

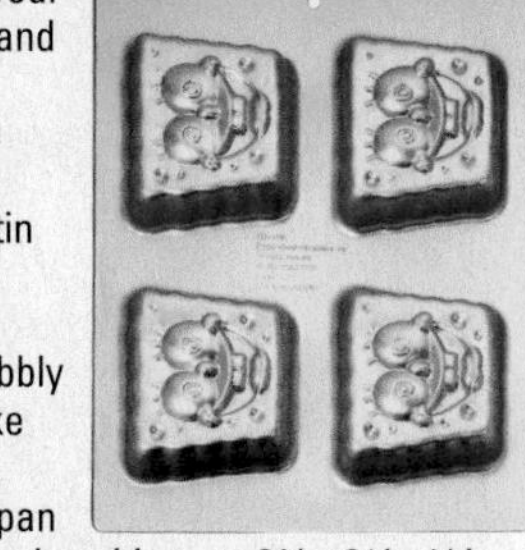

Get close-up with your favorite character and create all kinds of exciting single-size desserts. Great for cakes, candy, gelatin and brownies. The pan's intense color makes baking a bubbly good time. One cake mix makes 15 mini cakes. Four cavity pan is 11 x 9 in.; individual cavities are 3¾ x 3½ x ¾ in. deep. Aluminum.
2105-P-5131 $5.99

Gummy Making Kit

NEW!

Kids will have a great time making 16 yummy gummy candies in just minutes! Everything they need is included: mold with four exciting *SpongeBob SquarePants* designs, four .7 oz. pouches of gummy mix (Lemon, Blue Raspberry, Watermelon and Orange), .7 oz. packet of Sour Sugars for covering gummys, squeeze bottle and funnel. Just add water to the mix, shake, fill molds and pop in your refrigerator. Ages 4 and up.
2104-P-5136 $5.99

Baking Cups

Standard size, microwave-safe paper.
2 in. diameter.
415-P-5130
Pk./50 $1.69

Icing Color Set

Includes four .5 oz. jars: Yellow, Red, Blue and Brown. Certified Kosher.
601-P-5130 Set/4 $4.99

Edible Cake Decoration Set

Surround the neat-to-eat *SpongeBob* wafer with the cool icing decoration shapes and add the Happy Birthday message to create instant excitement on any birthday cake.
711-P-5130 Set/20 $2.99

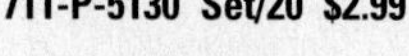

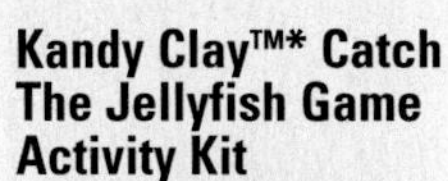

Kandy Clay™* Catch The Jellyfish Game Activity Kit

NEW!

It's the tastiest game ever—featuring the modeling clay you can eat! Includes twelve .5 oz. packs of Kandy Clay (Marshmallow White, Crystal Punch Light Blue, Banana Yellow and Bubble Gum Pink), 2 easy-to-fill Clay Molds for making game pieces, Sculpting Tool for trimming shapes and Game Board for playing the fun "Catch The Jellyfish" game with friends. When the game's over, the eating begins! Ages 4 and up.
2104-P-5140 $6.99

Candy Bar Kit

NEW!

Everything's included for you to make 8 of the yummiest candy bars anywhere, starring *SpongeBob*! Easy to make—just melt, mold and enjoy. Includes 1 candy bar mold (4 designs, 4 cavities), 10 oz. Candy Melts®† (Blue and Yellow), 2 oz. candy toppings (Rainbow Big Bits and Marshmallow Big Bits), plus 8 *SpongeBob* treat bags with matching stickers for fun gifts.
2104-P-5134 $7.99

Party Toppers

NEW!

He's surfing your party goodies on these cool handpainted toppers. Food-safe; great on cupcakes, brownies, cakes and other treats. 2 in. high.
2113-P-5130 Set/6 $3.99

Candle

SpongeBob is swimming in loot—giving you a cake to treasure! Bright handpainted details.
3½ in. high.
2811-P-5130 $3.99

Make-a-Cookie-Face Kit

Decorate 12 colorful cookies that capture *SpongeBob's* bubbly personality. Includes cookie cutter, 12 sets of *SpongeBob SquarePants* facial feature icing decorations, 4.25 oz. tube decorating icing, .75 oz. tube decorating gel, recipe and complete instructions. Certified Kosher.
2104-P-5131 $9.99

Lollipop Making Kit

Everything you need to create *SpongeBob* lollipops that will make waves! Includes lollipop mold (4 designs, 8 cavities), 10 oz. Candy Melts®† (Yellow, White and Pink), 3 disposable decorating bags, 1 decorating brush, 10 lollipop bags with ties and 10 lollipop sticks.
2104-P-5130 $7.99

*Brand edible modeling clay.
†Brand confectionery coating.

Barbie™

NEW!

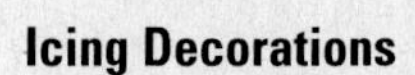

Icing Decorations
Mint-flavored edible sugar shapes. Certified Kosher.
710-P-8934 Pk./9 $2.29

Cake Pan
Celebration *Barbie*™ gets the party fun started for every birthday girl. This newest *Barbie*™ design features pretty pastels, romantic flowers and a fresh, fashionable look that's hers alone. Includes face maker (pictured below). One-mix pan is 9¾ x 13½ x 2 in. deep. Aluminum.
2105-P-8934 $10.99

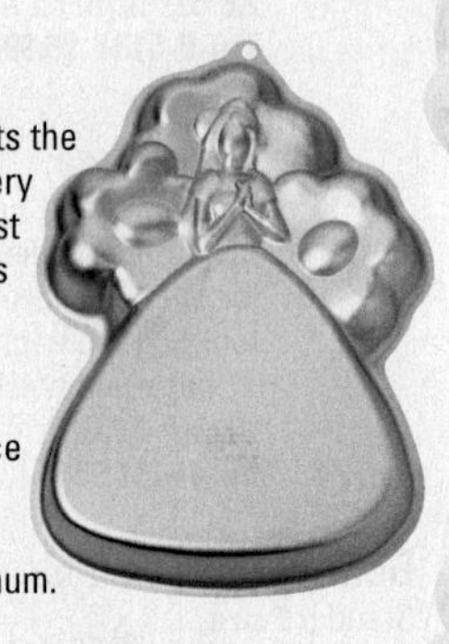

Shaped Sprinkles
Shake up your *Barbie*™ treats! 4-cell container is convenient for pouring and storing. 2.70 oz. Certified Kosher.
710-P-8901 $5.99

Face Maker
Place on cake top for the perfect look of Celebration *Barbie*™.
504-P-8934 $2.29

Candy Bar Kit
Everything's included for you to make 8 of the cutest, yummiest candy bars anywhere, featuring *Barbie*™! Easy and fun—just melt, mold and enjoy. Includes 1 candy bar mold (4 designs, 4 cavities), 10 oz. Candy Melts®† (Pink and Lavender), 2 oz. candy toppings (Strawberry and Marshmallow) and 8 *Barbie*™ treat bags with matching stickers for fun gifts.
2104-P-8934 $7.99

Kandy Clay™* Fashion Fun Activity Kit
Girls create the yummiest fashions—made from the modeling clay you can eat! Dress up the *Barbie*™ image on the Style Setter Board included. Kit includes twelve .5 oz. packs of Kandy Clay (Grape Purple, Banana Yellow, Crystal Punch Light Blue, Watermelon Hot Pink, Orange Orange, and Bubble Gum Pink), 2 easy-to-fill Clay Molds for making fashions, Sculpting Tool for trimming shapes and Style Setter Board for dressing up *Barbie*™. Not for use with actual doll. Ages 4 and up.
2104-P-8935 $6.99

Candle
Barbie® style makes any cake captivating! Handpainted, clean-burning quality. 3½ in. high.
2811-P-8934 $3.99

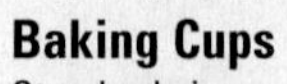

Baking Cups
Standard size, microwave-safe paper. 2 in. diameter.
415-P-8934
Pk./50 $1.69

Icing Color Set
Includes three .5 oz. jars (Pink, Yellow and Violet), and one .1 oz. jar of White Cake Sparkles™ edible glitter. Certified Kosher.
601-P-8934 Set/4 $4.99

Lollipop Making Kit
Everything you need to make delightful *Barbie*™ lollipops. Includes 1 lollipop mold (4 designs, 8 cavities), 10 oz. Candy Melts®† (Pink, White and Yellow), 3 disposable decorating bags, 1 decorating brush, 10 lollipop bags with ties, and 10 lollipop sticks.
2104-P-8903 $7.99

Treat Bags
Fill with candy, cookies and other goodies; great for gifts and surprises, too! Sixteen each 4 x 9½ in. bags and twist ties.
1912-P-8934
Pk./16 $1.99

*Brand edible modeling clay.

†Brand confectionery coating.

THE POWERPUFF GIRLS™

Cake Pan
The *Powerpuff Girls™* help you throw a party that rules! This fun pan features *Bubbles*, *Blossom* and *Buttercup* fighting evil and having a blast. One-mix pan is 13 x 10 x 2 in. deep. Aluminum.
2105-P-9902 $10.99

Candle
Pint-sized power rules as the *Powerpuff Girls™* arrive just in time to save the party! Their candle features handpainted details and clean-burning design to brighten every celebration. 3½ in. high.
2811-P-9902 $3.99

Icing Color Set
Includes four .5 oz. jars: *Blossom* Pink, *Buttercup* Green, *Bubbles* Blue and Peach. Certified Kosher.
601-P-9902
Set/4 $4.99

Icing Decorations
Mint-flavored edible shapes. Certified Kosher.
710-P-9902 Pk./9 $2.29

Baking Cups
Standard size, microwave-safe paper. 2 in. diameter.
415-P-9902
Pk./50 $1.69

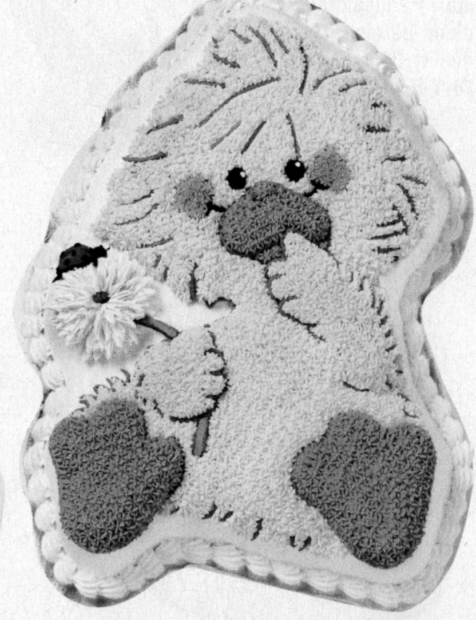

Cake Pan
A wonderful way to welcome baby—at a shower or a first birthday! *Witzy* makes an adorable friend for a day full of fun. One-mix pan is 13 x 8¼ x 2 in. deep. Aluminum.
2105-P-7810 $10.99

Icing Decorations
Mint-flavored edible sugar shapes decorate cupcakes, cookies, ice cream and cake. Certified Kosher.
710-P-7810
Pk./14 $2.29

Baking Cups
Standard size, microwave-safe paper. 2 in. diameter.
415-P-7810
Pk./50 $1.69

Icing Color Set
Includes four .5 oz. jars: Yellow, Orange, Red and Green. Certified Kosher.
601-P-7810 Set/4 $4.99

Candle
Wishin' with *Witzy* is so much fun! Handpainted, clean-burning quality. 3½ in. high.
2811-P-7810 $3.99

Treat Bags
Fill with candy, cookies and other goodies; great for gifts and surprises, too! Sixteen each 4 x 9½ in. bags and twist ties.
1912-P-7810
Pk./16 $1.99

Cake Pan
Fulfill every little girl's dream of becoming a princess with her very own magical Cinderella cake. One-mix pan is 14¼ x 9¼ x 2 in. deep. Aluminum.
2105-P-7475 $10.99

Mini Treats Cake Pan
NEW!
Get close-up with your favorite character and create all kinds of exciting single-size desserts. Great for cakes, candy, gelatin and brownies. The pan's intense color makes baking even more fun. One cake mix makes 15 mini cakes. Four cavity pan is 11 x 9 in.; individual cavities are 3½ x 4¾ x ¾ in. deep. Aluminum.
2105-P-7476 $5.99

Edible Cake Decoration Set
Surround the fun-to-eat *Cinderella* wafer with the magical icing decoration shapes and add the Happy Birthday message to create instant excitement.
711-P-7475 Set/20 $2.99

Icing Color Set
Includes four .5 oz. jars: Blue, Yellow, Pink and Skin Tone. Certified Kosher.
601-P-7475 Set/4 $4.99

Icing Decorations
Mint-flavored edible sugar shapes. Certified Kosher.
710-P-7475 Pk./9 $2.29

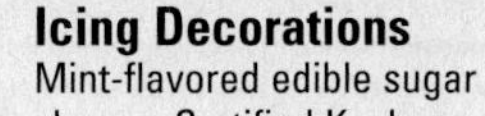

Shaped Sprinkles
4-cell container is convenient for pouring and storing. Includes Crown, Heart, Star and Flower shapes. 2.45 oz. Certified Kosher.
710-P-7479 $5.99

Baking Cups
Standard size, microwave-safe paper. 2 in. diameter.
415-P-7475 Pk./50 $1.69

Treat Bags
Fill with candy, cookies and other goodies; great for gifts and surprises, too! Sixteen each 4 x 9½ in. bags and twist ties.
1912-P-7475 Pk./16 $1.99

Party Toppers
NEW!
A royally fun way to top party treats. Handpainted, food-safe; great on cupcakes, brownies, cakes and other treats. 2 in. high.
2113-P-7475 Set/6 $3.99

Candle
Wish upon a *Disney* star! Handpainted, clean-burning quality. 3½ in. high.
2811-P-7475 $3.99

Gummy Making Kit
NEW!
Kids will have a great time making 16 yummy gummy candies in just minutes! Everything they need is included: mold with four fun *Disney Princess* designs, four .7 oz. pouches of gummy mix (Strawberry, Bubble Gum, Banana and Green Apple), .7 oz. packet of Sour Sugars for covering gummys, squeeze bottle and funnel. Just add water to the mix, shake, fill molds and pop in your refrigerator. Ages 4 and up.
2104-P-7477 $5.99

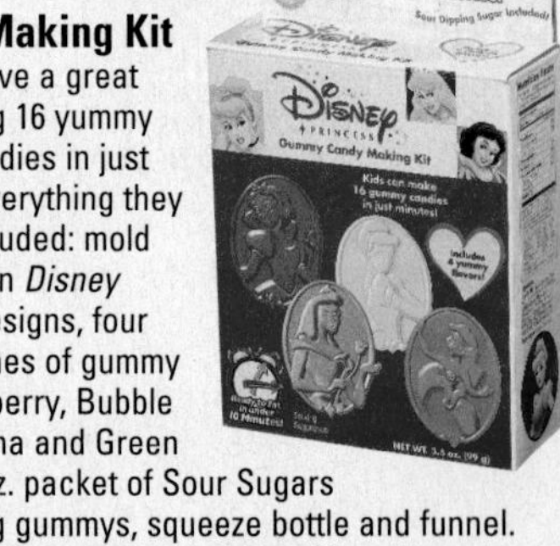

Flower Power

Cake Pan
One-mix pan is 11½ in. diameter x 2 in. deep. Aluminum.
2105-P-3055 $10.99

Floating Candles Set
Great for floating in punch bowls or decorating cakes, cupcakes and food platters. 1½ in. diameter.
2811-P-3055 Set/6 $3.99

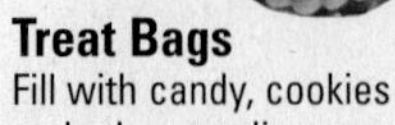

Treat Bags
Fill with candy, cookies and other goodies; great for gifts and surprises, too! Sixteen each 4 x 9 ½ in. bags and twist ties.
1912-P-3055 Pk./20 $1.99

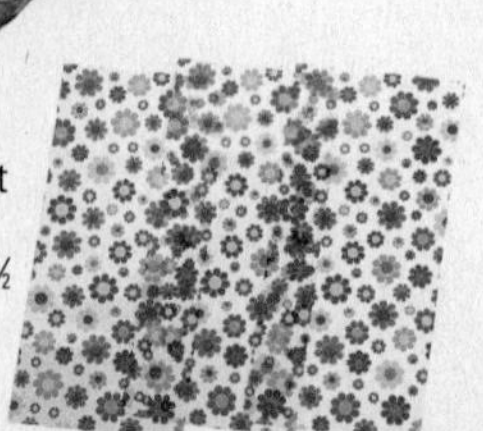

Icing Decorations
Mint-flavored edible shapes. Certified Kosher.
710-P-3055 Pk./9 $2.29

Party Cups
Standard size, microwave-safe paper. 2 in. diameter.
415-P-3055 Pk./50 $1.69

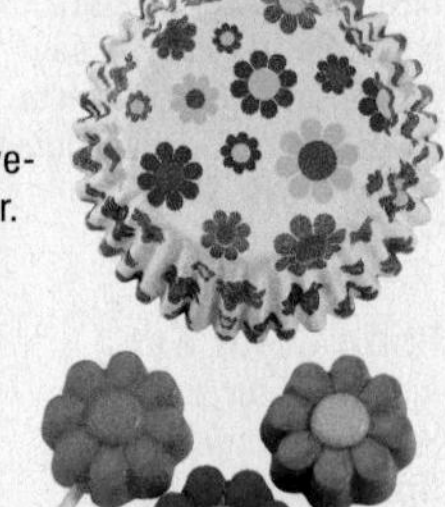

Lollipop Mold
1 design, 9 cavities.
2115-P-3055 $2.29

Disney Mickey Mouse

Mickey Face Pan
The world's most beloved mouse gets into the best parties! Easy-to-decorate; loved by all ages. One-mix pan is 10½ x 12 x 2 in. deep. Aluminum.

2105-P-3603 $10.99

Minnie Mouse Cake Pan
She'll win hearts with her adorable pose. One-mix pan is 15 x 11½ x 2 in. deep. Aluminum.
2105-P-3602 $10.99

Icing Color Set

Includes four .5 oz. jars: two Black, plus Mickey Peach, Copper (lt. skin tone). Certified Kosher.
601-P-3603 Set/4 $4.99

Mickey with Starburst Candle
Your favorite mouse with bright handpainted details. 3½ in. high.
2811-P-3609 $3.99

Minnie with Packages Candle
Handpainted details. 3 in. high.
2811-P-3605 $3.99

Icing Decorations
Mint-flavored edible sugar shapes. Certified Kosher.
710-P-3600 Pk./9 $2.29

Baking Cups
Standard size, microwave-safe paper. 2 in. diameter.
415-P-3610 Pk./50 $1.69

www.DISNEYPARTY.COM
www.disneyhome.com

Disney Winnie the Pooh

Stand-Up Cake Pan Set
Instructions for two different decorating ideas included. Each pan half is 8¼ high x 6½ wide x 2 ¾ in. deep. Pan takes 6 cups of pound cake batter. Includes heat conducting core and 3 clips. Aluminum.
2105-P-3002 Set/2 $17.99

Icing Decorations
Mint-flavored edible sugar shapes. Certified Kosher.
710-P-3000 Pk./9 $2.29

Shaped Sprinkles

Shake up your *Pooh* treats! 4-cell container for pouring and storing. 2.82 oz. Certified Kosher.
710-P-3004 $5.99

Baking Cups
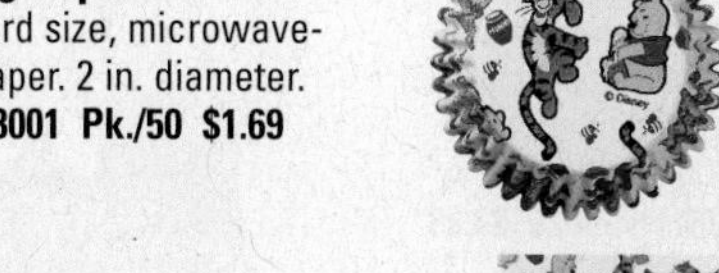
Standard size, microwave-safe paper. 2 in. diameter.
415-P-3001 Pk./50 $1.69

Treat Bags
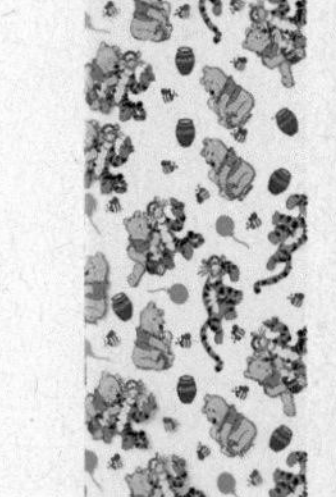
Fill with candy, cookies and other goodies; great for gifts and surprises, too! Sixteen each 4 x 9½ in. bags and twist ties.
1912-P-3001 Pk./16 $1.99

Tigger Cake Pan
One-mix pan is 15½ x 10½ x 2 in. deep. Aluminum.
2105-P-3001 $10.99

Pooh Face Cake Pan
One-mix pan is 11 x 9½ x 2 in. deep. Aluminum.
2105-P-3004 $10.99

Icing Color Set
Includes four .5 oz. jars: *Pooh* (gold), Red, Royal Blue and Black. Certified Kosher.
601-P-228 Set/4 $4.99

Candles
Pooh is ready for the party with bright handpainted details.
2-3 in. high.
$3.99

Pooh and Cake
2811-P-3007

Age 1 *Pooh*
2811-P-3001

Make-a-Cookie-Face Kit
Everything's here for you to decorate 12 colorful cookies that capture *Pooh's* personality. Includes cookie cutter, 12 sets of *Pooh* facial feature icing decorations, 4.25 oz. tube decorating icing, .75 oz. tube decorating gel, recipe and complete instructions.
2104-P-3005 $9.99

Lollipop Making Kit
Everything you need to make happy *Pooh* lollipops! Includes 1 lollipop mold (4 designs, 8 cavities), 10 oz. Candy Melts®† (Yellow, Red and Lavender), 3 disposable decorating bags, 1 decorating brush, 10 lollipop bags with ties and 10 lollipop sticks.
2104-P-3000 $7.99

†Brand confectionery coating.

Based on the "Winnie The Pooh" works, by A.A. Milne and E.H. Shepard.

www.DISNEYPARTY.COM
www.disneyhome.com

Bob the Builder™

Cake Pan
Build some fun with a cake featuring *Bob the Builder!™ Bob* and his construction scene friends are the latest sensation for kids. One-mix pan is 13¾ x 10 x 2 in. deep. Aluminum.
2105-P-5025 $10.99

Candle
Bob's built a birthday gift! Bright handpainted details—and the quality construction *Bob* demands. 3¼ in. high.
2811-P-5025 $3.99

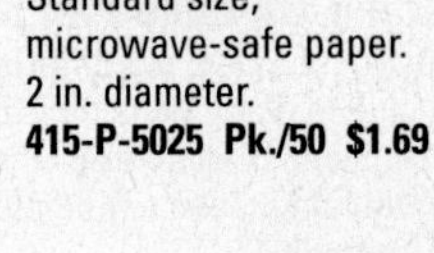

Baking Cups
Standard size, microwave-safe paper. 2 in. diameter.
415-P-5025 Pk./50 $1.69

Treat Bags
Fill with candy, cookies and other goodies; great for gifts and surprises, too! 4 x 9½ in. bags and twist ties.
1912-P-5025
Pk./16 $1.99

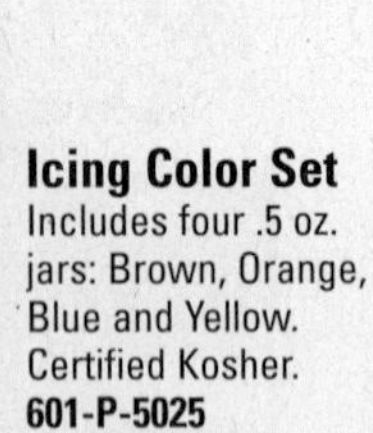

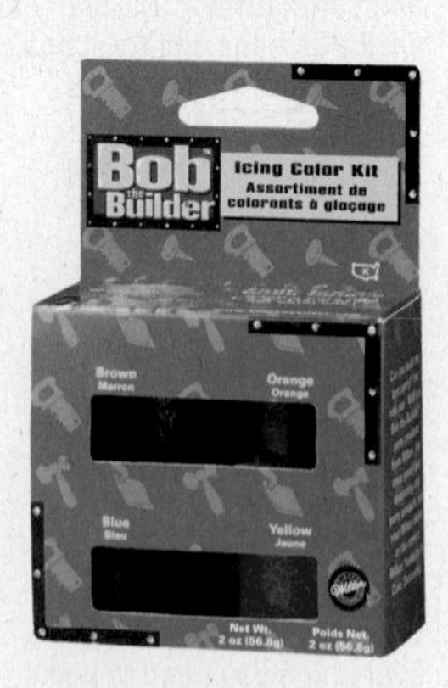

Icing Color Set
Includes four .5 oz. jars: Brown, Orange, Blue and Yellow. Certified Kosher.
601-P-5025
Set/4 $4.99

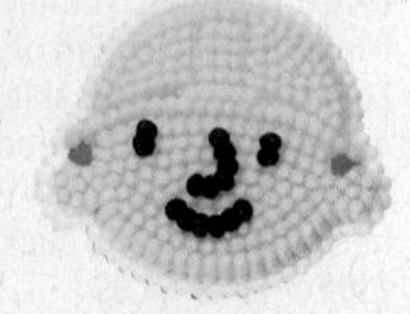

Icing Decorations
Mint-flavored edible sugar shapes decorate cupcakes, cookies, ice cream and cake. Certified Kosher.
710-P-5025 Pk./9 $2.29

Make-a-Cookie-Face Kit
Everything's here for you to decorate 12 fun, colorful cookies that capture *Bob the Builder's™* hardworking attitude. Includes cookie cutter, 12 sets of *Bob the Builder* facial feature icing decorations, 4.25 oz. tube decorating icing, .75 oz. tube decorating gel, recipe and complete instructions. Certified Kosher.
2104-P-5026 $9.99

Lollipop Making Kit
Everything you need to make fun *Bob the Builder™* lollipops! Includes 1 lollipop mold (4 designs, 8 cavities), 10 oz. Candy Melts®† (Blue, Yellow and White), 3 disposable decorating bags, 1 decorating brush, 10 treat bags with ties and 10 lollipop sticks.
2104-P-5025 $7.99

†Brand confectionery coating.

Cake Pan
Blue is bearing a banner with good wishes for the birthday boy or girl! One-mix pan is 13 x 11½ x 2 in. deep. Aluminum.
2105-P-3064 $10.99

Shaped Sprinkles
Shake up your *Blue's Clues* treats! 4-cell container is convenient for pouring and storing. 2.82 oz. Certified Kosher.
710-P-3062 $5.99

Icing Color Set
Includes four .5 oz. jars: Blue, Sky Blue, Dark Blue and Purple. Certified Kosher.
601-P-3064 Set/4 $4.99

NEW!

Party Toppers
A gift for *Blue,* and a treat for kids, too! Handpainted, food-safe; great on cupcakes, brownies, cakes and other treats. 2¼ in. high.
2113-P-3060 Set/6 $3.99

Candle
When *Blue* brings her friend *Joe* along, it's going to be a great party! Handpainted details. 3¼ in. high.
2811-P-3064 $3.99

Icing Decorations
Mint-flavored edible sugar shapes. Certified Kosher.
710-3061 Pk./9 $2.29

Baking Cups
Standard size, microwave-safe paper. 2 in. diameter.
415-P-3061 Pk./50 $1.69

Treat Bags
Fill with candy, cookies and other goodies; great for gifts and surprises, too! Sixteen each 4 x 9½ in. bags and twist ties.
1912-P-3060 Pk./16 $1.99

Food Making Kit
Everything you need to make great *Blue's Clues* treats! Includes 1 food mold (4 designs, 8 cavities), 10 oz. Candy Melts®† (Blue, Pink and Lavender), 3 disposable decorating bags, 1 decorating brush and 10 treat bags with ties.
2104-P-3060 $7.99

123 SESAME STREET®

Elmo Face Cake Pan
He's sweet, lovable and popular with kids of all ages. One-mix pan is 13½ x 10½ x 2 in. deep. Aluminum.
2105-P-3461 $10.99

Elmo with Crayons Candle
Elmo brings smiles to the party with bright, handpainted details. 3½ in. high.
2811-P-3463 $3.99

Icing Decorations
Mint-flavored edible sugar shapes decorate cupcakes, cookies, ice cream and cakes. Certified Kosher.
710-P-3460 Pk./9 $2.29

Baking Cups
Standard size, microwave-safe paper. 2 in. diameter.
415-P-3461 Pk./50 $1.69

Parade Cake Top Set
A fun birthday parade right on your cake. *Cookie Monster, Zoe, Elmo, Big Bird.* 1½ to 4 in. high.
2113-P-3460 Set/4 $4.99

Wedding

From ornaments to favors, cake stands to candle holders, Wilton gives brides the greatest variety of wedding products to create the wedding she has always dreamed about.

Wedding Figurines

More brides choose Wilton figurines to top their wedding cakes. The rich, sculpted crafting, realistic detailing and romantic designs make these figurines perfect wedding day keepsakes.

Always and Forever Petite Embrace
Height: 3¾ in. Base: 2½ in. diameter. Resin.
202-P-311 $21.99

Bianca
Height: 5¼ in. Resin.
202-P-207 $24.99

Platinum Bianca
Height: 5¼ in.
Painted resin.
202-P-418 $24.99

Always and Forever Musical Ornament
Plays "The Wedding March".
Height: 7¼ in.
Base: 4¼ in. diameter. Resin.
215-P-310 $49.99

Clear Bianca
Stunning figurine celebrates weddings and anniversaries. 5½ in. high x 4 in. wide x 3 in. deep. Acrylic. Shown on Lighted Revolving Base (sold below).
202-P-424 $24.99

Joyful Embrace
Height: 7½ in. Base: 4½ in. diameter. Resin.
110-P-904 $39.99

Horse & Carriage
4½ in. high x 7 in. long x 2½ in. wide. Resin.
110-P-862 $29.99

Castle
Lights from within using 2 D batteries (not included). 7½ in. high, 4½ in. square base. Resin.
111-P-2804 $59.99

Lighted Revolving Base
Choose to just light, just rotate or both at the same time. Uses 3 AA batteries (not included). Height: 2 in. Diameter: 5 in.
201-P-453 $24.99

Porcelain Gazebo
Height: 7½ in.
Base: 5½ x 5½ in. Porcelain.
117-P-507 $49.99

Porcelain Promenade
Height: 6½ in. Base: 5½ x 3 in. Porcelain.
117-P-508 $29.99

Just Married
Height: 5 in. Base: 5 x 3¼ in. Resin.
110-P-864 $44.99

Elegance
Height: 5½ in.
Base: 5 x 3 in. Resin.
110-P-863 $34.99

Forever In Your Eyes
Height: 6 in. Base: 5 in. diameter. Resin.
110-P-903 $39.99

Wedding Figurines

Caring Embrace
Height: 6 in.
Base: 3¾ in. Porcelain.
202-P-419 $34.99

With This Ring
Height: 4½ in. Resin.
202-P-313 $24.99

New Beginning
Height: 8⅝ in.
Base: 4½ x 3½ in.
Porcelain.
202-P-420 $39.99

Our Day
Height: 4¾ in. Poly Resin.
Blonde/White Gown
202-P-409 $6.99
Brunette/Ivory Gown
(not shown)
202-P-415 $6.99

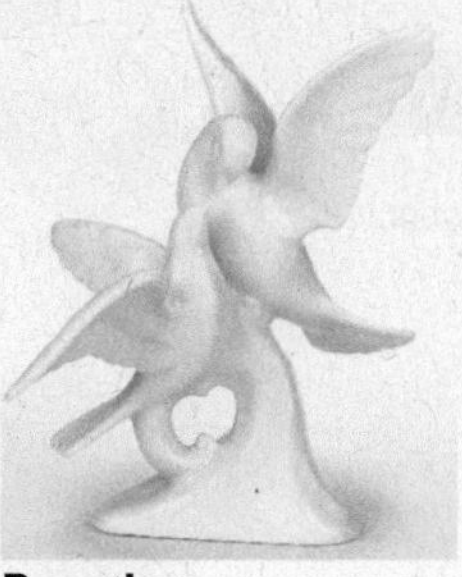

Devotion
Height: 7 in.
Base: 4 x 2½ in. Ceramic.
111-P-2803 $34.99

Inspirational Cross
Height: 5½ in.
Resin.
202-P-206 $24.99

Threshold Of Happiness
Height: 5 in. Resin.
202-P-202 $24.99

From This Day Forward (Non-musical)
Height: 7 in. Base:
4½ in. diameter. Resin.
202-P-417 $44.99

From This Day Forward
Height: 5 in. Resin.
202-P-319 $24.99

HUMOROUS WEDDING FIGURINES

Add a lighthearted touch to the celebration. Sure to bring a smile to the face of anyone who has ever planned a wedding!

Now I Have You
Height: 4¼ in. Base: 4¼ x 3¾ in. Resin.
115-P-101 $14.99

Oh No You Don't
Height: 4¼ in. Base: 6 x 3 in. Resin.
115-P-102 $14.99

Love's Duet
Height: 6 in.
Poly Resin.
202-P-402 $11.99

Ethnic Love's Duet
Height: 6 in.
Poly Resin.
202-P-412 $11.99

Lasting Love
Height: 4½ in.
Poly Resin.
202-P-302 $6.99
Petite Lasting Love
(not shown)
Height: 3½ in.
202-P-401 $5.99

The Tiff
Height: 4 in. Resin.
115-P-103 $14.99

Liberated Bride
Height: 4½ in. Plastic.
2113-P-4188 $5.99

Reluctant Groom
Height: 5 in. Plastic.
1316-P-9520 $5.99

WEDDING ATTENDANT FIGURINES

Want to add color? All resin figurines may be personalized using acrylic paint.

Bridesmaid
Height: 4½ in. Resin.
203-P-315 $5.99

NEW!

Groomsman
Height: 4½ in. Resin.
203-P-316 $5.99

NEW!

Ethnic Bridesmaid
Height: 4½ in. Resin.
203-P-318 $5.99

NEW!

Ethnic Groomsman
Height: 4½ in. Resin.
203-P-317 $5.99

Anniversary Ornaments

Petite 50th
Height: 5¾ in.
Base: 3¼ in. diameter.
105-P-4273 $8.99
Petite 25th
Silver 105-P-4265 $8.99

50 Years of Happiness
Height: 10 in.
Base: 4⅝ in. diameter.
102-P-223 $17.99

Wedding Ornaments

NEW!

Floral Topper
Beautiful handmade flowers, greenery, satin ribbon.
White resin base.
Height: 5¾ in.
Base: 3¼ in. Diameter
120-P-073 $39.99

Enduring Love
Height: 5 in. Base: 7 x 5 in. oval.
103-P-235 $35.99

Always and Forever
Height: 6½ in. Base: 7 x 5 in. oval.
118-P-200 $37.99

Romantic Moments
Height: 10½ in.
Base: 4½ x 6 in. oval.
118-P-651 $49.99

Our First Dance
Height: 9¼ in.
Base: 4⅝ in. diameter.
118-P-650 $44.99
Couple Only
Height: 6 in. Poly Resin
202-P-411 $14.99

Expression Of Love
Height: 7¾ in.
Base: 4½ in. diameter.
101-P-933 $35.99
Couple Only
Height: 4½ in. Poly Resin
202-P-306 $6.99

Expression Of Love
Height: 7¾ in.
Base: 4 ½ in. diameter.
101-P-931 $35.99

Sweetness
Height 7¾ in.
Base: 4½ in. diameter.
Blonde Bride 101-P-153
Brunette Bride 101-P-156
$29.99

Simple Joys
Height: 8 in.
Base: 4½ in. diameter.
103-P-150 $24.99

Promise
Porcelain couple.
Height: 9⅝ in.
Base: 4½ in. diameter.
117-P-315 $25.99

Reflections
Porcelain couple. Height: 8 in.
Base: 4¾ in. diameter.
117-P-268 $25.99

Spring Song
Height: 9½ in.
Base: 4⅝ in. diameter.
111-P-2802 $19.99
Kissing Lovebirds
5½ in. high.
1002-P-206 $4.99

Petite Spring Song
Height: 7 in.
Base: 3¼ in. diameter.
106-P-159 $12.99

Ornament Settings and Bases

A beautiful beginning to a cake top ornament you create. Simply add the figurine of your choice, and trim with flowers, fabric tulle and accents.

Floral Arch
Height: 10 in.
Base: 4 ⅝ in. diameter.
210-P-1987 $9.99

Chapel Windows
Use with base or alone.
6 ½ x 5 x 1 in. deep.
205-P-3060 $4.99

Gazebo Set
Easy to assemble plastic.
5 x 9 in.
205-P-3061 $4.99

Romantic Heart
2 pieces, 2 base sizes.
Regular 4 ⅝ in. diameter
201-P-7332 $2.99

Wedding Ensembles

Fulfill every bride's wish with the finest coordinated wedding accessories. Nicely presented, a complete collection makes a beautiful gift. Or enjoy the flexibility of choosing individual accessories that personalize the wedding day!

Flower Basket
Held by the flower girl, as she scatters Rose Petals along the bridal path. Petals not included.

Ring Bearer's Pillow
Lovingly carried by the Ring Bearer, this beautiful pillow adds elegance to your wedding ceremony.

Guest Book
The perfect wedding keepsake—guests sign and add their good wishes on your special day.

Guest Pen and Holder
To make signing the guest book easy and elegant.

Gift Card Bags
Beautiful and practical accessory for your wedding day! Use for gift envelopes, bride and groom's "dollar dance" money, bride's make-up, more— drawstring close keeps contents secure! Generous 7½ x 11 in. x 2 in. size.

Elegance
Sophistication abounds with tailored satin and ribbon trim.
Flower Basket
120-P-331 $14.99
Ring Bearer Pillow
120-P-334 $18.99
Guest Pen and Book Set
120-P-871 $29.99
Card Bag
(shown at right)
120-P-4007 $12.99

Eternity
Upscale quilting with floral trim—the essence of bridal chic. Ivory.
Flower Basket
120-P-339 $18.99
Ring Bearer Pillow
120-P-338 $24.99
Guest Pen and Book Set
120-P-328 $29.99
Card Bag
(shown at right)
120-P-4006 $12.99

Expressions
Lattice ribbon design with delicate floral blooms and ribbon trim
Flower Basket
120-P-872 $18.99
Ring Bearer Pillow
120-P-873 $24.99
Guest Pen and Book Set
120-P-874 $29.99
Card Bag
(shown at right)
120-P-4008 $12.99

Radiance
Beautifully designed and crafted with opulent rose blooms and wide organza ribbon trim. Set includes Flower Basket, Ring Bearer Pillow, Guest Pen and Guest Book.
120-P-261 Set/4 $69.99

Classic
Perfect choice for the bride who appreciates the allure of elegance. Satin with satin ribbon trim. Set includes Flower Basket, Ring Bearer Pillow, Guest Pen and Guest Book.
120-P-472 Set/4 $69.99

Enchanting
Inspired by the romance of a flower garden, designed in satin with fabric blooms. Set includes Flower Basket, Ring Bearer Pillow, Guest Pen and Guest Book.
120-P-083 Set/4 $69.99

Traditional
Gleaming white with lace and ribbon trim.

Flower Basket	**1006-P-603**	**$3.99**
Ring Bearer Pillow	**120-P-100**	**$15.99**
Guest Pen	**120-P-804**	**$14.99**
Guest Book	**120-P-800**	**$14.99**
Complete Set of 4	**120-P-095**	**$44.99**

Timeless
Beautiful woven satin ribbon design.

Flower Basket	**120-P-604**	**$14.99**
Ring Bearer Pillow	**120-P-101**	**$18.99**
Guest Pen	**120-P-831**	**$14.99**
Guest Book	**120-P-829**	**$18.99**
Complete Set of 4	**120-P-460**	**$69.99**

Legacy
Rich damask fabric covers this ensemble.

Flower Basket	**120-P-606**	**$14.99**
Ring Bearer Pillow	**120-P-102**	**$18.99**
Guest Pen	**120-P-832**	**$14.99**
Guest Book	**120-P-830**	**$18.99**

Simplicity
Adorned with shimmering fabric and pearls.

Flower Basket	**120-P-834**	**$14.99**
Ring Bearer Pillow	**120-P-833**	**$18.99**
Guest Pen	**120-P-836**	**$14.99**
Guest Book	**120-P-835**	**$18.99**

Wedding Day Accessories

SERVING PIECES

Keepsake-quality cake servers will be used again, on special occasions at gatherings with family and friends throughout your married life.

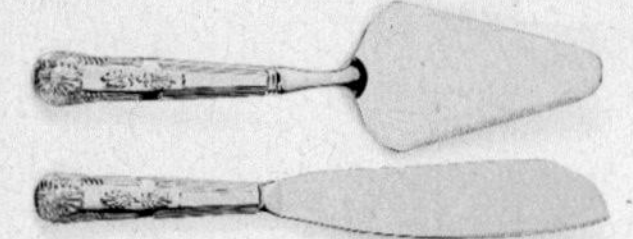

Cake Knife and Server Set
Silverplated, with sculpting on handles. Engravable.
120-P-4004 Set/2 $29.99

Cake Knife and Server Set
Stainless steel blades with acrylic handles. Engravable.
120-P-4003 Set/2 $24.99

Heart Silver Toasting Glasses and Servers Ensemble NEW!
For the toast to the bride and groom and cutting the cake. Elegant silver-plated heart design, organza ribbon and pearl trim. Silver–plated. Engrave for a beautiful keepsake.
120-P-232 Set/4 $49.99

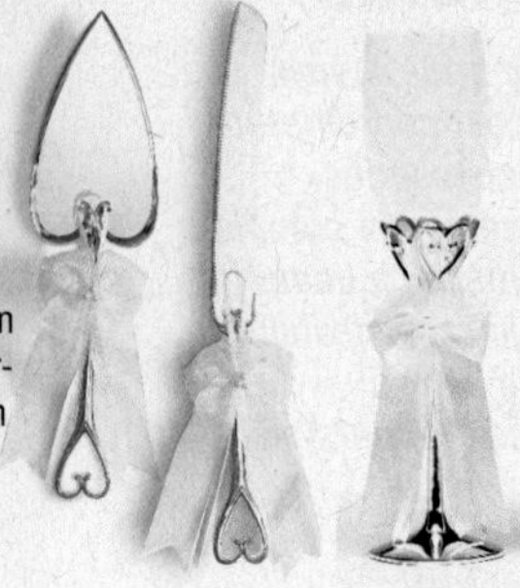

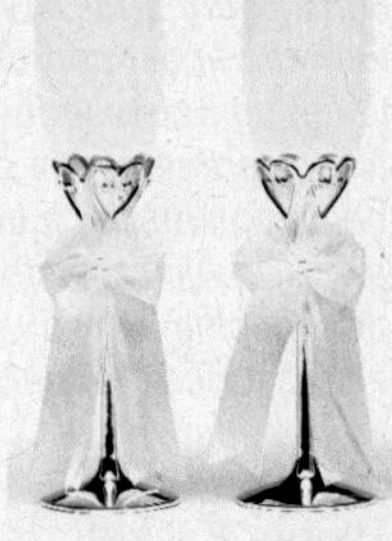

TOASTING GLASSES

Beautiful stemware to use at the reception, then at home!

Interlocking Hearts
Symbolic of true love, two fit together to form one heart. Silver-plated and engravable.
Height: 7 ½ in.
120-P-821
Set/2 $34.99

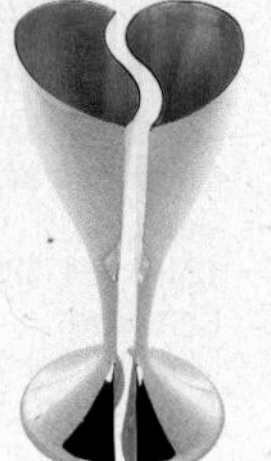

Pearl
Height: 9 ½ in.
120-P-783 Set/2 $21.99

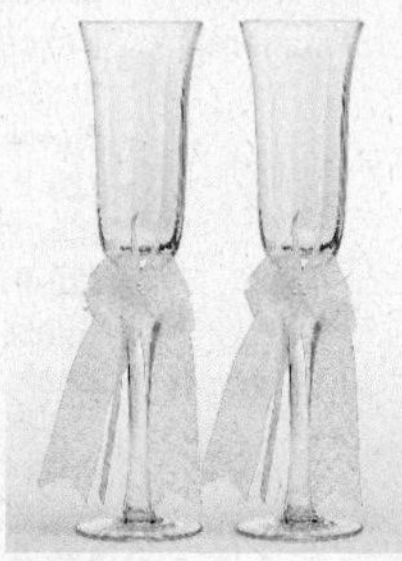

Fluted
Height: 10 in.
120-P-784 Set/2 $21.99

Champagne Bubbles
Height: 10 in.
120-P-652 Set/2 $21.99

Rosebud
Height: 8 ⅜ in.
120-P-708 Set/2 $21.99

Autograph Mat
Fits 11 x 14 in. frame, holds 5 x 7 in. photo. Includes black pen.
1009-P-508 $5.99

GLOVES

For all celebrations—weddings, prom, parties, Communion and costumes. In white.

Satin Long
120-P-827
$14.99

Satin Short
Adult 120-P-413 $9.99

Small
120-P-828 $6.99

GARTERS

Buy one to toss, one to keep. Beautifully appointed with lace and ribbon trim.

Keepsake White
Features engravable silver locket that holds two photos.
120-P-826 $9.99

Tossing
Ribbon, pearl and lace trim.
Blue
120-P-402 $5.99
White
120-P-401 $5.99

FLORAL ACCESSORIES

French Rose Wedding Bouquet
Perfect, beautiful blooms to keep or to use during the bouquet toss. Hand-crafted, fine silk flowers with wrapped stem. Bouquets approx. 8½ in. diameter with 4 in. stem.
120-P-1013 $24.99

White Rose Boutonniere
Perfect for weddings, prom, special occasions
1006-P-694 $4.99

Bouquet Holder NEW!
Create a bouquet just for the bride and her bridesmaids. At the reception, it converts into a standing arrangement. Arranging the silk bouquet is so simple, follow the easy step-by-step instructions included.
1006-P-641 $5.99

Bouquet Holder
Slip over stems to dress up any bouquet.
White Organza
10 ½ in. diameter.
1006-P-992 $1.99
White Lace (not shown)
10½ in. diameter.
1006-P-604 $1.99

Fresh Look Bouquet Holder
Make bouquets for the wedding party! It's easy to do, using your favorite silk or fabric flowers.
1006-P-611 $7.99

Silver Bouquet Holder
Arrange the bride's favorite flowers in this keepsake holder. Silver-plated.
7 ½ in. long.
120-P-651 $12.99

Flower Petals
Fill the flower girl's basket, scatter on the cake table, decorate favors. Lifelike 2½ in. diameter flower petals. Approx. 300 petals in Value Pack.
$9.99

Lavender Hydrangea
1006-P-879

White Rose
1006-P-698

Blush Rose
1006-P-697

Red Rose
1006-P-695

Latino Traditions NEW!

Kneeling Cushion
Heirloom-quality, designed for the First Communion, la quinceañera or wedding mass prayers. Crafted in satin. 18 in. x 14 in. pillow with 2 in. ruffle.
120-P-510 $39.99

Head Piece and Bouquet Set
Lightweight, life-like hand made flowers are fashioned into matching headpiece to wear and bouquet to carry on your special day.
120-P-211 Set/2 $69.99

Spanish Bible and Rosary Set
Use this beautiful set for the First Communion, la quinceañera, or wedding ceremony. Bible features updated, easy-to-read text in Spanish.
120-P-336 $39.99

Mis Quince Guest Book
Beautiful book with 16 full-color, removable pages documents la quinceañera ceremony and party. Includes room for signatures and wishes; photos; gift record, keepsake and more. Spanish text.
120-P-665 $39.99

La Quinceañera Figurine
Ideal as a cake top decoration or favor.
Height: 4½ in.
203-P-305 $3.99

Porcelain Celebration Doll
Heirloom quality keepsake doll is a cherished tradition for special life occasions —First Communion, la quinceañera, wedding. 22 in. tall; wood stand, simple assembly.
120-P-501 $89.99

LAZOS

In this popular wedding ceremony custom, one loop of the Lazo is placed around the bride, and the other loop around the groom, symbolically joining them together for all to see. Hand-crafted with the finest trims, each loop measures approximately 55 inches.

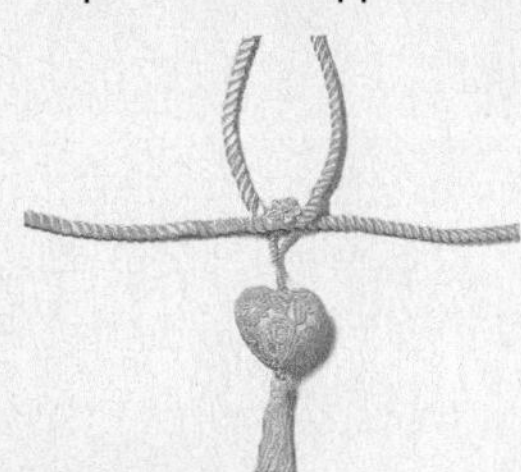

White Rope with Heart
Satin and embroidered lace.
120-P-602 $31.99

White Beaded with Cross
Pearl finish.
120-P-603 $18.99

Coin Box
Dazzling coin box with 13 coins—representative of Jesus and the 12 apostles—is presented during the wedding ceremony to symbolize the promise made by the bride and groom to provide and care for each other.
120-P-514 $19.99

Favor Tags
Attach to favors, decorations, flowers, celebration doll. Includes 11½ in. ribbon.
Mis Quince
1006-P-482
Pk./12 $2.99
Nuestra Boda
1006-P-484
Pk./12 $2.99

Accent Flowers
Add beautiful custom color to accessories and decorations. Attach with hot glue or sew on. 1 in. diameter.
Pink 211-P-1717
Pk./8 $1.29

Accent Leaves
Bend for a realistic silhouette. Attach with wire ends or hot glue in place. 1¼ in. wide leaf on 5 in. long stem.
Pink 211-P-1719
Pk./5 $1.29

Wedding Day Décor

Circle of Love Wreath
Use the attached ribbon loop to hang. Flowers on one side only. 7 in. diameter.
120-P-1011 $6.99

Flowering Heart
3 dimensional, the blooms cover all surfaces! Use the attached ribbon loop to hang. 9 in. diameter.
120-P-1012
$15.99

Iridescent Beaded Garland
⅞ in. diameter beads. 24 ft. length.
1006-P-196 $7.99

Sparkling Ice*
Container size: 1½ in. high x 4½ in. diameter.
1006-P-342 $9.99

*WARNING: CHOKING HAZARD–Small parts. Not intended for children. Not a toy–for decorative use only.

GIFT CARD HOLDERS

Keeps the wedding gift cards together at the reception, while acting as a distinctive centerpiece. Tulle accents not included.

Vertical Reception Gift Card Holder
16½ in. high x 7 in. long x 7 in. deep.
120-P-330 $24.99

Horizontal Reception Gift Card Holder
12 in. high x 10 in. long x 7 in. deep.
120-P-875 $24.99

Wedding Day Décor

LIGHTED BRIDAL GARLANDS

Romantic floral garland adds a soft glow to your wedding ambiance! You'll find so many uses for the ceremony and reception. Drape on pews and line the aisles, place along table edges and around the cake, wrap around pillars. 6 foot length, battery operated (uses 2 D Batteries, not included).

Organza Rose
1006-P-584 $23.99

Hydrangea
1006-P-581 $23.99

White Rose
1006-P-350 $23.99

French Rose Garland
Non-lighting; French roses strung together by organza ribbon. 6 foot length.
1006-P-345 $14.99

CANDLE RINGS AND HOLDERS

Lighted Candle Rings

Surround your candles with flowers and the gentle glow of romance. Uses 2 AA batteries, not included. Use with standard pillar candles up to 3 in. diameter. Shown on silver unity candleholder sold below (not included). **$14.99**

Organza Rose
1006-P-587

Hydrangea
1006-P-588

White Rose
1006-P-589

White Rose Candle Rings
Taper 120-P-782 Set/2 $8.99 **Unity 120-P-781 $10.99**

Silver Candleholder Set
Keepsake-quality set holds the unity candle and tapers for the candle lighting ceremony, then adds the romantic glow of candlelight to your reception table. At home, you'll use the candleholders year-round for special dates, dinner parties and holidays. Silver-plated; ribbon trim. Unity candle holder is 6¼ in. high; holds a pillar candle up to 3¾ in. diameter. Each taper candle holder is 5½ in. high; holds standard size tapers. Candles not included.
120-P-448 Set/3 $34.99

UNITY CANDLES

From This Day
Elegant pearl design. 9 in. high x 3 in. diameter.
120-P-738
$23.99

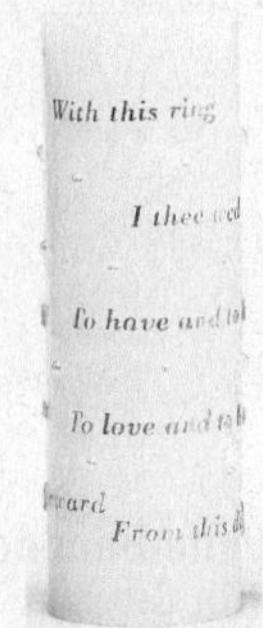

With This Ring
Words of love circle design. 9 in. high x 3 in. diameter.
120-P-737
$23.99

Love, Honor, Cherish
Contemporary design. 9 in. high x 3 in. diameter.
120-P-459
$23.99

Ribbon/Rings
Carved with ring-bearing doves. 9 in. high x 2¾ in. diameter.
120-P-710
$17.99

TAPER CANDLE SETS

Pearl
Candles read "From this Day". 10 in. high.
120-P-721
Set/2 $7.99

Love, Honor, Cherish
Ribbon and bow trim. 10 in. high.
120-P-217
Set/2 $7.99

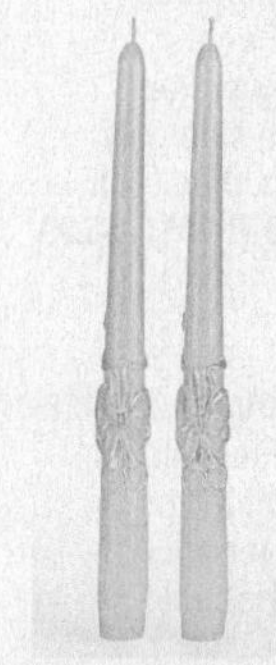

Ribbon/Rings
Elegant carved detail. 10 in. high.
120-P-726
Set/2 $2.99

Wedding Day Décor

CHAIR WRAP

Versatile fabric wrap beautifully accents party and reception chairs and more! Place on a table as a lush runner, wrap a large gift, make a magnificent bow. Fabric dye changes this wrap into a perfect-colored accent for your wedding day! 18 in. wide x 12 ft. long.

Organza Beaded
1006-P-382 $9.99

Satin
1006-P-384 $9.99

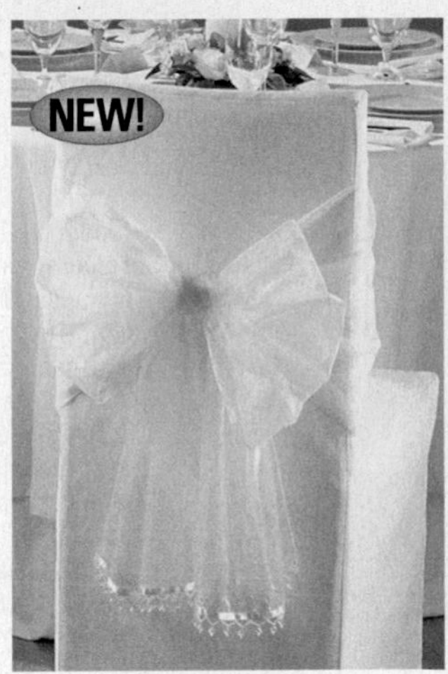

Satin Chair Cover
Distinguish wedding party and special guest seating at your celebration—fits most standard folding and party chairs. Luxurious satin fabric can be dyed using fabric dye to match your colors.
1006-P-131 $9.99

Pull-N-Fluff™ Bows
Create stunning bows in 3 easy steps—just pull the strings, tie and fluff! Perfect for weddings, holiday décor, gifts, more. Reusable and dyeable. Bows are 6 in. diameter.

Organza
1006-P-636
Pk./12 $19.99

Satin
1006-P-633
Pk./12 $29.99

Bubble Machine
Surround your celebration with shimmering bubbles! Compact size (4.5 high x 3.75 wide x 7 in. deep) allows for hiding in floral arrangements. Neutral white color blends with other wedding décor. Requires 2 C batteries, not included. Use with Wilton Bubble Solution.
1007-P-8015 $14.99

1 Liter Bubble Solution 1007-P-8016 $4.99

Car Decorating Kit
Eye-catching decorations trim the bride and groom's getaway vehicle with style! Includes: Magnetic "Just Married" sign, window clings, pre-fluffed pom-poms, streamers, balloons. Crafted of weather-resistant materials, reusable (except balloons).
1006-P-483 $14.99

CENTERPIECES

Lighted Gazebo
Looking for a distinctive way to decorate your wedding? Decorate the gazebo with flowers, greenery, ribbon or tulle. Create one for every table at your reception. Uses 4 AA batteries, not included. 4¾ in. deep x 3¾ in. long x 8 ½ in. high.
1006-P-223 $19.99

Silver Unlit Gazebo
1006-P-455 $14.99

Lighted Arch
What could be more elegant than a centerpiece matched to the celebration? Just add ribbon, tulle, and position your favorite ornament or photo. Uses 4 AA batteries, not included. 3½ deep x 8 in. long x 10 in. high.
1006-P-222 $19.99

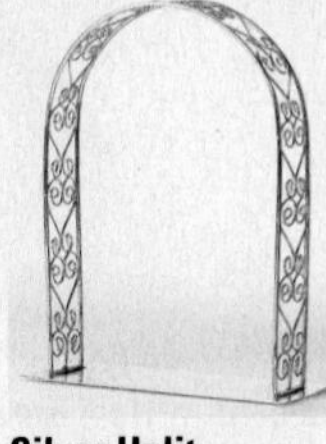

Silver Unlit Arch
1006-P-456 $14.99

Tiered Floral Centerpiece

NEW!

Create an elegant display for fresh or silk flowers. Use with or without cake. Can be displayed as single tiers. Contains three 2-piece tiers. Tops remove for easy cleaning. Assembly instructions included.
120-P-822 $29.99

Favor-Making Kits NEW!

Fun and festive kits personalize your favors with ease! Just add candy!

Heart Mega Favors
Makes 24 favors—includes heart containers, tulle circles, 5 in. ribbon lengths and favor tags.
1006-P-923 Pk./24 $23.99

Goblet Mega Favors
Makes 24 favors—includes goblet containers, tulle circles, 5 in. ribbon lengths and favor tags.
1006-P-924 Pk./24 $23.99

Favor Tins
Create personalized favor tins to match your celebration using your computer and printer, or hand design. Includes 12 tins, 12 adhesive labels and strips, complete instructions. Just download template from www.wilton.com and you're ready to go.
1006-P-481
Pk./12 $9.99

Candle Favors
Add a romantic touch to showers, receptions, every celebration. Includes 12 lightly-scented 4 in. mini candles, and 3 in. candle holders already decorated with white organza bows.
1006-P-643
Pk./12 $14.99

Sweet Things™ Champagne Bottles
Everything needed to make 12 beautiful favors! Includes champagne bottle favor pedestals, ribbon, tulle circles, favor tags.
1006-P-227 Pk./12 $14.99

Sweet Things™ Roses
Everything needed to make 12 beautiful favors! Includes rose favor pedestals, ribbon, tulle circles, favor tags.
1006-P-225 Pk./12 $14.99

Sweet Things™ Cakes
Everything needed to make 12 beautiful favors! Includes tiered cake favor pedestals, ribbon, tulle circles, favor tags.
1006-P-226 Pk./12 $14.99

Drawstring Wrappers
Create 12 cute favors in no time at all! Kit includes drawstring wrapper and blank favor tags. Just fill and tie.
Pk./12 $12.99
White 1006-P-921
Lavender 1006-P-922

Place Cards and Holders

An elegant way to indicate seating arrangements; and a stunning display for photos, special notes and thanks for your guests.

Silver Double Heart Place Cards
Use for every life celebration!
1006-P-752 Pk./40 $2.29

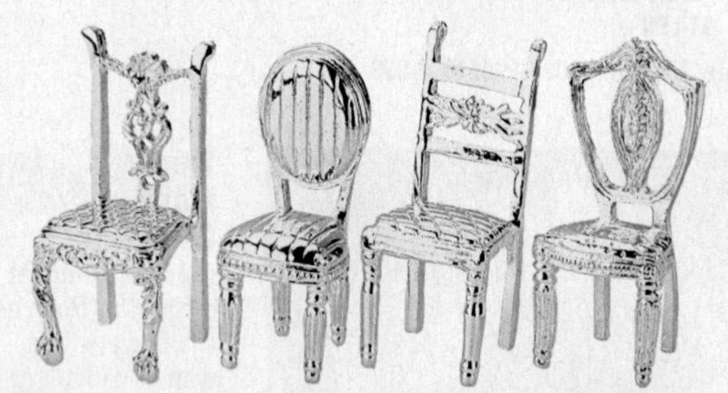

Chairs
Chair back is slotted to hold place card. 2¾ in. high.
1009-P-237 Pk./4 $12.99

Bell
Slotted handle holds place card. 2 in. high x 1¼ in. wide.
1006-P-886 Pk./4 $12.99

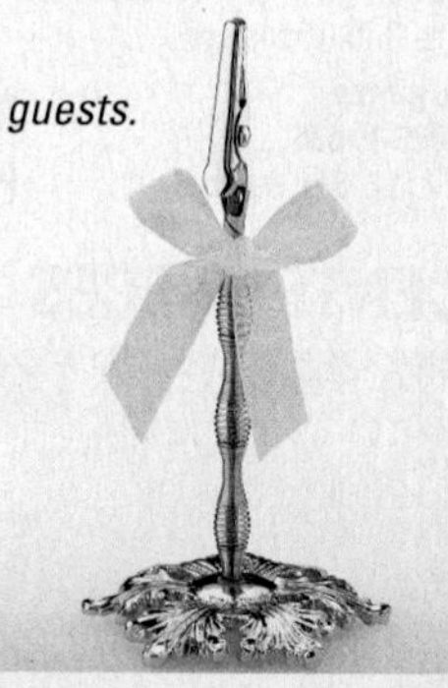

Silver Clip
3¾ in. high x 1¾ in. wide.
1009-P-223 Pk./4 $12.99

Silver Gazebo
Removable roof is slotted to hold place card. 3 in. high x 2½ in. wide.
1006-P-373 $1.29

Love Potion
Slotted cork holds place card. Includes recipe cards, funnel. 2¾ in. high x 1 in. wide.
1006-P-352 Pk./6 $5.99

"Glass" Slipper
Heel is slotted to hold place card. 1¾ in. high x 1 in. wide x 2 in. deep. Plastic.
1006-P-370 Pk./12 $5.99

Pedestal
3 in. high x 3¾ in. wide.
1009-P-236 $1.99

Glitter
2¼ in. high x 4½ in. wide.
1009-P-231 $1.99

Favor Containers

These beautiful containers hold favors for shower, wedding and anniversary celebrations. Perfect for mints, almonds, potpourri and small gifts.

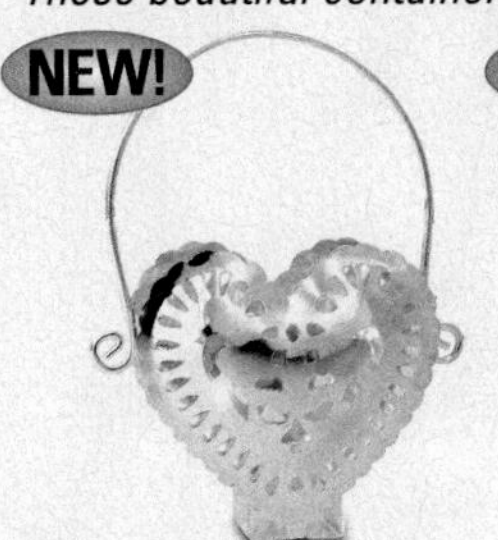

Silver Lace Heart Basket
3½ in. high x 3 in. wide. Metal.
1006-P-562 $1.29

Silver Heart Patterned Basket
3½ in. high x 3 in. wide. Metal.
1006-P-338 $1.29

Flower Shape Basket
3¾ in. high x 2 in. wide. Metal.
Silver 1006-P-167 $1.29
White 1006-P-165 $1.29

Silver Round Basket
3¾ in. high x 2 in. wide. Metal.
1006-P-168 $1.29

Swan
3 in. high x 1½ in. wide x 2 in. deep. Wings actually move! Acrylic.
1006-P-369 $1.29

Silver Heart Box
2 in. high x 2 in. wide. Metal.
1006-P-169 $1.29

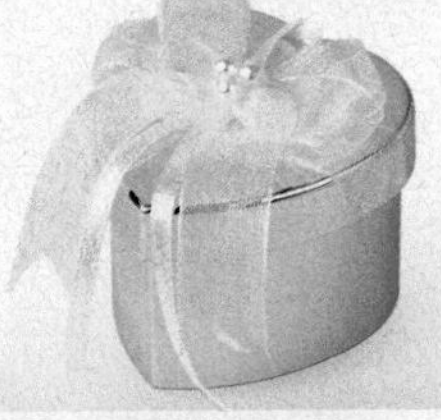

Mirrored Heart Box
1½ in. high x 1¾ in. long x 1¾ in. wide. Plastic.
1006-P-880 Pk./6 $9.99

Silver Trays
3½ in. diameter. Metal.
Heart 1006-883 Pk./6 $5.99
Round 1009-1101 Pk./6 $5.99

Champagne Glass
Clear. 2 in. high. Plastic.
1006-P-614 Pk./12 $2.49

Opalescent
5¼ in. high x 3 in. wide x 2 in. deep. Paper.
1006-P-355 Pk./12 $6.99

Champagne Flute
4 in. high x 1¼ in. wide. Plastic.
1006-P-193 Pk./12 $5.99

Tote
4 in. high x 2¼ in. wide x 1¼ in. deep. Vinyl.
1006-P-372 $1.29

Favor Cake Box
Shaped like a slice of cake. 20 boxes fit together to form a round cake tier. 4¼ in. long x 2¾ in. high.
1006-P-629 Pk./20 $6.99

Cake Slice Boxes
5 in. square x 3½ in. high.
415-P-955 Pk./20 $3.49

Double Heart Box
1 in. high x 4 in. wide x 2½ in. deep. Plastic.
1006-P-194 $1.29

Silver Chest
2 in. high x 3 in. wide x 2 in. deep. Paper.
1006-P-208 Pk./20 $9.99

White Bow
1¼ in. high x 2 in. long x 2 in. wide. Acetate and organza.
1006-681 Pk./6 $5.99

Silver Heart Pillow
1 in. high x 3 in. long x 2¼ in. wide. Paper.
1006-P-557 Pk./20 $9.99

Heart Tab
2¼ in. high x 2¼ in. long x 2¼ in. wide. Paper.
1006-P-517 Pk./20 $9.99

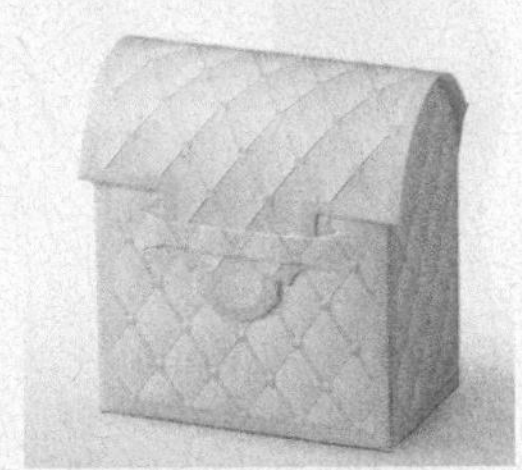

Ivory Chest
2½ in. high x 2¼ in. long x 1½ in. wide. Paper.
1006-P-515 Pk./20 $9.99

White Hexagon
2½ in. high x 1¼ in. long x 2½ in. wide. Paper.
1006-P-516 Pk./20 $9.99

Tuxedo
4 in. high. Paper.
1006-P-514 Pk./10 $9.99

Favor Frames

Insert a favorite photo or use as a place card holder by adding your guest's name. Silver metal.

Single Heart
1 in. high x 1 in. wide.
1009-P-239 $0.99

Double Heart
1 in. high x 2 in. wide.
1009-P-238 $1.49

Sachets and Tulle Circles

Perfect for favors, rose petals, rice, treats, gifts.

Drawstring Sachet Bags

Sheer organza fabric pouches close with a pull of the ribbons.
Medium measures 4½ x 6¾ in.
Pk./12 $7.99
Small measures 3¾ x 4 in.
Pk./12 $5.99

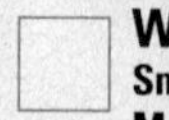

White
Small 1006-P-173
Medium 1006-P-184

Ivory
Small 1006-P-176
Medium 1006-P-183

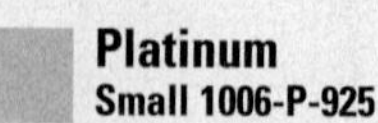

Platinum
Small 1006-P-925

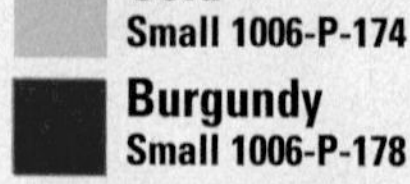

Gold
Small 1006-P-174

Burgundy
Small 1006-P-178

Lavender
Small 1006-P-189
Medium 1006-P-190

Red
Small 1006-P-188

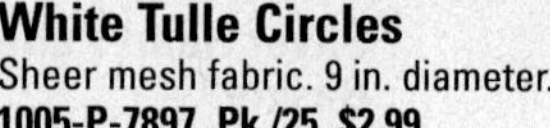

White Tulle Circles

Sheer mesh fabric. 9 in. diameter.
1005-P-7897 Pk./25 $2.99

Favor Accents

Romantic accents add sparkling beauty and elegance to favors, table decorations!

Engagement Rings

Use these sparkling favor accents to add beauty to favors, table decorations, centerpieces.
1006-P-115 Pk./12 $1.99

Anniversary Bands

¾ in. diameter.
Pk./48 $1.99
Silver 1006-P-101
Gold 1006-P-100
Pk./288 $6.99
Silver 1006-P-422
Gold 1006-P-421

Rose Flower Spray

8 in. long.
1006-P-507 $1.99

Lily Spray

9 in. long.
1006-P-503 Pk./12 $1.99

White Pearl Spray

8 in. long.
1006-P-506 Pk./12 $2.49

Iridescent Bells

Adds glamour to gifts, favors and ornaments.
2 in. high.
1006-P-195 Pk/24 $5.99
3 in. high.
1006-P-366 Pk/12 $5.99

Glittered Bells

Coated with non-edible glitter. Do not place directly on cake.
1 in. high.
1007-P-9061 Pk./12 $2.99

Doves

Glittered
Coated with non-edible glitter. Do not place directly on cake. 2 x 1½ in.
1006-P-166 Pk./12 $1.99
White 2 x 1½ in.
1002-P-1710 Pk./12 $1.99

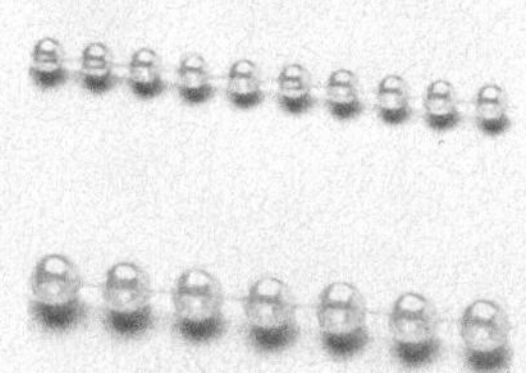

White Pearl Beading

Molded on one continuous 5-yard strand. Remove pearls before cutting and serving cake.
Large (6 mm)
211-P-1990 $3.99
Small (4 mm)
211-P-1989 $2.99

NEW!

Satin Stripe Favor Bands

Functional and decorative, a pretty way to accent favors. Use on Drawstring Sachets, Wedding Bubbles bottles and more for an instant decoration. 2 in. wide.
1007-P-8014 Pk./12 $2.99

LEAVES

Use these stunning accents to add sparkle and realism to floral arrangements, favors, centerpieces, decorations!

Shaping Leaves

Beautiful sheer leaves have wire edges to hold the precise shape you want. 1¼ in. wide leaf, 5 in. long stem.
Pk./6 $1.99

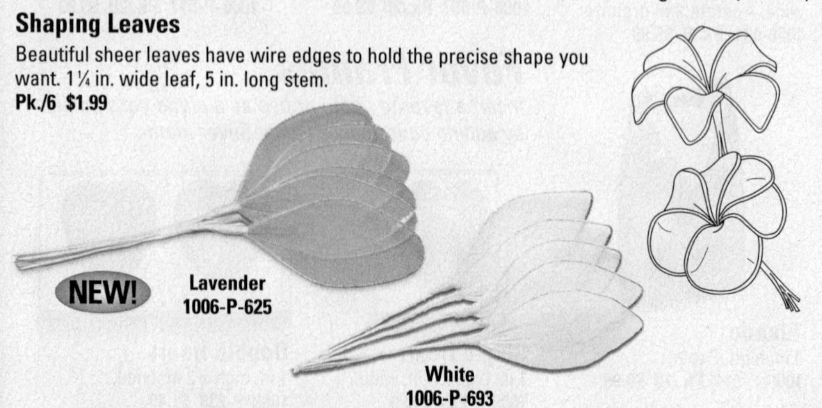

NEW!
Lavender
1006-P-625

White
1006-P-693

Gold
1⅞ in. wide.
1005-P-6518
Pk./144 $3.99
1¼ in. wide.
1005-P-6712
Pk./144 $3.49

Silver
1⅞ in. wide.
1005-P-6526
Pk./144 $3.99
1¼ in. wide.
1005-P-6720
Pk./144 $3.49

Green
2½ in. wide leaf, 2½ in. stem.
1005-P-401
Pk./12 $1.49

White
2½ in. wide leaf, 2½ in. stem.
1005-P-408
Pk./12 $1.49

Favor Decorations

WEDDING BUBBLES

Celebrate the wedding by showering the newly married couple with shimmering bubbles. It's a fun trend and a great way to wish the bride and groom good luck!

Contains 24 .6 oz. bottles of bubbles with wands. Decorate with Favor Band and tulle circles (shown on p. 210).
1007-P-8000 Pk./24 $4.99

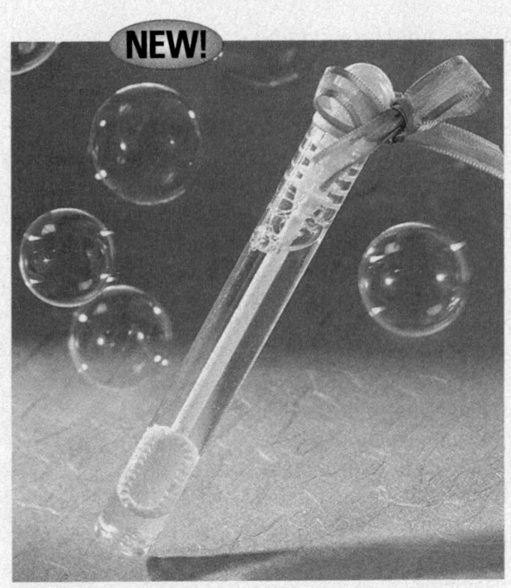

Love Knot Wands

Use after the ceremony, at the reception. 36 wands are packed in a convenient tray for reception table use. Ribbon not included. Each wand contains .16 fl. oz. bubble solution.
1007-P-8017 Pk./36 $8.99

Wedding Cake Charms

Charms are "hidden" under a slice of cake, bridesmaids pull the ribbons to reveal silver charms. Includes 8 silver-plated charms with ribbons attached.
120-P-1020 $10.49

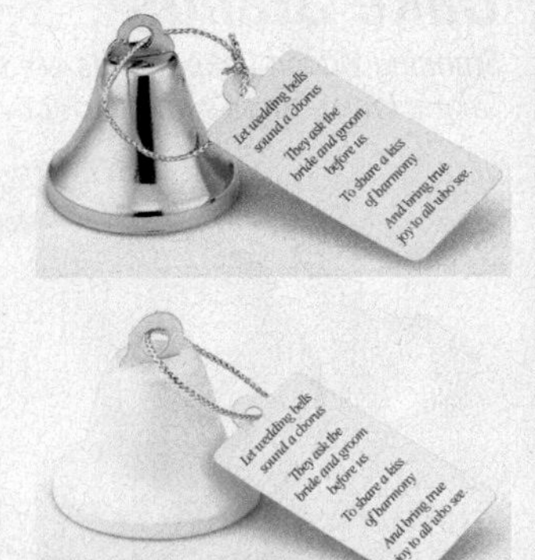

Celebration Bells

Ring for that special kiss after the marriage ceremony and at the reception. Hand to guests exiting the church, and place one at each setting at the reception. Contains 24 white bells, poem tags and white ties. Bell measures 1 ¼ in. tall x 1 ¼ in. wide.
Silver 1007-P-8012 $6.49
White 1007-P-8013 $6.49

Wedding Candy Favor Kits NEW!

Everything you need to make 10 beautiful favors for your wedding or shower celebration.

Includes 12 oz. white Candy Melts® brand confectionery coating, candy mold (1 design, 8 cavities), 2 disposable decorating bags and 10 white truffle boxes. Need more favors? Simply buy more Candy Melts (p. 146) and truffle boxes (p. 149); each 14 oz. package of Candy Melts makes 28 pieces to fill 14 boxes.
Each $7.99

Wedding Cakes
2104-P-1073

Wedding Bells
2104-P-1072

Melt **Mold** **Serve**

Candy Bar Molds NEW!

Create a sweet memory for your guests, a candy bar featuring a special message.

Molding is easy using Wilton Candy Melts® (p. 146). Present them beautifully in Candy Bar Boxes (p. 149). Each candy bar measures 3 ¼ in. wide x 1 ¾ in. tall x ¼ in. deep. 1 design, 4 cavities.
$1.99

Our Wedding
2115-P-1409

Thank You
2115-P-1410

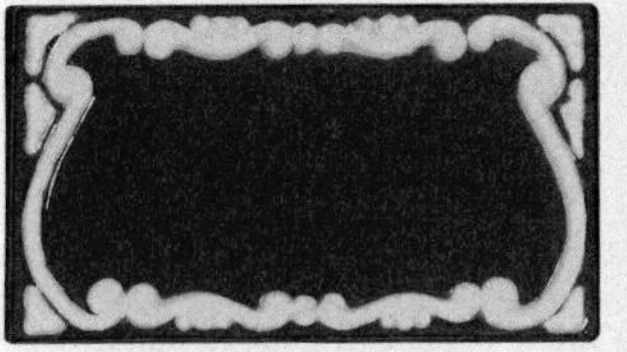

Add-A-Message
2115-P-1356

Candy

Trendy and traditional candy makes great fillers for favors and candy dishes at showers, weddings, celebrations!

Mini Hearts

12 oz. bag. Fruit flavored. Certified Kosher.
1006-P-797 $3.99

Wedding Message Hearts

10 oz. bag; approximately 90 pieces. Mint flavored.
1006-P-371 $3.99

Mint Drops

16 oz. bag. Assorted. Certified Kosher.
1006-P-788 $5.99

Pillow Mints

10 oz. bag. approximately 205 pieces. Assorted. Certified Kosher.
1006-P-858 $3.99

Jordan Almonds

16 oz. bag; approximately 100 pieces. Certified Kosher.
Assorted 1006-P-779 $6.99
White 1006-P-778 $6.99

Cake Stands

Stunning Wilton Cake Stands are the perfect way to display your special wedding cake. Take a look—there's one perfectly suited for your wedding cake size and design.

Silver Cake Plate and Serving Tray

Exquisitely detailed tray is the graceful way to serve cakes, appetizers and desserts. Its beautifully engraved handles and finely etched plate design add elegance to weddings, showers and other special occasions. Fine lacquer finish on silver-plated steel; will never tarnish. Serve with grease-proof doilies, p. 216. Displays cakes up to 12 in. diameter; tray is 17 in. diameter, measures 22 in. wide with handles.

307-P-500 $49.99

NEW!

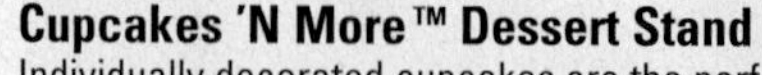

Cupcakes 'N More™ Dessert Stand

Individually decorated cupcakes are the perfect way to add a personal touch to celebrations. Now, with Cupcakes 'N' More, you have the perfect way to serve them! The look is fresh and fun, featuring bold silver-finished wire spirals to securely hold each cupcake. The twisting, towering design is perfect for any setting—kids' birthdays, holidays, weddings, showers, and more. Everyone will love serving themselves—and you'll love presenting your cupcakes, petit fours, candy cups, mini quiches and party favors in the center of the celebration!

Easy to assemble, collapsible for easy storage. Holds 23 cupcakes.

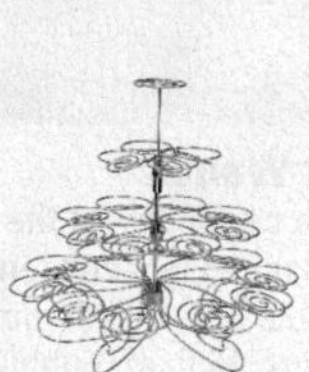

307-P-826 $29.99

Candlelight Cake Stand

- The magic of candlelight heightens the beauty of your cake
- Romantic swirls of scrollwork and hearts
- Great size for smaller weddings

Simple, graceful design reinforced with a crossbar for more support. Sturdy enameled metal design holds up to 40 lbs. Ideal for three stacked tiers supported by a 14 in. separator plate. Stand is 21½ in. diameter (13¼ in. center cake area) x 5 in. high and uses standard ⅞ in. candles. (Plates and candles not included.)

307-P-871 $34.99

Garden Cake Stand

Our beautiful Garden Cake Stand echoes the wrought-iron look found in many formal gardens. Simply place cakes on plates and set on the stand. Painted metal stand is 23 in. high x 22 in. wide and uses any standard 10 in., 14 in. and 18 in. separator plates. Satellite garden stands sold individually below.

307-P-860 $149.99

Satellite Garden Cake Stand

Painted metal; holds 12 in. separator plate.

307-P-861 $39.99

Super-Strong Cake Stand

- Made for heavy base tiers—holds up to 185 pounds of cake
- Ribbed underneath for added strength
- Subtle etched design

Large base tier will be stable when supported by our reinforced stand. High impact polystyrene. Height: 2¾ in.; Diameter: 18 in.

307-P-1200 $14.99

Scrollwork Cake Stands

- Three graduated stands let you create an elegant flowing presentation
- The cool, captivating look of silver metal, sculpted in graceful curves and scrolls

Presenting a stand design that truly enhances the look of your cake. Its graceful sense of motion begins with a beautiful stepped arrangement which positions three tiers on the cake table in a graceful, flowing fashion. Each stand features magnificent curves and swirls which create a sweeping style and rich texture. Simply place cake on Crystal-Look separator plate (included) and set on the stand. 17 in. stand has crossbar support for added strength. Compatible with any same-sized separator plate.

9 in. diameter x 12¼ in. high. **Includes** 9 in. Crystal-Look separator plate.	**307-P-880 $49.99**
13 in. diameter x 8 in. high. **Includes** 13 in. Crystal-Look separator plate.	**307-P-882 $59.99**
17 in. diameter x 4¼ in. high. **Includes** 17 in. Crystal-Look separator plate.	**307-P-884 $69.99**

FLOATING TIERS CAKE STAND SETS

- Dramatic illusion of decorated tiers suspended in mid-air
- Back support ideal for adding floral or ribbon treatments
- Great for modest size weddings

Round

Round plates present beautiful tiers. Set includes 17 in. high enamel coated white metal stand, 8, 12, and 16 in. smooth separator plates; instructions.

307-P-825
Set/4 $69.99

Replacement Plates
(Same plates as Crystal-Clear Cake Divider Set.)

8 in.	**302-P-9749**	**$3.99**
12 in.	**302-P-9765**	**$6.99**
16 in.	**302-P-9780**	**$10.99**

Heart

Heart shaped plates perfectly sized to heart shaped tiers. Set includes 17 in. high enamel coated white metal stand, 8, 12 and 16 in. Decorator Preferred® Heart Separator Plates; instructions.

307-P-872
Set/4 $69.99

Replacement Plates

8 in.	**302-P-60**	**$2.99**
12 in.	**302-P-62**	**$4.99**
16 in.	**302-P-64**	**$8.99**

Cake Assembly Sets

Tall Tier Cake Stand

Display your multi-tiered cakes up to 6 tiers high with this majestic stand. Lace-look plates enhance every cake design and hold tiers from 6 to 16 in. diameter. Easier to assemble than pillar construction, the twist-together center columns and strong, interchangeable plates provide sure stability. The optional Lady Windemere-Look 4-Arm Base, sold below, lets you surround up to 3 tiers with multiple small cakes for an even more dramatic presentation.

Basic Set

Includes five twist-apart columns 6½ in. high with one bottom and one top bolt; 18 in. footed base plate; 8, 10, 12, 14 and 16 in. separator plates (interchangeable, except footed base plate). Plastic.
304-P-7915 Set/13 $45.99

Replacement Parts

Top Column Cap Nut
304-P-7923 $0.79
Bottom Column Bolt
304-P-7941 $0.99

Additional Plates

8 in. **302-P-7894 $3.99**
10 in. **302-P-7908 $4.99**
12 in. **302-P-7924 $5.99**
14 in. **302-P-7940 $8.99**
16 in. **302-P-7967 $11.99**
18 in. **302-P-7983 $14.99**

Additional Columns

6½ in. **303-P-7910 $1.59**
7¾ in. **304-P-5009 $2.59**
13½ in. **303-P-703 $4.49**

Glue-On Plate Legs

Convert 14 or 16 in. separator plate into a footed base plate. Order 6 legs for each plate.
304-P-7930 $0.59

Lady Windemere-Look 4 Arm Base (For The Tall-Tier Stand)

Easily adds 4 base cakes to your tall tier cake. The 4-arm base can be used with any plate from the basic set, except the 18 in. footed base plate. Up to 3 graduated tiers can be added to the center columns. Use the 20 in. diameter 4-arm base with 4 stability pegs, 13½ in. column, bottom column bolt, base bolt and four 12 in. plates, sold above. Includes base bolt.
304-P-8245 $11.99

Additional Base Bolt **304-P-8253 $0.59**

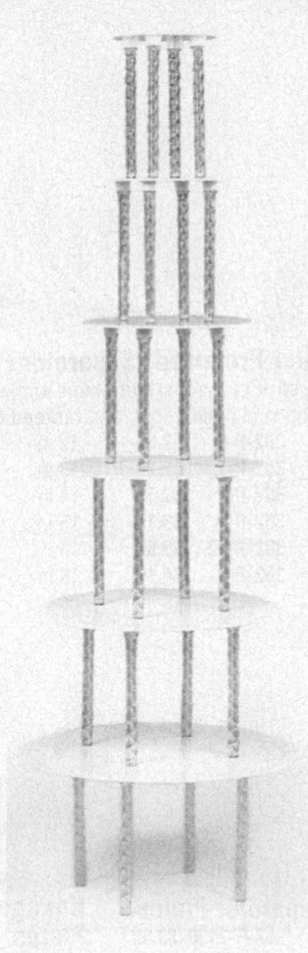

Crystal-Clear Cake Divider Set

- Sparkling clear twist legs beautifully accent your cake
- Designed for towering cakes from 6 to 14 in. diameter
- An elegant combination with Wilton crystal-look accessories

Clear plastic twist legs penetrate cake, rest on plate (dowel rods not needed). Includes 6, 8, 10, 12, 14 and 16 in. plastic separator plates plus 24 legs.
301-P-9450 Set/30 $47.99

Additional Plates

6 in. **302-P-9730 $2.99**
8 in. **302-P-9749 $3.99**
10 in. **302-P-9757 $4.99**
12 in. **302-P-9765 $6.99**
14 in. **302-P-9773 $8.99**
16 in. **302-P-9780 $10.99**

7½ in. Twist Legs

303-P-9794 Pk./4 $3.99

9 in. Twist Legs

Add more height to your tiers.
303-P-977 Pk./4 $3.99

Cake Corer Tube (not shown)

Essential tool easily and neatly removes center from cake tiers when tall tier stand columns are used. Ice cake before using. Serrated edge removes cake center with one push. Cleans easily.
304-P-8172 $1.99

Pillar and Plate Sets

Grecian Pillar and Plate Set

A deluxe money-saving collection for the serious cake decorator. Decorator Preferred® scalloped-edge separator plates and 5 in. pillars. Includes 54 pieces: two each 6 in., 8 in., 10 in., 12 in. and 14 in. plates; 20 Grecian pillars and 24 pegs.
SAVE 22% on set 301-P-8380 $45.99

Roman Column Tier Set

Includes 8 pieces: six 13¾ in. Roman columns and two strong 18 in. round Decorator Preferred® separator plates. Lovely with the Kolor-Flo Fountain (sold on pg. 216).
301-P-1981 $39.99

Harvest Cherub Separator Set

An idyllic setting for your romantic cake. Pillars snap on to plates for strong support. Set includes 6 pieces: four 7 in. Harvest Cherub pillars and two 9 in. separator plates (lower plate has 12 in. overall diameter).
301-P-3517 $11.99

Arched Tier Set

Dramatic when used with Kolor-Flo Fountain (sold on pg. 216), or Filigree Gazebo Kit (sold on pg. 216). Includes 14 pieces: Six 13 in. arched columns, two super strong 18 in. round Decorator Preferred® separator plates and six angelic cherubs to attach to columns with royal icing or glue.
301-P-1982 $48.99

Classic Separator Sets

Stately Grecian pillars and scalloped-edge plates create beautiful settings for all tiered cakes. Sets include 10 pieces: two Decorator Preferred® plates, four pillars and four pegs.

8 in. Plate Set
8 in. plates; 5 in. pillars
2103-P-256 $7.49

10 in. Plate Set
10 in. plates; 5 in. pillars
2103-P-108 $9.49

12 in. Plate Set
12 in. plates; 5 in. pillars
2103-P-124 $11.49

Separator Plates

Baker's Best® Disposable Plates
Recyclable plastic.

Size	Item	Price
6 in.	302-P-4000	$1.49
7 in.	302-P-4001	$1.69
8 in.	302-P-4002	$1.99
9 in.	302-P-4003	$2.49
10 in.	302-P-4004	$2.89
12 in.	302-P-4006	$3.79
14 in.	302-P-4008	$4.89

Decorator Preferred® Separator Plates
Our best, strongest separator plates with superior stability, beauty and scalloped edges. Guaranteed non-breakable.

Size	Item	Price	Size	Item	Price
6 in.	302-P-6	$2.09	12 in.	302-P-12	$4.69
7 in.	302-P-7	$2.29	13 in.	302-P-13	$5.49
8 in.	302-P-8	$2.59	14 in.	302-P-14	$5.79
9 in.	302-P-9	$3.19	15 in.	302-P-15	$6.99
10 in.	302-P-10	$3.59	16 in.	302-P-16	$7.79
11 in.	302-P-11	$4.19	18 in.	302-P-18	$11.49

Decorator Preferred® Heart Separator Plates
Perfectly sized to fit Wilton heart pans, for a stunning tiered heart creation. Lovely scalloped edges. Guaranteed non-breakable.

Size	Item	Price	Size	Item	Price
8 in.	302-P-60	$2.99	14 in.	302-P-63	$5.99
10 in.	302-P-61	$3.99	16 in.	302-P-64	$8.99
12 in.	302-P-62	$4.99	18 in.	302-P-65	$11.99

Square Separator Plates

Size	Item	Price
7 in.	302-P-1004	$2.99
9 in.	302-P-1020	$3.99
11 in.	302-P-1047	$4.99
13 in.	302-P-1063	$5.99

Oval Separator Plates

Size	Item	Price
8 ½ in.	302-P-2130	$3.99
11 ½ in.	302-P-2131	$4.99
14 ½ in.	302-P-2132	$5.99

Hexagon Separator Plates

Size	Item	Price
7 in.	302-P-1705	$2.99
10 in.	302-P-1748	$3.99
13 in.	302-P-1764	$5.99
16 in.	302-P-1799	$7.99

Crystal-Look Plates
Wilton crystal-look plates have an elegance like no other, with ridged sides that look like cut crystal. Built with the strength and support Wilton is famous for. Use with crystal-look pillars (sold on pg. 215).

Size	Item	Price
7 in.	302-P-2013	$3.49
9 in.	302-P-2035	$4.49
11 in.	302-P-2051	$5.99
13 in.	302-P-2078	$7.49
*17 in.	302-P-1810	$14.49

*Use only with 13 ¾ in. crystal pillars (sold on pg. 215).

17 in. Crystal-Look Plate and Pillar Set
Ideal style and height for use with fountains (sold on page 216). Contains four 13¾ in. pillars and two 17 in. plates. (not shown)
301-P-1387 $45.99

Dowel Rods and Pegs

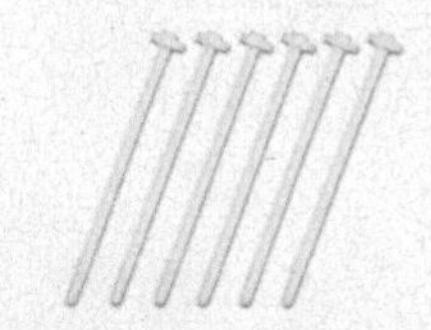

Plastic Dowel Rods
Heavy-duty hollow plastic provides strong, sanitary support for all tiered cakes. Cut with serrated knife to desired length. Length: 12¾ in. Diameter: ¾ in.
399-P-801 Pk./4 $2.49

Wooden Dowel Rods
Cut and sharpen with strong shears and knife. Length: 12 in. Diameter: ¼ in.
399-P-1009 Pk./12 $2.99

Plastic Pegs
Insure that cake layers and separator plates atop cakes stay in place. Pegs do not add support; dowel rod cake properly before using. Length: 4 in.
399-P-762 Pk./12 $1.44

Figurine Pillars

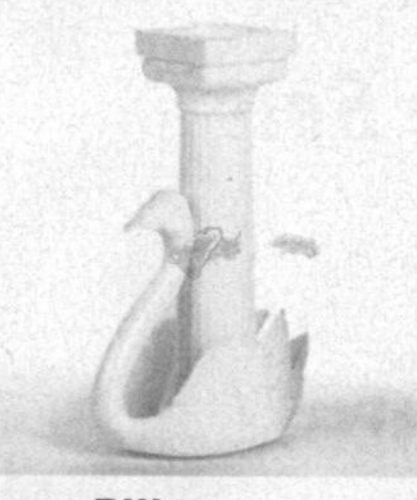

Swan Pillars
Grecian pillars with romantic swan bases add grace to your masterpiece. Height: 4 in.
303-P-7725 Pk./4 $3.49

Dancing Cupid Pillars
A delight for wedding shower or Valentine cakes. Height: 5 ½ in.
303-P-1210 Pk./4 $7.99

Cake Accents

Romantic accents add a sparkling beauty and elegance to cakes.

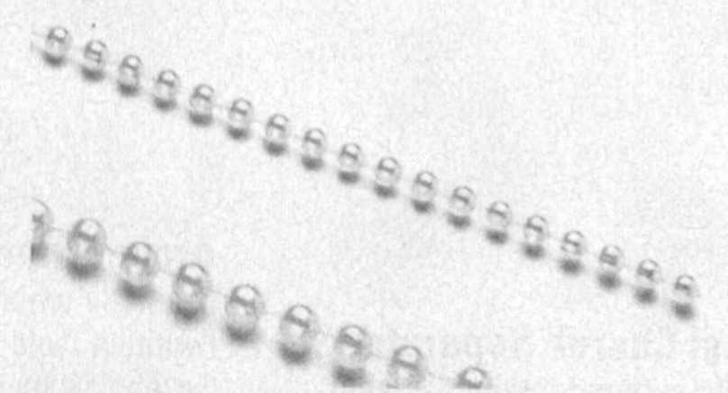

Happiness Ribbon Tier Top
Ribbon and tulle. Use on cake top or between tiers. Height: 3 in. Base: 5 in. diameter.
211-P-452 $7.00

Floral Puff Accent
5 ½ in. tulle puff with soft flowers and "pearl" sprays.
211-P-1011 $3.99

White Pearl Beading
Molded on one continuous 5-yard strand. Remove before cutting and serving cake.
Large (6 mm) **211-P-1990 $3.19** **Small** (4 mm) **211-P-1989 $2.69**

Scrolls
2 ¾ x 1 ¼ in.
1004-P-2801 Pk./24 $2.29

Angel Duet
Fluttering fancies. Each 2 in. high.
1001-P-457 Pk./2 $1.99

Separator Pillars

"Hidden" Pillars
Separate cake tiers slightly and create a floating illusion. Pushed into tiers as dowel rods, they fit onto all white separator plates except Tall Tier. Trimmable, hollow plastic. 6 in. high.
303-P-8 Pk./4 $2.49

Arched Pillars
Grecian-inspired with arched support.
4½ in.
303-P-452 Pk./4 $2.99
6½ in.
303-P-657 Pk./4 $4.99
13 in.
303-P-9720 Pk./2 $7.49

Roman Columns
Handsome pillars may be used with 16 and 18 in. plates and the Kolor-Flo Fountain (sold on pg. 216).
10¼ in.
303-P-8136 Pk./2 $5.49
13¾ in.
303-P-2130 Pk./2 $6.49

Grecian Spiked Pillars
Single plate pillars. Wide base for increased stability.
5 in. **303-P-3708**
Pk./4 $2.09
7 in. **303-P-3710**
Pk./4 $3.19
9 in. **303-P-3712**
Pk./4 $4.19

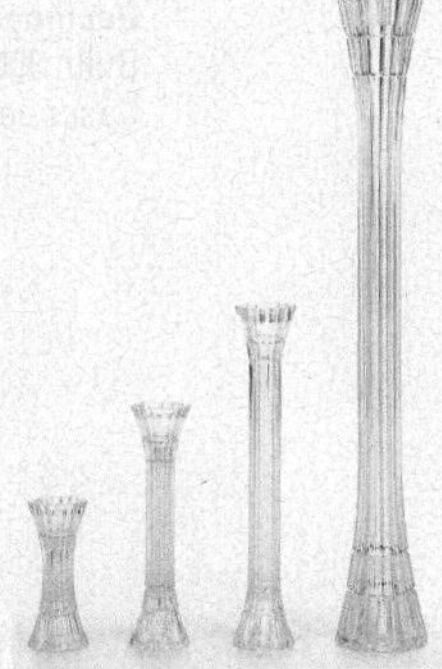

Crystal-Look Pillars
Use with crystal-look plates (sold on pg. 214) and Crystal Bridge and Stairway Set (sold below).
3 in. **303-P-2171**
Pk./4 $3.19
5 in. **303-P-2196**
Pk./4 $4.19
7 in. **303-P-2197**
Pk./4 $4.69
*13¾ in.
303-P-2242 $3.99
*Sold singly. Use only with 17 in. crystal plate (sold on pg. 214).

Baker's Best® Disposable Pillars with Rings
Single plate pillars.
7 in. **303-P-4000**
Pk./4 $2.79
9 in. **303-P-4001**
Pk./4 $2.89

Lattice Columns
Flattering garden-inspired design.
3 in. **303-P-2131**
Pk./4 $2.49
5 in. **303-P-2151**
Pk./4 $3.49
13 in. **303-P-2113**
Each $3.49

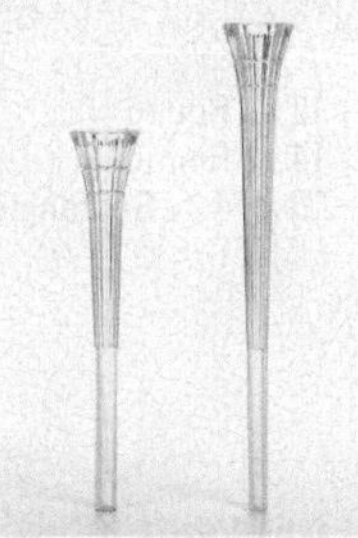

Crystal-Look Spiked Pillars
Single plate pillars. Double cake circles for extra support.
7 in. **303-P-2322**
Pk./4 $4.19
9 in. **303-P-2324**
Pk./4 $5.19

Grecian Pillars
Elegantly scrolled and ribbed.
3 in. **303-P-3606**
Pk./4 $2.09
5 in. **303-P-3703**
Pk./4 $3.19
7 in. **303-P-3705**
Pk./4 $4.19

Separator Rings

Use together or singly for a distinctive way to add height without pillars to wedding, anniversary and special occasion cakes.

Crystal Light Separator Ring Set
Adds a dramatic, soft illumination to cakes. Includes 3 rings (4 in. diameter x 4 in. high, 8 in. diameter x 4 in. high and 12 in. diameter x 3 in. high) and 6 plates (6 in., 8 in., 10 in., 12 in., 14 in., and 16 in. diameter). Includes 8 replacement bulbs. Uses 16 AA batteries, not included.
303-P-820 $149.99

Replacement Plates
302-P-2140
Set/6 $38.99

Always and Forever Oval Separator Ring Set
Designed for use with Wilton 7¾ x 5⅝ in. and 10¾ x 7⅞ in. oval pans. Contains everything needed to create a 3-tiered cake: One 7⅞ x 3 in. high oval separator ring with two corresponding oval 8½ in. x 6½ in. separator plates; and one 10⅝ x 3 in. high oval separator ring with two corresponding oval 11½ x 8½ in. separator plates. Rings crafted in highly polished, detailed resin.
303-P-812 Set/6 $44.99

Always and Forever Separator Ring
Use with any Wilton 10 in. Separator Plate Set. No pillars necessary. Made of highly polished, detailed resin. Height: 3 in.; Diameter: 9 in.
303-P-813 $15.99

Stairways and Bridges

Bridge the gap between lavish tiers.

Crystal Bridge and Graceful Stairway Set
Includes two stairways (16¾ in. long) and one platform (4¾ x 5 in.). Plastic.
205-P-2311 Set/3 $14.99

One Stairway Only
205-P-2315 $7.99

Filigree Bridge and Stairway Set
Includes two stairways (16¼ in. long) and one platform (4¾ x 5 in.). Plastic.
205-P-2109 Set/3 $11.99

One Stairway Only
205-P-1218 $4.99

Cake Fountains and Accessories

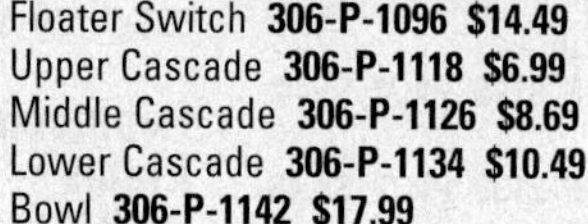

Kolor-Flo Fountain

Professional quality fountain looks spectacular with every tiered cake design. Water cascades dramatically from three levels; simply remove top levels for smaller fountain arrangements. Intricate light system with two bulbs for added brilliance. Use with 14 in. or larger plates, 13 in. or taller pillars for tallest cascade. Coordinates with our 17 in. Crystal-Look Plate and Pillar Set, p. 214. Plastic fountain bowl is 9¾ in. diameter. 110-124 V, AC motor with 65 in. cord. Pumps water electrically. Directions, replacement part information included.
306-P-2599 $109.99

Replacement Parts
Pump **306-P-1002 $48.99**
Piston **306-P-1029 $3.99**
Pump/Bulb Bracket **306-P-1037 $3.39**
Light Socket **306-P-1045 $5.49**
Light Bulb **306-P-1053 $5.99**
Bottom Base **306-P-1170 $13.99**
Cascade/Pump Connector **306-P-1088 $3.49**
Floater Switch **306-P-1096 $14.49**
Upper Cascade **306-P-1118 $6.99**
Middle Cascade **306-P-1126 $8.69**
Lower Cascade **306-P-1134 $10.49**
Bowl **306-P-1142 $17.99**

Cascade Set for Kolor-Flo Fountain
Dome shapes redirect water over surface in non-stop streams. Set includes 4 pieces: 2½ in., 4½ in., 8 in., and 11½ in. diameter (Kolor-Flo Fountain sold separately).
306-P-1172 Set/4 $14.99

Fanci Fountain

Economical fountain in crystal-clear design enhances any tiered cake. Adjustable, smooth water flow. Use with 14 in. or larger plates. Set-up instructions included. Height: 12 in. Diameter: 10 in.
306-P-2000 $59.99

Replacement Parts
Bulb **306-P-1790 $1.79**
Cascade Set **306-P-1791 $9.99**

Fresh Flower Accessories

Flower Holder Ring

Put at base of Kolor-Flo Fountain shown above. 12½ in. diameter x 2 in. high. Plastic.
305-P-435 $4.99

Crystal-Look Bowl

4½ in. diameter.
1½ in. deep.
205-P-1404 $2.99

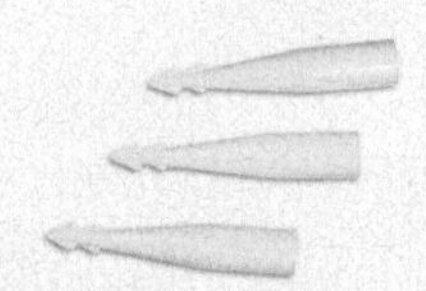

Flower Spikes

Fill with water, push into cake, add flowers. Makes cakes safe for insertion of stems or wires. 3 in. high.
1008-P-408 Pk./12 $2.49

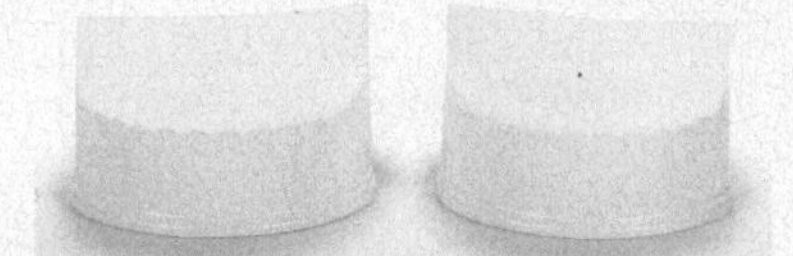

Fresh Flower Holders

Insert easily under cake tiers to hold blooms, greenery, pearl sprays, tulle puffs and more. Use with floral oasis to keep flowers fresh.
205-P-8500 Pk./2 $2.99

Construction Settings

Filigree Gazebo Kit

Intricate arch and trellis pieces wrap around Wilton Arched Pillars (not included, sold on p. 213 and 215) to create an elegant garden look for tiered cakes. Easy assembly—just insert tabs into slots to link pieces. Includes instructions for 3 cake designs.
2104-P-2942 $19.99

Cathedral Cake Kit

Includes: 5 easy-to-assemble white church pieces, 4 white plastic cake supports, a church window that can be illuminated from within. Opening in tower is 8½ in. high x 2½ in. wide.
2104-P-2940 $15.99

Cake Doilies

Add instant elegance to cake plates, dessert trays, entrée and sandwich servings. Use under table centerpieces and plants, for decorations and crafts, too.

Grease-Proof White

Size	Item	Pack	Price
4 in. Round	**2104-P-90204**	**Pk./30**	**$1.99**
6 in. Round	**2104-P-90206**	**Pk./20**	**$1.99**
8 in. Round	**2104-P-90208**	**Pk./16**	**$1.99**
10 in. Round	**2104-P-90210**	**Pk./10**	**$1.99**
12 in. Round	**2104-P-90212**	**Pk./6**	**$1.99**
14 in. Round	**2104-P-90214**	**Pk./4**	**$1.99**
10 x 14 in. Rectangle	**2104-P-90224**	**Pk./6**	**$1.99**

Silver Foil

4 in. Round
2104-P-90404
Pk./12 $2.49

6 in. Round
2104-P-90116
Pk./18 $2.49

8 in. Round
2104-P-90006
Pk./12 $2.49

10 in. Round
2104-P-90007
Pk./6 $2.49

12 in. Round
2104-P-90412
Pk./4 $2.49

Gold Foil

4 in. Round
2104-P-90304
Pk./12 $2.49

6 in. Round
2104-P-90306
Pk./18 $2.49

8 in. Round
2104-P-90308
Pk./12 $2.49

10 in. Round
2104-P-90310
Pk./6 $2.49

12 in. Round
2104-P-90312
Pk./4 $2.49

Cake Boards and Accents

Your cake will look its best when presented with quality Wilton boards, doilies and ruffled trims.

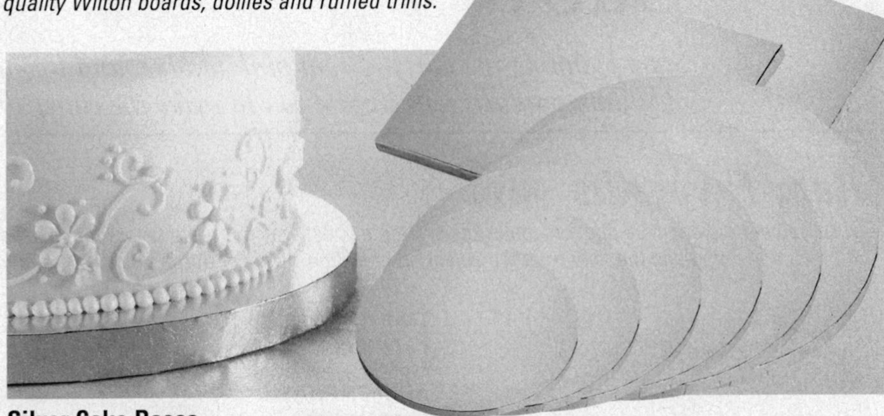

Cake Boards

Shaped cakes look best on boards cut to fit! Strong corrugated cardboard, generously-sized in rectangular shapes. Perfect for sheet and square cakes. For shaped cakes, use the pan as a pattern and cut out board to fit cake.

10 x 14 in.	**2104-P-554**	**Pk./6**	**$4.79**
13 x 19 in.	**2104-P-552**	**Pk./6**	**$5.29**

Silver Cake Bases

Convenient ½ in. thick silver-covered bases are grease-resistant, food-safe and reusable. Strong to hold heavy decorated cakes without an additional serving plate. Perfect for all types of cakes and craft creations—fondant cakes, stacked tiers, gingerbread houses, school projects, more!

10 in. Round	**2104-P-1187**	**Pk./2**	**$6.99**
12 in. Round	**2104-P-1188**	**Pk./2**	**$7.99**
14 in. Round	**2104-P-1189**	**Pk./2**	**$9.99**
16 in. Round	**2104-P-1190**	**Pk./2**	**$11.99**
18 in. Round	**2104-P-1191**	**Pk./2**	**$12.99**
20 in. Round	**2104-P-1192**	**Pk./2**	**$13.99**
11 x 15 in. Rectangle	**2104-P-1193**	**Pk./2**	**$8.99**
14 x 20 in. Rectangle	**2104-P-1194**	**Pk./2**	**$11.99**

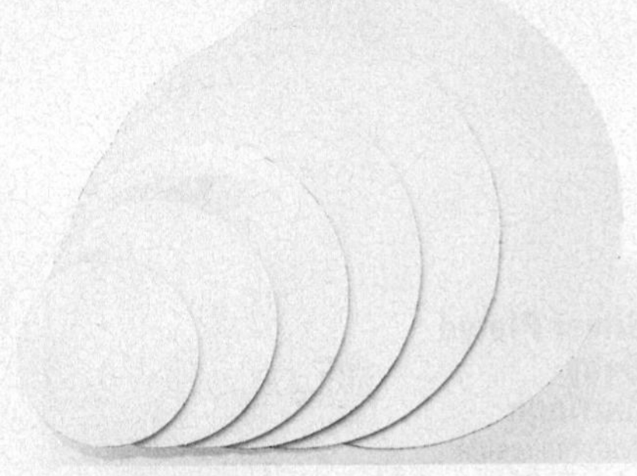

Cake Circles

Corrugated cardboard for strength and stability.

6 in. diameter	**2104-P-64**	**Pk./10**	**$3.19**
8 in. diameter	**2104-P-80**	**Pk./12**	**$4.19**
10 in. diameter	**2104-P-102**	**Pk./12**	**$5.29**
12 in. diameter	**2104-P-129**	**Pk./8**	**$5.29**
14 in. diameter	**2104-P-145**	**Pk./6**	**$5.29**
16 in. diameter	**2104-P-160**	**Pk./6**	**$6.29**

Show 'N' Serve™ Cake Boards

Scalloped edge has the look of intricate lace. Food-safe, grease-resistant coating.

10 in. diameter	**2104-P-1168**	**Pk./10**	**$4.49**
12 in. diameter	**2104-P-1176**	**Pk./8**	**$4.99**
14 in. diameter	**2104-P-1184**	**Pk./6**	**$5.49**
14 x 20 in. Rectangle	**2104-P-1230**	**Pk./6**	**$5.99**

Ruffle Boards®

Ready-to-use cake board and ruffle in one. Bleached white board and all-white ruffling complement any cake.

8 in. (for 6 in. round cake)	**415-P-950**	**$2.49**
10 in. (for 8 in. round cake)	**415-P-960**	**$2.99**
12 in. (for 10 in. round cake)	**415-P-970**	**$3.99**
14 in. (for 12 in. round cake)	**415-P-980**	**$4.49**
16 in. (for 14 in. round cake)	**415-P-990**	**$5.49**
18 in. (for 16 in. round cake)	**415-P-1000**	**$7.49**

Tuk-'N'-Ruffle®

A pretty touch that attaches to edge of your serving tray or board with royal icing or tape.
60 ft. bolt per box.
White **802-P-1008 $14.99**
6 ft. pkg. White **802-P-1991 $2.99**

Fanci-Foil

Serving side has a non-toxic grease-resistant surface. FDA-approved for use with food.
Continuous roll: 20 in. x 15 ft.
White **804-P-191 $7.99**
Gold **804-P-183 $7.99**
Silver **804-P-167 $7.99**

Cake Boxes

Sturdy cardboard boxes are the safe way to protect and transport your beautiful decorated cakes and cupcakes. Flip-top design keeps the box securely closed. Also great as gift and storage boxes!

NEW!

10 x 10 x 5 in.

For 8 in. round cakes.
Plain 415-P-942 $0.99

12 x 12 x 6 in.

For 10 in. round cakes.
Plain 415-P-944 $1.49
Window 415-P-946 $1.89

10 x 14 x 4 in.

For 9 x 13 in. sheet cakes or 12 cupcakes.
Plain 415-P-943 $1.19

14 x 19 x 4 in.

For 12 x 18 in. sheet cakes or 24 cupcakes.
Plain 415-P-945 $1.89
Window 415-P-947 $2.39

Baby

Start planning the party—from pink to blue, and themes in between, this dazzling array of Wilton products will inspire you to make the cutest things for your baby celebration.

Baby Favor Kits NEW!

Designed to be distinctive and fun, these kits are the easiest way to create favors for your baby celebration. All components of the kit are included—you add the filler from the selection of Wilton candy or Jordan almonds, and you're done!

Drawstring Wrappers
Create these favors in no time at all—they're pre-assembled! Just fill, tie ribbons, and add favor tag. Candy not included.
Pk./12 $12.99
Pink 1006-P-218
Blue 1006-P-219
White 1006-P-340

Sweet Things™ Pacifiers
Everything needed to make 12 oh-so-cute favors! Includes pacifier favor pedestals, ribbon, tulle circles, place cards, assembly instructions. Candy not included.
1006-P-531
Pk./6 $9.99

Sweet Things™ Teddy Bears
Everything needed to make 12 adorable favors! Includes teddy bear favor pedestals, ribbon, tulle circles, place cards, assembly instructions. Candy not included.
1006-P-530
Pk./6 $9.99

Favor Containers

Perfect as favors—filled with candy and treats, and as gift and cake accents.

Drawstring Sachets
Ready to fill with Jordan Almonds, Rose Petals, Pillow Mints, small gifts.
3¾ in. x 4 in.
Pk./12 $5.99
Pink 1006-P-179
Blue 1006-P-180

White Flower Basket
3¾ in. wide x 2 in. high.
Metal.
1006-P-890 $1.29

Silver Plated Baby Carriage
With moveable wheels. 3 in. long x 2 in. wide x 3½ in. high.
1006-P-878 $7.99

Baby Favor Bags
Delightful container for candies, small gifts and other favor treats.
3 x 5½ in. high.
1006-P-362 Pk./12 $7.99

Porcelain Baby Block
2 in. wide x 1¾ in. high.
Favor and candy not included.
1006-P-324 $2.99

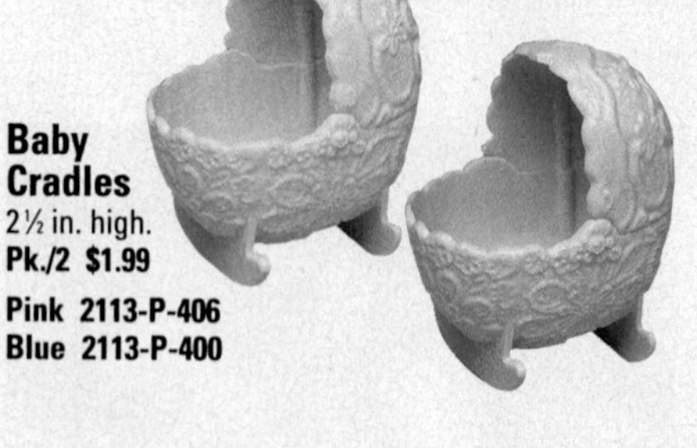

Baby Cradles
2½ in. high.
Pk./2 $1.99
Pink 2113-P-406
Blue 2113-P-400

Baby Blocks Container*
Removable lid for easy filling. Each 1¼ in. high.
2113-P-419 Set/4 $2.99

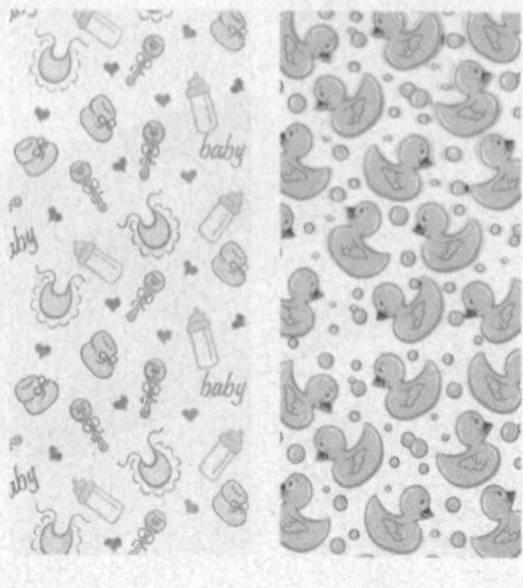

Party Bags
Colorful designs for candy and cookie treats. 20 plastic bags, 20 ties included.
4 x 9½ in.
Pk./20 $1.99
Baby
1912-P-2365
Rubber Ducky
1912-P-1275

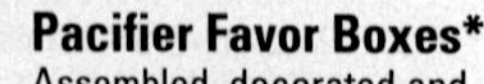

Pacifier Favor Boxes*
Assembled, decorated and ready to fill with Wilton candies. Each box is 2 in. x 2 in. x 1¼ in. high.
Pk./6 $7.99
Pink 1006-P-330
Blue 1006-P-331
Yellow 1006-P-332

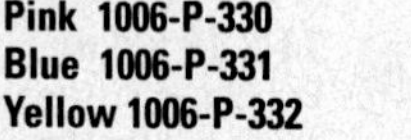

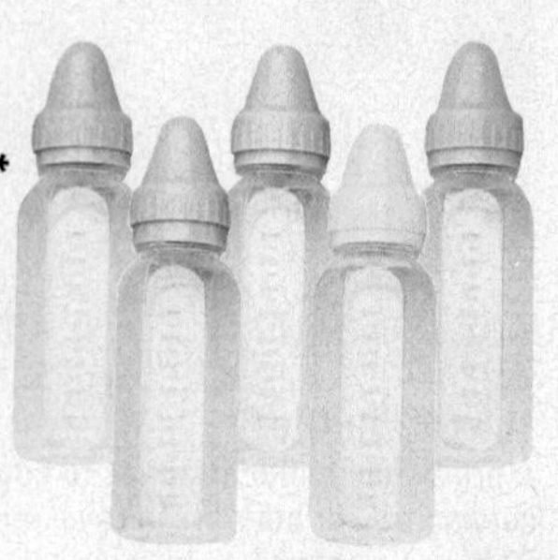

Baby Bottles*
Open for easy filling. Pink, lavender, blue, yellow, mint.
4 in. high; opening ½ in. diameter.
1006-P-696
Pk./6 $5.99

*WARNING: CHOKING HAZARD–Small parts. Not intended for children. Not a toy–for decorative use only.

Favor Accents

Add special touches to your baby favors, gift tie-ons and table decorations.

Ethnic Newborn Baby Figurines*
1 in. high.
1103-P-30 NEW!
Pk./6 $1.99

Newborn Baby Figurines*
1 in. high.
1103-P-62
Pk./6 $1.99

Mini Rocking Horses*
1¼ in. high. Pink, lavender, blue, yellow, mint.
1103-P-52
Pk./6
$1.99

Mini Clothes Pins*
Pink, lavender, blue, yellow, mint.
1⅜ in. high
1103-P-27
Pk./20 $1.99

Small Safety Pins*
1½ in. long.
Pk./20 $1.99

Pink 1103-P-21
Blue 1103-P-26

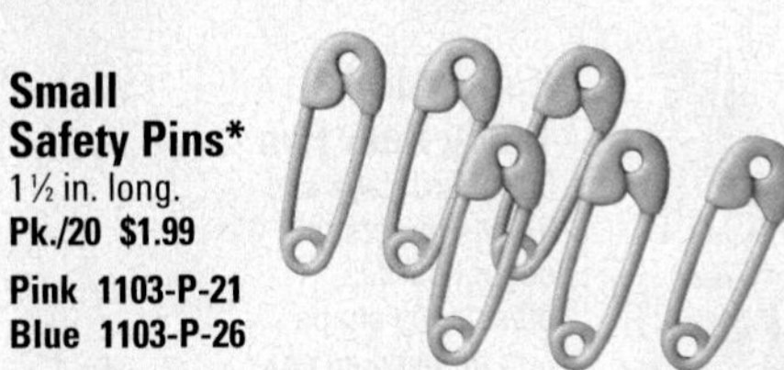

Mini Baby Bottles*
Pink, lavender, blue, yellow, mint. 1¼ in. high.
1103-P-16
Pk./20 $1.99

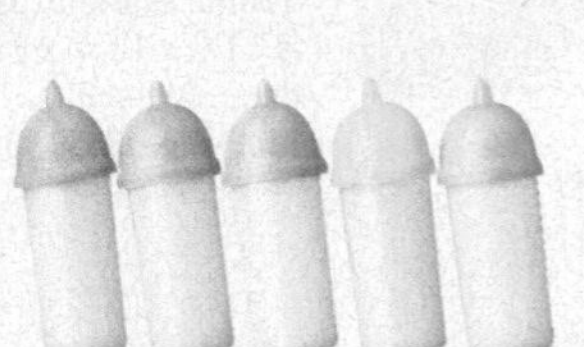

Baby Bears*
1 in. high.
Pk./6 $2.99

Blue 1103-P-7
Pink 1103-P-8

Rocking Horses
Three blue, three pink.
2½ in. high.
1103-P-28
Pk./6 $3.99

Shower Rattles*
Pink, lavender, blue, yellow, mint.
3¾ in. high.
1103-P-29
Pk./6 $2.99

Sleeping Angels Set
A precious pose, one pink and one blue. 2 in. high x 3 in. long.
2113-P-2325
Set/2 $1.99

Baby Bracelets*
Three pink, three blue.
1¼ in. high.
1103-P-56 Pk./6 $2.29

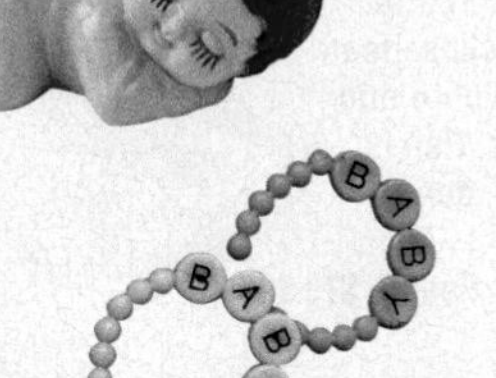

FAVOR BANDS

Instant decoration for favors, bubbles, gifts. Slip one on to close filled bags and tulle favor puffs, or use to decorate any baby favor.

Multicolor Flower
Accented with satin ribbon.
1006-P-683 Pk./12 $4.99

Baby Bottle
Accented with a cute baby bottle.
Pk./6 $2.49

Pink 1006-P-509
Blue 1006-P-508

Baby Pacifier
Accented with a baby pacifier.
Pk./6 $2.49

Pink 1006-P-566
Blue 1006-P-567

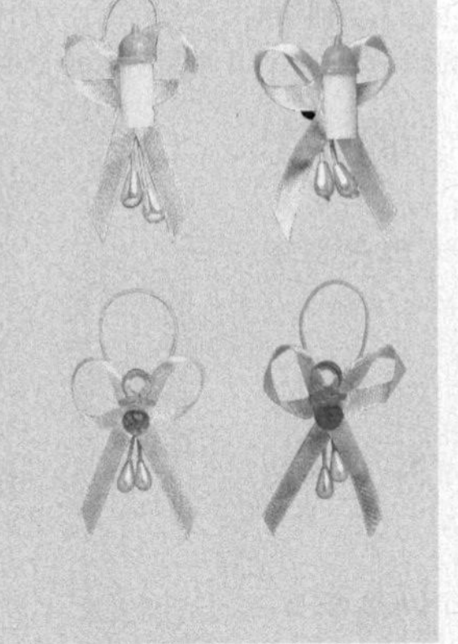

*WARNING: CHOKING HAZARD–Small parts. Not intended for children. Not a toy–for decorative use only.

Candy Molds

Fun shaped molds celebrate baby over and over again. Making candy is easy to do, complete directions are included with each mold! Use Wilton Candy Melts® brand confectionery coating, sold on p. 146.

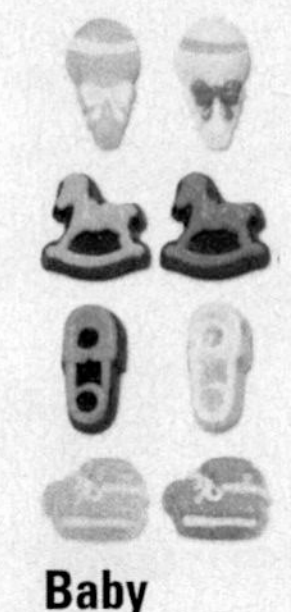

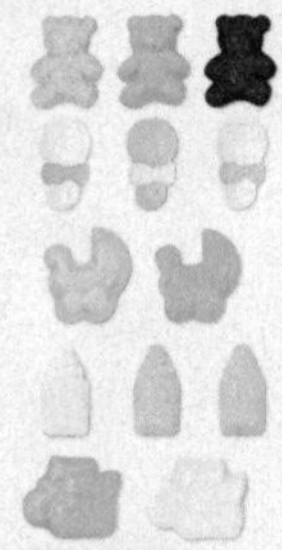

Baby Bottles
1 design, 6 cavities.
2115-P-1560
$1.99

Baby Shower
4 designs, 11 cavities.
2115-P-1710
$1.99

Mini Baby Icons
5 designs, 20 cavities.
2115-P-1537
$1.99

Candies

Perfect filler for favors, treat bags, candy dishes!

Certified Kosher.

Mint Drops
16 oz. bag. Assorted.
1006-P-788 $5.99

NEW!

Mini Hearts
10 oz. bag. Assorted.
1006-P-797 $3.99

Jordan Almonds
16 oz. bag; approx. 100 pieces. **$6.99**
Assorted 1006-P-779
White 1006-P-778

Pillow Mints
10 oz. bag. approx. 205 pieces. Assorted.
1006-P-858 $3.99

Mini Favor Frames

Perfect shower favors, keepsakes, crafts. Hand out instead of cigars!

Mini Favor Frames
6 different designs per box, each 3 x 3 in. Holds 1½ x 1½ photo.
1009-P-1131 Pk./6 $12.99

Baby Memories

NEW!

Best Wishes Bear
Create a precious keepsake for the new baby. It's easy and fun—add your personal touches, go pink or blue, or decorate to match the baby's room. Use fabric paint, markers or other favorite craft supplies. Includes blue and pink sheer ribbons and pen. 9¼ in. high, holds 4 x 3 in. photo.
1009-P-1140 $16.99

Shadow Box Frame
Small Treasures shadow box holds and safely keeps baby mementos, and makes a permanent display and keepsake. Add photos, booties, other fun first things. 11 x 13 x 3½ in. deep.
1009-P-1117 $29.99

Memory Box
Wooden hinged box holds photos outside, precious keepsakes inside. Displays two 3 x 4 in. and two 1 x 3 in. photos. Painted white, ready for you to decorate or simply add photos. 8½ x 8½ in., 2 in. deep.
1009-P-1114 $19.99

Baby Frame
Create a keepsake for the new baby that becomes a personalized, permanent record! Fine wood frame is painted white, ready for you to decorate with your own designs, names, etc. 11 x 14 in.
1009-P-1110 $19.99

Baby Frame Autograph Mat
Holds a 5 x 7 in. photo, with room for autographs and good wishes of friends and family. Few gifts touch so many like this one! For use in an 11 x 14 in. frame.
1009-P-1106 $5.99

Baking Accessories

BAKEWARE

Cuddly Lamb Pan
NEW!

His sweet smile is the perfect welcome for baby showers. See the label for four great decorating ideas. One-mix pan is 11¾ in. x 8¾ in. x 2 in. deep. Aluminum.
2105-P-4947 $9.99

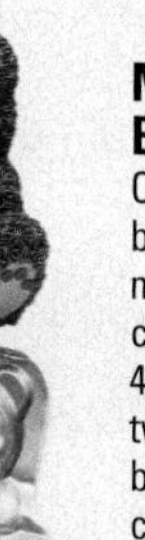

Stand-Up Cuddly Bear Pan Set
Five decorating ideas on one box! Two-piece pan takes 6⅔ cups of firm textured batter. Includes 6 clips, heat-conducting core and instructions. Pan is 9½ x 8⅝ in. deep. Aluminum.
2105-P-603 Set/10 $19.99

Mini Stand-Up Bear Pan Set
Convenient size for baking cakes and molding candy, ice cream and sugar. 4¾ in. high. Includes two-piece pan, baking stand, four clips and instructions. Aluminum.
2105-P-489 Set/8 $10.99

Huggable Teddy Bear Pan
From birthdays and baby showers to school parties, classic toy shape can be used all year 'round. One-mix pan is 13½ x 12 ¼ x 2 in. deep. Aluminum.
2105-P-4943 $9.99

BAKING CUPS
Everyone loves the convenience of cupcakes—easy to make, to carry to the party, and simple to serve! Now, you'll make the cutest ones for every baby celebration using Wilton Baking Cups! Perfect for treats, favors, and as nut or candy cups.

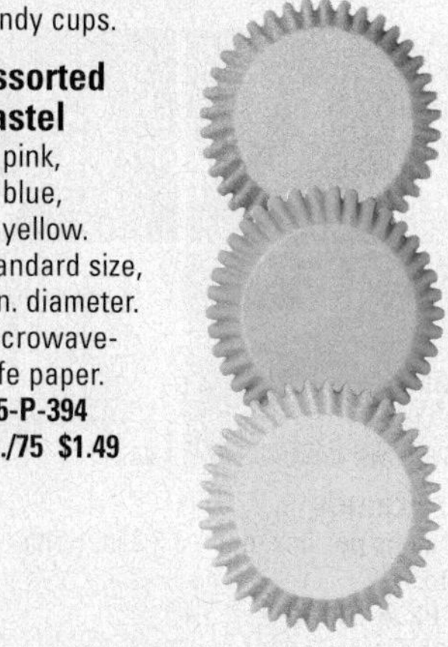

Assorted Pastel
25 pink, 25 blue, 25 yellow. Standard size, 2 in. diameter. Microwave-safe paper.
415-P-394 Pk./75 $1.49

CANDLES
Cute candles brighten the little one's first celebration. Handpainted details, clean-burning design.

Baby Things
Approx. 2 in. high.
2811-P-855 Set/4 $3.29

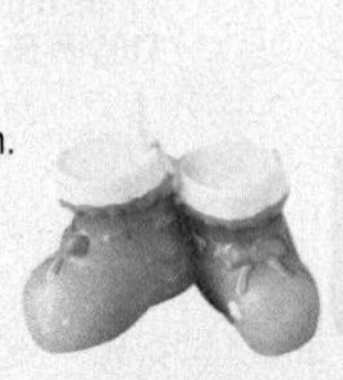

Soft Colors Candles
From classic to shimmer in yellow, pink, blue and mint.

Shimmer NEW!
Shown, 2½ in. high.
2811-P-3664 Pk./8 $1.99

Also available, shown on p. 153:

Rounds
2½ in. high.
2811-P-291 Pk./24 $0.69

Corkscrew
2½ in. high.
2811-P-775 Pk./8 $2.49

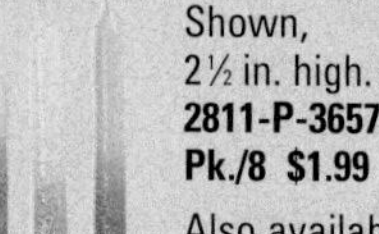

Lattice NEW!
Shown, 2½ in. high.
2811-P-3657 Pk./8 $1.99

Also available, shown on p. 153:

Tricolor
2½ in. high.
2811-P-782 Pk./10 $1.99

Twist NEW!
Shown, 2½ in. high.
2811-P-3661 Pk./8 $2.49

Also available, shown on p. 153:

Party Thins
8 in. high.
2811-P-255 Pk./20 $0.99

Jumbo Crayons
3¼ in. high.
2811-P-292 Pk./8 $1.49

Cake Pan

A wonderful way to welcome baby—at a shower or a first birthday! *Witzy* makes an adorable friend for a day full of fun. One-mix pan is 13 x 8¼ x 2 in. deep. Aluminum.
2105-P-7810 $10.99

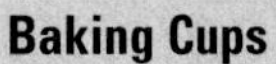

Candle

Wishin' with *Witzy* is so much fun! Handpainted, clean-burning quality. 3½ in. high.
2811-P-7810 $3.99

Icing Color Set

Includes four .5 oz. jars: Yellow, Orange, Red and Green. Certified Kosher.
601-P-7810 Set/4 $4.99

NEW!

Mailable Frame

Fun birth announcement, thank you note, first birthday invitation. Holds 3½ x 5 in. photo. Includes envelopes.
1006-P-7811
Pk./12 $6.99

Place Card/ Favor Tag

NEW!

Tent fold with cut out top.
1006-P-7814
Pk./24 $1.99

Icing Decorations

Mint-flavored edible sugar shapes decorate cupcakes, cookies, ice cream and cake. Certified Kosher.
710-P-7810 Pk./14 $2.29

Baking Cups

Standard size, 2 in. diameter. Microwave-safe paper.
415-P-7810 Pk./50 $1.69

Treat Bags

Fill with candy, cookies and other goodies; great for gifts and surprises, too! Sixteen each 4 x 9½ in. bags and twist ties.
1912-P-7810 Pk./16 $1.99

NEW!

Favor Box

Fill with candy and tiny treats. Easy to assemble. Size: 2¼ x 3⅛ in. unassembled.
1006-P-7810
Pk./24 $6.99

Rubber Ducky

3-D Cake Pan

This bath-time favorite will make a big splash at baby showers. Five adorable designs included. Two-piece pan takes 5½ cups batter, Aluminum.
2105-P-2094 $12.99

Candles

Handpainted details, clean-burning design. 1½ in. high.
2811-P-9337 Set/6 $3.29

Sprinkles

2.34 oz. plastic shaker bottle for convenient pouring and storing. Certified Kosher.
710-P-798 $1.99

NEW!

Mailable Frame

Cute birth announcement, thank you note, or first birthday party invitation. Holds 3½ x 5 in. photo. Includes envelopes.
1006-P-542
Pk./12 $6.99

Place Card/Favor Tag

NEW!

Tent fold with cut out top.
1006-P-543
Pk./24 $1.99

NEW!

Favor Box

Fill with candy and tiny treats. Easy to assemble. Size: 2¼ x 3⅛ in. unassembled.
1006-P-545
Pk./24 $6.99

Icing Decorations

Mint-flavored edible sugar shapes decorate cupcakes, cookies, ice cream and cake. Certified Kosher.
710-P-293 Pk./12 $2.09

Baking Cups

Microwave-safe paper. Standard size, 2 in. diameter.
415-P-378
Pk./50 $1.49

Party Bags

Fill with candy, cookies and other goodies; great for gifts and surprises, too! 20 plastic bags, 20 ties included. 4 x 9½ in.
1912-P-1275 Pk./20 $1.99

Candy Mold

Making candy is easy to do, complete directions are included with each mold! Use Wilton Candy Melts®† sold on p. 146. 1 design, 6 cavities.
2115-P-1565 $1.99

†Brand confectionery coating.

Instructional

Find inspiration with Wilton how-to books and videos. There's something perfect for your next celebration, from kids' birthday cakes to multi-tiered wedding designs.

Specialty Publications

Cake Decorating Beginner's Guide

With this exciting book, anyone can decorate a fantastic-looking cake the very first time! Wilton, the #1 name in cake decorating, shows beginners everything they need to know, step-by-step. The *Beginner's Guide* makes decorating easy to learn and fun to do for everyone!

- How to bake and ice perfect cakes
- How to mix any color icing with ease
- 15 fantastic cake ideas to decorate in 6 steps or less
- Step-by-step decorating instructions for stars, rosettes, drop flowers and more

Soft cover, 40 pages.
902-P-1232 $3.99

Uses of Decorating Tips

Valuable quick reference and idea book for any decorator. Features five of the most popular decorating tip families and explains what each does. Shows the versatility of many tips by presenting varied cake designs. Soft cover, 48 pages.
902-P-1375 $8.99

Candy Making Beginner's Guide

You'll be amazed at the fantastic candies you can make using this book. The possibilities are endless, using the great selection of Wilton Candy Melts® and Candy Molds. The *Beginner's Guide* shows you how, step-by-step, so you will make great-looking candies your very first time. It's a great new way to add fun to parties and create impressive gifts. The *Beginner's Guide* has the information you need to start making candy like a pro.

- 20 incredible candy ideas—all made in a few easy steps!
- Easy ways to melt perfectly every time
- Painting color details in candy
- How to make classic creme-filled and dipped candies
- Great candy gift and favor ideas

Soft cover, 40 pages.
902-P-1231 $3.99

2005 Yearbook of Cake Decorating — NEW!

The #1 annual decorating book helps you create great cakes and desserts throughout the year! It's the ultimate resource for professional bakers and anyone who wants to serve something special. Over 200 exciting decorating ideas—including cakes for every occasion, holiday candies and cookies, favorite character desserts and more. The Fondant Fun special section features exciting ways to decorate with this easy-to-handle icing. Featuring step-by-step decorating instructions, technique resource guide, product section and website link to more cake designs. Soft cover, 224 pages.
English 1701-P-2034 $9.99
Spanish 1701-P-2037 $9.99

2005 Pattern Book — NEW!

Duplicate many of the beautiful cake designs featured in the 2005 Yearbook and on the Wilton website. Includes over 100 decorating outlines to transfer to your cake. Easy-to-follow instructions. Soft cover, 60 pages of patterns.
408-P-2005 $6.99

The Wilton School—Decorating Cakes

This exciting book presents what Wilton has learned in 75 years of teaching cake decorating, in an easy-to-follow format that reflects today's lifestyles. *Decorating Cakes* is designed to appeal to anyone who wants to make great-looking cakes for families and friends.

- 30 exciting cakes with complete instructions and product listings
- 103 technique instructions, shown step-by-step, including borders, flowers, fondant and more
- Helpful recipes, tip chart, serving and cutting charts, glossary of terms
- In-depth sections on baking cakes, preparing icing, using decorating tips, cutting and transporting cakes
- Product guide, which shows and explains the equipment and ingredients required for decorating

Soft cover, 116 pages.
902-P-904 $12.99

Instructional Videos

How to Make Wedding Cakes

Invaluable lessons on how to design and assemble tiered cakes for weddings, showers, anniversaries and other special occasions. Hints for transporting and serving also included in this 60-minute video. DVD material matches VHS.
DVD 901-P-256 $19.99
VHS 901-P-128 $19.99

Cake Decorating—Easy as 1-2-3!

Learn how to level and frost a cake perfectly, make simple borders, flowers, leaves and more. 60 minutes. DVD material matches VHS.
DVD 901-P-257 $19.99
VHS 901-P-115 $19.99

How to Make Icing Flowers

Learn how to make roses, Easter lilies, violets, pansies, daisies, poinsettias and more! Five cake designs incorporate all the flowers included in this 60-minute video. DVD material matches VHS.
DVD 901-P-258 $19.99
VHS 901-P-119 $19.99

Wedding Publications

Wilton Party Favors

This exclusive collection is filled with dozens of designs to suit every taste and budget. You'll find a great favor in this book to enhance any wedding, holiday or themed party. Organized to suit the season of the celebration (with an extra section for anniversaries), *Wilton Party Favors* includes all you need to know about making these favors with ease. Step-by-step instructions to help you complete a party's worth of favors in just a few hours. A convenient section on favor-making tools and techniques. Plus information on buying the great Wilton products used to make each design. Soft cover, 48 pages.

908-P-119 $12.99

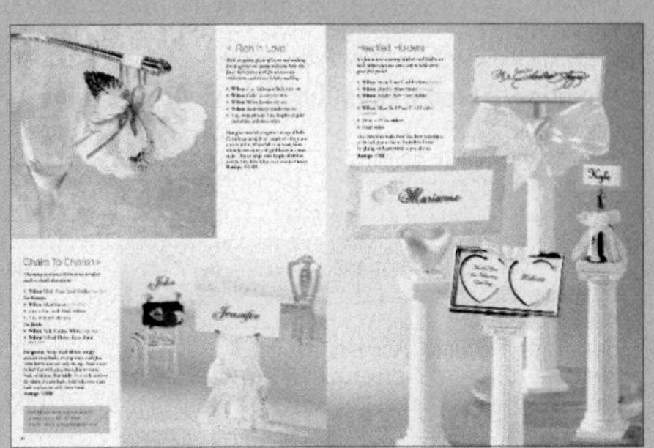

Wilton Wedding Cakes— A Romantic Portfolio

Our exciting new collection of tiered cakes makes the romantic wedding of every bride's dreams a reality. *A Romantic Portfolio* sets the bride's imagination free, with 38 exquisite cakes that express love in many ways. It's all here—beautiful seasonal designs, elegant shapes, classic and contemporary looks. There is a cake for every taste—along with coordinating ornament, favor suggestions and tiered cake accessories.

A Romantic Portfolio will inspire decorators as well as brides. Every design includes step-by-step decorating instructions, product checklists and serving amounts. Used with our comprehensive construction guide, patterns, techniques and recipes, *A Romantic Portfolio* has everything decorators need to recreate each cake to perfection. Soft cover, 144 pages.

902-P-907 $16.99

Also included is a special pull-out supplement, *My Wedding Planner*. This invaluable booklet is filled with ideas and worksheets to help you organize the perfect wedding in every detail.

Wilton Weddings

For planning and organizing your wedding—garden weddings, at-home and hotel receptions are covered—from budgets to interior designs. Pull-out Planning Guide includes a budget checklist and 12-month organizer, plus tips on getting the most for your money. 25 cake designs and instructions. Soft cover, 148 pages.

908-P-115 $14.99

A Treasury of Wilton Wedding Cakes

This exquisite collection of wedding cakes and ornaments reflects the more than 75 years of experience Wilton has in designing wedding cakes, Victorian to contemporary.

Soft cover, 96 pages.

908-P-105 $8.99

Wilton Wedding Dream Cakes

A truly distinctive collection for today's bride, reflecting a new freedom in wedding cake design. More than 45 designs with complete instructions, from elegant classic tiers to colorful cakes with contemporary flair. A special pull-out supplement features ideas from budgeting to floral options. Soft cover, 128 pages.

908-P-101 $14.99

Wilton Bridal Cakes

A showcase for many favorite wedding cake styles—Victorian, country garden and contemporary. Includes 27 designs, ideal for large or intimate celebrations. Complete instructions, patterns and cutting guide make it easy to achieve the cake of your dreams.

Soft cover, 96 pages.

908-P-110 $8.99

GENERAL INDEX

Cake Tools & Supplies

Candy Supplies

Cookie Supplies

Fondant and Gum Paste Supplies

Icing Supplies

Instructional

Ornaments & Figurines

Party Favors & Accents

Wedding/Tiered Cakes Supplies & Accessories

BAKEWARE INDEX

Numbers in parentheses indicate page numbers for designs which feature these pans.

Bakeware Essentials

Seasonal Pans

Novelty Pans

Mini Pans

Tier Pan Sets

PARTY THEME INDEX

Licensed Characters

Party Themes

*Brand confectionery coating.